# SYNTACTIC AND STRUCTURAL
# PATTERN RECOGNITION
# THEORY AND APPLICATIONS

**World Scientific Series in Computer Science**

*Published*

1: Computer-Aided Specification Techniques (*J Demetrovics, E Knuth & P Rado*)

2: Proceedings of the 2nd RIKEN International Symposium on Symbolic and Algebraic Computation by Computers (Eds. *N Inada & T Soma*)

3: Computational Studies of the Most Frequent Chinese Words and Sounds (*Ching Y Suen*)

4: Understanding and Learning Statistics by Computer (*M C K Yang & D H Robinson*)

5: Visualizing Abstract Objects and Relations — A Constraint-Based Approach (*T Kamada*)

6: DC Flux Parametron — A New Approach to Josephson Junction Logic (*E Goto & K F Loe*)

7: Syntactic and Structural Pattern Recognition — Theory and Applications (Eds. *H Bunke & A Sanfeliu*)

8: Information, Randomness & Incompletenesss — Papers on Algorithmic Information Theory, Second Edition (*G J Chaitin*)

9: P-Prolog — A Parallel Logic Programming Language (*Rong Yang*)

10: Intelligent Chinese Language Pattern and Speech Processing (Ed. *P S-P Wang*)

11: Control Theory of Robotic Systems (*J M Skowronski*)

12: An Introduction to Chinese, Japanese, and Korean Computing (*J K T Huang & T D Huang*)

13: Mathematical Logic for Computer Science (*Z W Lu*)

14: Computer Vision and Shape Recognition (Eds. *A Krzyzak, T Kasvand & C Y Suen*)

15: Stochastic Complexity in Statistical Inquiry (*J Rissanen*)

16: A Perspective in Theoretical Computer Science — Commemorative Volume for Gift Siromoney (Ed. *R Narasimhan*)

17: Computer Transformation of Digital Images and Patterns (*Z C Li, T D Bui, Y Y Tang & C Y Suen*)

18: Array Grammars, Patterns and Recognizers (Ed. *P S P Wang*)

19: Structural Pattern Analysis (Eds. *R Mohr, Th Pavlidis & A Sanfeliu*)

20: A Computational Model of First Language Acquisition (*N Satake*)

*Forthcoming*

21. The Design and Implementation of ConcurrentSmalltalk (*Y Yokote*)

Series in Computer Science — Vol. 7

# SYNTACTIC AND STRUCTURAL PATTERN RECOGNITION
# THEORY AND APPLICATIONS

edited by

**Horst Bunke**

Institut für Informatik und
Angewandte Mathematik
Universität Bern
Switzerland

**Alberto Sanfeliu**

Instituto de Cibernética
Universitat Politecnica de
Barcelona
Spain

**World Scientific**

*Singapore • New Jersey • London • Hong Kong*

*Published by*

World Scientific Publishing Co. Pte. Ltd.
P O Box 128, Farrer Road, Singapore 9128
*USA office:* 687 Hartwell Street, Teaneck, NJ 07666
*UK office:* 73 Lynton Mead, Totteridge, London N20 8DH

**Library of Congress Cataloging-in-Publication Data**

Syntactic and structural pattern recognition — theory and applications
   (Series in computer science; vol. 7)

1. Pattern recognition systems. 2. Pattern perception. I. Bunke,
Horst, 1925 —   II. Sanfeliu, Alberto. III. Series.
TK7882.P3S96    1990          006.4'2          88-33983
ISBN 9971-50-552-5
ISBN 9971-50-566-5 (pbk.)

Printed in Singapore by JBW Printers & Binders Pte. Ltd.

# PREFACE

Pattern recognition has been an area of research for more than thirty years. In the beginning the main interest was focussed on statistical and numerical methods. However, it was as early as in the 1960s that there was a growing interest in symbolic representations with emphasis on pattern structure. During the 1970s and the first half of the 1980s the field was mainly influenced by the work of K.S. Fu and his students, until his unexpected and untimely death. As a matter of fact, it was K.S. Fu in the first place who formed our understanding of the field of syntactic and structural pattern recognition. It took place when we both visited him and worked together with him at Purdue University from 1980 to 1981 and 1979 to 1981, respectively.

Today, syntactic and structural pattern recognition is still an active area of research. In 1982 when Technical Committees within the International Association for Pattern Recognition (IAPR) were founded there was one committee established on syntactic and structural methods. The activities of this committee included the publication of a special issue of a journal and the organization of a workshop, both in 1986. As past and present chairmen of this committee, we were both engaged in its activities from the beginning and could get a vivid insight into contemporary research in syntactic and structural pattern recognition.

This book is directed to a broad readership with varying background and motivation. At the one end, our aim is to present fundamental concepts and notations developed in syntactic and structural pattern recognition. For example, Chapters 1 to 7 and 9 can be used as a text for an introductory course on the topic at an undergraduate or graduate level. At the other end, it is our intention to report on the current state of the art with respect to both methodology and applications, thus satisfying the needs of the practising professional who already has experience and knowledge on the subject. Readers belonging to the second category will perhaps find Chapters 8 and 10-18 most useful. For the introductory Chapters 1 to 7 and 9 no previous knowledge of the field is required. However, some familiarity with calculus and basic concepts in computer science will certainly lead to a more effective use of the book.

The book consists of individual chapters written by different authors. The chapters are grouped into broader subject areas like "Syntactic Representation and Parsing", "Structural Representation and Matching", "Learning", etc. Each chapter is a self-contained presentation of one particular topic. In order to keep the original flavor of each contribution, no efforts were undertaken to unify the different chapters with respect to notation. Naturally, the self-containedness of the individual chapters results in some redundancy. However, we believe that this handicap is compensated by the fact that each contribution can be read individually without prior study of the preceding chapters. A unification of the broad spectrum of material covered by the individual chapters is provided by the subject and author index included at the end of the book.

We are very glad about the positive response which we received from our colleagues when we asked them to write the different chapters of this book. We want to thank them very much for their cooperation and the timely submission of their manuscripts. Particular thanks are due to Dr. K. K. Phua, Editor-in-Chief of World Scientific Publ. Co., Singapore. The cooperation with him has always been a pleasure to us.

H. Bunke
*Berne, Switzerland*

A. Sanfeliu
*Barcelona, Spain*

*December, 1987*

# CONTENTS

Preface     v

## PART I: THEORY

Chapter 1   Introduction and Overview     3
*Michael G. Thomason*

### Syntactic Representation and Parsing

Chapter 2   String Grammars for Syntactic Pattern Recognition     29
*H. Bunke*

Chapter 3   Parsing and Error-Correcting Parsing for
String Grammars     55
*E. Tanaka*

Chapter 4   Array, Tree and Graph Grammars     85
*Azriel Rosenfeld*

### Structural Representation and Matching

Chapter 5   String Matching for Structural Pattern Recognition     119
*H. Bunke*

Chapter 6   Matching Tree Structures     145
*Alberto Sanfeliu*

Chapter 7   Matching Relational Structures Using
Discrete Relaxation     179
*Linda G. Shapiro and Robert M. Haralick*

Contents

Chapter 8 Random Graphs 197
A.K.C. Wong, J. Constant and M.L. You

Learning

Chapter 9 Grammatical Inference 237
Laurent Miclet

Chapter 10 An Algorithm for Inferring Context-Free
Array Grammars 291
P.S.P. Wang and X.W. Dai

Hybrid Approaches

Chapter 11 Hybrid Pattern Recognition Methods 307
H. Bunke

Chapter 12 Combining Statistical and Structural Methods 349
Wen-Hsiang Tsai

PART II: APPLICATIONS

Chapter 13: Industrial Applications 369
Henry S. Baird

Chapter 14 Three-Dimensional Object Recognition by
Attributed Graphs 381
E.K. Wong

Chapter 15 Chinese Character Recognition 415
J.W. Tai and Y.J. Liu

Chapter 16 Table Driven Parsing for Shape Analysis 453
T.C. Henderson and A. Samal

Chapter 17 A General Purpose Line Drawing Analysis System 479
Roger Mohr

Chapter 18 ECG Analysis 499
E. Skordalakis

Author Index 533

Subject Index 541

# PART I: THEORY

# 1

# INTRODUCTION AND OVERVIEW

MICHAEL G. THOMASON
*Department of Computer Science*
*University of Tennessee*
*Knoxville, TN 37996*
*USA*

## 1. STRUCTURE IN PATTERNS

Two principal areas of contemporary pattern recognition are the *decision-theoretic* approach and the *syntactic/structural* approach. Decision-theoretic methods are based primarily on using numerical-valued features as a means for distinguishing one class of patterns from other classes[1]. By contrast, syntactic and structural methods are based on explicit or implicit representations of a class's structure, where *structure* conceptually means the characteristic way in which the subpatterns (or elements or components) of a pattern are related or configured together. Syntactic methods use the models and techniques of formal language theory; general structural methods use other models and techniques as well.

**Example 1.** In practice, it is frequently useful to define the *pattern primitives* as the simplest subpatterns identified in the raw data output of sensors. Then various relations among the primitives define subpatterns at a higher level. Related groups of these subpatterns may define more complex subpatterns in turn, and the analysis continues until the overall pattern is described.

Consider the five curved line segments $a, b, c, d, e$ in Fig. 1a as primitives for the boundary of the chromosome in Fig. 1b. A hierarchical description of the complete chromosome is given in the tree (Fig. 1c) in which the leaves are primitives and the interior nodes are subpatterns. Traversing the tree from its root towards its leaves indicates that the structure encountered in a clockwise scan of the boundary of this ⟨telocentric chromosome⟩ is a ⟨bottom⟩ attached to an ⟨armpair⟩, where a ⟨bottom⟩ is primitive $e$, an ⟨armpair⟩ is a ⟨side⟩ attached to an ⟨armpair⟩, a ⟨side⟩ is primitive $b$, and so on. ∎

Syntactic and structural pattern recognition is based on *discrete mathematical relations*[2,3] as the detailed descriptions of structure. Recall that the Cartesian product of set $A$ with set $B$ is denoted $A \times B$ and is the set of all ordered pairs

$$\{(a,b) | a \text{ in } A, b \text{ in } B\} .$$

A *relation* $R$ from $A$ to $B$ is a subset of $A \times B$, $R \subseteq A \times B$. The relations that can be defined from $A$ to $B$ range from the entire Cartesian product $A \times B$ itself to the null relation $\phi$, where $\phi$ is the null set with no elements. If the pair $(a,b)$ is in relation $R$, we say that "$a$ is $R$-related to $b$" and write

(a) Pattern primitives.

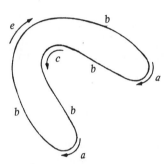

(b) Telocentric chromosome.

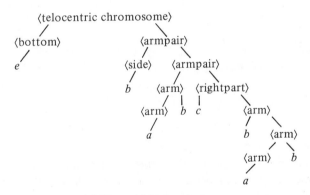

(c) Hierarchical description.

Fig. 1. Boundary structure of telocentric chromosome.

$aRb$ for short. If $R$ is a subset of $A \times A$, then $R$ is a relation *on the set A*.

The idea of a relation in $A \times B$ extends naturally to a relation in a product of a larger number of sets. Thus, an element of a relation in

$A \times B \times C$ is an ordered triple of three related items $(a, b, c)$, $a$ in $A$, $b$ in $B$, $c$ in $C$. A relation in $A \times B \times C \times D$ is a set of lists of four related items and relations in larger products are similarly defined.

As an illustration with finite strings of symbols, suppose that an infinite class $L$ contains the strings $abc, aabcc, aaabccc, \ldots$ but no other forms. The structure of the elements of $L$ is defined by a left-to-right ordering relation involving substrings of the symbols $a, b, c$; specifically, $x$ is in class $L$ iff in a left-to-right scan of $x$ there is a sequence of $n$ $a$'s, followed by one $b$, followed by $n$ $c$'s, for $n \geq 1$.

Structural relations in patterns may be defined *implicitly* or *explicitly*, that is, the relations may be implicit in the models and algorithms used or may be explicitly defined in detail. One method based on implicitly defined relations is the syntactic approach in which a pattern class is the language generated by a formal grammar[4,5,6]; in this case, the structural relations satisfied by every element in the language are implied by the syntactic and semantic rules of the grammar. An illustration of explicitly defined relations is the representation of a pattern class by a perfect prototype in which all details of the relations among subpatterns are fully listed, say, in the explicit form of a directed graph with nodes labeled as subpatterns and arcs labeled as relations[7,8].

## 2. AREAS OF RESEARCH

Among the topics of research in syntactic and structural techniques are the following four general areas.

### 2.1. Flexible Recognition Using Inexact Matching

Syntactic and structural representations are useful for defining quantitative similarity or distance measures from a candidate pattern to a model of a class and for developing algorithms for error-tolerant recognition based on those measures. An algorithm for an optimal classification (e.g. for minimum distance or maximum likelihood) is reasonable to compute in some cases; in others, suboptimal algorithms that perform well in practice are available. In the realm of discrete mathematics, it often occurs that optimal solutions of important problems can be found only by algorithms that exhaustively search through a prohibitively large number of possible solutions. As a result, considerable attention is given to restricted searches and to other techniques for developing algorithms that are not too complex to compute, yet yield "good" — even though possibly suboptimal — average classification performance.

## 2.2. Analysis of Syntactic and Structural Models

Discrete mathematical models of pattern structure may be analyzed themselves to compute quantitative measures of structural complexity, structural information content, or structural distance between classes. When stochastic models are used for environments in which there are natural variations or deformations due to noise, properties of various random variables and entropies of various probability measures are part of the analysis.

## 2.3. Inference and Machine Learning

*Inference* in syntactic and structural pattern analysis usually means machine learning in the form of an algorithm that automatically or semi-automatically constructs a structural representation when presented with a training set of items from a class. One example is grammatical inference, the inference of a grammar from a set of items known to belong to a particular language. Another example is analysis of the structure in a prototype in order to produce an explicit relational model.

When multiple samples are available, structure-learning algorithms are often designed to search for correspondences among subpatterns in the samples and attempt to generalize this structure into generic class descriptions; that is, inductive inference is attempted[9]. An extension is to refine an inferred model by using also some "negative samples" that must be excluded from the class. An algorithm may be unsupervised, in which case it is completely automatic and does not require any inputs other than the samples themselves; a supervised algorithm is semi-automatic and will at times require additional information, for example, a human expert's approval or disapproval of hypotheses about structure generated by the algorithm while it is being executed.

## 2.4. Integration of Syntactic and Structural Methods with Other Techniques

Methods that combine syntactic or structural aspects with other techniques of pattern recognition are called *hybrid approaches*[10]. Many pattern recognition systems are not purely syntactic or structural, but use instead a combination of techniques for pattern analysis. For example, the initial extraction of pattern primitives from raw data and their labeling as symbols with features or attributes, is often approached as a non-structural recognition problem; then the subsequent analysis of relations among the primitives deals with structural aspects[11].

A hybrid system is characterized by some degree of interaction between its structural and non-structural components. Structural relations may be used at times to improve the performance of the non-structural pattern recognition, for instance, by eliminating certain primitives from consideration by assigning probability 0 to those primitives that cannot satisfy relations already known to exist. In this way, structural constraints may help to minimize the complexity and maximize the likelihood of correct recognition of the non-structural processing.

## 3. SYNTACTIC METHODS

### 3.1. Grammars

The structure of many classes of patterns may be effectively represented by the discrete mathematical models of formal language theory[4,5,6]. Those primarily used are formal grammars and the algorithms for pattern analysis based on grammars.

The standard definition of a string-generating grammar $G = (N, T, P, S)$ gives its finite sets of nonterminals $N$, terminals $T$ and productions $P$, and the unique initial nonterminal $S$. It is required that $N \cap T = \phi$. This definition emphasizes that $P$ specifies a *rewriting* or *production relation* $\rightarrow$ on strings by listing each production in the form $x \rightarrow y$ for $x$ and $y$ in $(N \cup T)^*$. $(N \cup T)^*$ is the set of all finite strings using symbols in $N \cup T$ and includes the empty string $\varepsilon$.

In this production relation, $x \rightarrow y$ means that "$x$ may be rewritten as, or replaced by, $y$". For practical reasons, the grammars actually used are rarely more complex than context-free grammars; this means that each production has the form $A \rightarrow y$ in which $A$ is a single nonterminal.

The set of productions $P$ in a grammar $G$ imposes a structure or *syntax* on the language generated by $G$ via an implicit relation on strings; specifically, the *derivation relation* $\overset{*}{\Rightarrow}$ is the reflexive-transitive closure of the production relation $\rightarrow$, and *the language generated by $G$* is

$$L(G) = \{z | z \text{ is a string of terminals, } S \overset{*}{\Rightarrow} z\} \ .$$

**Example 2.** A straightforward use of a grammar to define a pattern class is to specify the terminals $T$ as the pattern primitives, the nonterminals $N$

as labels for subpatterns of related primitives or subpatterns and the productions $P$ as the rewriting rules needed to impose the required structure on each item in the language $L(G)$.

The string *ebabcbab*, which represents the sequence of primitives in a clockwise scan of the telocentric chromosome boundary in Fig. 1b, is in the language generated by the context-free grammar $G = (\{S, A, B, C, D, E, F\}, \{a, b, c, d, e\}, P, S)$ with the following seventeen productions:

$$
\begin{array}{lllll}
S \rightarrow BA & A \rightarrow CA & A \rightarrow AC & A \rightarrow DE & A \rightarrow ED \\
B \rightarrow e & B \rightarrow bB & B \rightarrow Bb & C \rightarrow b & C \rightarrow bC \\
C \rightarrow Cb & C \rightarrow d & D \rightarrow a & D \rightarrow bD & D \rightarrow Db \\
E \rightarrow cD & F \rightarrow Dc & & &
\end{array}
$$

Nonterminal $S$ stands for ⟨telocentric chromosome⟩, $A$ for ⟨armpair⟩, $B$ for ⟨bottom⟩, $C$ for ⟨side⟩, $D$ for ⟨arm⟩, $E$ for ⟨rightpart⟩ and $E$ for ⟨leftpart⟩. Figure 1c is a *derivation tree* for this string in $L(G)$. The other strings in $L(G)$ are encodings of boundaries of various telocentric chromosomes.

Terminals may also represent operations whereby subpatterns are related. Languages with operator symbols among the terminals include the Picture Description Languages[12] in which the terminal + means "connect head to tail", the terminal − means "connect head to head" and several other combining operations are defined. A production like $A \rightarrow B + C$ means that the subpattern $A$ consists of the subpattern $B$ joined head-to-tail to the subpattern $C$. ∎

The definition of a grammar may be extended to include features or attributes assigned to the nonterminals and terminals by attribute-value computation rules, usually called *semantic rules*. In formal terms, there is a syntax vs. semantics trade-off in the sense that, to define a specific language by a grammar, one has a choice of less complex syntax with more complex semantics, or vice versa[13]. But semantic rules are often useful in practice because they focus directly on the attributes or features of subpatterns[14]. A grammar may also be extended to weighted derivations, for example, to create a stochastic grammar by attaching probabilities to the productions so that stochastic aspects of natural or noise-induced variations in structure are described[4,5,6].

There is a one-to-one correspondence between grammars as generators of languages and *automata* as recognizers of languages[4,5,6]. An automaton is a mathematical model of a computing machine that scans an input item $x$

and determines whether $x$ is in a specific language $L$ or not. As conceptual models of computation, automata are often used as the bases of language recognition algorithms.

## 3.2. Syntax-Directed Translations

An aspect of formal languages of interest in syntactic pattern recognition is syntax-directed translation — a method of defining a translation relation that takes structure into account. A *translation* from language $L_1$ to language $L_2$ is a relation $M$ in $L_1 \times L_2$ where $xMy$ means "output string $y$ in $L_2$ is a translation of input string $x$ from $L_1$."

To study translation formally with a model based on syntactic structure, we generalize context-free grammar $G = (N, T, P, S)$ to a *syntax-directed translation schema* $T = (N, T_i, T_\theta, R, S)$ where $N$ is a finite set of nonterminals, $T_i$ and $T_\theta$ are finite sets of input and output terminals respectively, $R$ is a finite set of translation rules and $S$ is the unique starting nonterminal. It is required that $N \cap T_i = \phi$ and that $N \cap T_\theta = \phi$. A translation rule in $R$ is basically two context-free productions locked together to allow simultaneous derivation of an input string and its translation as an output string. Each rule has the form $A \to \alpha, \beta$ where $A$ is a nonterminal, $\alpha$ is a string in $(N \cup T_i)^*$; $\beta$ is a string in $(N \cup T_\theta)^*$ and each nonterminal in $\alpha$ has an identical, associated nonterminal in $\beta$. The left-to-right order of nonterminals in $\alpha$ may be different from the order of their associates in $\beta$, but associated nonterminals must always be rewritten simultaneously.

A rule like $A \to \alpha, \beta$ is used to rewrite nonterminal $A$ in the input derivation by $\alpha$ and simultaneously to rewrite the associated nonterminal $A$ by $\beta$ in the output derivation. Thus, $A \to \alpha$ is considered to be an input-string production and $A \to \beta$ is a corresponding output-string production. The translation relation defined by schema $T$ is

$$\chi(T) = \{(x, y) | S \overset{*}{\Rightarrow} x \text{ as an input string derivation}$$
$$\text{for } x \text{ in } T_i{}^*, S \overset{*}{\Rightarrow} y \text{ simultaneously as an output}$$
$$\text{derivation for } y \text{ in } T_\theta{}^* \} \ .$$

**Example 3.** In a formal sense, error-correction in languages is often syntax-directed[15]. Suppose it is discovered that primitive $c$ in Fig. 1a is occasionally mislabeled as $e$. As a correcting translation based on the grammar $G$ in Ex. 2 above, we create a schema $T = (\{S, A, B, C, D, E, F, \}, \{a, b, c, d, e\}, \{a, b, c, d, e\}, R, S)$ with the two rules needed to change an erroneous $e$ into a $c$, namely:

$$E \to eD, cD \qquad F \to De, Dc$$

The other rules in the schema describe no error, so they are identical to the seventeen productions in $G$ and are the same for input as for output; these rules include items like $B \to bB, bB$ and $S \to BA, BA$.

Suppose the $c$ in the string $ebabcbab$ for the chromosome boundary in Fig. 1b is mislabeled as an $e$, so that the actual input string to be recognized is $ebabebab$. Using the syntax-directed translation schema $T$ with its error-correcting rules, we can derive this input string and simultaneously derive a corrected output translation:

Input:   $S \quad BA \quad eA \quad eCA \quad ebA \quad ebDE$
$\quad\quad\quad \Rightarrow \quad\ \Rightarrow \quad\ \Rightarrow \quad\ \ \Rightarrow \quad\ \ \Rightarrow \quad\quad\ \Rightarrow$
Output:   $S \quad BA \quad eA \quad eCA \quad ebA \quad ebDE$

$\quad\quad ebDbE \quad\ ebabE \quad\ ebabeD$
$\quad\quad\quad\ \Rightarrow \quad\quad\ \ \Rightarrow \quad\quad\ \ \Rightarrow$
$\quad\quad ebDbE \quad\ ebabE \quad\ ebabcD$

$\quad\quad ebabebD \quad\ ebabebDb \quad\ ebabebab$
$\quad\quad\quad\ \Rightarrow \quad\quad\quad\ \Rightarrow$
$\quad\quad ebabcbD \quad\ ebabcbDb \quad\ ebabcbab$

The first eight translation rules used in this sequence of eleven are

$$S \to BA, BA \quad B \to e, e \quad A \to CA, CA \quad C \to b, b$$
$$A \to DE, DE \quad D \to Db, Db \quad D \to a, a \quad E \to eD, cD$$

The first seven of these represent no error, but the eighth $E \to eD, cD$ accomplishes the error-correcting translation of $e$ (as an erroneous symbol in the input string) into $c$ (as a corrected output string symbol). ∎

Syntax-directed translation may be extended to multiple output languages by defining an *order n translation* to be a relation in $L_i \times L_{\theta_1} \times L_{\theta_2} \times \ldots \times L_{\theta_n}$ where $L_i$ is the output language and $L_{\theta_j}$ is the $j$th output language, $1 \le j \le n$. An order $n$ syntax-directed translation schema is a system $T = (N, T_i, T_{\theta_1}, \ldots, T_{\theta_n}, R, S)$ with nonterminals $N$; terminal sets $T_i, T_{\theta_1}, \ldots, T_{\theta_n}$ for the various languages, starting nonterminal $S$ and rules of the form $A \to \alpha, \beta_1, \beta_2, \ldots, \beta_n$ where $\alpha$ is in $(N \cup T_i)^*$ and each $\beta_j$ is in $(N \cup T_{\theta_j})^*$. Each $\beta_j$ has identical, associated nonterminals for those in

$\alpha$. The output languages are generally viewed as a left-to-right translation sequence derived from the input string.

Order $n$ schemata[16] have been proposed to study time-varying images where the structural aspects change as subpatterns move relative to one another or as the image sensor is shifted. The syntax-directed model is also extended to tree grammars for tree-to-tree translations[17]. This model has been used to study a registered sequence of images with objects in motion (vehicles moving through an intersection); the information in each image is represented as a tree and the translation of one tree to the next must obey the constraints on the expected object motion during the time between images. The idea is to embed in the translation rules all the known constraints on the way images may vary.

**Example 4**. To demonstrate translation representing simple movement in one dimension, we create a schema that translates a string like $+|++$ into the string $++|+$, that is, the terminal symbol $|$ shifts one position to the right within a string of $+$'s. The schema is $T = (\{S, A\}, \{+, |\}, \{+, |\}, R, S)$ with these three rules:

$$S \rightarrow A + | + A, A + +|A \qquad A \rightarrow +A, +A \qquad A \rightarrow \varepsilon, \varepsilon \ .$$

The derivation of the string $+|++$ as input and its simultaneous translation to output are as follows:

$$
\begin{array}{lllll}
\text{Input: } S & A+|+A & \varepsilon+|+A & +|++A & +|++\varepsilon \\
 & \Rightarrow & \Rightarrow & \Rightarrow & \Rightarrow \\
\text{Output: } S & A++|A & \varepsilon++|A & ++|+A & ++|+\varepsilon
\end{array}
$$

Thus, the pair $(+|++, ++|+)$ is in $\chi(T)$, the translation relation defined implicitly by the schema $T$. The string $++|+$ itself translates to $+++|$. The string $+++|$ has no translation defined by the schema because $+++|$ cannot be derived as an input string.

In a more elaborate translation, suppose that the terminal $|$ may remain stationary or move one position to the left or right until it reaches one end of the string. The new schema $T' = (\{S, A\}, \{+, |\}, \{+, |\}, R', S)$ for these translations has five rules:

$$
\begin{array}{ll}
S \rightarrow A+|+A, A+|+A \qquad & S \rightarrow A+|+A, A|++A \\
S \rightarrow A+|+A, A++|A \qquad & A \rightarrow +A, +A \\
A \rightarrow \varepsilon, \varepsilon &
\end{array}
$$

The translations may be described in more detail if probabilities of movement are available. Suppose that stationarity of the terminal | is estimated to occur with probability $p$, left movement with probability $q$, and right movement with probability $(1-p-q)$. These probabilities may be incorporated into the schema $T'$ by assigning probabilities to the selection of a rule for rewriting the nonterminal $S$, so that $T'$ becomes a *stochastic schema*:

$$p : S \rightarrow A + | + A, A + | + A \qquad q : S \rightarrow A + | + A, A| + +A$$
$$(1 - p - q) : S \rightarrow A + | + A, A + +|A$$

Note that $S$ will be rewritten as $A + | + A$ with probability 1 in the input derivation but as $A + | + A, A| + +A$, or $A + +|A$ with the appropriate probability in the output translation. Assigning probabilities to the two rules for rewriting the nonterminal $A$ completes the specification of $T$ as a stochastic schema; then various aspects may be studied via the stochastic process that describes its translations[5,15]. ∎

### 3.3. Grammars for Non-String Languages

As defined above, a grammar $G$ gives a finite rewriting relation implicitly defining a string language $L(G)$. This idea may be generalized to a grammar for a language with elements more complex than strings. Trees, arrays, webs and graphs are primary examples[4,5,18−24]. These discrete mathematical items have a more complex relational structure than strings in their own right and they are useful in applications in which a rich structure must be described or in which the patterns themselves have a natural form conveniently mapped into a non-string representation. The structure of a tree, for example, immediately defines two partial ordering relations on the nodes, namely, (1) a *top-to-bottom relation* in which node $a$ is related to node $b$ iff $b$ is reachable from $a$ along a path from the root, and (2) a *left-to-right relation* in which node $a$ is related to node $b$ iff the path from the root to $a$ is obtained by following arcs equal to or left of the arcs on the path from the root to $b$.

Some aspects of string grammars are carried over to non-string environments in a straightforward way. The underlying interpretation of any grammar $G$ is that $G$ provides a finite set of rules of syntax for its language $L(G)$, and a non-string grammar may include items that function like "nonterminals", "terminals" and a rewriting relation. But descriptions of the way in which the rewritings occur are more subtle and intricate. For example, if $x \rightarrow y$ is a production in a graph grammar, the actual replacement of $x$ by $y$ as a subgraph contained in a larger graph requires a detailed specification of how to carry out the rewriting[19,20]; that is, the production $x \rightarrow y$ needs an associated *embedding rule* telling how to remove subgraph $x$ and install subgraph $y$ in its place.

As would be expected, investigation of the properties of these higher order systems is generally more difficult than with string grammars. But in various applications, a language of trees, webs, or graphs is a more natural description of pattern structure than a language of strings.

## 4. EXPLICIT STRUCTURAL RELATIONS
### 4.1. Digraphs

The most effective approach to a variety of pattern recognition problems is the use of explicit descriptions of structural relations for the classes of interest. As an explicit representation of a relation $R$ in $A \times B$, it is often convenient to use a *directed graph* or *digraph* in which (1) the nodes are the elements of $A \cup B$, and (2) there is an arc directed from node $a$ to node $b$ iff $(a, b)$ is in $R$. In this way, $R$ becomes the "arc-connection relation" of the equivalent digraph. More than one relation from $A$ to $B$ may be given in the same digraph, in which case each arc must be labeled with its own relation's name. Figure 2 illustrates these ideas for relations $R_1$ and $R_2$ from $A = \{a, b\}$ to $B = \{x, y, z\}$.

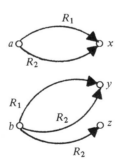

Fig. 2. Relation $R_2$ and function $R_1$.

A powerful approach to structural pattern analysis with explicit relations is the use of digraphs with attributes attached to nodes or arcs[7,8,25]. For example, an "equal length" relation $R$ might be defined such that $xRy$ means "edge $x$ has the same length as edge $y$". $R$ is an example of establishing a relationship by comparing the values of a specific attribute or feature for two primitives. An important extension in practice is based on ideas of approximate structural matching because we would often want to define $R$ as the relation "approximately equal in length" and have "approximately" taken into account by allowing inexact matching of $x$ with $y$, say, by using an algorithm to compute a weight to reflect the inexactness.

Probabilities are incorporated into structural digraph representations with attributes by Wong and You[26] to study random graphs. The distribution assigned to a graph is estimated as the structural probability distribution of a class and an entropy-based distance measure between graphs is defined for purposes of comparison and analysis of classes. Information-theoretic concepts have also been used by Kak *et al.*[27] for stereo vision in robotic assembly, in which structural descriptions of left and right images of the same scene must be matched. The approach is to use information-theoretic measures to guide the search to find a correspondence between the primitives in the left image and the primitives in the right image of the same scene.

### 4.2. Functions and Homomorphisms

Suppose $R$ is a relation from $A$ to $B$ such that, for each element $a$ in $A$, there is exactly one ordered pair $(a, b)$ in $R$; then $R$ is a *function* from $A$ to $B$, denoted $R : A \rightarrow B$. If the pair $(a, b)$ is in function $R$, we write $R(a) = b$. In a digraph, a function $R$ has the property that exactly one $R$-arc leaves each node in $A$. In Fig. 2, $R_1 = \{(a, x), (b, y)\}$ is a function but $R_2 = \{(a, x), (b, y), (b, z)\}$ is not because element $b$ is $R_2$-related to too many things.

Consider further the digraph arcs for a function $R : A \rightarrow B$. If each node in $B$ has at least one entering arc, then $R$ is an *onto* function, also called a *surjection*. If each node in $B$ has at most one entering arc, then $R$ is a *one-to-one* function, also called an *injection*. If $R$ is both onto and one-to-one, then each node in $B$ has exactly one entering arc and $R$ is a *bijection*. Various properties of these kinds of functions are well known[2,3]. For example, if $h : P \rightarrow Q$ is a bijection, then so is its inverse function from $Q$ to $P$; and if $h : P \rightarrow Q$ and $g : Q \rightarrow T$ are both in (or sur- or bi-)jections, so is the composite map $h \circ g : P \rightarrow T$ in this diagram:

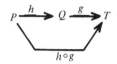

Suppose that $P$ in $A \times A$ is a structural relation for pattern components in $A$ and that $Q$ in $B \times B$ is a structural relation for pattern components in $B$. Suppose further that we want to compare the structure defined by $P$ on $A$ with the structure defined by $Q$ on $B$. Adopting a concept from modern algebra, we search for a function $R : A \to B$ which "preserves the relation $P$ as the relation $Q$" in the sense that, for each pair $(a_i, a_j)$ in $P$, we find $(R(a_i), R(a_j))$ in $Q$. A function with that property is a *homomorphism*, and we say that "$R : A \to B$ is a homomorphism carrying relation $P$ into relation $Q$." The notation $R : (A, P) \to (B, Q)$ is sometimes used to indicate this.

A homomorphism that is also a bijection is an *isomorphism*. An isomorphism $R : (A, P) \to (B, Q)$ establishes that when the elements of $A$ are associated with those of $B$ by the function $R$, then the two patterns have a totally identical structure insofar as the relations $P$ on $A$ and $Q$ on $B$ are concerned. A homomorphism $R : (A, P) \to (B, Q)$ that is also an onto function is an *epimorphism* and indicates that $(A, P)$ maybe "larger" than $(B, Q)$ because $(B, Q)$ involves fewer components; this can also be expressed as an isomorphism carrying $Q$ on $B$ to a subgraph of $P$ on $A$. A homomorphism $R : (A, P) \to (B, Q)$ that is also a one-to-one function is a *monomorphism* and indicates that $(A, P)$ may be "smaller" than $(B, Q)$ because $(B, Q)$ involves more components; this can also be expressed as an isomorphism carrying $P$ on $A$ to a subgraph of $Q$ on $B$.

**Example 5**. Consider Fig. 3a, the digraph of relation $P = \{(4,3), (3,1), (3,2), (2,2)\}$ on set $A = \{1, 2, 3, 4\}$. The function $h_1 : (A, P) \to (B1, Q1)$ defined in Fig. 3b is an isomorphism for relation $Q1$ on $B1 = \{w, x, y, z\}$; this means that the inverse relation $h_1^{-1} : (B1, Q1) \to (A, P)$ is also an isomorphism. In Fig. 3c, the function $h_2 : (A, P) \to (B2, Q2)$ is an epimorphism for relation $Q2$ on $B2 = \{w, x, z\}$; relation $Q2$ on $B2$ is isomorphic to a subgraph of relation $P$ on $A$. In Fig. 3d, the function $h_3 : (A, P) \to (B3, Q3)$ is a monomorphism for relation $Q3$ on $B3 = \{v, w, x, y, z\}$; relation $P$ on $A$ is isomorphic to a subgraph of relation $Q3$ on $B3$. ∎

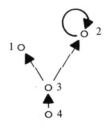

(a) $P$ relation on $A$.

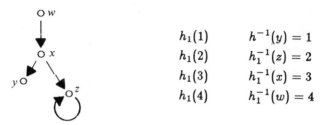

$$h_1(1) \qquad h^{-1}(y) = 1$$
$$h_1(2) \qquad h_1^{-1}(z) = 2$$
$$h_1(3) \qquad h_1^{-1}(x) = 3$$
$$h_1(4) \qquad h_1^{-1}(w) = 4$$

(b) $Q1$ relation on $B1$, isomorphism $h_1:(A, P) \rightarrow (B1, Q1)$ and inverse isomorphism $h_1^{-1}$: $(B1, Q1) \rightarrow (A, P)$.

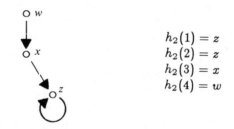

$$h_2(1) = z$$
$$h_2(2) = z$$
$$h_2(3) = x$$
$$h_2(4) = w$$

(c) $Q2$ relation on $B2$ and epimorphism $h_2: (A, P) \rightarrow (B2, Q2)$.

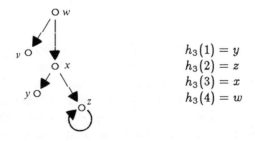

$$h_3(1) = y$$
$$h_3(2) = z$$
$$h_3(3) = x$$
$$h_3(4) = w$$

(d) $Q3$ relation on $B3$ and monomorphism $h_3: (A,P) \rightarrow (B3, Q3)$.

Fig. 3. Aspects of homomorphisms.

## 5. FLEXIBLE MATCHING: GENERAL COMMENTS

Given a candidate item $z$ and a structural specification of a class $C$, the recognition task involves determining how well the structure of $z$ matches that of $C$. In the syntactic approach, class $C$ is implicitly defined by grammar $G$, that is, $C = L(G)$. Given a candidate item $z$ and a grammar $G$, the process of searching for a sequence of productions to derive $z$ is called *parsing*[4,5,6,28]. If $z$ is successfully parsed, then a structural analysis of $z$ is also available because a production sequence has been found.

When relations are given as explicit digraphs, the comparison of a candidate $z$ with a class $C$ is expressed as a subgraph isomorphism problem or a graph homomorphism problem, that is, as a search for a function which satisfies requirements for (at least approximate) preservation of structure[7,8]. This general category of search problems has been studied by Haralick and Shapiro as *consistent labeling*[29].

In environments in which candidate $z$ may be deformed by noise or may have natural variations not completely defined in the representation of a class $C$, one must consider error-tolerant comparison based on similarity or distance measures. In using relational digraphs with attributes, Shapiro and Haralick[7] study computational methods using tree search with look-ahead operations to search for a function to compare prototype and candidate structure according to various criteria for inexact matching. Also using an attributed relational digraph $P$ as a model of a pure pattern, Tsai and Fu[8] define local deformations in a candidate digraph $P'$ to be changes in node labels. If changes are also present in relational arcs, then $P'$ has structural deformations. A state-space search approach to "correcting" $P'$ into $P$ using deformation weights is developed for some constrained cases.

An approach used successfully in many applications, including error-correcting parsing with a grammar, is to define a finite set of structure-modifying operations as "errors" or "mutations" that can occur in candidate patterns and to compute quantitative measures that take the costs of these operations into account. For structural matching with strings, for example, a standard method for computing the dissimilarity $d(z, C)$ of a candidate string $z$ from a class $C$ is to define the individual costs of the four atomic operations of *match* (or no change), *substitution*, *deletion* and *insertion* on the symbols in $z$; then $d(z, C)$ is computed as the summed costs of a sequence of these operations to edit $z$ into a string $y$ in $C$ where the dissimilarity $d(z, y)$ of $z$ from $y$ is minimized[4,5,6,30].

If no specialized knowledge about an application is available, we may set the costs at $+0$ for each match of a symbol in $z$ with a symbol in $y$ and $+1$ for each substitution, deletion, or insertion in $z$. Then $d(z, y)$ is the count of the minimum number of changes to make $z$ identical to $y$ and is called the *Levenshtein distance*[4].

More subtle models take probabilities into account, for example, the *a priori* probability of $y$ and the individual error-in-symbol probabilities. Minimal cost editing of a string $x$ into a string $y$ is also used at times as a nearest-neighbor calculation for comparing two classes $C_1$ and $C_2$; that is, we search for $x$ in $C_1$ and $y$ in $C_2$ that minimize a relevant string-to-string measure $d(x, y)$. Stochastic models may, of course, allow a prototype item to be defined as the class representative for purposes of comparing statistical cluster centers of classes. If attribute values are attached to symbols, then approximate matching of these values may also be incorporated as computations with weights.

The idea of error-correction is extended in a rigorous way to trees by defining tree-editing operations, typically, substitution of a node label, insertion of a node between an existing node and its predecessor, insertion of a node to the left of all successors of a node, insertion of a node to the right of an existing node and deletion of a node of rank 0 or 1. A generalized error-correcting tree automaton is available for minimum cost correcting when costs of the individual edit operations are known[4].

Error-correction has been extended to graph-to-graph matching for graphs with node and arc labels by defining graph-edit operations, typically, insertion or deletion of node or arc, label substitution at node or on arc and node label merging or splitting. A distance measure between non-hierarchical attributed digraphs that reflects the cost of editing a candidate graph into a reference graph but also includes the cost of recognition of the nodes, is used by Sanfeliu and Fu[24]. The similarity of feature values at nodes in the candidate graph to those in the prototype graph is taken into account in the overall cost.

## 6. INFERENCE AND MACHINE LEARNING: GENERAL COMMENTS

Work in inference and machine learning includes the efforts to develop algorithms that can reduce the human labor-intensiveness of producing syntactic or structural descriptions of pattern classes, usually via automatic or semi-automatic processing of training samples. In some cases, an inference algorithm might also be able to find a less obvious or more complex structure than a human would describe.

Fundamental considerations for any inference algorithm are the nature of its search for structure and the form taken by its generalizations (if generalization is in fact attempted). An objective of many inference methods is to find a substructure common to a training set of samples by searching for comparable instances of repetitive subpatterns; these instances are then represented in a generalized form. For example, in grammatical inference, recurrent subpatterns may be considered to be instances of "pumping by recursion" and may be formally represented by recursion in the productions of a grammar[5]. More elaborate inference methods may also estimate weights for options in structure, typically by using relative frequencies of occurrence as probabilities[4,5,6].

An illustration of both inference and inexact matching with a stochastic generator of strings is provided by a method in which the four string-edit operations described above are used to infer a Markov chain from a set of sample strings[30]. Each sample in turn is installed in the Markov chain by an alignment that gives the sample its maximum achievable probability as a realization. The edit costs are based on the relative frequencies with which symbols occur in aligned samples and are used in the cost function for dynamic programming to compute optimal (maximum probability) alignments. As a consequence of this method, the more (or less) frequently a substring is found in the sample set, the higher (or lower) is its probability as a network realization. Entropies are valuable analysis measures; using a candidate string's probability computed by the same cost function as a similarity measure has proven useful for error-tolerant pattern recognition.

**Example 6.** The strings *BMRMJ*, *BRMLJ* and *BMLJ* are samples of the same class. (Specifically, they are string encodings of acoustic information in isolated utterances of the spoken word "two".) The alignment of the first two strings for maximum re-enforcement of substrings is

$$
\begin{array}{cccccc}
B & M & R & M & \varepsilon & J \\
| & | & | & | & | & | \\
B & \varepsilon & R & M & L & J
\end{array}
$$

where the empty string $\varepsilon$ is used for convenience to show alignment details.

This alignment yields the Markov network,

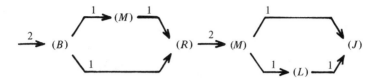

in which the six states are $(B), (M), (R), (L)$ and $(J)$, and the arcs are labeled with their relative frequencies of use in sample alignments. The network clearly shows the initial $B$, the midstring $RM$ and the final $J$ as "landmarks" that occur in left-to-right order in every sample, whereas the $M$ before the $R$ and the $L$ before the $J$ occur at their relative positions in half the samples.

The third string aligns for maximum probability as

$$
\begin{array}{cccccc}
B & M & R & M & \varepsilon & J \\
| & | & | & | & | & | \\
B & \varepsilon & R & M & L & J \\
| & | & | & | & | & | \\
B & \varepsilon & \varepsilon & M & L & J
\end{array}
$$

to yield the new network,

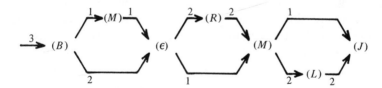

A new state $(\varepsilon)$ with the unobservable empty string has been added for convenience in arc fan-in or fan-out and arcs have been adjusted to reflect the new sample. The new network now shows the initial $B$, the midstring $M$, and the final $J$ as substrings occurring with probability 1. The first $M$ occurs only one time in three, the midstring $R$ is an event with probability $2/3$ and the $L$ before the $J$ also occurs with probability $2/3$.

Although this illustration uses strings of four or five symbols, the method can be used effectively to search for quite complex pattern structure in sample strings with lengths of hundreds of symbols[30]. The fundamental idea of this inference — to look for recurrent structure as landmark substrings with relative frequency weightings — is reasonable in some applications; in others, re-enforcement of substrings in a Markov model does not yield a useful structural description and other inference techniques should be considered. ■

## 7. COMPUTATIONAL COMPLEXITY OF ALGORITHMS

As mentioned earlier, finding an optimal solution to a structural problem often requires an algorithm that carries out a complex search. With respect to computations in "real world" applications, a *complexity measure* of an algorithm indicates an amount of a resource required to execute the algorithm on a computer, expressed as a function of the size of the problem input to the algorithm[3]. A "resource" is a practical computational requirement like CPU time or core memory and is measured in units used. Typically, complexity would reflect the total CPU time required or the maximum memory needed as an algorithm is executed for a certain sized input problem.

The complexity of computations ultimately affects syntactic and structural pattern recognition because algorithms yielding optimal solutions frequently involve very large searches, at the worst, searches that exhaustively examine all combinations of options. Since the search space often expands in an exponential way as the size of the input problem increases, the demand for computational resources quickly becomes excessive. As a result, less complex algorithms are often implemented to avoid exhaustive searches, but at the risk of finding a suboptimal solution rather than a truly optimal one.

As a specific illustration in pattern analysis of finite strings of symbols, suppose we wish to compare the structure of a string $x = x_1 x_2 \ldots x_n$ of $n$ symbols with a string $y = y_1 y_2 \ldots y_m$ of $m$ symbols. The comparison is a search for a sequence of edit operations (substitutions, deletions, insertions and matches performed independently on a symbol-by-symbol basis in $x$) that modifies $x$ and makes it identical to $y$. An additive cost for each operation is defined using any available information about the specific application and the search is for an alignment of $x$ with $y$ in which the summed cost of all edits of $x$ is minimized.

This is a minimum-cost, error-correcting comparison of $x$, say, as a candidate pattern to be classified, with $y$, say, as a prototype string for a pattern class. The method extends in a logical way to comparing a candidate string $x$ with a network that defines more than one string[26].

**Example 7.** Figure 4 shows a dynamic programming matrix for computing the optimal alignment(s) of $x = ab$ with $y = acb$ when the additive cost is $+1$ for each substitution, $+3$ for each deletion, $+2$ for each insertion and $+0$ for each match. The matrix is filled in by looping over columns and rows from the upper left entry $m(0,0)$ to the lower right $m(3,2)$. The entry at row-$i$ and column-$j$ is $m(i,j)$ and is computed as the minimum summed cost among the three paths into $m(i,j)$ from its three neighbors $m(i-1, j-1), m(i, j-1)$, and $m(i-1, j)$:

$$m(i,j) = \min \begin{cases} m(i, j-1) + 3 & \text{[delete]} \\ m(i-1, j-1) + \begin{cases} 0 & \text{if } x_i = y_j & \text{[match]} \\ 1 & \text{if } x_i \neq y_j & \text{[substitute]} \end{cases} \\ m(i-1, j) + 2 & \text{[insert]} \end{cases}.$$

The optimal cost is the lower right entry, in this case, $m(3,2) = 2$. The optimal alignment which gives the detailed edit sequence to transform $x$ into $y$ with the minimum cost, is

$$\begin{array}{rccc} x = & a & \varepsilon & b \\ & |\text{match} & |\text{insert} & |\text{match} \\ y = & a & c & b \\ & |+0 & |+2 & |+0 \\ \text{total cost} = & 0 & 2 & 2 \end{array}$$

where $\varepsilon$ is the empty string, the unobservable string with no symbols, used here for convenience in showing the optimal alignment. ∎

|   | $x$ | |
|---|---|---|
|   | $a$ | $b$ |
| $a$ | 0 | 2 |
| $y$ $c$ | 2 | 1 |
| $b$ | 4 | 2 |

Fig. 4. Dynamic programming matrix for string-to-string comparison.

A useful measure of the computational complexity of comparing a string $x$ of $n$ symbols with a string $y$ of $m$ symbols is the number of entries that must be computed in a dynamic programming matrix, that is, $nm$ entries, interpreted as a measure of the storage of the matrix entries or the time to compute them. The complexity for the matrix in Fig. 4 is only $(2)(3) = 6$, but applications may involve much longer strings. For $n = m = 100$, for instance, the complexity has reached 10,000. A basic approach to reducing this complexity is to inhibit the computation of matrix entries highly unlikely to be in an optimal alignment: at the price of some extra book-keeping and at the risk of missing the optimal solution, many entries might be avoided, thereby yielding substantial net reduction in computations.

A standard method of inhibiting computations is to keep running counts of the number of deletions count $(d)$ and insertions count $(i)$ performed as the matrix is being filled in, and to set a threshold $t$ on the absolute value | count $(d)$ – count $(i)$| such that entries for which

$$|\text{ count }(d) - \text{count }(i)| > t$$

are not computed (equivalently, these entries are immediately assigned a symbol for "infinite cost"). The idea is to set the threshold value such that a preponderance of either deletions or insertions larger than $t$ is unlikely to be optimal. Essentially, the threshold constrains the dynamic programming to compute matrix entries inside a diagonal channel and to avoid entries outside the channel; hence, $t$ must be established to balance the reduction of complexity (lower $t$) with the risk of missing the optimal solution (higher $t$).

## 8. CONCLUSION

This chapter has given an overview of syntactic and structural pattern recognition based on implicit and explicit representations of relations. The chapters following in Part I discuss in detail syntactic representation and parsing, structural representation and matching, machine learning and hybrid approaches. The chapters in Part II discuss state-of-the-art applications of syntactic and structural techniques in industry and in areas such as 3-D object recognition, Chinese characters, line drawings, analysis of shapes and ECGs.

REFERENCES

1. J.T. Tou and R.C. Gonzalez, *Pattern Recognition Principles* (Addison-Wesley, Reading, MA, 1974).
2. S. MacLane and G. Birkhoff, *Algebra* (MacMilland, Toronto, Canada, 1967).
3. D.F. Stanat and D.F. McAllister, *Discrete Mathematics in Computer Science* (Prentice-Hall, Englewood Cliffs, NJ, 1977).
4. K.S. Fu, *Syntactic Pattern Recognition and Applications* (Prentice-Hall, Engelwood Cliffs, NJ, 1982).

5. R.C. Gonzalez and M.G. Thomason, *Syntactic Pattern Recognition: An Introduction* (Addison Wesley, Reading, MA, 1978).

6. L. Miclet, *Structural Methods in Pattern Recognition* (Springer-Verlag, New York, 1986).

7. L.G. Shapiro and R.M. Haralick, "Structural descriptions and inexact matching", *IEEE Trans. PAMI* **3** (1981) 504-519.

8. W.H. Tsai and K.S. Fu, "Error-correcting isomorphisms of attributed relational graphs for pattern analysis", *IEEE Trans. SMC* **9** (1979) 757-768.

9. D. Angluin and C.H. Smith, "Inductive inference: Theory and Methods", *Computing Surveys* **6** (1983) 237-269.

10. H. Bunke, "Hybrid methods in pattern recognition", in *Pattern Recognition Theory and Applications*, eds. P.A. Devijver and J. Kittler (Springer Verlag, New York, 1987) pp. 367-382.

11. K.S. Fu, *et al.*, reprinted papers in "Special Memorial Issue for Professor King-Sun Fu", *IEEE Trans. PAMI* **8** (3) (1986).

12. A.C. Shaw, "Parsing of graph representable pictures", *J. ACM* **17** (1970) 453-481.

13. A. Pyster and H.W. Buttleman, "Semantic-syntax-directed translation", *Information and Control* **39** (1978) 320-361.

14. W.H. Tsai and S.S. Yu, "Attributed string matching with merging for shape recognition", *IEEE Trans. PAMI* **7** (1985) 453-462.

15. M.G. Thomason, "Stochastic SDTS for correction of errors in context-free languages", *IEEE Trans. Comp.* **24** (1975) 1211-1216.

16. T.I. Fan and K.S. Fu, "A syntactic approach to time-varying image analysis", *Comp. Graphics and Image Processing* **11** (1979) 138-149.

17. K.S. Fu and T.I. Fan, "Tree translation and its application to a time-varying image analysis problem", *IEEE Trans. SMC* **12** (1986) 856-867.

18. H. Bunke, "Attributed graph grammars and their application to schematic diagram interpretation", *IEEE Trans. PAMI* **4** (1982) 574-582.

19. M. Nagl, "A tutorial and bibliographical survey on graph grammars", in *Graph-Grammars and Their Application to Computer Science and Biology*, Lecture Notes in Computer Science (Springer-Verlag, New York, 1979).

20. T. Pavlidis, "Structural descriptions and graph grammars" in *Pictorial Information Systems* (Springer-Verlag, New York, 1980).

21. T. Pavlidis, *Structural Pattern Recognition*, (Springer-Verlag, New York, 1977).

22. A. Rosenfeld, *Picture Languages* (Academic Press, New York, 1979).

23. A. Rosenfeld and D.L. Milgram "Web automata and web grammars", in *Machine Intelligence-7*, eds. B. Meltzer and D. Richie (Wiley, New York, 1972).

24. A. Sanfeliu and K.S. Fu, "A distance measure between attributed relational graphs for pattern recognition", *IEEE Trans. SMC* **13** (1983) 353-362.

25. L.G. Shapiro, "A structural model of shape", *IEEE Trans. PAMI* **2** (1980) 111-126.

26. A.K.C. Wong and M. You, "Entropy and distance of random graphs with application to structural pattern recognition", *IEEE Trans. PAMI* **7** (1985) 599-609.

27. A.C. Kak, K.L. Boyer, C.H. Chen, R.J. Safranek. and H.S. Yang, "A knowledge-based robotic assembly cell", *IEEE Expert* **1** (1986) 63-83.

28. E. Tanaka, M. Ikeda and K. Ezure, "Direct parsing", *J. Patt. Recog.* **19** (1986) 315-324.

29. R.M Haralick and L.G. Shapiro, "The consistent labeling problem: Part II", *IEEE Trans. PAMI* **2** (1980) 193-204.

30. M.G. Thomason and E. Granum, "Dynamic programming inference of Markov networks from finite sets of sample strings", *IEEE Trans. PAMI* **8** (1986) 491-502.

# Syntactic Representation and Parsing

# 2

# STRING GRAMMARS FOR SYNTACTIC PATTERN RECOGNITION

H. BUNKE

*Universität Bern*
*Institut für Informatik und angewandte Mathematik*
*Länggass-Strasse 51, CH-3012 Bern*
*Switzerland*

The aim of this chapter is to give an introduction to string grammars and their application to pattern recognition. First we discuss formal grammars as they are known from the theory of formal languages and consider, from a general point of view, how they can be used in pattern recognition. Then we review approaches particularly developed for application in pattern recognition. These include probabilistic grammars, attributed grammars, and higher-dimensional extensions of string grammars.

## 1. INTRODUCTION

The basic idea underlying any approach to syntactic and structural pattern recognition is the explicit use of structure for pattern representation. So the structural properties of unknown patterns to be classified or analyzed are stressed as well as the structural properties which are common to all members of a pattern class. A structural representation puts emphasis on how a complex pattern is recursively built up from elementary components, including relations of various types which exist between the individual parts of a pattern.

In the syntactic approach, formal grammars are used for pattern class representation. The productions of a grammar describe how complex (sub)patterns can be built up from simpler constituents. The recognition procedure is based on the concept of formal language parsing.

Generally, the use of a grammar for pattern class representation has some advantages if there is either recursivity in the patterns under consideration, or there are many common substructures shared by the members of a pattern class. Another advantage of the syntactic approach is its foundation on the theory of formal languages. This theory is very well understood today and has proven useful in many subfields of computer science. For the area of syntactic pattern recognition, it provides many useful results about descriptive power, limitations and computational complexity of different representation schemas and recognition, i.e. parsing, procedures. Thus many different (and complicated) algorithms can be represented on a well-developed and fairly standardized common basis.

On the other hand there are problems with the syntactic approach. For complex patterns, the productions of a grammar lack sufficient representational power. Augmenting the grammar by particular heuristics can solve the problem. However, in this case the resulting approach is no longer founded on the theory of formal languages. Also the lack of automatic inference and learning procedures, which can be practically applied, puts some limitations on the syntactic approach.

Well-known books in syntactic pattern recognition addressing both theory and applications are those by Fu (1977)[1], Fu (1982)[2], Gonzalez and Thomason (1978)[3] and Miclet (1986)[4]. Although the origin of syntactic pattern recognition dates back to the 1960s, the field is still an area of active research. Recent work is reported in Refs. 5 and 6.

Many different types of grammars and parsing algorithms for syntactic pattern recognition have been proposed in the past. The most fundamental concept is string grammars. They operate on strings of symbols, i.e. words over a finite alphabet. The aim of this chapter is to give an introduction to string grammars and their application to pattern recognition, providing the basic concepts and notations for the following chapters of this book. The subject of parsing will be treated separately in Chapter 3. Particular applications of string grammars can be found in Chapters 15-18 of this book.

A generalization of string grammars are grammars operating on more complex data structures, like arrays, trees, or graphs. They are the subject of Chapter 4 of this book. For other work on tree and graph grammars see also Refs. 2, 7, 8 and 9. A detailed survey on the present state of the art in automatic inference is given in Chapter 9, and a discussion about the relations between syntactic methods and other approaches to pattern recognition, including combinations of different approaches, is given in Chapters 11 and 12.

## 2. FORMAL GRAMMARS AND LANGUAGES

Formal grammars operate on words over finite sets of symbols. First, we will provide some elementary notations and concepts.

An *alphabet A* is a finite set of symbols. A *word x* over *A* is a sequence of symbols

$$x = a_1 \ldots a_n \text{ where } a_i \in A; \ i = 1, \ldots, n \ .$$

The *empty word ε* is the sequence with no symbols. The *length* of a word, denoted by $|x|$, is equal to the number of symbols contained in it. Thus $|\varepsilon| = 0$. The set of all words over an alphabet is denoted by $A^*$. For example, if

$$A = \{a, b\} \ ,$$

then
$$A^* = \{\varepsilon, a, b, aa, ab, ba, bb, aaa, aab, \ldots\} \ .$$

The set of all words over an alphabet excluding the empty word is denoted by $A^+$, i.e. $A^+ = A^* - \{\varepsilon\}$.

We write $a^n$ for $aa \ldots a$ (*n* consecutive occurrences of symbol *a*). The *concatenation* of two words

$$x = a_1 \ldots a_n \text{ and } y = b_1 \ldots b_m$$

is given by

$$xy = a_1 \ldots a_n b_1 \ldots b_m \ .$$

Notice that $x\varepsilon = \varepsilon x = x$ and $(xy)z = x(yz)$ for any $x, y, z \in A^*$. Concatenation can be extended to sets of words $X$ and $Y$ by defining

$$XY = \{xy | x \in X, y \in Y\} \ .$$

For example, if

$$X = \{01, 10\} \text{ and } Y = \{00, 11\}, \text{ then}$$
$$XY = \{0100, 0111, 1000, 1011\} \ .$$

**Definition 2.1.** A *formal grammar* is a four-tuple
$G = (N, T, P, S)$ where
$N$ is a finite set of *nonterminal symbols*,
$T$ is a finite set of *terminal symbols*,
$P$ is a finite set of *productions*, or *rewriting rules*, and
$S \in N$ is the *initial* or *starting symbol*.

It is required that $N \cap T = \emptyset$; the union of $N$ and $T$ is called the *vocabulary* $V = N \cup T$. Each production $p \in P$ is of the form $\alpha \rightarrow \beta$ where $\alpha$ and $\beta$ are called the *left-hand* and *right-hand side*, respectively, with $\alpha \in V^+$ and $\beta \in V^*$.

The most important part of a grammar is the set of productions. The intuitive meaning of a production $\alpha \rightarrow \beta$ is to replace the occurrence of the left-hand side in a word by the right-hand side, obtaining a new word thus. This idea is captured in a formal way by the following definition.

**Definition 2.2.** Let $G$ be a grammar and $\alpha \rightarrow \beta$ a production in $P$. Any word $v = x\alpha y$ with $x, y \in V^*$ can be *derived* into the word $w = x\beta y$. We write $v \rightarrow w$ in this case, and $v \xrightarrow{*} w$ if there exist words $v = v_0, v_1, \ldots, v_n = w$ such that $v_i \rightarrow v_{i+1}; i = 0, 1, \ldots, n - 1$.

**Definition 2.3.** The *language* generated by a grammar $G$ is given by

$$L(G) = \{x | x \in T^*, S \xrightarrow{*} x\} \ .$$

Thus in the derivation of an element $x \in L(G)$ we start with the initial symbol $S$ and successively apply rules until a word is obtained which contains only symbols from the terminal alphabet.

**Example 2.4.** Consider the grammar $G = (N, T, P, S)$ where

$$N = \{S, A, B\}, T = \{a, b, c\} \,,$$
$$P = \{S \rightarrow cAb, \ A \rightarrow aBa, \ B \rightarrow aBa, \ B \rightarrow cb\} \,.$$

This grammar generates the language

$$L(G) = \{ca^n cba^n b | n \geq 1\} \,.$$

For example, for the generation of the word *caacbaab*, i.e. $n = 2$, the following sequence of substring replacements are applied:

$$S \rightarrow cAb \rightarrow caBab \rightarrow caaBaab \rightarrow caacbaab \,. \qquad \blacksquare$$

From this example we conclude that the language generated by a grammar is an infinite set of words in general, although all components of a grammar are finite.

According to the form of the productions, we can distinguish different types of grammars.

**Definition 2.5.**
(a) A grammar according to Def. 2.1 is called *unrestricted*, or of *type 0*.
(b) A grammar is called *context-sensitive*, or of *type 1*, iff any production is of the form $xAy \rightarrow xzy$ where $x, y \in V^*; A \in N; z \in V^+$.
(c) A grammar is called *context-free*, or of *type 2*, iff any production is of the form $A \rightarrow z$ where $A \in N; z \in V^+$.
(d) A grammar is called *regular*, or of *type 3*, iff any production is of the form $A \rightarrow aB$, or $A \rightarrow a$ where $A, B \in N; a \in T$.

In a context-sensitive grammar, the nonterminal symbol $A$ can be replaced by the non-empty string $z$ only if it occurs within the context $x$ and $y$. Such a contextual condition for replacement does not exist in a context-free grammar. A regular grammar is a special type of context-free grammar where the right-hand side of each production fulfills additional restrictions. There exist slightly different definitions in the literature which can be shown equivalent to Def. 2.5. Obviously, the grammar in Ex. 2.4 is context-free.

**Definition 2.6.** A language is of type $i$ iff it is generated by a grammar of type $i$.

It can be easily seen from Def. 2.5 that any grammar of type $i$ is also of type $i - 1; i = 1, 2, 3$. Thus any language of type $i$ is also of type $i - 1$. This imposes a hierarchical inclusion relation between the classes of languages generated by grammars of different types. It can be shown that this kind of inclusion is a proper one.

**Theorem 2.7.** For $i = 0, 1, 2$ there exists a language $L(G)$ of type $i$ which cannot be generated by a grammar of type $i + 1$.

The proof can be found in any textbook on formal language theory, for instance Ref. 10. For example, the language in Ex. 2.4, which is generated by a context-free grammar, cannot be generated by any regular grammar.

For various reasons, it is useful to restrict the productions of a grammar to some standard form. Two well-known standard forms are introduced in the next definition.

**Definition 2.8.** Let $G$ be a context-free grammar.
  (a) $G$ is in *Chomsky normal form* if each of its productions is either of the form $A \rightarrow BC$ with $A, B, C \in N$, or of the form $A \rightarrow a$ with $A \in N, a \in T$.
  (b) $G$ is in *Greibach normal form* if each of its productions is of the form $A \rightarrow ax$ with $A \in N, a \in T, x \in N^*$.

**Theorem 2.9.** Let $G$ be a context-free grammar. Then there exists a grammar $G_1$ in Chomsky normal form and a grammar $G_2$ in Greibach normal form such that $L(G) = L(G_1) = L(G_2)$.

Again, the proof can be found in textbooks on formal language theory, for example, Ref. 10.

## 3. FUNDAMENTAL CONCEPTS IN PARSING

A fundamental task in syntactic pattern recognition is to decide, given a grammar $G$ and a word $x$ over the terminal alphabet, if $x \in L(G)$. In this section we will discuss basic concepts related to this task. Detailed algorithms will be presented in Chapter 3 of this book.

**Definition 3.1.** Let $G = (N, T, P, S)$ be a context-free grammar. A *derivation tree* is a tree where
  (1) each node is labeled with a symbol $z \in V$ such that
      – each leaf is labeled with a symbol $a \in T$,
      – each non-leaf is labeled with a symbol $A \in N$,
      – the root is labeled with the initial symbol $S$;

(2) if there exists a node with label $A \in N$ such that its successor nodes are labeled with $x_1, \ldots, x_n \in V$ then there exists a production $A \to x_1 \ldots x_n$ in $P$.

We will use derivation trees for the representation of the derivation steps applied to generate a word $x \in L(G)$. Since context-free grammars play the most important role in syntactic pattern recognition, we will limit our considerations to this type of grammar. For non-context-free grammars, the concept of derivation tree can be extended resulting in a *derivation graph*.

**Example 3.2.** Consider the grammar in Ex. 2.4 and the word *caacbaab*. Its derivation tree is given in Fig. 1.

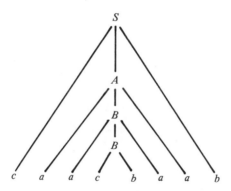

Fig. 1. An example of a derivation tree.

**Definition 3.3.** Let $G = (N, T, P, S)$ be a context-free grammar. A word $x \in L(G)$ is called *unambiguous* if there exists only one derivation tree of $x$ with respect to $G$. It is called *ambiguous* if there exists more than one derivation tree.

**Example 3.4.** Consider the following grammar $G = (N, T, P, S)$. $N = \{S, A\}, T = \{a\}, P = \{S \to aA, S \to aaA, A \to aa, A \to a\}$. Obviously $L(G) = \{aa, aaa, aaaa\}$.

We notice that the word $aaa \in L(G)$ can be generated in two different ways, namely $S \to aA \to aaa$, and $S \to aaA \to aaa$.

Accordingly, there exist two different derivation trees which are shown in

Fig. 2. An example of an ambiguous word.

Fig. 2. Thus $aaa$ is ambiguous. By contrast, the two other words generated by $G$ are unambiguous. As it will be seen later, ambiguous strings represent a situation where one pattern has different interpretations.     ■

It can be easily seen that, for any grammar $G$ and any word $x \in T^*$, there exists a derivation tree according to $G$, if and only if $x \in L(G)$. So the task of deciding if $x \in L(G)$ is equivalent to the construction of a derivation tree. This problem is also called *parsing* (of $x$ according to $G$). There are two principal classes of parsing algorithms. In *top-down* parsing, the derivation tree is constructed from the root towards the leaves. That is, starting with the initial symbol of the grammar, successive application of productions is tried until $x$ is generated. In *bottom-up* parsing, the derivation tree is built from the bottom towards the root by rule application in reverse order. Detailed examples of both top-down and bottom-up parsing algorithms and a more comprehensive treatment of the general subject area of parsing will be given in Chapter 3 of this book.

## 4. FORMAL GRAMMARS FOR PATTERN RECOGNITION

A formal grammar $G$ is a suitable tool for the description of a possibly infinite set of strings, i.e. the language $L(G)$. Use of grammars in pattern recognition is based on the following idea. The terminals of the grammar correspond to primitive, or elementary, pattern constituents which can be directly extracted from an input pattern by means of suitable preprocessing and segmentation methods. The set of grammar *nonterminals* corresponds to subpatterns of greater complexity, which are hierarchically built up from primitive elements. The process of constructing complex (sub)patterns from simpler parts is modeled by the productions of the grammar. Finally, the *language* generated by the grammar represents a whole class of patterns.

In order to illustrate these ideas consider the grammar in Ex. 2.4. Assume that the terminal symbols represent line segments of fixed length

Fig. 3. Line segments as primitives for contour representation.

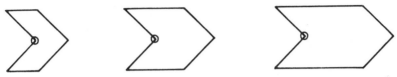

Fig. 4. Sample patterns of a class.

according to Fig. 3. A class of arrow-like shapes is shown in Fig. 4. Each shape can be represented by a string of terminal symbols if we surround the pattern in a clockwise direction. For the purpose of normalization we assume the starting point to be at the middle of the tail, as indicated by the small circles in Fig. 4. So the class of patterns in Fig. 4 can be represented by the set of words

$$\{cacbab, \ caacbaab \ , caaacbaaab, \dots \}$$

which is identical with $L(G)$.

Almost any task in pattern recognition belongs to the category of either *pattern classification* or *pattern analysis*. In the former case, given an unknown input pattern $x$, we want to assign $x$ to one out of $N$ classes, $N \geq 2$. Typical examples are character recognition, industrial quality control, or medical decision making. In pattern analysis we desire to infer a symbolic data structure describing the contents or the meaning of the input pattern. What is precisely meant by "meaning of a pattern" depends on the particular problem. Examples of pattern analysis can be found in automatic document analysis, aerial image understanding and robot vision.

Given $N$ grammars $G_1, \dots, G_N$ each describing a pattern class, the task of pattern classification can be solved by a recognition procedure according to Fig. 5. We may think of each rectangle in Fig. 5 as a parser which tries, given a string $x$ representing an unknown input pattern, to construct the derivation tree of $x$ according to $G_i; i = 1, \dots, N$. If there does not exist any $G_i$ with $x \in L(G_i)$, then the input pattern is rejected.

It is very important to notice that the derivation tree of an unknown input pattern $x$ provides not only a decision about its class but also structural

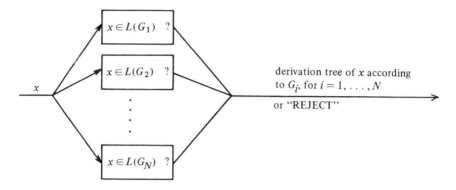

Fig. 5. Block diagram of syntactic recognition.

information describing how $x$ is hierarchically built up from its primitive constituents. Thus the derivation tree can be used in pattern analysis either directly as a symbolic data structure describing $x$, or it can be input to another procedure which extracts the desired information. For example, one might be interested in the length of an arrow in Fig. 4. This length is directly related with the number of occurrences of either the symbol $B$ or $a$, and can be easily extracted from a derivation tree like in Fig. 1. In conclusion, we notice that the recognition scheme in Fig. 5 is suitable not only for pattern classification but also for pattern analysis.

Until now, we have discussed only the noise free case. In many real applications, however, there are noise and distortions corrupting the patterns under consideration. For such a case, there exist three different strategies which can be followed. First, if there is precise and complete knowledge available about the possible errors occurring in the patterns, then it may be possible to augment the ideal, i.e. error free, grammar rules by error productions. In this way, the language $L(G)$ represents not only all possible ideals, but also all possible distorted patterns. For both pattern recognition and pattern analysis, the schema shown in Fig. 5 can be used.

Secondly, if it is the case that one pattern can be generated by more than one grammar (i.e. different pattern classes overlap each other such that $x \in L(G_i)$ and $x \in L(G_j)$ for $i \neq j$) then it may be useful to apply knowledge about relative frequencies, or likelihood, of patterns and subpatterns. This results in one of the stochastic approaches which will be discussed in greater detail in Sec. 5.

Lastly, if there is neither knowledge about relative frequencies nor about possible distortions available, we can still establish some general implicit assumptions about possible errors in patterns and use an *error-correcting parsing algorithm*. The basic idea in error-correcting parsing is to find, given a grammar $G$ and a word $x \notin L(G)$, that string $y \in L(G)$ which most resembles $x$, and construct its derivation tree according to $G$. So in order to cope with noisy and distorted patterns, the recognition schema in Fig. 5 can be generalized such that each rectangle corresponds to an error-correcting parser. A detailed treatment of the subject of error-correcting parsing will be given in Chapter 3 of this book.

## 5. GRAMMARS WITH PROBABILISTIC INFORMATION

We will now discuss how a grammar describing a class of patterns can be augmented by probabilistic information. In Sec. 5.1 we will review stochastic grammars as a classical way to incorporate probabilistic information into a grammar, following standard texts like those by Gonzalez and Thomason (1978)[3], and Fu (1982)[2]. In Sec. 5.2 a more recent approach will be described (see Refs. 11 and 12).

### 5.1. Stochastic Grammars and Languages

In the following we will consider only context-free grammars. For the purpose of notational convenience let the set of nonterminals of a grammar $G$ be

$$N = \{A_1, \dots, A_m\}$$

and let the set of productions be

$$A_1 \to X_{11}, \dots, A_1 \to X_{1,n1}$$
$$\vdots$$
$$A_m \to X_{m1}, \dots, A_m \to X_{m,nm} \qquad \text{where } X_{ij} \in V^+.$$

**Definition 5.1.**

   (a) A *stochastic* (context-free) *grammar* is a four-tuple $G^s = (N, T, P^s, S)$ where

      – $N, T,$ and $S$ are the same as in Definition 2.1 (nonterminal alphabet, terminal alphabet, initial symbol)

- $P^s$ is a finite set of productions of the form $p_{ij} : A_i \rightarrow X_{ij}$ with

$$A_i \in N; \quad X_{ij} \in V^+; \quad 0 < p_{ij} \leq 1; \quad \sum_{j=1}^{ni} p_{ij} = 1; i = 1, \dots, m \ .$$

(b) The *characteristic grammar* $G = (N, T, P, S)$ of a stochastic grammar $G^s$ is obtained by deleting the numbers $p_{ij}$ from each production in $P^s$.

Intuitively, a stochastic context-free grammar is obtained from its characteristic grammar if we add a *probability* to each production in $P$ such that the probabilities of productions with identical left-hand sides sum up to the value one. We can think of $p_{ij}$ as the probability of applying the rule $A_i \rightarrow X_{ij}$ in the derivation of a word.

If a rule $r \in P^s$ is given by $p_{ij} : A_i \rightarrow X_{ij}$ we also use the notation $p(r)$ for $p_{ij}$ (probability of the rule $r$).

**Definition 5.2.** Let $G^s = (N, T, P^s, S)$ be a stochastic grammar and $G = (N, T, P, S)$ its characteristic grammar.

(a) If $x \in L(G)$ is unambiguous and has a derivation $S = w_0 \overset{r_1}{\rightarrow} w_1 \overset{r_2}{\rightarrow} \dots \overset{r_k}{\rightarrow} w_k = x$ where $r_1, \dots, r_k \in P$, then the probability of $x$ with respect to $G^s$ is given by

$$p(x|G^s) = \prod_{i=1}^{k} p(r_i) \ .$$

(b) If $x \in L(G)$ is ambiguous and has $l$ different derivation trees with corresponding probabilities $p_1(x|G^s), \dots, p_l(x|G^s)$ then the probability of $x$ with respect to $G^s$ is given by

$$p(x|G^s) = \sum_{i=1}^{l} p_i(x|G^s) \ .$$

To get the probability of an unambiguous string $x$ we simply multiply the probabilities of all productions applied in the derivation of $x$. If $x$ is ambiguous then we first calculate the probability of $x$ under each different derivation and secondly, sum up all those values.

**Example 5.3.** We augment the grammar in Ex. 3.4 by the following probabilities:

$$0.5: S \rightarrow aA \ , \qquad 0.5: S \rightarrow aaA \ ,$$
$$0.3: A \rightarrow aa \ , \qquad 0.7: A \rightarrow a \ .$$

Consequently, we obtain the following probabilities $p(x|G^s)$ for $x$:

$$aa : 0.35, \quad aaa : 0.5, \quad aaaa : 0.15 .$$

**Definition 5.4.** Let $G^s = (N, T, P^s, S)$ be a stochastic grammar. The *language* generated by $G^s$ is given by $L(G^s) = \{[x, p(x|G^s)]|x \in T^*, S \xrightarrow{*} x\}$.

**Example 5.5.** Let $G^s = (N, T, P^s, S)$ with $N = \{S\}, T = \{a, b\}, P = \{p : S \rightarrow aSb, 1 - p : S \rightarrow ab\}$. We observe $L(G) = \{a^n b^n | n \geq 1\}$. Each element $x \in L(G)$ is unambiguous. Thus

$$L(G^s) = \{[a^n b^n, p^{n-1}(1-p)]|n \geq 1\} . \qquad \blacksquare$$

Let the *a priori* probability of the pattern class represented by the grammar $G_i^s$ be $p(G_i^s)$ and let $p(x)$ denote the probability of the string, i.e. pattern, $x$. According to Bayes' formula[13] we may write

$$p(G_i^s|x)p(x) = p(x|G_i^s)p(G_i^s) \qquad (5.1)$$

where $p(x|G_i^s)$ is given according to Def. 5.2 and $p(G_i^s|x)$ is the *a posteriori* probability of $G_i^s$. If $x$ can be generated by more than one grammar $G_j^s, j = 1, \ldots, N$, a meaningful decision rule is

$$x \in L(G_i^s) \text{ if } p(G_i^s|x) = \max\{p(G_j^s|x)|j = 1, \ldots, N\} . \qquad (5.2)$$

The probability $p(G_i^s|x)$ can be calculated according to (5.1). Since the maximum in (5.2) is independent of $p(x)$, we may use, instead of $p(G_j^s|x)$, the probability

$$p'(G_j^s|x) = p(x|G_j^s)p(G_j^s) . \qquad (5.3)$$

If the *a priori* probabilities $p(G_i^s)$ are not known, it is straightforward to use $p(G_i^s) = N^{-1}$ for $i = 1, \ldots, N$. In this case we may directly use $p(x|G_j^s)$ for $p(G_j^s|x)$ in (5.2).

So the desired decision procedure can be implemented in the following way:

(1) Given an unknown input pattern $x$, parse $x$ according to $G_i, i = 1, \ldots, N$.

(2) For all $j$ with $x \in L(G_j)$ compute $p(x|G_j^s)$ according to Def. 5.2.

(3) Make a decision according to (5.2).

A very important problem in stochastic grammars is *consistency*. As a matter of fact the decision procedure described above is sound only if each grammar $G_i$ is consistent, i.e.

$$\sum_{x \in L(G_i)} p(x|G_i^s) = 1 \qquad \text{for } i = 1, \ldots, N \ .$$

Detailed procedures for checking consistency are described in Refs. 2 and 3. Applications of stochastic grammars are reported in Ref. 1.

## 5.2. Parsing Strings with Multiple Choices

While in Sec. 5.1 the uncertainty which may be present in a pattern recognition problem is expressed in terms of probabilities of grammar productions, in this section we follow a different approach, incorporating the uncertainty into the pattern primitives. This method is realistic in applications where, due to noise and distortions, the primitives cannot be reliably detected. Instead of assuming an input string of length $m$, i.e.

$$x = x_{i1} \ldots x_{im}, x_{ij} \in T, \quad T = \{x_1, \ldots, x_n\}$$

where a terminal symbol is uniquely determined at each position, we consider a sequence of vectors

$$\begin{bmatrix} c_1(x_1) \\ c_1(x_2) \\ \vdots \\ c_1(x_n) \end{bmatrix} \begin{bmatrix} c_2(x_1) \\ c_2(x_2) \\ \vdots \\ c_2(x_n) \end{bmatrix} \cdots \begin{bmatrix} c_m(x_1) \\ c_m(x_2) \\ \vdots \\ c_m(x_n) \end{bmatrix} \tag{5.4}$$

where $c_i(x_j)$ is a measure of certainty that the symbol $x_j \in T$ is correct at position $i; i = 1, \ldots, m; j = 1, \ldots, n$. So there are multiple choices at each input position, with different certainties. Depending on the particular application, we might wish to impose the restriction

$$\sum_{j=1}^{n} c_i(x_j) = 1 \ ; \qquad i = 1, \ldots, m$$

which can be easily obtained by suitable normalization. Given certainties $c_1(x_{i1}), c_2(x_{i2}), \ldots, c_m(x_{im})$, we define the certainty of the string $x_{i1} x_{i2} \ldots x_{im}$ by

$$c(x_{i1} x_{i2} \ldots x_{im}) = \sum_{j=1}^{m} c_j(x_{ij}) \ .$$

In general, a sequence of vectors according to (5.4) corresponds to $n^m$ different strings, each with a different certainty. The task of the parsing procedure is to determine that string $x$ which is compatible with the considered grammar and has maximum certainty, i.e.

$$x \in L(G) \text{ and } c(x) = \max\{c(y)|y \in L(G)\} . \qquad (5.5)$$

A fast and simple parsing procedure for solving (5.5) for the case of a regular grammar was described in Ref. 11. An extension to context-free grammars is proposed in Ref. 12. As an application of this method consider Fig. 6. A class of sinusoidal patterns is described by a grammar. One pattern instance is shown in Fig. 6a. A noisy version of it is presented in Fig. 6b. For detecting the sinusoidal pattern in Fig. 6b, an edge detector is applied first. After normalization, its response in line $i$ and column $j$ can directly be used as the certainty measure $c_i(x_j)$, i.e. each line in Fig. 6 corresponds to an input position $i = 1, \ldots, m$, and there is one terminal symbol $x_j$ for each column position $j = 1, \ldots, n$. If $x_j$ is correct in line $i$ then this means that the contour of the pattern under consideration passes through line $i$ and column $j$. The application of the parser to Fig. 6b yields the contour shown in Fig. 6c. We notice that the pattern in Fig. 6a can be perfectly recognized regardless of the noise.

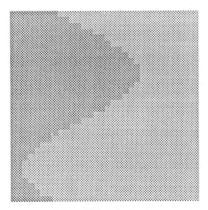

(a) Original pattern.

Fig. 6. An example of the parsing method by Bunke and Pasche[12].

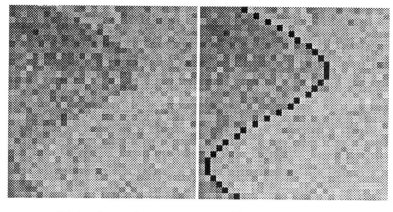

(b) A noisy version.          (c) Result of parsing.

Fig. 6. Cont'd.

In Fig. 7, an additional pattern is superimposed on the contents of Fig. 6a. Since this pattern is not compatible with the given grammar, the parser finds the sinusoidal line in Fig. 7b, although its contrast is lower than the contrast of the other pattern. Figure 7c shows the result of parsing a noisy version of Fig. 7b. For more details see Ref. 12.

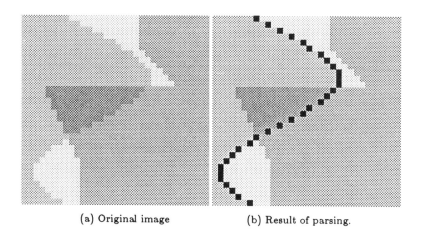

(a) Original image          (b) Result of parsing.

Fig. 7. Two overlapping patterns.

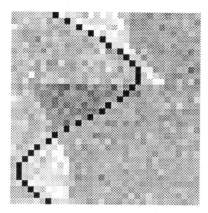

(c) Parsing a noisy version of Fig. 7b.

Fig. 7. Cont'd.

## 6. ATTRIBUTED GRAMMARS

The rules of a formal grammar are a suitable tool for modeling structural properties of patterns, particularly for describing how a complex pattern is hierarchically composed of simpler constituents. However, there are deficiencies in adequately representing quantitative information such as the length and orientation of lines, textural parameters of regions, or 3-D surface orientation. A solution to this problem is provided by attributed grammars. The idea is to augment each grammar symbol $Y \in V$ by a vector of attribute values

$$m(Y) = (x_1, \dots, x_k) \tag{6.1}$$

where an *attribute* $\alpha$ is a function

$$\alpha : Y \to D_Y$$

mapping a symbol $Y \in V$ into a domain $D_Y$ of numerical values. In (6.1) we observe $x_1, \dots, x_k \in D_Y$. An attribute vector can be interpreted as a numerical feature vector in the sense of statistical pattern recognition[13]. A detailed discussion on the relations between attributed grammars and statistical pattern recognition can be found in Chapters 11 and 12 of this book.

Considering a production $A_1 \dots A_n \to B_1 \dots B_m$ with $A_i, B_j \in V$, there is usually a relationship between the attributes of the symbols in the left-hand side and those of the right-hand side. Two cases must be distinguished. First, the attributes in the left-hand side can be dependent on those in the right-hand side, i.e.

$$\alpha(A_i) = f_i(\alpha(B_1), \ldots, \alpha(B_m)), \quad i = 1, \ldots, n , \qquad (6.2)$$

or the attributes in the right-hand side can be dependent on those in the left-hand side, i.e.

$$\alpha(B_i) = g_i(\alpha(A_1), \ldots, \alpha(A_n)), \quad i = 1, \ldots, m . \qquad (6.3)$$

Attributed grammars have originally been proposed for modeling the semantics of programming languages, and according to Knuth[14], the attributes following Eq. (6.2) are called *synthesized*, while attributes according to Eq. (6.3) are referred to as *inherited*. Theoretically, a grammar can contain symbols with attributes of both types, but for the sake of simplicity, it is advised that only one attribute type within one grammar if possible be used.

In bottom-up recognition one starts with a segmented pattern with all the primitives extracted in such a way that the attributes of the non-terminal symbols can successively be computed during analysis according to Eq. (6.2). Conversely, in top-down recognition attribute values for the grammar start symbol must be known and are successively inherited to other grammar symbols according to Eq. (6.3). One remark is that $f_i$ and $g_i$ in Eqs. (6.2) and (6.3), respectively, may be any closed-form mathematical function or any other algorithm which takes some attribute values as input and produces some attribute values as output.

As a simple example of an attributed grammar, suppose we have to take into account the length of the contour of the patterns in Fig. 4. This can be easily achieved by introducing the length $l$ as an attribute for each grammar symbol. For the case of synthesized attributes, the productions of the grammar in Ex. 2.4 can be augmented by the following functions:

$$
\begin{aligned}
l(S) &= l(c) + l(A) + l(b) , & &\text{for } S \to cAb , \\
l(A) &= 2l(a) + l(B) , & &\text{for } A \to aBa , \\
l(B) &= 2l(a) + l(B) , & &\text{for } B \to aBa , \\
l(B) &= l(c) + l(b) , & &\text{for } B \to cb .
\end{aligned}
$$

Detailed examples of attributed grammars can be found in Chapters 15-18 of this book. Other examples known from the literature are in Refs. 15-17.

## 7. HIGHER-DIMENSIONAL EXTENSIONS

Until now, we have considered string representations of patterns where the terminal symbols correspond to pattern primitives. Since the only possible relation between the symbols in a string is the concatenation relation, this schema is very restricted if two-dimensional or even higher-dimensional patterns are to be described.

There are two possible extensions leading to more effective representations of higher-dimensional patterns. The first is a representation formalism which is intrinsically more-dimensional, like arrays, trees, or graphs. This subject will be covered in greater detail in Chapter 4 of this book (see also Chapter 10). The second possible extension is to incorporate into the string representation relations which are more general than concatenation. Two well-known approaches following this idea are the picture description language PDL[18] and plex grammars[19] which will be described in the following sections.

### 7.1. Picture Description Language (PDL)

Throughout this section we assume that each primitive part of a pattern has exactly two points, called *tail* and *head*, where it can be linked to other primitives. Thus we can represent each primitive by a directed and labeled edge of a graph as shown in Fig. 8. In the picture description language, there are four ways of joining a pair of primitives. These four binary operations are denoted by $+, -, \times$, and $*$. Additionally there are two unary operators. The four binary operations and their geometric interpretation are shown in Fig. 9. Each entity resulting from the linking of two primitives has a tail and a head, too, as shown in Fig. 9. So we can extend the four binary operations $+, -, \times$, and $*$ to higher level structures, i.e. we can use more complex PDL expressions as arguments of the operators. An example is shown in Fig. 10. In this example the unary operator $\sim$ is used, which reverses tail and head of a primitive, or a more complex expression.

It can be shown that any directed graph with labeled edges can be represented by a PDL expression. (Usually there are more than one possible expression for one graph.) Consequently, there exists a PDL expression for any pattern which can be represented by a graph of primitive elements.

The fundamental idea in syntactic pattern recognition is to represent a pattern class by a formal grammar generating all the members of this class. This idea can be applied to the PDL formalism in a straightforward way.

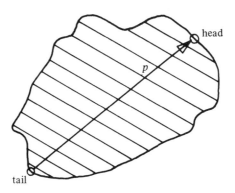

Fig. 8. A pattern primitive *p* and its representation by a directed and labeled edge.

| Operator | Meaning | Geometric interpretation |
|---|---|---|
| *a* + *b* | head (*a*) linked to tail (*b*)<br><br>head (*a* + *b*) = head (*b*)<br>tail (*a* + *b*) = tail (*a*) | 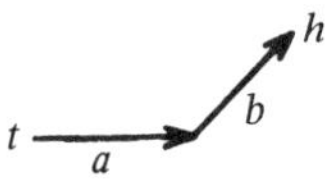 |
| *a* − *b* | head (*a*) linked to head (*b*)<br><br>head (*a* − *b*) = head (*b*)<br>tail (*a* − *b*) = tail (*a*) | 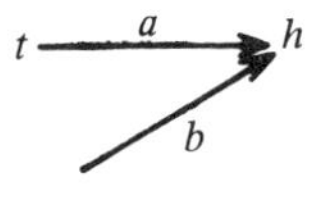 |
| *a* × *b* | tail (*a*) linked to tail (*b*)<br><br>head (*a*×*b*) = head (*b*)<br>tail (*a*×*b*) = tail (*b*) | 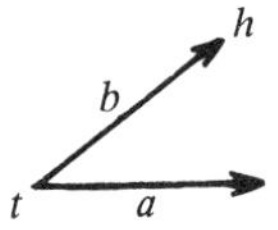 |
| *a*\**c* | tail (*a*) linked to tail (*c*)<br>and<br>head (*a*) linked to head (*c*)<br>head (*a*\**c*) = head (*a*)<br>tail (*a*\**c*) = tail (*a*) | 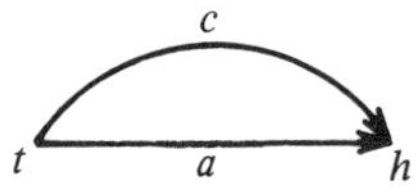 |

Fig. 9. The four binary PDL-operators.

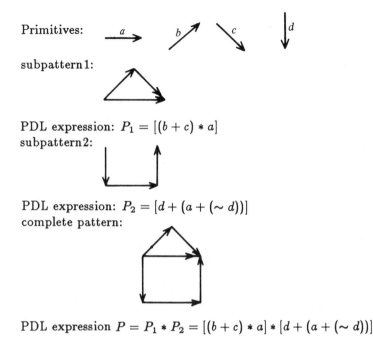

Primitives:

subpattern 1:

PDL expression: $P_1 = [(b + c) * a]$
subpattern 2:

PDL expression: $P_2 = [d + (a + (\sim d))]$
complete pattern:

PDL expression $P = P_1 * P_2 = [(b + c) * a] * [d + (a + (\sim d))]$

Fig. 10. An example of a PDL expression and its corresponding pattern.

The language $L(G)$ generated by a grammar $G$ consists of a number of PDL expressions each describing an individual pattern. A whole pattern class is represented by one grammar. Consequently, the recognition schema shown in Fig. 5 can be applied. Each rectangle corresponds to a (string) language parser which examines an input PDL expression $x$ if it can be generated by one of the grammars $G_1, \ldots G_N$.

An example of a grammar generating PDL expressions is

$$G = (N, T, P, S) \text{ with}$$
$$N = \{S, A, HOUSE, TRIANGLE\}$$
$$T = \{a, b, c, d, (\,,\,), +, -, \times, *, \sim\}$$
$$P : S \to A, \quad S \to HOUSE$$
$$A \to b + ((TRIANGLE) + c)$$
$$HOUSE \to (d + (a + (\sim d))) * (TRIANGLE)$$
$$TRIANGLE \to (b + c) * a$$

Obviously,

$$L(G) = \{b + (((b + c) * a) + c) , \quad (d + (a + (\sim d))) * ((b + c) * a)\} \ .$$

If we interpret the terminals $a, b, c, d$ according to Fig. 10, then this language represents the patterns shown in Fig. 11.

Fig. 11. Two patterns which can be represented by a string grammar generating PDL expressions.

A straightforward way of incorporating attributes according to Sec. 6, into a grammar generating PDL expressions is to use the $x$- and $y$-coordinates of the tail and head of each primitive and more complex subexpression. Early applications of PDL included the analysis of bubble chamber events[18]. A more recent application is the analysis of line drawings. This application is described in Chapter 17 of this book.

## 7.2. Plex Grammars

The main drawback of PDL is its limitation to only two concatenation points of subexpressions, including primitives. This limitation is overcome by *plex structures* introduced by Feder[19].

A symbol with $n$ attaching points is called an *n-attaching point entity* or *nape*. Structures formed by joining napes are called plex structures. Formally, a nape is represented by an identifier and a list of its attaching points. For example, "hor(1,2,3)" represents a nape with name "hor" and three attaching points, "1", "2", and "3". A plex structure is described by three components, namely, a list of napes, a list of internal connections between napes, and a list of attaching points where the plex structure can be joined with other napes or plex structures.

Two napes are shown in Fig. 12. They represent a vertical and a horizontal line segment with three and two attaching points respectively. These napes can be joined in a variety of ways yielding different patterns which can be described by plex structures. Three examples are shown in Fig. 13. The first pattern consists of two vertical and one horizontal line segment.

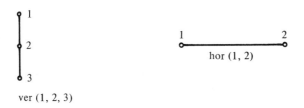

ver (1, 2, 3)

Fig. 12. An example of two napes.

So the napes ver, hor, and ver are listed in the first component of the plex structure. The napes in a plex structure may be listed in any order. The second component consists of two elements, namely, 210 and 022. This means that there are two internal connections between napes in the pattern. The first connection is made up by attaching point 2 of the first nape, i.e. ver, and attaching point 1 of the second nape, i.e. hor, while the second connection is given by the joining of attaching point 2 of hor to attaching point 2 of the second nape ver. The two other plex structures are to be interpreted in the same way. The list of external attaching points, i.e. the third component of the plex structures, is empty for all three patterns shown in Fig. 13.

A string grammar generating a set of plex structures is called a *plex grammar*. In such a grammar, the napes correspond to the terminals. The productions of a grammar generating the patterns in Fig. 13 are

LETTER( ) → TWOPART( )
LETTER( ) → THREEPART( )
TWOPART( ) → L( )
L( ) → (ver, hor)(31)( )
THREEPART( ) → H( ), THREEPART( )→ F( )
H( ) → (HELP, ver)(22)( )
F( ) → (HELP, hor)(11)( )
HELP(1,2,3) → (ver, hor)(21)(10, 02, 30).

The nonterminal nape HELP(1,2,3) has three external attaching points 1,2,3. A graphical illustration is given in Fig. 14.

As an application of plex grammars, the recognition of 3-D objects has been proposed recently[20]. A parser for plex grammars is described in Ref. 21.

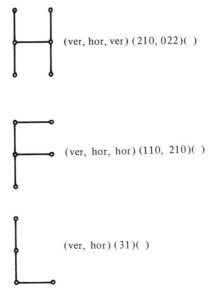

(ver, hor, ver) (210, 022)( )

(ver, hor, hor) (110, 210)( )

(ver, hor) (31)( )

Fig. 13. An example of three patterns and their corresponding descriptions as plex structures, using the napes shown in Fig. 12.

Fig. 14. A graphical illustration of the nonterminal nape HELP (1,2,3); see text.

## 8. CONCLUSIONS

The theory of formal languages can be used as a formal framework for classification and analysis of patterns. For many practical applications, the concepts from pure formal language theory must be generalized in a suitable way. Possible extensions include probabilistic grammars, attributed grammars and higher-dimensional approaches.

According to the experience made in pattern recognition during the past thirty years, there does not exist *the* optimal class of algorithms. So syntactic methods can give a contribution to only a limited number of problems. Nevertheless, there is contemporary research on combining syntactic methods with other approaches from statistics and artificial intelligence. It can be expected that this will result in more powerful and flexible techniques. It can also be expected that future research in pattern recognition will put more emphasis on parallel algorithms, including the theoretical investigation of their computational complexity and possible VLSI-implementations.

## REFERENCES

1. K.S. Fu (ed.) *Syntactic Pattern Recognition Applications* (Springer Verlag, Berlin, 1977).
2. K.S. Fu, *Syntactic Pattern Recognition and Applications* (Prentice Hall, Englewood Cliffs, NJ, 1982).
3. R.C. Gonzalez and M.G. Thomason, *Syntactic Pattern Recognition* (Addison Wesley, Reading, MA, 1978).
4. L. Miclet, *Structural Methods in Pattern Recognition* (North-Oxford Academic, 1986).
5. H. Bunke and A. Sanfeliu (eds.), *Advances in Syntactic Pattern Recognition, Special Issue of Pattern Recognition* **19**, (4) (1986).
6. G. Ferrate, T. Pavlidis, A. Sanfeliu and H. Bunke (eds.), *Syntactic and Structural Pattern Recognition* (Springer-Verlag, 1988).
7. K.S. Fu and B.K. Bhargava, "Tree systems for syntactic pattern recognition", *IEEE Trans. Comp.* **22** (1973) 1087-1099.
8. H. Bunke, "Attributed graph grammars and their application to schematic diagram interpretation", *IEEE Trans. PAMI* **4** (1982) 574-582.
9. A. Sanfeliu and K.S. Fu, "Tree-graph grammars for pattern recognition", in *Graph Grammars and Their Application to Computer Science* eds. H. Ehrig, M. Nagl and G. Rozenberg (Springer Verlag, Berlin, 1982) pp. 349-368.
10. J.E. Hopcroft and J.D. Ullmann, *Introduction to Automata Theory, Languages, and Computation*, (Addison Wesley, Reading, MA, 1979).
11. H. Bunke, K. Grebner and G. Sagerer, "Syntactic analysis of noisy input strings with an application to the analysis of heart-volume curves", *Proc. 7th ICPR*, Montreal, 1984, pp. 1145-1147.
12. H. Bunke and D. Pasche, "A new syntactic parsing method and its application to the tracking of noisy contours in images", in *Signal Processing IV-Theories and Applications*, eds. J. L. Lacoume *et al.* (North-Holland, 1988) pp. 1201-1204.
13. R.O. Duda and P.E. Hart, *Pattern Classification and Scene Analysis* (J. Wiley, New York, 1973).
14. D.E. Knuth, "Semantics of context-free languages", *Math. Syst. Theory* **2**(1968) 127-146.
15. T. Pavlidis and F. Ali, "A hierarchical syntactic shape analyser", *IEEE Trans. PAMI* **1** (1979) 2-9.
16. G.Y. Tang, "A syntactic-semantic approach to image understanding and creation", *IEEE Trans. PAMI* **1** (1979) 135-144.
17. K.C. You and K.S. Fu, "Distorted shape recognition using attributed grammars and error-correcting techniques", *Computer Graphics and Image Processing* **13** (1980) 1-16.
18. A.C. Shaw, "Parsing of graph-representable pictures", *J. ACM* **17** (1969) 453-487.
19. T. Feder, "Plex languages", *Info. Sciences* **3** (1971) 225-241.

20. W.C. Lin and K.S. Fu, "A syntactic approach to 3-D object representation", *IEEE Trans. PAMI* **6** (1984) 351-364.
21. W.C. Lin and K.S. Fu, "A Syntactic Approach to 3D Object Representation and Recognition", TR-EE 84-16, Purdue University, West Lafayette, IN 47907, 1984.

# 3

# PARSING AND ERROR-CORRECTING PARSING FOR STRING GRAMMARS

E. TANAKA

*Department of Information Science*
*Utsunomiya University*
*2753 Ishiimachi, Utsunomiya 321*
*Japan*

From the linguistic point of view, syntactic pattern recognition concerns the problem of deciding whether a string $X$ belongs to a language $L(G)$ or not, if $X$ is not deformed or garbled. This is called a recognition or a parsing problem. The two tabular parsing methods for context-free languages, the Cocke-Kasami-Younger and the Earley, are described. If $X$ is erroneous, an error-correcting recognition or an error-correcting parsing method is required. The two error-correcting parsing methods for context-free languages based on the above methods are described. Furthermore, the latest trends of research on parsing and error-correcting parsing are stated and several comments are given.

## 1. PARSERS FOR CONTEXT-FREE LANGUAGES

### 1.1. Introduction

In syntactic pattern recognition, we assume that a pattern can be represented by a sequence of primitives and a class of patterns makes a language $L(G)$. Consider two grammars $G_1$ and $G_2$ which represent the class 1 and the class 2, respectively. If a sequence of primitives $X$ belongs to $L(G_1)$, $X$ is determined to be a pattern of the class 1. If $X$ belongs to neither $L(G_1)$ nor $L(G_2)$, $X$ is rejected.

Parsing is nothing but constructing the syntactic tree(s) of a given string. This is a simple problem. A recognition problem and a parse problem for a given string $I$ and a grammar $G$, are stated as follows.

(1) A recognition problem is a problem to decide whether $I$ is in $L(G)$ or not. A machine to recognize a string is called a recognizer.

(2) A parse problem is a problem to decide whether or not $I$ is in $L(G)$ and to make the syntactic tree(s) of $I$, if $I$ is in $L(G)$. A machine to parse a string is called a parser.

A pushdown automaton[1-4] is a recognizer of a context-free language. Parsers can be classified into the following four categories:

(a) parsers with pushdown lists[5],

(b) direct parsers[6],

(c) transition diagram parsers[7],

(d) tabular parsers[5].

Parsers with pushdown lists ("backtrack parsing" in Ref. 1) seem to be reduced versions of direct parsers. The time and space complexities of both parsers are $O(c^n)$ and $O(n)$, respectively, for a string of length $n$, where $c$ is a constant. Transition diagram parsers are usually used for a deterministic context-free language without cycles and left-recursion. Those three kinds of parsers are hard to extend to error-correcting parsers. Only tabular parsers have error-correcting versions. Here we will concentrate on tabular parsers of a general context-free language, because error-correction is indispensable to syntactic pattern recognition.

### 1.2. A Bottom-Up Parser

The bottom-up tabular parsing method for a context-free language is called the Cocke-Kasami-Younger method (the CKY, for short). Let $I =$

$a_1 a_2 \ldots a_n$ be the input string to be parsed, where $a_i$ is in alphabet $\Sigma$ for $1 \leq i \leq n$. Parse table Ta consists of $n(n+1)/2$ entries $t[i,j] (1 \leq i \leq n, 1 \leq j \leq n - i + 1)$.

Input: CFG $G = (N, T, P, S)$ in Chomsky normal form and an input string $I = a_1 a_2 \ldots a_n$ .

Output: The parse table Ta .

Algorithm 1
```
1   begin {* of the CKY *}
2     for i := 1 to n do
3     for each A → a_i ∈ P do t[i, 1] := t[i, 1] ∪ {A} ;
4     for j := 2 to n do begin
5       for i := 1 to n − j + 1 begin
6         for k := 1 to j − 1 do begin
7           for each A → BC ∈ P do
8           if (B ∈ t[i, k]) and (C ∈ t[i + k, j − k])
9           then t[i, j] := t[i, j] ∪ {A} ;
10          end ;
11      end ;
12    end ;
13    if S ∈ t[1, n] then I is accepted
14    else I is rejected ;
15  end {* of the CKY *}
```

The CKY has the following properties.

(1) If $A \in t[i,j]$, then $A \overset{*}{\rightarrow} a_i a_{i+1} \ldots a_{i+j-1}$.
(2) The space and time complexities to construct Ta are $O(n^2)$ and $O(n^3)$, respectively. The time complexity to make all syntactic trees of a string is $O(c^n)$.

The method to make syntax trees from the parse table is described in Ref. 5.

**Example 1.1.** Consider a grammar $G1 = (N, T, P, S)$ such that $N = \{S, A\}, T = \{a, b\}$ and $P = \{S \rightarrow AS, A \rightarrow AS, A \rightarrow AA, S \rightarrow b, A \rightarrow a\}$.

$L(G) = \{a^{m1} b a^{m2} b \ldots a^{ms} b \mid mi \geq 1, s \geq 1\}$ .

Let $I = aaab$ be the input string to be parsed.

Table 1 is the parse table Ta1 for $I = aaab$. Since $S$ is in $t[1,4]$, $I$ is accepted.

Consider another data structure. Let an item be of the form "$t : (A, l, r)$", where $t, A, l$ and $r$ are the numbers assigned to the item, a symbol, the left child of the item $t$ and the right child of the item $t$, respectively. Table 2 is the parse table Ta2 using this type of an item. $t[1,4]$ of Ta2 includes five symbols $S$ which correspond to five syntax trees for $I$ shown in Fig. 1. However, $t[1,4]$ of Ta1 has only one $S$. This $S$ represents five symbols $S$, these are $S_{16}, S_{20}, S_{23}, S_{26}$ and $S_{28}$. It is easier to make syntactic trees for $I$ from Ta2 than from Ta1, but Ta2 requires more memory than Ta1.

Ikeda proposed an interesting data structure for an item such as "$t : (A, D)$", where $t, A$ and $D$ are the numbers assigned to an item, a symbol and the set of pairs of children of the item, respectively. Table 3 is the parse table Ta3 for $I$ using this data structure. This table contains the same number of items as Ta1, but it enables us to make the parse tree(s) easier after completing the parse table.

### 1.3. A Top-Down Parser

In this section, a parser for a context-free language proposed by Earley[7] is described. This parser uses an item of the form $(A \rightarrow \alpha \cdot \beta, i)$ which means that $\alpha$ has been parsed. A list $L[i] (i = 0, 1, \ldots, n)$ is a set of items. The number "$i$" in $(A \rightarrow \alpha \cdot \beta, i)$ indicates that the item is generated from an item in $L[i]$. Let $\lambda$ be the null string.

Define the operation $L[k] \cup \{(X \rightarrow \alpha \cdot \beta, j)\}$ in the two ways as follows:

**Definition 1.2.** If $(X \rightarrow \alpha \cdot \beta, i) \in L[k]$ and $i \leq j$, do nothing. Otherwise, add $(X \rightarrow \alpha \cdot \beta, j)$ to $L[k]$.

**Definition 1.3.** If $(X \rightarrow \alpha \cdot \beta, i) \in L[k]$ and $i = j$, do nothing. Otherwise, add $(X \rightarrow \alpha \cdot \beta, j)$ to $L[k]$.

Definition 1.2 suffices for the recognition problem and the parse problem to construct only one parse tree of an input. If all parse trees of an input are required, we must use Definition 1.3.

Input:  CFG $G = (N, T, P, S)$ and an input string $I = a_1 a_2 \ldots a_n$ .

Output:  The parse lists $L[0], L[1], \ldots, L[n]$ .

Table 1. Parse table Ta1 for *aaab*.

| $S, A$ | | | |
|---|---|---|---|
| $A$ | $S, A$ | | |
| $A$ | $A$ | $S, A$ | |
| $A$ | $A$ | $A$ | $S$ |
| *a* | *a* | *a* | *b* |

Table 2. Parse table Ta2 for $I = aaab$.

| | | | |
|---|---|---|---|
| 16 : $(S, \quad 1, \ 11)$ <br> 17 : $(A, \quad 1, \ 11)$ <br> 18 : $(A, \quad 1, \ 12)$ <br> 19 : $(A, \quad 1, \ 13)$ <br> 20 : $(S, \quad 1, \ 14)$ <br> 21 : $(A, \quad 1, \ 14)$ <br> 22 : $(A, \quad 1, \ 15)$ <br> 23 : $(S, \quad 5, \ 7)$ <br> 24 : $(A, \quad 5, \ 7)$ <br> 25 : $(A, \quad 5, \ 8)$ <br> 26 : $(S, \quad 9, \ 4)$ <br> 27 : $(A, \quad 9, \ 4)$ <br> 28 : $(S, \ 10, \ 4)$ <br> 29 : $(A, \ 10, \ 4)$ | | | |
| 9 : $(A, \quad 1, \ 6)$ <br> 10 : $(A, \quad 5, \ 3)$ | 11 : $(S, \quad 2, \ 7)$ <br> 12 : $(A, \quad 2, \ 7)$ <br> 13 : $(A, \quad 2, \ 8)$ <br> 14 : $(S, \quad 6, \ 4)$ <br> 15 : $(A, \quad 6, \ 4)$ | | |
| 5 : $(A, \quad 1, \ 2)$ | 6 : $(A, \quad 2, \ 3)$ | 7 : $(S, \quad 3, \ 4)$ <br> 8 : $(A, \quad 3, \ 4)$ | |
| 1 : $(A, \quad 0, \ 0)$ | 2 : $(A, \quad 0, \ 0)$ | 3 : $(A, \quad 0, \ 0)$ | 4 : $(S, \quad 0, \ 0)$ |
| *a* | *a* | *a* | *b* |

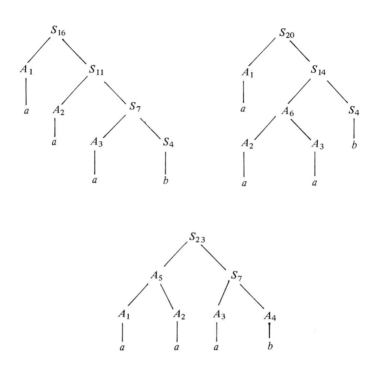

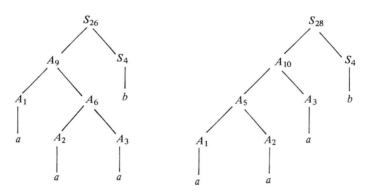

Fig. 1. Syntactic trees for $I = aaab$.

Table 3. Parse table Ta3 for $I = aaab$.

| | | | |
|---|---|---|---|
| 12 : $(S, \{(1, 10), (5, 10), (9, 4)\})$<br>13 : $(A, \{(1, 10), (1, 11),$<br>$(5, 10), (5, 11), (9, 4)\})$ | | | |
| 9 : $(A, \{(1, 6), (5, 3)\})$ | 10 : $(S, \{(2, 7), (6, 4)\})$<br>11 : $(A, \{(2, 7), (2, 8), (6, 4)\})$ | | |
| 5 : $(A, \{(1, 2)\})$ | 6 : $(A, \{(2, 3)\})$ | 7 : $(S, \{(3, 4)\})$<br>8 : $(A, \{(3, 4)\})$ | |
| 1 : $(A, \phi)$ | 2 : $(A, \phi)$ | 3 : $(A, \phi)$ | 4 : $(S, \phi)$ |
| $a$ | $a$ | $a$ | $b$ |

**Algorithm 2**

```
1 begin {* of the Earley *}
2    L[0] := {($ → •S, O)} ;
3    for i := 1 to n do L[i] := φ; (φ is the null set)
4    i := 0 ;
5    while i ≤ n do begin
6       for each (X → α•Yβ, j) ∈ L[i] do begin
7       if Y ∈ N then begin {* PREDICTOR *}
8          for each Y → γ ∈ P do
9             L[i] := L[i] ∪ {(Y → •γ, i)} ;
10      end
11      else if (Y ∈ T and i ≠ n) then begin {* SCANNER *}
12         if Y = a_{i+1} then
13            L[i + 1] := L[i + 1] ∪ {(X → αY•β, i)} ;
14         end
15         else if (Yβ = λ) then begin {* COMPLETER *}
16            for each (A → δ•Xς, k) ∈ L[j] do
17               L[i] := L[i] ∪ {(A → δX•ς, k)} ;
18            end ;
19         end {* of for *}
20      if (no new item has been generated in L[i] from lines 6–19)
21         then i := i + 1 ;
22   end ; {* of while *}
23   if ((S → α• , 0) ∈ L(n)) then I is accepted
        else I is rejected ;
24 end {* of the Earley *} .
```

The Earley has the following properties.

(1) If $(A → α•β, i)$ is in $L[j]$, then $α \xrightarrow{*} a_{i+1}a_{i+2} \ldots a_j$.

(2) The space and time complexities to construct the parse lists are $O(n^2)$ and $O(n^3)$, respectively. The time complexity to make all syntactic trees of a string is $O(c^n)$.

The method to make syntax trees from the parse lists is described in Ref. 5.

**Example 1.4.** Consider CFG $= (N, T, P, S)$, where $N = \{S, T, A, B\}, T = \{a, b, c\}, P = \{S → T, S → Sc, S → AB, T → aTb, T → ab, A → aA, A → a, B → bB, B → b\}$. $L(G) = \{a^t b^u c^v \mid t \geq 1, u \geq 1, v \geq 0\}$. The parse list for $I = abcc$ is shown in Table 4. First, generate $(\$ → •S, 0)$. By PREDICTOR,

$(S \rightarrow \bullet T, 0), (S \rightarrow \bullet Sc, 0)$ and $(S \rightarrow \bullet AB, 0)$ are created, since $S \rightarrow T, S \rightarrow Sc$ and $S \rightarrow AB$ are in $P$ and $S$ is active. Nonterminals $T, S$ and $A$ become active. Since $T \rightarrow aTb$ and $T \rightarrow ab$ are in $P, (T \rightarrow \bullet aTb, 0)$ and $(T \rightarrow \bullet ab, 0)$ are created. Similarly, PREDICTOR makes $(A \rightarrow \bullet aA, 0)$ and $(A \rightarrow \bullet a, 0)$ since $A \rightarrow aA$ and $A \rightarrow a$ are in $P$. For active $S$ of $(S \rightarrow \bullet Sc)$, three items $(S \rightarrow \bullet T, 0), (S \rightarrow \bullet Sc, 0)$ and $(S \rightarrow \bullet AB, 0)$ are generated, but they have been stored already. No item can be created by PREDICTOR. List $L[0]$ has been completed. Applying SCANNER to items 5, 6, 7 and 8, $(T \rightarrow a \bullet Tb, 0), (T \rightarrow a \bullet b, 0), (A \rightarrow a \bullet A, 0)$ and $(A \rightarrow a \bullet, 0)$ are generated. PREDICTOR generates $(T \rightarrow \bullet aTb, 1)$ and $(T \rightarrow \bullet ab, 1)$ for active $T$ of item 9, and $(A \rightarrow \bullet aA, 1)(A \rightarrow \bullet a, 1)$ for active $A$ of item 11. From items 4 and 12, COMPLETER makes $(S \rightarrow A \bullet B, 0)$. For active $B$ of item 17, PREDICTOR creates $(B \rightarrow \bullet bB, 1)$ and $(B \rightarrow \bullet b, 1)$. Then $L(1)$ has been completed. The rest is omitted. The two parse trees for $I$ and the subtrees corresponding to the items which are the components of the parse trees are depicted in Fig. 2.

## 1.4. Other Approaches

In 1980, Graham, Harrison and Ruzzo[8] reported a parser for a general context-free language (the GHR, for short). This parser has interesting features. (1) The GHR has close connections with both the Earley and the CKY, and unifies the two superficially dissimilar parsers. (2) The GHR is conceptually simpler than the Earley and may be much faster than the Earley by word-parallel Boolean operations. At the same time, it may be much faster than the CKY, since it has "predictors". The space and time complexities of the GHR are the same as those of the CKY. Another type of parsing[6] was reported in 1986, that is, "direct parsing". Direct parsers use neither "lists" as the Earley nor "tables" as the CKY, since the syntax tree of an input is expressed by a pointer type data structure. Two parsers were presented. The first makes a parse tree in preorder of vertices. If the parser is faced with the unsuccessful match of an input symbol or cannot find any possible forward steps, it backtracks. If the parser finds one parse tree, it accepts the input and stops. The second is a modified version of the first with no backtracking. Though the space complexity of the parsers is $O(n)$ and the time complexity is $O(c^n)$, we can find practical examples where the parsers analyze faster than the CKY and the Earley. Casacuberta[9] proposed extended versions of the Earley in order to apply syntactic methods to speech recognition.

Table 4. Parse lists for $I = abcc$. PRED: PREDICTOR, SCAN: SCANNER, COMP: COMPLETER.

| | | | |
|---|---|---|---|
| $L[0]$ | 1 | $[\$ \rightarrow \cdot S,\ 0]$ | initial setting |
| | 2 | $[S \rightarrow \cdot T,\ 0]$ | PRED(1), PRED(3) |
| | 3 | $[S \rightarrow \cdot Sc,\ 0]$ | PRED(1), PRED(3) |
| | 4 | $[S \rightarrow \cdot AB,\ 0]$ | PRED(1), PRED(3) |
| | 5 | $[T \rightarrow \cdot aTb,\ 0]$ | PRED(2) |
| | 6 | $[T \rightarrow \cdot ab,\ 0]$ | PRED(2) |
| | 7 | $[A \rightarrow \cdot aA,\ 0]$ | PRED(4) |
| | 8 | $[A \rightarrow \cdot a,\ 0]$ | PRED(4) |
| $L[1]$ | 9 | $[T \rightarrow a\cdot Tb,\ 0]$ | SCAN(5) |
| | 10 | $[T \rightarrow a\cdot b,\ 0]$ | SCAN(6) |
| | 11 | $[A \rightarrow a\cdot A,\ 0]$ | SCAN(7) |
| | 12 | $[A \rightarrow a\cdot,\ 0]$ | SCAN(8) |
| | 13 | $[T \rightarrow \cdot aTb,\ 1]$ | PRED(9) |
| | 14 | $[T \rightarrow \cdot ab,\ 1]$ | PRED(9) |
| | 15 | $[A \rightarrow \cdot aA,\ 1]$ | PRED(11) |
| | 16 | $[A \rightarrow \cdot a,\ 1]$ | PRED(11) |
| | 17 | $[S \rightarrow A\cdot B,\ 0]$ | COMP(12, 4) |
| | 18 | $[B \rightarrow \cdot bB,\ 1]$ | PRED(17) |
| | 19 | $[B \rightarrow \cdot b,\ 1]$ | PRED(17) |
| $L[2]$ | 20 | $[T \rightarrow ab\cdot,\ 0]$ | SCAN(10) |
| | 21 | $[B \rightarrow b\cdot B,\ 1]$ | SCAN(18) |
| | 22 | $[B \rightarrow b\cdot,\ 1]$ | SCAN(19) |
| | 23 | $[S \rightarrow T\cdot,\ 0]$ | COMP(20, 2) |
| | 24 | $[S \rightarrow AB\cdot,\ 0]$ | COMP(22, 17) |
| | 25 | $[\$ \rightarrow S\cdot,\ 0]$ | COMP(23, 1) , COMP(24, 1) |
| | 26 | $[S \rightarrow S\cdot c,\ 0]$ | COMP(23, 3), COMP(24, 3) |
| | 27 | $[B \rightarrow \cdot bB,\ 2]$ | PRED(21) |
| | 28 | $[B \rightarrow \cdot b,\ 2]$ | PRED(21) |
| $L[3]$ | 29 | $[S \rightarrow Sc\cdot,\ 0]$ | SCAN(26) |
| | 30 | $[\$ \rightarrow S\cdot, 0]$ | COMP(29, 1) |
| | 31 | $[S \rightarrow S\cdot c,\ 0]$ | COMP(29, 3) |
| $L[4]$ | 32 | $[S \rightarrow Sc\cdot,\ 0]$ | SCAN(31) |
| | 33 | $[\$ \rightarrow S\cdot,\ 0]$ | COMP(32, 1) |
| | 34 | $[S \rightarrow S\cdot c,\ 0]$ | COMP(32, 3) |

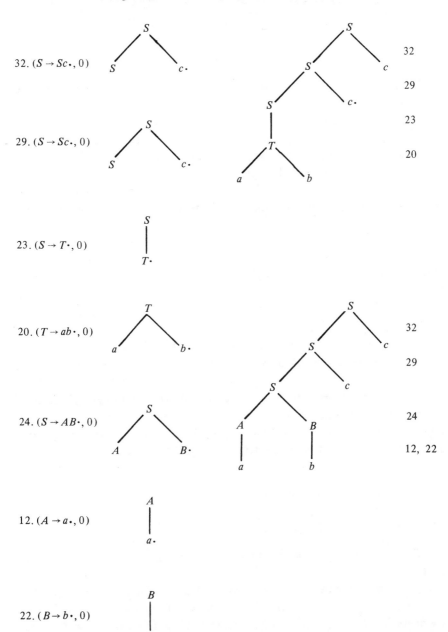

32. $(S \to Sc\cdot, 0)$

29. $(S \to Sc\cdot, 0)$

23. $(S \to T\cdot, 0)$

20. $(T \to ab\cdot, 0)$

24. $(S \to AB\cdot, 0)$

12. $(A \to a\cdot, 0)$

22. $(B \to b\cdot, 0)$

32

29

23

20

32

29

24

12, 22

**Fig. 2.** Correspondences between items and sub-syntactic trees, and two syntactic trees for $I = abcc$.

## 2. ERROR-CORRECTING PARSERS FOR CONTEXT-FREE LANGUAGES

### 2.1. Introduction

Consider again the two classes case. If an input string $x$ is deformed or garbled by noise, the parsing techniques in the previous section cannot decide whether $x$ belongs to the class 1 or the class 2. If $x$ is erroneous, we have to know whether $x$ is closer to $L(G_1)$ or $L(G_2)$. To realize this, first, a distance $D(L(G), x)$ or a similarity $S(L(G), x)$ from $L(G)$ to $x$ must be defined, and second, an algorithm to compute $D(L(G), x)$ or $S(L(G), x)$ must be developed. This algorithm is called an error-correcting recognizer or an error-correcting parser. An error-correcting recognition problem and an error-correcting parsing problem are defined as follows.

(1) An error-correcting recognition problem is the problem of finding the distance or similarity between $I$ and $J$, where $I$ is an input string, and $J$ is a string in $L(G)$ closest to $I$.

(2) An error-correcting parse problem is a problem of finding the closest string(s) $J$ to $I$, to make syntactic tree(s) of $J$ and to determine the distance or the similarity between $I$ and $J$.

In the following, we will introduce the weighted Levenshtein distance[10] which is a basis for error-correcting parsers. This distance and some of its modifications are also described in Chapter 5 of this book. Let $X = x_1 x_2 \ldots x_m$ and $Y = y_1 y_2 \ldots y_n$ be two finite strings of symbols from a given alphabet and define $M_s$ to be a mapping from $X$ to $Y$. $M_s$ is a set of pairs of integers $(i, j)$ which satisfies the following conditions, where $i$ and $j$ are labels for $x_i$ and $y_j$, respectively.

(1) $1 \leq i \leq m$,    $1 \leq j \leq n$.
(2) For $(i_1, j_1)$,    $(i_2, j_2) \in M_s$,
    (a) $i_1 = i_2$    iff    $j_1 = j_2$.
    (b) $i_1 < i_2$    iff    $j_1 < j_2$.

These conditions prohibit one-to-many, many-to-one and cross mappings.

Let $u_s$ be the number of elements $(i, j)$ in $M_s$ such that $x_i \neq y_j$. Let $v_s = n - |M_s|$ and $w_s = m - |M_s|$, where $|M_s|$ denotes the number of elements in $M_s$. $u_s, v_s$ and $w_s$ are considered as the number of substitutions, of insertions of extra symbols and of deletions to transform $X$ to $Y$, respectively. The one-dimensional weighted Levenshtein distance (1WLD) from $X$ to $Y$, denoted by $D(X, Y)$, is

$$D(X, Y) = \min_s\{p * u_s + q * v_s + r * w_s\} ,$$

where $p, q$ and $r$ are non-negative weights assigned to a substitution, an insertion and a deletion, respectively. The following are the properties of 1WLD:

(1) $D(X, Y) \geq 0$, with equality iff $X = Y$,

(2) $D(X, Z) + D(Z, Y) \geq (X, Y)$,

(3) $D(X, Y) = D(Y, X)$, if $q = r$.

$D(X, Y)$ can be computed by

$$d(i, j) = \min\{d(i - 1, j) + r, \quad d(i - 1, j - 1) + p(i, j), \quad d(i, j - 1) + q\} ,$$

where $d(i, 0) = i * r, d(0, j) = j * q$.

$$p(i, j) = \begin{cases} p, & \text{if } x_i \neq y_j . \\ 0, & \text{otherwise} . \end{cases}$$

Then

$$D(X, Y) = d(m, n) .$$

The computational complexity of computing $D(X, Y)$ is proportional to $mn$.

Define $D(L(G), I)$ as follows:

$$D(L(G), I) = \min\{D(\xi, I)|\xi \in L(G)\} .$$

This is 1WLD from a language $L(G)$ to a string $I$. Note that 1WLD is not symmetric, that is, the equality $D(X, Y) = D(Y, X)$ does not hold in general. Then $D(L(G), I)$ is not always equal to $D(I, L(G))$. A correct string $X$ in $L(G)$ is deformed or garbled to $I$, not $I$ to $X$. Therefore, we must compute $D(L(G), I)$. Error-correcting parsers can be characterized by $D(L(G), I)$.

Assume we derive $\alpha \gamma b \delta \beta$ by applying a production $B \to \gamma b \delta (b \in T)$ to $\alpha B \beta$. If we obtain $\alpha \gamma a \delta \beta (a \neq b, a \in T)$ by applying $B \to \gamma b \delta$ to $\alpha B \beta$, then this is an erroneous derivation with a substitution error and is denoted as follows

$$\alpha B\beta \rightarrow \alpha\gamma a\delta\beta \quad \text{with weight } p \ .$$

In the same way, a deletion error is written as

$$\alpha B\beta \rightarrow \alpha\gamma\delta\beta \quad \text{with weight } r$$

or

$$\alpha\gamma a\delta\beta \rightarrow \alpha\gamma\delta\beta \quad \text{with weight } r \ .$$

An insertion error can be expressed as

$$\alpha B\beta \rightarrow \alpha a B\beta \quad \text{with weight } q \ ,$$
$$\alpha B\beta \rightarrow \alpha B a\beta \quad \text{with weight } q \ .$$

Assume that $A \xrightarrow{*} \alpha B\beta$ is obtained with weight $w$, we have

$$A \xrightarrow{*} \alpha\gamma b\delta\beta \quad \text{with weight } w \ ,$$
$$A \xrightarrow{*} \alpha\gamma a\delta\beta \quad \text{with weight } w+p \ ,$$
$$A \xrightarrow{*} \alpha\gamma\delta\beta \quad \text{with weight } w+r \ ,$$
$$A \xrightarrow{*} \alpha a B\beta \quad \text{with weight } w+q \ ,$$
$$A \xrightarrow{*} \alpha B a\beta \quad \text{with weight } w+q \ .$$

## 2.2. A Bottom-Up Error-Correcting Parser

The bottom-up error-correcting parser for a context-free language was proposed by Fung and Fu[11] for substitution errors. Tanaka and Fu[12] and Yamasaki and Tonomura[13] proposed independently this type of error-correcting parser for substitution, insertion and deletion errors. Here we call it the TFY. The error-correcting parser described here is an extension of the CKY. Define $h(A) = \min\{|\alpha| * r | A \xrightarrow{*} \alpha, \alpha \in T^*\}$, where $|\alpha|$ is the length of one of the shortest strings derived from nonterminal $A$. Let $W\text{max}$ be a predetermined threshold.

Define the operation $t[i,j] \cup \{(A,w)\}$ as follows:

If $(A, w') \in t[i,j]$ and $w' \leq w$, do nothing.

If $(A, w') \in t[i,j]$ and $w' > w$, replace $(A, w')$ with $(A, w)$.

Otherwise, if $w \leq W\text{max}$, add $(A, w)$ to $t[i,j]$.

Input:  CFG $G = (N, T, P, S)$ in Chomsky normal form and an input string $I = a_1 a_2 \ldots a_n$. $p$, $q$ and $r$ are the weights for a substitution, an insertion and a deletion, respectively.

Output: The parse table Ta .

**Algorithm 3**

```
1  begin {* of the algorithm *}
2      for i := 1 to n do begin
                  {* match or substitution *}
3      for each A → b ∈ P do
4        if b = aᵢ then t[i, 1] := t[i, 1] ∪ {(A, 0)}
5        else t[i, 1] := t[i, 1] ∪ {(A, p)}
6      repeat {* deletion *}
7        for each A → BC ∈ P do begin
8          if ((B, w) ∈ t[i, 1])  {*C is deleted *}
             then t[i, 1] := t[i, 1] ∪ {(A, w + h(C)} ;
9          if ((C, w) ∈ t[i, 1])  {*B is deleted *}
             then t[i, 1] := t[i, 1] ∪ {(A, w + h(B)} ;
10         end ;
11     until {* No new item has been generated from lines 7–10 *}
       {* insertion *}
12       for each (A, w) ∈ t[i, 1] do begin
13         if i > 1 then t[i − 1, 2] := t[i − 1, 2] ∪ {(A, w + q)}
14         if i < n then t[i, 2] := t[i, 2] ∪ {(A, w + q)}
15       end ;
16     end ; {* of for i *}
17     for j := 2 to n do begin
18     for i := 1 to n − j + 1 do begin
19       for k := 1 to j − 1 do begin {* complete *}
20         for each A → BC ∈ P do
21           if ((B, w_B) ∈ t[i, k]) and ((C, w_C) ∈ t[i + k, j − k])
22             then t[i, j] := t[i, j] ∪ {(A, w_B + w_C)} ;
23         end ;
24       repeat {* deletion *}
25         for each A → BC ∈ P do begin
26           if ((B, w) ∈ t[i, j])  {*C is deleted *}
               then t[i, j] := t[i, j] ∪ {(A, w + h(C))} ;
27           if ((C, w) ∈ t[i, j])  {*B is deleted *}
               then t[i, j] := t[i, j] ∪ {(A, w + h(B))} ;
28         end
29       until {*No new item has been generated from lines 25–28*}
         {* insertion *}
30         for each (A, w) ∈ t[i, j] do begin
```

31          if $i > 1$ and $j < n$ then $t[i-1, j+1] := t[i-1, j+1] \cup \{A, w+q)\}$
32          if $i < n$ and $j < n$ then $t[i, j+1] := t[i, j+1] \cup \{(A, w+q)\}$
33      end ;
34    end ; {* of for $i$ *}
35    end ; {* of for $j$*}
36    if $(S, w) \in T[1, n]$, then $I$ is accepted with weight $w$
37    else $I$ is rejected:
38 end .   {* of the algorithm *}

The TFY has the following properties.

(1)  If $(A, w) \in T[i, j]$, then $A \xrightarrow{*} a_i a_{i+1} \ldots a_{i+j-1}$ with weight $w$.
(2)  The space and time complexities of this algorithm are the same as those of the CKY.

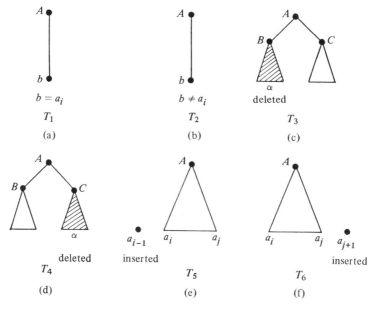

Fig. 3.  Sub-syntactic trees corresponding to the operations in a bottom-up error-correcting parser.

The operation described from lines 3–7 treats substitution errors. If $b = a_i$ and $A \to b$ is in $P$, $(A, 0)$ is added to $t[i, 1]$. This corresponds to tree $T_1$ in Fig. 3a. If $b \neq a_i$, $(A, p)$ is created in $t[i, 1]$. This is the hypothesis that $a_i$ is substituted for $b$ (Fig. 3b). Deletion errors are treated by the operations from lines 6–11 and lines 24–29. If $A \rightarrow BC$ is in $P$ and $(B, w_B)$ is in $t[i, j]$, $(A, w_B + h(C))$ is created in $t[i, j]$. This is the hypothesis that $\alpha$ is deleted. Here $\alpha$ is one of the shortest strings such that $C \xrightarrow{*} \alpha (\alpha \in T^*)$ and $h(C) = |\alpha| * r$. This is depicted in Fig. 3c. Another case is illustrated in Fig. 3d. The operation from lines 30–33 treats insertion errors. If $(A, w_A)$ is in $t[i, j]$, $(A, w_A + q)$ is added to $t[i, j + 1]$ and $t[i - 1, j + 1]$. This means that $a_{i+j+1}$ and $a_{i-1}$ are assumed to be inserted (Figs. 3e and 3f).

**Example 2.1.** Consider $G3 = (N, T, P, S)$, where $N = \{S, A\}, T = \{a, b\}$, $P = \{S \rightarrow AS, A \rightarrow SA, S \rightarrow b, A \rightarrow a\}$.

$L(G) = \{a^{m1} b a^{m2} b \ldots a^{ms} b|$ if $s = 1, m1 \geq 1$; if $s > 1, m1 \geq 0$ and $mi \geq 1$ $(i = 2, 3, \ldots, s)$. We set $p = q = r = 1$.

Table 5 is the parse table Ta1 for $I = abb$. $I$ is accepted with weight 1. Table 6 is the parse table Ta2 which uses an item of the form "$t :$ $(A, w, l, r)$", where $t, A, l$ and $r$ are defined in Ex. 1.1 and $w$ is the weight. "1:$(S, 1, \text{SUB}, -)$" denotes $a$ is substituted for $b$ which is reduced to $S$, and SUB means a substitution error. MAT, INS and DEL stand for a match, an insertion error and a deletion error, respectively. $I$ has seven corrected syntax trees shown in Fig. 4.

### 2.3. A Top-Down Error-Correcting Parser

Aho and Peterson[14] proposed a top-down error-correcting parser based on the Earley. Since they used error productions, the parser requires enormous time and memory. In 1974, Lyon[15] reported an error-correcting parser which is a natural extension of the Earley. In the following, we will describe a simplified version of the Lyon. Define the operation $L[k] \cup \{(X \rightarrow \alpha \cdot \beta, j, w)\}$ in the two ways as follows:

**Definition 2.2.** If $(X \rightarrow \alpha \cdot \beta, i, w') \in L[k], i \leq j$ and $w' \leq w$, do nothing. If $(X \rightarrow \alpha \cdot \beta, i, w') \in L[k], i \leq j$ and $w' > w$, replace $(X \rightarrow \alpha \cdot \beta, i, w')$ with $(X \rightarrow \alpha \cdot \beta, j, w)$.
Otherwise, if $w \leq W \max$, add $(X \rightarrow \alpha \cdot \beta, j, w)$ to $L[k]$.

**Definition 2.3.** If $(X \rightarrow \alpha \cdot \beta, j, w') \in L[k]$ and $w' \leq w$, do nothing. If $(X \rightarrow \alpha \cdot \beta, j, w') \in L[k]$ and $w' > w$, replace $(X \rightarrow \alpha \cdot \beta, j, w')$ with $(X \rightarrow \alpha \cdot \beta, j, w)$.
Otherwise, if $w \leq W \max$, add $(X \rightarrow \alpha \cdot \beta, j, w)$ to $L[k]$.

Definition 2.2 is for the recognition problem and the parse problem to construct only one parse tree of an input. Definition 2.3 is useful to construct

Table 5. Parse table Ta1 for *I=abb*.

| | | |
|---|---|---|
| (S, 1)<br>(A, 1) | | |
| (A, 1)<br>(S, 0) | (A, 1)<br>(S, 1) | |
| (S, 1)<br>(A, 0) | (S, 0)<br>(A, 1) | (S, 0)<br>(A, 1) |
| *a* | *b* | *b* |

Table 6.  Parse table Ta2 for *I = abb*.  Item 8 is deleted after creating item 14.

| | | |
|---|---|---|
| 16 : (S, 1, 14, INS)<br>21 : (S, 1, 2, 9)<br>22 : (S, 1, 2, 13)<br>23 : (S, 1, 2, 19)<br>24 : (S, 1, 2, 20)<br>25 : (S, 1, 4, 10)<br>26 : (A, 1, 14, 11)<br>27 : (A, 1, 14, 12)<br>28 : (S, 1, 15, 10) | | |
| 4 : (A, 1, 2, INS)<br>14 : (S, 0, 2, 5)<br>15 : (A, 1, 14, DEL) | 9 : (S, 1, 5, INS)<br>13 : (S, 1, INS, 10)<br>17 : (A, 1, 5, 11)<br>18 : (A, 1, 5, 12)<br>19 : (S, 1, 6, 10)<br>20 : (S, 1, 7, 10) | |
| 1 : (S, 1, SUB, −)<br>2 : (A, 0, MAT, −)<br>3 : (S, 1, 2, DEL) | 5 : (S, 0, MAT, −)<br>6 : (A, 1, SUB, −)<br>7 : (A, 1, 5, DEL) | 10 : (S, 0, MAT, −)<br>11 : (A, 1, SUB, −)<br>12 : (A, 1, 10, DEL) |
| *a* | *b* | *b* |

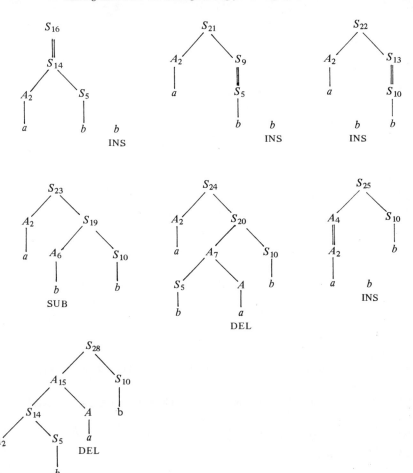

Fig. 4. Corrected syntactic trees for $I = abb$. $S_{14}$ is exactly the same as $S_{16}$. Similarly, $S_5 = S_9$, $S_{10} = S_{13}$ and $A_2 = A_4$.

all parse trees of an input.

Input: $G = (N, T, P, S)$ and an input string $I = a_1 a_2 \ldots a_n$. $p, q$ and $r$ are the weights for a substitution, an insertion and a deletion, respectively.

Output: $L[0], L[1], \ldots, L[n]$.

**Algorithm 4**
1 begin {* of the Lyon *}

2    $L(0) := \{(\$ \rightarrow \cdot S\#, 0, 0)\}$ ;
3    for $i := 1$ to $n$ do $L[i] := \phi$ ;
4    $i := 0$ ;
5    while $(i \leq n)$ do begin
6        for each $(X \rightarrow \alpha \cdot Y\beta, j, w)$ do begin
7            if $Y \in N$ then begin {* PREDICTOR *}
8            for each $Y \rightarrow \gamma \in P$ do
9                $L[i] := L[i] \cup \{(Y \rightarrow \cdot\gamma, i, 0)\}$ ;
10           end
11           else if $Y \in T$ then begin {* SCANNER *}
12               if $i \neq n$ then begin
13                   if $Y = a_{i+1}$ then
14                       $L[i+1] := L[i+1] \cup \{(X \rightarrow \alpha Y \cdot \beta, i, w)\}$
                                                      {* match *}
15                   else
16                       $L[i+1] := L[i+1] \cup (X \rightarrow \alpha Y \cdot \beta, i, w + p)$ ;
                                                      {* substitution *} ;
17                       $L[i+1] := L[i+1] \cup \{(X \rightarrow \alpha \cdot Y\beta, i, w + q)\}$
                                                      {* insertion *} ;
18               end
19               $L[i] : L(i) \cup \{(X \rightarrow \alpha Y \cdot \beta, i, w + r)\}$ {* deletion *};
20           end
21           else if $Y\xi = \lambda$ then begin {* COMPLETER *}
22               for each $(A \rightarrow \delta \cdot Y\xi, k) \in L[j]$ do
23                   $L[i] := L[i] \cup \{(A \rightarrow \delta X \cdot \xi, k)\}$
24           end
25           else if $(Y = \#)$ then begin {* insertion at the end of the sentence *}
26               $L[n] := L[n] \cup \{(\$ \rightarrow S\# \cdot, j, w + (n - i) * q)\}$ ;
27           end {* of for *} ;
28    if (no new item has been generated in $L[i]$ from lines 5–27)
29        then $i := i + 1$ ;
30    end {* of while *}
31    if $((\$ \rightarrow S \cdot, 0, w) \in L[n]$ then $I$ is accepted with weight $w$
32    else $I$ is rejected ;
33 end {* of the Lyon *} .

The Lyon has the following properties.

(1) If $(A \rightarrow \alpha \cdot \beta, i, w) \in L[j]$, then

$\alpha \overset{*}{\to} a_{i+1} a_{i+2} \ldots a_j$ with weight $w$.

(2) The space and time complexities of the Lyon are the same as those of the Earley.

**Example 2.4.** Consider the CFG $G4 = (N, T, P, S)$, where $N = \{S, T\}$, $T = \{a, b, c\}$, $P = \{S \to T, S \to Sc, T \to aTb, T \to ab\}$. $L(G) = \{a^t b^t c^u | t \geq 1, u \geq 0\}$. We set $p = q = r = 1$ and $W \max = 1$. The result for $I = abb$ is shown in Table 7. The five corrected parse trees are listed in Fig. 5.

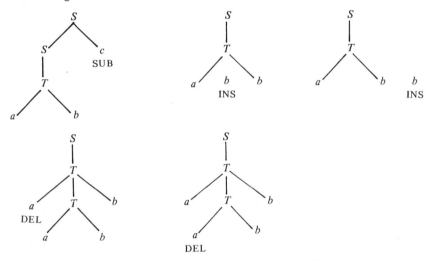

Fig. 5. Corrected syntactic trees for $I = abb$.

## 2.4. Other Approaches

The GHR was extended to an error-correcting parser for context-free languages[16]. This parser has similar characteristics to that of the GHR.

(1) The parser unifies both the top-down error-correcting parser by Lyon and the bottom-up error-correcting parsers by Tanaka-Fu and Yamasaki-Tonomura.

(2) The parser is conceptually simpler than the Lyon, and may be much faster than the bottom-up error-correcting parsers. This error-correcting parse is the optimum parser in the sense of the WLD. The time and space complexities of the parser are the same as those of the CKY.

Table 7. Parse lists for $I = abb$. MAT: MATCH, SUB: SUBSTITUTION, INS: INSERTION, DEL: DELETION.

| | | | |
|---|---|---|---|
| $L[0]$ | 1 | $[\$ \rightarrow \bullet S\#, 0, 0]$ | |
| | 2 | $[S \rightarrow \bullet T, \ 0, \ 0]$ | PRED(1), PRED(3) |
| | 3 | $[S \rightarrow \bullet Sc, \ 0, \ 0]$ | PRED(1), PRED(3) |
| | 4 | $[T \rightarrow \bullet aTb, \ 0, \ 0]$ | PRED(2), PRED(6) |
| | 5 | $[T \rightarrow \bullet ab, \ 0, \ 0]$ | PRED(2), PRED(6) |
| | 6 | $[T \rightarrow a\bullet Tb, \ 0, \ 1]$ | DEL(4) |
| | 7 | $[T \rightarrow a\bullet b, \ 0, \ 1]$ | DEL(5) |
| $L[1]$ | 8 | $[T \rightarrow a\bullet Tb, \ 0, \ 0]$ | MAT(4) |
| | 9 | $[T \rightarrow \bullet aTb, \ 0, \ 1]$ | INS(4) |
| | 10 | $[T \rightarrow a\bullet b, \ 0, \ 0]$ | MAT(5) |
| | 11 | $[T \rightarrow \bullet ab, \ 0, \ 1]$ | INS(5) |
| | 12 | $[T \rightarrow \bullet aTb, \ 1, \ 0]$ | PRED(8), PRED(15) |
| | 13 | $[T \rightarrow \bullet ab, \ 1, \ 0]$ | PRED(8), PRED(15) |
| | 14 | $[T \rightarrow ab\bullet, \ 0, \ 1]$ | DEL(10) |
| | 15 | $[T \rightarrow a\bullet Tb, \ 1, \ 1]$ | DEL(12) |
| | 16 | $[T \rightarrow a\bullet b, \ 1, \ 1]$ | DEL(13) |
| | 17 | $[S \rightarrow T\bullet, \ 0, \ 1]$ | COMP(14, 2) |
| | 18 | $[\$ \rightarrow S\bullet\#, \ 0, \ 1]$ | COMP(17, 1) |
| | 19 | $[S \rightarrow S\bullet c, \ 0, \ 1]$ | COMP(17, 3) |
| $L[2]$ | 20 | $[T \rightarrow ab\bullet, \ 0, \ 0]$ | MAT(10) |
| | 21 | $[T \rightarrow a\bullet b, \ 0, \ 1]$ | INS(10) |
| | 22 | $[T \rightarrow a\bullet Tb, \ 1, \ 1]$ | SUB(12) |
| | 23 | $[T \rightarrow \bullet aTb, \ 1, \ 1]$ | INS(12) |
| | 24 | $[T \rightarrow a\bullet b, \ 1, \ 1]$ | SUB(13) |
| | 25 | $[T \rightarrow \bullet ab, \ 1, \ 1]$ | INS(13) |
| | 26 | $[T \rightarrow ab\bullet, \ 1, \ 1]$ | MAT(16) |
| | 27 | $[S \rightarrow T\bullet, \ 0, \ 0]$ | COMP(20, 2) |
| | 28 | $[T \rightarrow aT\bullet b, \ 0, \ 1]$ | COMP(20, 6), COMP(26, 8) |
| | 29 | $[T \rightarrow \bullet aTb, \ 2, \ 0]$ | PRED(22), PRED(33) |
| | 30 | $[T \rightarrow \bullet ab, \ 2, \ 0]$ | PRED(22), PRED(33) |
| | 31 | $[\$ \rightarrow S\bullet\#, \ 0, \ 0]$ | COMP(27, 1) |
| | 32 | $[S \rightarrow S\bullet c, \ 0, \ 0]$ | COMP(27, 3) |
| | 33 | $[T \rightarrow a\bullet Tb, \ 2, \ 1]$ | DEL(29) |
| | 34 | $[T \rightarrow a\bullet b, \ 2, \ 1]$ | DEL(30) |
| | 35 | $[S \rightarrow Sc\bullet, \ 0, \ 1]$ | DEL(32) |

Table 7. Cont'd.

| | | | |
|---|---|---|---|
| | 36 | $[T \to ab\bullet,\ 0,\ 1]$ | MAT(21) |
| | 37 | $[T \to ab\bullet,\ 1,\ 1]$ | MAT(24) |
| | 38 | $[T \to aTb\bullet,\ 0,\ 1]$ | MAT(28) |
| | 39 | $[T \to a\bullet Tb,\ 2,\ 1]$ | SUB(29) |
| | 40 | $[T \to \bullet aTb,\ 2,\ 1]$ | INS(29) |
| | 41 | $[T \to a\bullet b,\ 2,\ 1]$ | SUB(30) |
| | 42 | $[T \to \bullet ab,\ 2,\ 1]$ | INS(30) |
| | 43 | $[\$ \to S\bullet\#,\ 0,\ 1]$ | INS(31), INS(51) |
| $L[3]$ | 44 | $[S \to Sc\bullet,\ 0,\ 1]$ | SUB(32) |
| | 45 | $[S \to S\bullet c,\ 0,\ 1]$ | INS(32), COMP(44, 3), COMP(48, 3) |
| | 46 | $[T \to ab\bullet,\ 2,\ 1]$ | MAT(34) |
| | 47 | $[T \to aT\bullet b,\ 0,\ 1]$ | COMP(36, 6), COMP(37, 8) |
| | 48 | $[S \to T\bullet,\ 0,\ 1]$ | COMP(36, 2), COMP(38, 2) |
| | 49 | $[T \to \bullet aTb,\ 3,\ 0]$ | PRED(39) |
| | 50 | $[T \to \bullet ab,\ 3,\ 0]$ | PRED(39) |
| | 51 | $[\$ \to S\bullet\#,\ 0,\ 1]$ | COMP(44, 1), COMP(48, 1) |
| | 52 | $[T \to a\bullet Tb,\ 3,\ 1]$ | DEL(49) |
| | 53 | $[T \to a\bullet b,\ 3,\ 1]$ | DEL(50) |

Vowels in continuous speech are highly context-dependent. These kinds of context-dependent phonological rules in English are described in Ref. 17. To treat this context-dependency, a context-dependent similarity was proposed[18]. An error-correcting parser based on this similarity is reported in Ref. 19.

Yoshino and Aoki[20] applied the bottom-up error-correcting parser[12] to hand-printed character recognition in order to realize a segmentation free recognizer.

## 3. RECENT DEVELOPMENTS IN PARSERS AND ERROR-CORRECTING PARSERS FOR CONTEXT-SENSITIVE LANGUAGES

It is well-known that the language $\{a^n b^n c^n | n \geq 1\}$ is not a context-free language but a context-sensitive language. This means that even a simple shape such as a triangle cannot be expressed by a context-free language. Almost all pictures are intrinsically context-sensitive. However, the analysis of a context-sensitive language is more complicated than that of a context-free language. We will explain it using examples. The normal form of productions of a context-sensitive grammar are of the form

(1) $A \rightarrow a$ ,

(2) $A \rightarrow BC$ ,

(3) $AB \rightarrow CB$ ,    $AB \rightarrow AC$ ,

where $a \in T$, and $A, B, C \in N$.

Let us make a correspondence between context-sensitive productions and graphs (Fig. 6). Consider bottom-up parsing.

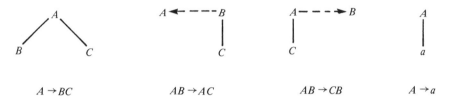

$A \rightarrow BC$          $AB \rightarrow AC$          $AB \rightarrow CB$          $A \rightarrow a$

Fig. 6. Sub-syntactic graphs corresponding to the productions in context-sensitive normal form.

(a) The production $F \rightarrow AC$ cannot be applied to the syntactic graph $T_1$ in Fig. 7a. If it is applied to $T_1$, we have the syntactic graph $T_2$ in which $H$ has two fathers.

(b) The production $AC \rightarrow BC$ cannot be applied to the syntactic graph $T_1$ in Fig. 8a. If it is applied to $T_1$, we have $T_2$ which has a crossing.

(c) The syntactic graph $T_1$ in Fig. 9a denotes the coexistence of two syntactic graphs $T_2$ and $T_3$. The production $A \rightarrow BC$ cannot be applied to $B$ and $C$. If it is applied, we obtain $T_4$ which has a crossing.

Therefore, there are some restrictions on applying productions to a syntactic graph. Another problem is loop detection.

(d) If $w_1 = w_{n+1}$ in the following deriviation

$$S \xrightarrow{*} \alpha w_1 \beta \rightarrow \alpha w_2 \beta \rightarrow \ldots \rightarrow \alpha w_{n+1} \beta$$

"$\alpha w_1 \beta \xrightarrow{*} \alpha w_{n+1} \beta$" is called a loop of length $n$. A loop must be detected in parsing to terminate parsing.

These restrictions (a)–(d) make a parse algorithm for a context-sensitive language complicated.

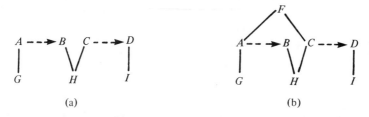

Fig. 7. (a) Two sub-syntactic graphs $T_1$, and (b) an incorrect syntactic graph $T_2$ obtained by applying production $F \rightarrow AC$ to $T_1$ wrongly.

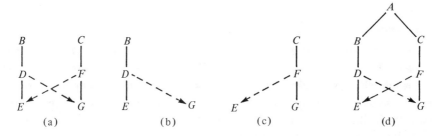

Fig. 8. (a) A sub-syntactic graph $T_1$, and (b) an incorrect sub-syntactic graph $T_2$ obtained by applying production $BC \rightarrow EC$ to $T_1$ wrongly.

Fig. 9. (a) A syntactic graph $T_1$ which consists of $T_2$ and $T_3$, (b) a syntactic graph $T_2$, (c) a syntactic graph $T_3$ and (d) an incorrect syntactic graph obtained by applying production $A \rightarrow BC$ to $T_1$ wrongly.

## 1. Parsers using stacks

A bottom-up parser and a top-down parser using stacks are described in Refs. 21 and 22, respectively. The former is a natural extension of Ref. 5 to a context-sensitive language.

## 2. Parsers using tables and lists

Bottom-up parsers for a context-sensitive language are reported in Refs. 12, 23 and 24. Top-down parsers are found in Refs. 25 and 26. Each item of these parsers has indices that indicate the children of the item for a bottom-up parser and the father of the item for a top-down parser. For example, in a bottom-up parser an item is expressed as $E = (A, i, j, k, l)$, where $A, i$ and $l$ denote a symbol, the number assigned to this item and an index for loop detection, respectively. $j$ and $k$ are the numbers of items that generate $E$, that is, the children of $E$. Memorizing ancestor-descendant relationship in an item makes a context check and a loop check easier in constructing a parse table, and makes parse trees easier after completing the parse table. However, these parsers are not based on dynamic programming. They are similar to direct parsing, but are not really direct parsing, because they use a table or a set of lists. Here, we call them pseudo-direct parsing.

*3. Error-correcting parsers*

Bottom-up error-correcting parsers for a context-sensitive language are reported in Refs. 12 and 27, and top-down ones in Refs. 28 and 29. They are not based on dynamic programming.

*4. Parsers to analyze a string from left to right based on dynamic programming*

A new attempt is found in the report by Hitaka, Nakamura and Yoshida[28]. They try to construct a parser for a general context-sensitive language which analyzes a string from left to right using a bracket grammar. Though the idea is interesting, the loop detection problem is left to be solved. Ikeda and Tanaka[29] proposed a parser for a loop-free context-sensitive language which is an extension of the Earley.

## 4. CONCLUDING REMARKS

Parsers and error-correcting parsers (EC parsers, in short) except stack type parsers are classified as shown in Table 8. The author does not have a strong impression that filling all the blanks is worthy.

Error-correcting parsers in formal language theory have not been applied to speech recognition. However, since an error-correcting parser takes much computing time and memory to analyze English, even a computer with some $M$ bytes of memory can only analyze a sentence of a few words if the number of syntax rules is more than several hundred. With respect to time, a high speed error-correcting parser is needed. To realize such a high speed error-correcting parser, a high speed parser must be constructed.

Table 8. Parsers and error-correcting parsers.

| Language | Method | Dynamic programming parsing | | Pseudo direct parsing | | Direct parsing |
|---|---|---|---|---|---|---|
| | | Parser | EC Parser | Parser | EC Parser | Parser |
| CF | Top-down method | Earley[5] | Lyon[15] ITK[19] | | | TIE[6] |
| | Bottom-up method | CKY[5] | TFY[12,13] | | | |
| | Combined method | GHR[8] | Tanaka[16] | | | |
| CS | Top-down method | IT[29] | Ikeda[32] | TSK[25] AK[26] | KIT[30] KM[31] | |
| | Bottom-up method | | | Kuno[23] TF[12] Kamata[24] | TF[12] Kamata[27] | |

Two attempts, one for English and the other for Japanese, can be found in Refs. 33 and 34 respectively.

# REFERENCES

1. A.V. Aho and J.D. Ullman, *The Theory of Parsing, Translation, and Compiling, Vol. 1: Parsing*, (Prentice-Hall, Englewood Cliffs, NJ, 1972).
2. K.S. Fu (ed.), *Syntactic Pattern Recognition, Applications* (Springer, Berlin 1977).
3. R.C. Gonzalez and M.G. Thomason *Syntactic Pattern Recognition, An Introduction* (Addison-Wesley, London, 1978).
4. S. Ginsburg, *The Mathematical Theory of Context-free Languages* (McGraw-Hill, N.Y., 1966).
5. Chapter 4 of Ref. 1.
6. E. Tanaka, M. Ikeda and K. Ezure, "Direct parsing," Pattern Recognition **19** (1986) 315-323.
7. Chapter 4 of Ref. 3.
8. S.L. Graham, M.A. Harrison and W.L. Ruzzo, "An improved context-free recognizer," *ACM Trans. Program. Lang. & Syst.* **2** (1980) 415-449.
9. F. Casacuberta, "A syntactic method for substring segmentation and recognition," in *Syntactic and Structural Pattern Recognition*, eds. G. Ferrate, T. Pavlidis, A. Sanfeliu and H. Bunke (Springer, Berlin, 1988).
10. T. Okuda, E. Tanaka and T Kasai, "A method for the correction of garbled words based on the Levenshtein metric," *IEEE Trans. Comp.* **25** (1976) 172-178.
11. L.W. Fung and K.S. Fu, "Maximum-likelihood syntactic decoding," *IEEE Trans. Info. Theory* **21** (1975) 423-430.
12. E. Tanaka and K.S. Fu, "Error-correcting parsers for formal languages," Purdue Univ. Tech. Rep., TR-EE 76-7 (1976); also *IEEE Trans. Comp.* **27** (1978) 605-616 and *IEEE Trans. Comp.* **31** (1982) 327-328.
13. S. Yamasaki and T. Tonomura, "On a bottom-up least error-correcting algorithm for context-free languages," *J. Info. Process. Soc.* **18** (1977) 781-788.
14. A.V. Aho and T.G. Peterson, "A minimum distance error-correcting parser for context-free languages," *SIAM J. Comput.* **1** (1972) 305-312.
15. G. Lyon, "Syntax-directed least-errors analysis for context-free languages: a practical approach," *CACM* **17** (1974) 3-14.
16. E. Tanaka, "An improved error-correcting parser for a context-free language," *Trans. Inst. Electron. Commun. Engin.* **E67** (1984) 379-385.
17. B. Oshika, V. Zue, V. Weeks, H. New and J. Aurbach, "The role of phonological rules in speech understanding research," *IEEE Trans. ASSP* **23** (1975) 104-112.
18. E. Tanaka, "A string correction method based on the context-dependency," in *Syntactic and Structural Pattern Recognition*, eds. G. Ferrate, T. Pavlidis, A. Sanfeliu and H. Bunke (Springer, Berlin, 1988).
19. M. Ikeda, E. Tanaka and O. Kakusho, "An error-correcting parser based on the context-dependent similarity," in *Syntactic and Structural Pattern Recognition*, eds. G. Ferrate, T. Pavlidis, A. Sanfeliu and H. Bunke (Springer, Berlin, 1988).
20. K. Yoshino and K. Aoki, "Recognition of handwritten script English words using a syntactic method," Report of research group of pattern recognition and learning, Inst. Electron. Commun. Engin., PRL82-47 (1982).

21. W.A. Woods, "Context-sensitive recognition," Mathematical linguistics and automatic translation, Rep. NSF–18, The Computing Laboratory, Harvard Univ., 1967.

22. K. Kamata, "A parsing method for a context-sensitive language using a grammar without context-sensitive productions," *Trans. Inst. Electron. Commun. Engin.*, **64** (1981) 17-23

23. S. Kuno, "A context-sensitive recognition procedure," Mathematical linguistics and automatic translation, Rep. NSF–18, The Computing Laboratory, Harvard Univ., 1967.

24. K. Kamata, "A bottom-up parsing method for a context-sensitive language using a grammar without context-sensitive productions," *Trans. Inst. Electron. Commun. Engin.*, (1982) 1-7.

25. E. Tanaka, K. Sakuramoto and T. Kasai, "A top-down parsing algorithm for a context-sensitive language," *Trans. Inst. Electron. Commun. Engin.* **62-D** (1979) 97-103.

26. H. Adachi and K. Kamata, "A top-down parsing method for a context-sensitive language using a grammar without context-sensitive productions," *Trans. Inst. Electron. Commun. Engin.*, **J66-D** (1983) 880-887.

27. K. Kamata, "A bottom-up error-correcting method for a context-sensitive language using a grammar without context-sensitive productions," *Trans. Inst. Electron. Commun. Engin.*, **J66-D** (1983) 653-659.

28. T. Hitaka, T. Nakamura and S. Yoshida, "Characterization of a phrase structure grammar and its parsing," Report of research group on natural language processing, Info. Process. Soc. 47-1 (1985).

29. M. Ikeda and E. Tanaka, "A recognizing algorithm for a loop-free context-sensitive language based on the dynamic programming method", *Trans. Inst. Electron. Commun. Engin.* **69-D** (1986) 1371-1381.

30. H. Kobayashi, M. Ikeda and E. Tanaka, "A top-down error-correcting parser for a context-sensitive language", *Trans. Inst. Electron. Commun. Engin.* **J68-D** (1985) 1505-1512.

31. K. Kamata and O. Miyazawa, "A top-down error-correcting parsing for context-sensitive languages using a grammar without context-sensitive rules", *Trans. Inst. Electron. Commun. Engin.* **E68** (1985) 579-585.

32. M. Ikeda, "Parsing methods for a context-sensitive language", Master's thesis, Department of Information Science, Utsunomiya University (1986).

33. E. Tanaka, I. Tamada, T. Nagasawa and K. Wakahara, "High speed English analysis by pattern matching," *Proc. Int. Comput. Symp.* 1986, Vol. 1, Taiwan, 1986, pp. 308-316.

34. K. Ozeki, "A multi-stage decision algorithm to select optimum bunsetsu sequences based on degree of kakariuke dependency," *Trans. Inst. Electron. Commun. Engin.* **J70-D** (1987) 601-609.

# 4

# ARRAY, TREE AND GRAPH GRAMMARS

AZRIEL ROSENFELD
*Center for Automation Research*
*University of Maryland*
*College Park, MD 20742*
*USA*

This tutorial paper reviews several generalizations of string grammars that are directly applicable to syntactic pattern recognition. One class of generalizations includes grammars whose languages are sets of arrays of symbols, where the arrays may be rectangular-shaped or may be arbitrary connected arrays. The other class includes grammars whose languages are sets of labeled graphs, or in particular, labeled trees.

## 1. INTRODUCTION

Ordinary (string) grammars have languages that are sets of (one-dimensional) strings of symbols. In this chapter we review several generalized types of grammars whose languages are multidimensional. As a preliminary, Sec. 2 reviews some basic string grammar concepts that are used in defining these generalizations, and Sec. 3 discusses some variations on conventional grammars that are needed in defining array grammars.

Strings are one-dimensional arrays; thus it is natural to consider grammars whose languages are sets of two-dimensional arrays. We can require these arrays to be rectangular (e.g. a string of length $n$ is a $1 \times n$ rectangle), or we can allow them to have arbitrary shapes (but require them to be connected). Section 4 discusses various types of array grammars.

A string can also be regarded as a special type of connected graph in which each node (with two exceptions) has exactly two neighbors, and where the symbols in the string are regarded as labels of the nodes. Thus it is natural to consider grammars whose languages are sets of labeled graphs. In particular, since a string is an acyclic directed graph, and in particular a directed tree, we can also consider grammars whose languages are sets of labeled trees. Graph and tree grammars are discussed in Sec. 5.

String grammars of various types are known to be equivalent to "acceptors" (i.e. automata) of various types, in the sense that they have the same classes of languages. Section 6 briefly discusses acceptors that are equivalent to various types of array, tree, and graph grammars. Finally, Sec. 7 discusses some important generalizations of grammars, including programmed grammars and parameterized ("attributed") grammars.

The literature on these types of grammars is extensive; we only give some general references here. An introduction to array grammars and acceptors of various types can be found in Ref. 1, and an introduction to graph grammars can be found in Ref. 2. A general introduction to syntactic methods in pattern recognition with emphasis on tree grammars can be found in Ref. 3. Graph grammars have a large literature, and have been the subject of a series of international workshops; collections of papers derived from these workshops, including a major bibliography, can be found in Refs. 4, 5 and 6.

## 2. PRELIMINARIES ON STRING GRAMMARS

We begin by briefly reviewing, in Secs. 2.1–2, grammars whose languages are sets of strings.

## 2.1. String Grammars

Formally, a *string grammar* is a 4-tuple $G \equiv (V, V_T, S, P)$, where

$V$ is a nonempty, finite set of *symbols*, called the *vocabulary* of $G$,

$V_T$ is a nonempty proper subset of $V$ called the *terminal vocabulary* of $G$,

$S \in V_N \equiv V - V_T$ is called the *initial symbol* (or "start symbol"),

$P$ is a nonempty, finite set of pairs $(\alpha, \beta)$, where $\alpha, \beta$ are non-null strings of elements of $V$.

The pairs in $P$ are called the *rules* (or "productions") of $G$, and are usually written in the form $\alpha \to \beta$ (denoting the fact that $\alpha$ can be replaced by $\beta$, as discussed immediately below).

In order to define the language of $G$, we must introduce the notion of a "derivation" in $G$. We say that the string $\tau$ is *directly derived* from the string $\sigma$ in $G$ (notation: $\sigma \underset{G}{\Rightarrow} \tau$) if there exists a rule $\alpha \to \beta$ of $G$ such that $\alpha$ is a substring of $\sigma$, and $\tau$ is the result of replacing some occurrence of $\alpha$ (as a substring of $\sigma$) by $\beta$. We say that $\tau$ is *derived* from $\sigma$ in $G$ (notation: $\sigma \underset{G}{\Rightarrow}^* \tau$) if there exists a sequence of strings $\sigma = \sigma_0, \sigma_1, \dots, \sigma_n = \tau$, where $n \geq 0$, such that $\sigma_i$ is directly derived from $\sigma_{i-1}$ in $G, 1 \leq i \leq n$. The set of strings of elements of $V_T$ ("terminal strings") that can be derived in $G$ from the initial string $S$ (consisting of the single symbol $S$) is called the *language* of $G$, and is denoted by $L(G)$. A sequence of strings $S = \sigma_0, \sigma_1, \dots, \sigma_n = \tau \in L(G)$ for which $\sigma_{i-1} \underset{G}{\Rightarrow} \sigma_i$ is called a *derivation* of $\tau$ in $G$. (We shall omit "in $G$" and the subscript $G$ from now on, since there will be no danger of confusion.)

Given any grammar $G$, there exists a grammar $G'$ in which terminal symbols are never rewritten by a rule, and such that $L(G') = L(G)$. In fact, we can define $G'$ to have nonterminal vocabulary $(V - V_T) \cup V_T'$, where $V_T'$ is a set of primed copies of the symbols in $V_T$. For each rule $\alpha \to \beta$ of $G$, we have the rule $\alpha' \to \beta'$ in $G'$, where the primes denote the fact that each symbol in $V_T$ is replaced by the corresponding symbol in $V_T'$. In addition, $G'$ has the rules $x' \to x$ for all $x \in V_T$. Evidently, a string on $V_T$ is derivable in $G'$ if it is derivable in $G$ (since $G'$ can derive the corresponding string on $V_T'$, which can then be changed into a $V_T$ string using the $x' \to x$ rules), and conversely (since the $x' \to x$ rules are the only rules of $G'$ that produce symbols in $V_T$). We shall assume from now on that grammars never rewrite terminal symbols.

The following examples may serve to illustrate how string grammars work. In all of them we have $V_T = \{a, b\}$, while the symbols in $V_N$ are denoted by capital letters.

(1) *Repetitions of a specified string.* Let $\alpha$ be any specific string of $a$'s and $b$'s, and let $G$ have the rules

$$S \to \alpha S, \quad S \to \alpha\alpha .$$

The first rule can be used any number of times to produce a string of the form $\alpha \ldots \alpha S$. As soon as the second rule is used, the process terminates, since there are no more $S$'s. Thus the final result is a string of the form $\alpha \ldots \alpha$, i.e. a periodic string with period $\alpha$, and consisting of at least two periods.

(2) *Symmetric strings.* Let the rules of $G$ be

$$S \to aSa, \quad S \to bSb, \quad S \to aa, \quad S \to bb, \quad S \to a, \quad S \to b .$$

When the first two rules are used in any sequence, they create a string of the form $\sigma S \sigma^R$, where $\sigma^R$ is the reversal of $\sigma$, and $\sigma$ is any string of $a$'s and $b$'s. When one of the last four rules is used, the process terminates, since no $S$'s remain. Thus the language of this grammar is the set of all non-null symmetric strings of $a$'s and $b$'s, i.e. strings of the form $\sigma\sigma^R$ or $\sigma a\sigma^R$ or $\sigma b\sigma^R$.

(3) *Repeated strings.* We begin with the rules

$$S \to aa, \quad S \to bb, \quad S \to aCT, \quad S \to bDT,$$
$$T \to ACT, \quad T \to BDT, \quad T \to Aa, \quad T \to Bb .$$

These rules create a string of $AC$'s and $BD$'s, beginning with an $aC$ or $bD$ and ending with an $Aa$ or $Bb$. (There may be no $A$'s, $B$'s, $C$'s, or $D$'s in the string, in which case it is just $aa$ or $bb$.) We also have the rules

$$CA \to AC, \quad CB \to BC, \quad DA \to AD, \quad DB \to BD .$$

These rules allow $C$'s and $D$'s to shift rightward relative to the $A$'s and $B$'s. Note that the order of the $A$'s and $B$'s, and of the $C$'s and $D$'s, does not change. Thus the sequence of $C$'s and $D$'s, omitting its first term, is always the same as the sequence of $A$'s and $B$'s, omitting its last term, since $AC$'s and $BD$'s were originally created in pairs. Finally, we have the rules

$$aA \to aa, \quad aB \to ab, \quad bA \to ba, \quad bB \to bb,$$
$$Ca \to aa, \quad Da \to ba, \quad Cb \to ab, \quad Db \to bb .$$

These rules change $A$'s and $B$'s to $a$'s and $b$'s when they have $a$'s or $b$'s on their left, and change $C$'s and $D$'s to $a$'s and $b$'s when they have $a$'s or $b$'s on their right. Thus we can obtain a string $\tau$ consisting entirely of terminal symbols ($a$'s and $b$'s) provided all the $C$'s and $D$'s have shifted to the right of all the $A$'s and $B$'s. Note that $\tau$ must be composed of two identical substrings (i.e. $\tau$ is of the form $\sigma\sigma$) since the sequence of $A$'s and $B$'s corresponds to the sequence of $C$'s and $D$'s. In other words, the language of this grammar is the set of all strings of the form $\sigma\sigma$, where $\sigma$ is any non-null string of $a$'s and $b$'s.

Up to now we have considered a grammar as *generating* its language by repeated application of rules starting from $S$. Conversely, we can think of $G$ as *accepting* or *parsing* the strings of its language by reducing them to $S$ using repeated application of the rules of $G$ in reverse. In other words, we say that $G$ parses the terminal string $\tau$ if there exists a sequence of strings $\tau = \sigma_n, \sigma_{n-1}, \ldots, \sigma_0 = S$ such that $\sigma_i$ is directly derivable from $\sigma_{i-1}$ in $G$, $1 \leq i \leq n$. Although these definitions are equivalent, in practice parsing may be much harder than generation. A simple illustration of this is provided by Ex. (2). If we are given a symmetric string $\sigma$ of $a$'s and $b$'s, we can apply the reverse of one of the rules $S \to a$ or $S \to b$ to it in any position, and we can probably also apply the reverse of $S \to aa$ or $S \to bb$ to it in many positions as well; but if we pick the wrong rule or the wrong position (not at the center of $\sigma$), we will not be able to complete the parse.

## 2.2. Special Types of Grammars

The general type of grammar defined in Sec. 2.1 is sometimes called a "type 0" grammar.

A grammar $G$ is called *monotonic* if, for each rule $\alpha \to \beta$ of $G$, we have $|\alpha| \leq |\beta|$, where $|\sigma|$ denotes the length of $\sigma$. It is called *context-sensitive*, or "type 1", if for each rule $\alpha \to \beta$ of $G$ there exists strings $\xi, \eta$, and $\omega$, where $\omega$ is non-null, and a symbol $A \in V_N$, such that $\alpha = \xi A \eta$ and $\beta = \xi \omega \eta$. In other words, in a context-sensitive grammar, each rule replaces a single symbol $(A)$ by a non-null string $(\omega)$ when it occurs in a specified context $(\xi, \eta)$. Evidently context-sensitive implies monotonic. It can be shown, conversely, that for any monotonic grammar there exists a context-sensitive grammar having the same language. Examples (1) and (2) of grammars given in Sec. 2.1 are context-sensitive, and Ex. (3) is monotonic. To make (3) context-sensitive, we can replace the rule $CA \to AC$ by the three rules $CA \to C'A, C'A \to C'C, C'C \to AC$, and similarly for the rules $CB \to BC, DA \to AD$, and $DB \to BD$.

$G$ is called the *context-free*, or "type 2", grammar if its rules are all of the form $A \rightarrow \beta$, where $A \in V_N$. Evidently context-free implies context-sensitive. Examples (1) and (2) of Sec. 2.1 are both context-free. $G$ is called *linear* if its rules are all of the form $A \rightarrow B$ where $A \in V_N$ and $\beta$ contains at most one nonterminal symbol. $G$ is called *finite-state*, or "type 3", if its rules are all of the form $A \rightarrow \tau B$ or $A \rightarrow \tau$, where $A, B \in V_N$ and $\tau$ is a (non-null) terminal string[a]. Evidently finite-state implies linear implies context-free. Example (1) of Sec. 2.1 is finite-state and Ex. (2) is linear. A language is called monotonic, context-sensitive, context-free, linear, or finite-state if it is the language of a monotonic, context-sensitive, context-free, linear, or finite-state grammar, respectively.

As we saw at the end of Sec. 2.1, parsing is difficult even for linear grammars. It is somewhat simpler for finite-state grammars. When a string is generated using such a grammar, it grows only at its right end; thus it can be parsed by applying reversed rules ($\beta \rightarrow \alpha$) at that end to shrink it back to a single $S$. For example, parsing is straightforward and unambiguous for the grammar in Ex. (1) of Sec. 2.1.

## 3. ISOMETRIC GRAMMARS AND PARALLEL GRAMMARS

### 3.1. Isometric Grammars

In this section we consider a modified way of defining string grammars that will be needed in order to extend the definition of a grammar from strings to arrays.

Formally, an *isometric string grammar* is a 5-tuple $G \equiv (V, V_T, S, \#, P)$, where $V, V_T, S$, and $P$ are as in the definition of a grammar, and $\# \in V_N$ is called the *blank symbol*. In addition, we require that the rules $\alpha \rightarrow \beta$ in $P$ all satisfy the following conditions:

(a)  $|\alpha| = |\beta|$($\alpha$ and $\beta$ have the same length).
(b)  $\alpha$ does not consist entirely of #'s.
(c)  Replacing $\alpha$ by $\beta$ cannot disconnect or eliminate the non-#'s.

(Readily, this is equivalent to requiring that the non-#'s in $\beta$ exist and are connected, and if $\alpha$ has a non-# as its left(right) end, so has $\beta$.)

Derivations in $G$ are defined exactly as in Sec. 2.1. We define the language of $G$ as the set of terminal strings $\tau$ such that the infinite string

---

[a]It is not difficult to show that, without loss of generality, we can assume that $\tau$ consists of a single terminal symbol.

$\#^{\infty}\tau\#^{\infty}$ (i.e. $\tau$ embedded in an infinite string of $\#$'s) can be derived in $G$ from the infinite initial string $\#^{\infty}S\#^{\infty}$.

It is not hard to show that the languages of isometric grammars are the same as those of ordinary grammars — in other words, for any grammar $G$, there exists an isometric grammar having the same language as $G$, and vice versa.

**Proof.** For any grammar $G$, we can define an isometric grammar $G'$ that generates $L(G)$ exactly as follows:

(1) For every rule $\alpha \to \beta$ of $G$ such that $|\alpha| \leq |\beta|$, $G'$ has the rule $\alpha\natural^{|\beta|-|\alpha|} \to \beta$, where $\natural$ is a special nonterminal symbol.

(2) For every rule $\alpha \to \beta$ of $G$ such that $|\alpha| \geq |\beta|$, $G'$ has the rule $\alpha \to \beta\natural^{|\alpha|-|\beta|}$.

(3) In addition, $G'$ has the rules $X\# \to X\natural, X\natural \to \natural X$, and $\#\natural X \to \#\#X$, for all non-$\#$ nonterminal $X$. These rules allow $\#$'s to be changed into $\natural$'s at the right end of the string of non-$\#$'s; $\natural$'s to be shifted leftward; and $\natural$'s to be changed back to $\#$'s at the left end of the string.

It is easy to see that $G'$ can generate a terminal string $\sigma$ (surrounded by $\#$'s) iff just enough $\natural$'s are created, and these $\natural$'s are shifted into just the right positions, to allow a derivation of $\sigma$ in $G$ to be simulated using rules in (1) and (2). (The terminal vocabulary of $G'$ is the same as that of $G$.) Thus $L(G') = L(G)$.

Conversely, given an isometric grammar $G'$, we can define $G$ such that, for every rule $\alpha \to \beta$ of $G'$, $G$ has the rule $\alpha' \to \beta'$, where $\alpha'$ and $\beta'$ are the same as $\alpha$ and $\beta$ but with $\#$'s, if any, omitted. It is not hard to see that $G$ can generate a terminal string $\tau$ iff $G'$ generates $\#^{\infty}\tau\#^{\infty}$. (We recall that under $G'$, the non-$\#$'s remain connected; thus derivations in $G$ differ from those in $G'$ only in that when $G'$ destroys or creates $\#$'s at its ends, $G$ simply grows or shrinks.) ∎

The languages generated by isometric grammars that never create $\#$'s (i.e. for all rules $\alpha \to \beta$, there can be $\#$'s in $\beta$ only in positions corresponding to $\#$'s in $\alpha$) are the same as those generated by monotonic grammars.

**Proof.** In the first part of the proof that grammars and isometric grammars are equivalent, if $G$ is monotonic, there are no rules of type (2) (except those that are also of type (1)); hence we can omit the rules $\#\natural x \to \#\#x$ and still guarantee that derivations in $G$ can be simulated, by creating and shifting in just enough $\natural$'s to allow the rules of type (1) to operate. Thus if $G$ is monotonic, we can define $G'$ so that it never creates $\#$'s. In the second part of the proof, if $G'$ never creates $\#$'s, then for all rules $\alpha \to \beta$ of $G'$ we have $|\alpha'| \leq |\beta'|$, so that $G$ is monotonic. ∎

There are several ways of defining a class of isometric grammars whose languages are the same as those of the finite-state grammars. It is evident that if the rules of $G$ are all of the form $A\#^m \to \beta$, where $|\beta| = m + 1$ and $\beta$ is a string of terminals ending in at most one nonterminal, then $L(G)$ is finite-state; and conversely, if $G'$ is finite-state, there is an isometric $G$ of the above form such that $L(G') = L(G)$. We can also establish a stronger result: the languages generated by isometric grammars in which, for all rules $\alpha \to \beta$, $\alpha$ consists of a single nonterminal symbol together with $\#$'s, and $\beta$ consists of non-$\#$'s, are the same as the languages generated by finite-state grammars. (Note that rules of this form are analogous to *context-free* rules, rather than to finite-state rules.)

**Proof.** By the preceding paragraph, any language generated by a finite-state grammar is generated by an isometric grammar of the above form. Conversely, suppose that $G$ is of the above form. Note first that if we have generated the string $\omega$ in $G$, and $X$ is a symbol in the interior of $\omega$, then $X$ (if it is nonterminal) can only be rewritten by rules of the form $X \to Y$, since there are no $\#$'s adjacent to $X$ to serve as context. Now eventually we must be able to turn $\omega$ into a string of terminals by applying rules of $G$; if we combine these rules with the rules that generated $\omega$, we obtain a set of strings $\omega'$ in which $X$ has been replaced by all the terminals to which it can give rise, without changing $L(G)$. Thus we can assume that any string generated by $G$ has nonterminals only at its ends. In particular, we can assume that the right-hand side of any rule of $G$ has nonterminals only at its ends. Similarly, if $X$ is a nonterminal at the right end of such a string (of length $> 1$), it can only be rewritten by the rules of the form $X\#^m \to \beta$ (as in the preceding paragraph), and analogously for an $X$ at the left end.

Suppose that the first rule used in a derivation in $G$ has a nonterminal only at one end, say the right. Then subsequent rules must all be of the form $X\#^m \to \beta$, as explained above, so that the part of $L(G)$ generated by derivations that begin in this way is finite-state. The argument is analogous if the first rule has a nonterminal only at the left end, since it is easily seen that if we reverse the definition of a finite-state grammar (i.e. every rule's right-hand side *begins* with at most one nonterminal), we still obtain exactly the finite-state languages.

If $G$ has rules of the form $S \rightarrow X$, they can be eliminated by letting $S$ go directly into the strings of length $> 1$ that are derivable from $X$, or into the singleton terminal symbols that are derivable from $X$. Note that in the latter case, these rules can contribute only finitely many strings to $L(G)$.

Finally, suppose that the first rule used in a derivation has nonterminal symbols at both ends and has length $> 1$. As we have already seen, the nonterminal at the right end can only be rewritten by rules of the form $A\#^m \rightarrow \beta$, and analogously for the nonterminal at the left end. Thus the strings derivable in this way are essentially concatenations of pairs of strings, each belonging to a finite-state language, and it is well-known that the set of such concatenations is also a finite-state language. Combining this with the results of the previous two paragraphs, we see that $L(G)$ is a finite union of finite-state languages, and this implies that it too is a finite-state. ∎

## 3.2. Parallel Grammars

In an ordinary grammar $G$, at any given step in a derivation, a given rule may be applicable in more than one place. In this section we discuss several approaches to defining *parallel grammars*, in which rules are applied in all possible places simultaneously.

We first consider an approach in which we still apply only a single rule $\alpha \rightarrow \beta$ at a given time, but apply this rule by replacing *every* instance of $\alpha$ by $\beta$. For example, we can generate the set of strings $\sigma\sigma$ (Ex. (3) of Sec. 2.1) using the parallel context-free grammar whose rules are

$$S \rightarrow TT \quad T \rightarrow aT, \quad T \rightarrow bT, \quad T \rightarrow a, \quad T \rightarrow b .$$

One problem with this approach is that instances of $\alpha$ can overlap. For example, if we apply the rule $XX \rightarrow ZZ$ to the string $XXX$, in parallel, the result is (presumably) $ZZZZ$, since $XXX$ contains two instances of $XX$; thus application of the isometric rule $XX \rightarrow ZZ$ changes the length of the string. (Indeed, if we apply $XXX \rightarrow ZZ$ to $X^m$ in parallel, we get $Z^{2(m-2)}$, so that applying a length-decreasing rule can increase the string length.) In ordinary ("sequential") rule application, this could not happen; applying the rule $XX \rightarrow ZZ$ to $XXX$ yields either $ZZX$ or $XZZ$, to which the rule no longer applies.

Another problem with parallel rule application is that parsing and generating are no longer inverses of one another. For example, applying $XX \rightarrow ZZ$ to $XXX$ in parallel yields $ZZZZ$, but applying $ZZ \rightarrow XX$ to

$ZZZZ$ in parallel yields $XXXXXX$, since $ZZZZ$ contains three instances of $ZZ$. In fact it is not hard to exhibit a grammar $G$ such that the sets of strings generated and parsed by $G$ in parallel are disjoint from one another and from $L(G)$.

The *parallel language* $L_P(G)$ generated by a given grammar $G$ when each rule is applied in parallel is not the same as $G$'s "sequential language" $L(G)$ in general, but it is the same in certain simple cases. For example, consider the linear grammars; it is evident that these have the property that, at any stage of a derivation, at most one nonterminal symbol is present. Since the rules of a linear grammar all have left-hand sides consisting of a single nonterminal symbol, it is clear that at any stage of a derivation, a given rule can apply in at most one place; thus it makes no difference whether a rule is applied sequentially (i.e. in one place at a time) or in parallel. In other words, if $G$ is a linear grammar, we have $L_P(G) = L(G)$.

It can also be shown that the *class* of languages generated in parallel by grammars is the same as the class of languages generated in the usual way; and similarly for the classes of languages generated sequentially and in parallel by monotonic grammars. To prove that any (sequential) language is a parallel language, we show that for any grammar $G$, there exists a grammar $G'$ with $L(G') = L(G)$, such that at any step of a derivation in $G'$, no rule applies at more than one place. Specifically, for each rule $X_1 \ldots X_m \to Z_1 \ldots Z_n$ of $G$, $G'$ has the rule $\overline{X}'_1 \overline{X}_2 \ldots \overline{X}_m \to \overline{Z}'_1 \overline{Z}_2 \ldots \overline{Z}_n$, where the barred symbols are all nonterminals. We also give $G'$ the rule $S \to \overline{S}'$ and the set of rules

$$\overline{X}'\overline{Y} \to \overline{X}\overline{Y}' \quad \text{and} \quad \overline{X}\overline{Y}' \to \overline{X}'\overline{Y} \,,$$

for all pairs of nonterminals one of which is primed and the other is not. These rules initially create a prime and allow it to shift from symbol to symbol. Since the rules that correspond to those of $G$ all involve the prime, it is clear that any rule applies at only one place (evidently, more than one prime never exists). Finally, we give $G'$ the rules

$$\overline{x}'\overline{y} \to \overline{x}y' \quad \text{and} \quad \overline{x}'\# \to x\#$$

for all $\overline{x}, \overline{y}$ corresponding to terminal symbols $x, y$ of $G$ (or, if we do not want to introduce the $\#$ symbol, we design $G'$ so that the rightmost symbol of any string derivable in it is always uniquely marked). These last rules allow the prime to shift rightward through symbols that correspond to terminals, turning them into terminals as it goes, until it reaches the right end of the string and vanishes. It is evident that this process can result in a terminal string iff $G'$ generated a string of symbols corresponding to terminals, by imitating a derivation in $G$ that leads to a string of terminals; thus the resulting terminal string must be in $L(G)$. (If the last rules are used too soon, or are not started with the prime at the left end of the string, a string consisting entirely of terminals will not be created.) Since in $G'$, no rule can apply in more than one place, we have $L_P(G') = L(G')$; thus $L(G) = L(G') = L_P(G')$, which proves that any language is a parallel language. Note also that if $G$ is monotonic, so is $G'$.

Conversely, we can show that for any grammar $G$ there exists a grammar $G''$ that, in effect, applies the rules of $G$ in parallel; thus $L_P(G) = L(G'')$, so that any parallel language is a sequential language. Basically, we define $G''$ to simulate an automaton $A$ (see Sec. 5). Suppose that, at a given stage in the operation of $A$, we are ready to apply a rule of $G$ in parallel to the current string $\sigma$ (initially, this string is $S$). $A$ picks a rule $\alpha \to \beta$, scans $\sigma$, and marks every position in $\sigma$ at which a match to $\alpha$ begins. It then scans $\sigma$ again and replaces each instance of $\alpha$ by $\beta$. (If instances overlap, the part of $\sigma$ from the start of one instance of $\alpha$ to the start of the next is replaced by $\beta$.) When this process is complete, we are ready to apply another rule of $G$. It is not hard to see that if $G$ is monotonic, so is $G''$.

The remarks in the preceding three paragraphs show that any (arbitrary, monotonic, linear) language is a (arbitrary, monotonic, linear) parallel language, and vice versa. The analogous result about context-free languages is false. For example, consider the context-free grammar whose rules are $S \to SS$ and $S \to x$. It is not hard to see that the parallel language of this grammar is the set of strings $\{x^{2^n} | n = 0, 1, 2, \dots\}$; but it is well-known that this is not a context-free language in the ordinary sense. Conversely, it can be shown that the parenthesis-string language, which is context-free, is not parallel context-free.

Parallel rule application has a particularly convenient interpretation for rules that are in the context-sensitive form $\xi A \eta \to \xi \omega \eta$: For each instance of $\xi A \eta$ in the given string $\sigma$, we replace the $A$ by an $\omega$. (Note that this is not the same as replacing each instance of $\xi A \eta$ by $\xi \omega \eta$; for the rule $XX \to XZ$, applied to the string $XXX$, replacing $XX$'s by $XZ$'s gives $XZXZ$, whereas replacing $X$'s by $Z$'s when they have $X$'s on their left gives $XZZ$.) In this case, some of the problems mentioned at the beginning of this subsection do not arise, since the substrings being replaced (i.e. the $A$'s) cannot overlap, even if the $\xi A \eta$'s do overlap. Parsing and generation are still not always inverses of one another, e.g. if we apply $XX \to XZ$ to $XXX$, we obtain $XZZ$, whereas if we apply $XZ \to XX$ to $XZZ$, we obtain $XXX$. On the other hand, string length can never decrease, since $A$'s are being replaced by non-null strings ($\omega$'s). The results in the preceding paragraphs all continue to hold for this modified concept of parallel rule application.

Another approach to defining parallelism for context-sensitive grammars is to apply all possible rules in all possible positions at the same time. In other words, given a string $\sigma = A_1 \ldots A_n$, for each $A_i$ we choose a rule $\xi_i A_i \eta_i \to \xi_i \omega_i \eta_i$ of $G$ that applies to $A_i$ in $\sigma$ (i.e. such that $\xi_i$ precedes $A_i$ in $\sigma$, and $\eta_i$ follows it) and replace $A_i$ by $\omega_i$. (If no such rule exists, we leave $A_i$ unchanged.) This is done in parallel for every symbol in $\sigma$; the rule used is chosen independently for each $A_i$. Parallel rule application systems of this kind are called *L-systems*; if the rules are all context-free, they are called *OL-systems*. L-systems have been extensively studied as models of biological growth; they will not be discussed here in detail.

The proofs given above apply also to isometric grammars; in fact, in the proof that any sequential language is a parallel language, if $G$ is isometric, so is $G'$, while in the proof that any parallel language is a sequential language, an isometric $G''$ can simulate an automaton of the desired type that applies the rules in $G$.

## 4. MATRIX GRAMMARS AND ARRAY GRAMMARS

We are now ready to define grammars whose languages are sets of two-dimensional arrays. Section 4.1 briefly discusses matrix grammars whose languages are sets of rectangular arrays. Section 4.2 discusses array grammars whose languages are connected two-dimensional arrays of arbitrary shape.

### 4.1. Matrix Grammars

A class of grammars that generate rectangular arrays can be informally defined as follows:

(a) A string grammar $G$ generates a string $\sigma$ which will become the top row of the array.

(b) The symbols in $\sigma$ are initial symbols of a set of finite-state string grammars $G_1, \ldots, G_n$. After $\sigma$ has been completely generated, these grammars operate in parallel (compare Sec. 3.2) to generate the columns of the array. The parallel rule application must be defined so as to insure that in every column, at any given time, a rule of the same length is applied, and that the terminating rules are all applied at the same time[b]. (We use finite-state grammars $G_i$ to insure that the columns can only grow in one direction, namely downward. This also makes parsing easier, as pointed out at the end of Sec. 2.2.)

Formally, a *matrix grammar* $M$ is an $(n + 1)$-tuple $(G, G_1, \ldots, G_n)$, where $G$ is a grammar and $G_1, \ldots, G_n$ are finite-state-grammars such that the terminal vocabulary of $G$ is the set $\{S_1, \ldots, S_n\}$ of initial symbols of the $G_i$'s. (We can assume that the nonterminal vocabularies of the $G_i$'s are disjoint.) $M$ operates by generating a (horizontal) string $\sigma$ of $S_i$'s using the rules of $G$, then generating a rectangular array from the top row $\sigma$ by applying rules in the $G_i$'s in parallel, where the set of rules applied at a given step all have the same length, and are either all non-terminating or all terminating.

A number of other grammar-like mechanisms can be used to generate rectangular array languages, but we will not describe them in detail here.

## 4.2. Array Grammars

We now introduce grammars whose languages are sets of connected arrays of symbols. Such an array can be regarded as a mapping from the set of (integer-coordinate) lattice points $(i, j)$ into the vocabulary $V$ where all but finitely many lattice points are mapped into # ("blank"). In other words, an array is constructed by placing symbols ($\in V$) in integer-coordinate positions on the plane. Two symbols are called *neighbors* if they are in positions $(i, j), (h, k)$ such that $|i - h| + |j - k| = 1$. An array $\Sigma$ is called *connected* if for all non-# symbols $A, B$ in $\Sigma$ there exists a sequence $A = A_0, A_1, \ldots, A_n = B$ of non-# symbols in $\Sigma$ (a "path") such that $A_i$ is a neighbor of $A_{i-1}, 1 \leq i \leq n$.

An *array grammar* is defined analogously to an isometric string grammar (Sec. 3.1) except that the rules are pairs of connected arrays rather than pairs of strings. To see why we require array grammars to be isometric, note that a derivation in an array grammar operates by replacing subarrays by subarrays, just as a string grammar replaces substrings by substrings. However, if the two subarrays ($\alpha$ and $\beta$, say) are not identical in size and shape, it is not clear how to replace $\alpha$ by $\beta$. One can presumably shift the

---

[b]If we assume, as we can without loss of generality, that the rules of each $G_i$ are all of the forms $X \to zZ$ and $X \to z$, where $X, Z$ are nonterminals and $z$ is a terminal, then it suffices to require that the terminating rules be applied in every column at the same time.

rows or columns of the host array relative to one another so as to make room for $\beta$, but this may cause changes in symbol adjacencies arbitrarily far away from $\beta$, since adjacent rows or columns may shift by different amounts. Thus applying a local rewriting rule $\alpha \to \beta$ may cause non-local changes in the host array, which seems undesirable. In the string case, this problem does not arise; even if $\beta$ does not have the same length as $\alpha$, the adjacency relationships in the rest of $\sigma$ do not change when we replace $\alpha$ by $\beta$. When we require array grammars to be isometric, $\alpha$ and $\beta$ in any rule $\alpha \to \beta$ are geometrically identical, so it is obvious how to replace $\alpha$ by $\beta$. As in the string case, the array grows (or shrinks) by rewriting (or creating) #'s.

It is not immediately obvious how to insure that an array grammar preserves connectedness (and nonemptiness) of the set of non-#'s. Before formulating conditions for this, we first observe that in any rule $\alpha \to \beta, \alpha$ must contain non-#'s, but they need not be connected. (In one dimension, as long as the non-#'s remain connected, a rule in which $\alpha$ has nonconnected non-#'s could never apply; but in two dimensions, a globally connected array can contain locally nonconnected parts.) On the other hand, if $\alpha$ has more than one connected component of non-#'s, every such component must touch the border of $\alpha$. Our conditions on $\beta$ are then as follows:

(1) If the non-#'s of $\alpha$ do not touch the border of $\alpha$, then the non-#'s of $\beta$ must be connected (and nonempty).

(2) Otherwise,

(a) every connected component of non-#'s in $\beta$ must contain the intersection of some component of non-#'s in $\alpha$ with the border of $\alpha$;

(b) conversely, every such intersection must be contained in some component of non-#'s in $\beta$.

It can be shown that if conditions (1) and (2) hold, applying the rule $\alpha \to \beta$ does not disconnect or eliminate the non-#'s.

**Proof.** We assume that non-#'s existed and were connected before $\alpha \to \beta$ was applied. In case (1), the non-#'s of $\alpha$ must be the only non-#'s that exist; there cannot be any outside $\alpha$, since they would have to be connected to those in $\alpha$, which would require that non-#'s exist on the border of $\alpha$. Hence when we replace $\alpha$ by $\beta$, the non-#'s of $\beta$ are the only ones that exist, and they are connected as a consequence of condition (1).

In case (2), we first show that any two non-#'s $A, B$ not in $\alpha$ remain connected when $\alpha$ is replaced by $\beta$. If there is a path of non-#'s from $A$ to $B$ that does not meet $\alpha$, this is clear. Otherwise, note that each time the path enters and leaves $\alpha$, it meets only one component of non-#'s in $\alpha$, and by condition (2b) the intersection of this component with the border of $\alpha$ is contained in a component of non-#'s in $\beta$; hence each such segment of the path can be replaced by a segment in $\beta$.

Similarly, if $A$ is not in $\alpha$ and $B$ is in $\beta$, then by condition (2a), the component of non-#'s in $\beta$ that contains $B$ also contains the intersection of some component of non-#'s in $\alpha$ with the border of $\alpha$. Now $A$ was connected (outside $\alpha$) to this component and hence to the intersection; thus $A$ is connected to $B$.

Finally, if $A$ and $B$ are both in $\beta$, and are not connected, they are both in components of non-#'s that, by condition (2a), contain intersections of components of non-#'s in $\alpha$ with the border of $\alpha$. But these components were connected outside $\alpha$; hence so were these intersections. ∎

It is clear that if condition (1) did not hold, applying $\alpha \to \beta$ would disconnect (or annihilate) the non-#'s. If condition (2a) did not hold, a component of non-#'s in $\beta$ might be created that failed to be connected to the other non-#'s; while if condition (2b) did not hold, some non-#'s outside $\beta$ might be disconnected from the other non-#'s.

Formally, an (isometric) *array grammar* is a 5-tuple $G = (V, V_T, P, S, \#)$, where all of these are defined just as in Sec. 3.1, except that $P$ is a set of pairs of connected arrays $(\alpha, \beta)$, for all of which

(a) $\alpha$ and $\beta$ are geometrically identical,

(b) $\alpha$ does not consist entirely of #'s, and

(c) $\beta$ satisfies conditions (1) and (2) above.

The *language* of $G, L(G)$, is the set of all (non-null) connected terminal arrays $\Sigma$ such that $\Sigma$ (embedded in an infinite array of #'s) can be derived in $G$ from the initial array, which consists of a single $S$ (embedded in an infinite array of #'s). Derivations are defined exactly as in Sec. 2.1, except that they involve replacement of one subarray by another, rather than of one substring by another. Parsing is also defined just as in Sec. 2.1. By the proof given just above and induction, the array resulting from any derivation always has its non-#'s connected.

An array grammar is called *monotonic* if #'s are never created by any rule — in other words, for all rules $\alpha \to \beta$, there are #'s in $\beta$ only in positions corresponding to #'s in $\alpha$. We call an array grammar *context-free* if it is monotonic and, for all rules $\alpha \to \beta, \alpha$ consists of a single non-terminal symbol and (possibly) of #'s; note that such rules do use #'s as "context." As we shall see later, there does not seem to be a good analog of "finite-state" for array grammars.

The following simple example of a context-free isometric array grammar generates upright rectangles of $a$'s on a background of #'s:

$$S\# \to aS, \quad S \to A, \quad S \to a, \quad \begin{matrix} A \\ \# \end{matrix} \to \begin{matrix} a \\ B \end{matrix} .$$

These rules generate a horizontal row of $a$'s from left to right, possibly ending in an $A$; if so, the $A$ turns into an $a$ and create a $B$ below it.

$$\begin{matrix} a \\ \#B \end{matrix} \to \begin{matrix} a \\ Ba \end{matrix}, \quad \begin{matrix} \# \\ \#B \end{matrix} \to \begin{matrix} \# \\ \#a \end{matrix}, \quad \begin{matrix} \# \\ \#B \end{matrix} \to \begin{matrix} \# \\ \#C \end{matrix}, \quad \begin{matrix} C \\ \# \end{matrix} \to \begin{matrix} a \\ D \end{matrix} .$$

The $B$ moves leftward, leaving a trail of $a$'s. When it reaches the end of the row of $a$'s above it, it turns into either an $a$ or a $C$; in the latter case, the $C$ turns into an $a$ and creates a $D$ below it.

$$\begin{matrix} a \\ D\# \end{matrix} \to \begin{matrix} a \\ aD \end{matrix}, \quad \begin{matrix} \# \\ D\# \end{matrix} \to \begin{matrix} \# \\ a\# \end{matrix}, \quad \begin{matrix} \# \\ D\# \end{matrix} \to \begin{matrix} \# \\ A\# \end{matrix} .$$

The $D$ moves rightward, leaving a trail of $a$'s. When it reaches the end of the row of $a$'s above it, it turns into either an $a$ or an $A$, in which case the previous processes can be repeated.

Parallel array grammars are defined just as in Sec. 3.2. The proofs that they generate the same classes of languages as sequential array grammars are straightforward.

## 5. GRAPH GRAMMARS AND TREE GRAMMARS

### 5.1. (Labeled) Graph Grammars

Strings and arrays can be regarded as special cases of *labeled graphs*. We can think of the symbols in a string as labels attached to the nodes of a graph in which all but two of the nodes have exactly two neighbors. Similarly, we can think of the symbols in an array as labels attached to the nodes of a graph in which each node has at most four neighbors. (Further restrictions on the graph structure are needed to insure that the graph is isomorphic to an array but we will not give the details here.)

There are many ways of defining grammars whose languages consist of labeled graphs. (We shall usually omit the word "labeled" from now on. When such grammars were first introduced, labeled graphs were called "webs" for short.) The simplest approach is to use a definition exactly analogous to that of a string grammar, except that in a rule $\alpha \to \beta$, $\alpha$ and $\beta$ are graphs rather than strings. In a derivation, we apply the rule $\alpha \to \beta$ to a graph $\sigma$ by replacing some occurrence of $\alpha$, as a subgraph of $\sigma$, by $\beta$. However, a new complication arises that did not arise for strings (nor for arrays, because we required array grammars to be isometric). When we replace substring $\alpha$ by substring $\beta$, or subarray $\alpha$ by geometrically identical subarray $\beta$, it is obvious how to "embed" $\beta$ into $\sigma$ in place of $\alpha$. In the case of graphs, however, it is not obvious how to do this. Thus a rule $\alpha \to \beta$ in a graph grammar must specify how $\beta$ is to be "embedded" into $\sigma - \alpha$, i.e. which nodes of $\beta$ should become neighbors of (i.e. be connected by arcs to) which nodes of $\sigma - \alpha$ (for simplicity, only to those that were neighbors of nodes of $\alpha$). Given such a specification, the language of such a grammar can be defined as the set of graphs, having labels in the terminal vocabulary, that can be derived by successive rule applications, starting from a one-node graph labeled $S$.

Similarly, we can define grammars for languages consisting of directed graphs ("digraphs," for short). Here $\alpha$ and $\beta$ are digraphs, and the embedding of $\beta$ into $\sigma - \alpha$ consists of two parts; we must specify which nodes of $\beta$ should be joined by in-arcs to which nodes of $\sigma - \alpha$ that were originally joined by in-arcs to nodes of $\alpha$, and similarly for out-arcs.

To illustrate the concept of a graph grammar, we give four simple examples, corresponding to four basic types of digraphs: strings, cycles, trees and binary trees. In these examples, for simplicity, we use only a single terminal symbol (so that the resulting languages can, if desired, be regarded as consisting of unlabeled graphs).

(1) Let the rules be

$$S \to a\ S, \qquad S \to a$$

where all nodes that were joined by in-arcs to the rewritten $S$ node become joined to the $a$ node. It is evident that the language of this grammar is the set of all directed strings whose nodes are all labeled $a$, i.e. the set of all digraphs of the form

(2) Let the rules be

$$S \to \begin{array}{c} T \\ \nearrow \quad \nwarrow \\ a\bullet \to \bullet a \end{array} \,, \qquad T \to \underset{\bullet \to \bullet}{a \;\; T}\,, \qquad T \to \underset{\bullet}{a}$$

where in the second rule, nodes that were joined to the $T$ by in-arcs are joined to the $a$, while those joined to the $T$ by out-arcs are joined to the new $T$; and in the third rule, all arcs to or from the $T$ are transferred to the $a$. Readily, the language of this grammar is the set of all directed cycles labeled $a$, i.e.

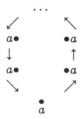

(3) Let the rules be

$$S \to \underset{\bullet \to \bullet}{S \;\; S}\,, \qquad S \to \underset{\bullet}{a}$$

where all arcs to or from the $S$ become transferred to the left-hand $S$ in the first rule, and to the $a$ in the second rule. Here the language is the set of all directed trees labeled $a$, rooted at the initial node.

(4) Let the rules be

$$S \to a\bullet \begin{array}{c} S \\ \nearrow \\ \searrow \\ S \end{array} \,, \qquad S \to \underset{\bullet}{a}$$

where in both rules, all the $S$'s arcs are transferred to the $a$. Here the language is the set of all directed binary trees labeled $a$, rooted at the initial node.

In the examples given above, only the nodes are labeled; but it is also possible to define graph grammars in which both the nodes and the arcs are labeled. Grammars for multigraphs can also be defined; we omit the details here. Note that all these examples are "context-free" in the sense that in any rule $\alpha \to \beta, \alpha$ is a single nonterminally labeled node; but the embedding makes the results of applying a rule depend on the context of the rewritten node.

We have not formally defined the embedding process. In our examples, the embeddings were all defined by specifying two correspondences between the nodes of $\alpha$ and those of $\beta$, one for in-arcs and one for out-arcs; the in-arcs of a given node of $\alpha$ are transferred to the corresponding node of $\beta$, and similarly for the out-arcs. There are many other ways of defining embeddings, but we will not discuss them here; for details see Refs. 4, 5 and 6.

## 5.2. Tree Grammars

An important special case of a graph grammar is a *tree grammar*; here, in the rule $\alpha \rightarrow \beta$, $\alpha$ and $\beta$ are labeled (sub)trees, and we apply the rule to a tree $\sigma$ by replacing some occurrence of $\alpha$, as a subtree of $\sigma$, by $\beta$. Note that in this case it is obvious how we attach $\beta$ to $\alpha$'s neighborhood; the (unique) parent of $\alpha$'s root simply becomes the parent of $\beta$'s root. The language of a tree grammar is the set of terminally labeled trees that can be generated in this way from a one-node tree labeled $S$. Example (4) of a graph grammar in Sec. 5.1 can be regarded as a tree grammar, but Ex. (3) cannot, since it allows a new outgoing arc to be added to a tree node without replacing the entire subtree at that node.

Tree grammars can also be defined in other ways; for further discussion of the subject see Ref. 3. An important advantage of tree grammars over general graph grammars is that in a tree grammar, trees are generated by rewriting entire subtrees, so that they grow only from the ends of their branches. This makes parsing easier, as was pointed out at the end of Sec. 2.2.

## 6. ACCEPTORS

Grammars can be used as both generators or acceptors of languages; the language of a grammar is the set of strings (or arrays, graphs, etc.) that can be generated by derivations beginning with the start symbol, and it is also the set of strings that can be "parsed," i.e. reduced to the start symbol, by reverse derivations. As we have pointed out in Sec. 2, however, parsing is usually more difficult than generation.

Automata are another class of language acceptors. In this section we briefly discuss automata that accept the same classes of languages as various types of string, array, or graph grammars.

## 6.1. String Acceptors

A *deterministic string acceptor* is a 7-tuple $A \equiv (V, V_I, \#, Q, q_i, q_a, \delta)$ where

$V$ is a nonempty, finite set of symbols, called the *tape vocabulary* of $A$ ,

$V_I$ is a nonempty subset of $V$ called the *input vocabulary* of $A$ ,

$\# \in V_I$ is called the *blank symbol* ,

$Q$ is a nonempty, finite set called the *state set* of $A$ ,

$q_i \in Q$ is called the *initial state* ,

$q_a \in Q$ is called the *accepting state* ,

$\delta$ is a mapping form $V \times Q \times \{L, R, N\}$ into itself called the *transition function* of $A$ .

Informally, we can think of $A$ as a "bug" that moves along an input tape, which initially contains an infinite string of the form $\#^\infty \sigma \#^\infty$, where $\sigma$ is a non-null string of symbols in $V_I$. $A$ is initially placed on some non-$\#$ symbol of this string, and is initially in state $q_i$ (and has not yet moved). It moves along the tape, rewrites symbols, and changes state by repeated application of the transition function $\delta$; thus if it is in state $q$, is located on the symbol $x$, and has just moved in direction $d \in \{L, R, N\}$, and $\delta(x, q, d) = (x', q', d')$, it rewrites $x$ as $x'$, changes to state $q'$, and moves in direction $d'$. ($L$ means "left", $R$ means "right," and $N$ means "no move.") If $A$ ever enters the accepting state $q_a$, we say it has accepted the input string $G$. The set of input strings that $A$ accepts is called its *language*, and is denoted by $L(A)$. It can be shown that the sets of strings that are languages of acceptors are the same as the sets that are languages of (type 0) grammars.

$A$ is called *nondeterministic* if $\delta$ is a mapping from $V \times Q \times \{L, R, N\}$ into $2^{V \times Q \times \{L,R,N\}}$ — in other words, if $\delta$ takes triples $(x, q, d)$ into *sets* of triples $(x', q', d')$. When a nondeterministic acceptor is in state $q$ and located on symbol $x$, it nondeterministically chooses any $(x', q', d') \in \delta(x, q, d)$, rewrites $x$ as $x'$, changes to state $q'$, and moves in direction $d'$. We say that a nondeterministic acceptor $A$ accepts the input string $\sigma$ if it is possible for $A$ to enter state $q_a$, starting from state $q_i$ somewhere on the input string $\#^\infty \sigma \#^\infty$.

The starting position of $A$ on $\sigma$ does not affect $A$'s ability to accept strings, since $A$ can always find (say) the left end of $\sigma$; thus an arbitrary starting position is equivalent to a standardized starting position. As we shall see, the situation is more complicated in the array and graph cases.

A will be called *tape-bounded* if it "bounces off" #'s — i.e. whenever it reads a #, it does not rewrite it, and moves back in the direction from which it has just come. A will be called *monotonic* if it cannot rewrite #'s as non-#'s (so that it can move across #'s, but cannot rewrite them). It is easily seen that the classes of languages accepted by the tape-bounded and monotonic acceptors are the same, and it can be shown that these languages are the same as the languages of context-sensitive grammars.

A is called *finite-state* if it cannot rewrite any symbols (whether #'s or non-#'s). It is easily seen that the class of languages accepted by finite-state acceptors is the same whether or not the acceptors are required to be tape-bounded; and it can be shown that this class consists of just the languages of finite-state grammars. It is also well-known that the class of languages accepted by finite-state acceptors is the same whether or not the acceptors are required to be deterministic, even if they are allowed to move in only one direction, say to the right (provided that they always start at the left end of $\sigma$). As we shall see, many of these results break down in the array and graph cases.

## 6.2. Array Acceptors

An array acceptor A is defined in almost exactly the same way as a string acceptor. It is initially placed on a non-# symbol, where we assume that the non-# portion $\sigma$ of the input array is finite and connected. Of course, in the two-dimensional case there are four possible directions of movement — left, right, up, and down — rather than only two directions; thus we use $\{L, R, U, D, N\}$ in the definition of $\delta$.

The definitions of tape-bounded, monotonic and finite-state acceptors are the same as in the string case; and tape-bounded is equivalent to monotonic, at least for deterministic acceptors.

### (a) The rectangular case

If the input array (of non-#'s) is rectangular, A's ability to accept its input array does not depend on its starting position; it can always find a standard starting position (e.g. the northwest corner of the array, by moving left and up), since the array is rectangular. (This is not so for arbitrary connected input arrays.) Note that a deterministic, tape-bounded, finite-state array acceptor can be designed to test whether or not its input array $\sigma$ is rectangular by doing a raster scan and checking the sides for local straightness at the beginning and end of each row, as well as checking the straightness of the top and bottom; thus such acceptors cannot be fooled by giving them nonrectangular input.

Unfortunately, the classes of rectangular array languages generated by matrix grammars are not the same as the classes accepted by the various types of array acceptors. To see this, we consider the following examples:

(1) If its top-row grammar $G$ is finite-state, the language $L$ of the matrix grammar $M$ is a finite-state array language. Indeed, we can define a finite-state array acceptor $A$ that accepts $L$ as follows: Given a rectangular array $\Sigma$, $A$ scans the last column $C_m$ of $\Sigma$, simulates acceptors for the finite-state column languages (which we can assume to have grammars of the special form indicated in Sec. 4.1), and thus determines to which of these languages, if any, $C_m$ belongs. $A$ can thus verify whether a terminating rule of $G$ could have produced any of the initial symbols $S_m$ that began the generation of $C_m$. $A$ then scans the next-to-last column $C_{m-1}$, determines which symbols $S_{m-1}$ could have begun its generation, and verifies whether a rule of $G$ could have produced any of these symbols together with a nonterminal that then results in $S_m$. This process is repeated until it has accounted for all of $\Sigma$. Conversely, however, there are (deterministic, tape-bounded) finite-state rectangular array languages that cannot be generated by any such $M$. For example, consider the set $L$ of square arrays of even side length whose rows are all of the form $x^n y^n$. No such $M$ can generate $L$, since the string language $\{x^n y^n | n = 1, 2, \ldots \}$ is not finite-state. On the other hand, a finite-state array acceptor can verify that its input array $\Sigma$ is in $L$ as follows: Verify squareness (and evenness of side length) by moving "diagonally"; then move alternately two steps upward and one leftward, starting at the lower right corner, to find a middle column; finally, move down that column and verify that, in each row, there are $x$'s on its left and $y$'s on its right. Thus the class of matrix languages for which $G$ is finite-state is a proper subset of the class of finite-state array languages. It is not hard to see that we can require $A$ in the first part of the proof to be deterministic and tape-bounded; thus these matrix languages are a proper subset of the deterministic, tape-bounded, finite-state array languages.

(2) If $G$ is context-free, the language of $M$ is not necessarily finite-state. For example, the set $L$ of rectangular arrays of even width whose rows are all of the form $x^n y^n$ can be generated by such an $M$ ($G$ generates $S_1^n S_2^n$; the rules of $G_1$ are $S_1 \rightarrow x S_1, S_1 \rightarrow x$, and those of $G_2$ are $S_2 \rightarrow y S_2, S_2 \rightarrow y$), but $L$ cannot be accepted by a finite-state array acceptor,

since $\{x^n y^n | i = 1, 2, \dots\}$ is not a finite-state string language (consider the arrays of height 1). Thus the matrix languages in general (even for context-free $G$'s) are not a subset of the finite-state array languages. Conversely, there are (deterministic, tape-bounded) finite-state array languages that are not matrix languages, for any choice of $G$. For example, the set $L$ consisting of all square arrays is not a matrix language since the termination decision in generating the columns does not depend on the array width. (The step numbers at which column termination can occur depend on the set of $S_i$'s that initiated the columns; there are only finitely many such sets and they cannot carry enough information to provide for a different termination step for every top row width.) Thus the matrix languages and the finite-state array languages are incomparable.

(3) The matrix languages for which $G$ is context-sensitive are a proper subset of the tape-bounded array languages. For example, the arrays whose columns are all of the form $x^n y^n$ are a tape-bounded array language, but are not a matrix language (since $\{x^n y^n | n = 1, 2, \dots\}$ is not a finite-state string language). Conversely, a tape-bounded acceptor can scan the columns of a rectangular array, determine which $S_i$'s could have initiated their generation, record these (sets of) $S_i$'s in the top row, and then simulate a one-dimensional tape-bounded acceptor to verify whether some such set of $S_i$'s could have been generated by $G$; thus any such matrix language is a tape-bounded array language. On the other hand, there are matrix languages (which have non-context-sensitive top rows and height 1) that are not tape-bounded array languages; thus the tape-bounded array languages and the matrix languages are incomparable. Finally, the matrix languages are a proper subset of the rectangular array languages in which the top rows are generated by arbitrary (type 0) grammars by arguments similar to those already given.

## (b) The general case

The definitions of array acceptors for arbitrary connected arrays are exactly as in the case of rectangular arrays. In this case, however, we cannot always insure that $A$ can find a standard starting position on its input array (e.g. the leftmost non-# in the uppermost row that contains non-#'s). This can be done by a tape-bounded $A$, but not by an $A$ that is finite-state.

The languages of array grammars are the same as the languages accepted by array acceptors.

**Proof.** Given an array grammar $G$, we define an acceptor $A$ that accepts exactly $L(G)$ as follows: Given an array $\Sigma$ of non-#'s in the terminal vocabulary $V_T$ of $G$, embedded in an infinite array of #'s, $A$ moves around nondeterministically, starting at some point of $\Sigma$, and rewrites each symbol $x$ (possibly #) that it encounters as $(x, \#)$.[c] Finally, at some step, $A$ rewrites some $x$ as $(x, S)$; this can only happen once. After it happens, $A$ begins to simulate rules of $G$ on the second terms of pairs; pairs with no second term are regarded as having second term #. Suppose that at some step, $A$ decides to apply the rule $\alpha \to \beta$ of $G$. It then searches (nondeterministically) for one of the non-# symbols in $\alpha$ (as a second term), marks it, checks (deterministically) for the other symbols as second terms (these are in known positions relative to the given symbol), marks them, and when they have all been found, rewrites these second terms as the corresponding symbols in $\beta$; after this is done, $A$ is ready to simulate another rule. (While searching, $A$ continues to rewrite $x$'s as $(x, \#)$'s.) At any stage after applying a rule of $G$, $A$ can systematically scan the array of non-#'s and check whether (a) every non-# is a pair and (b) the second term of every pair is the same as its first term. $A$ can also check, during such a scan, whether the non-# first terms are in fact all in $V_T$. If this is found to be true, $A$ accepts $\Sigma$; otherwise, $A$ can resume the simulation of $G$. Evidently, $A$ accepts $\Sigma$ iff a derivation in $G$ exists that generates a copy of $\Sigma$; thus $A$ accepts exactly $L(G)$ (from some starting point).

Conversely, given $A$, we define a grammar $G$ that generates exactly $L(A)$ as follows: Starting with an $S$ on a background of #'s, $G$ begins by generating an arbitrary array $\Sigma$ of triples of the form $(x, x, 0)$ or $(x, x, 1)$, where $x$ is any non-# symbol in the vocabulary $V$ of $A$, and where there is always exactly one 1. This can be done using the rules

(1a)  $S \to (x, x, 1)$,

(1b)  rotations (by multiples of $90°$),

(1c)  $(x, x, 1)(y, y, 0) \to (x, x, 0)(y, y, 1)$ and its rotations, and

(1d)  $(x, x, 1) \to (x, x, (q_i, N))$,

for all $x, y \neq \#$ in $V$. When (1d) is used, the 1 turns into a pair $(q_i, N)$ representing the initial state and (fictitious) previous move direction of $A$.

Next, $G$ simulates the operation of $A$ on the array of second terms of the triples; the first terms remain unaffected. This is done using the rules

---

[c] This is done in order to insure that $A$ is always on a connected set of non-#'s; if $A$ moved into the #'s without rewriting them as pairs, it might be unable to find $\Sigma$ again.

(for all $x, u, v$ in $V$)

(2a) $(x, y, (q, d)) \rightarrow (x, z, (q', N))$ for all $(q', z, N) \in \delta(q, y, d)$;

(2b) $(x, y, (q, d))(d')(u, v, 0) \rightarrow (x, z, 0)(d')(u, v, (q', d'))$

for all $(q', z, d') \in \delta(q, y, d)$; and

(2c) $(x, y, (q, d))(d')\# \rightarrow (x, z, 0)(d')(\#, \#, (q', d'))$ (similarly),

where $\delta$ is the transition function of $A$, provided that $q$ is not $q_a$. (Here $(\alpha)(A')(\beta)$ means that $(\alpha)$ lies in direction $d'$ relative to $(\beta)$.)

Finally, if the simulation of $A$ enters the accepting state $q_a$, the triples are turned into their first terms using the rules

(3a) $(x, y, (q_a, d)) \rightarrow x$ for all $x, y \in V$, and

(3b) $(u, v, 0)x \rightarrow ux$ and its rotations, for all $u, v, x \in V$.

Since $V - \{\#\}$ is the terminal vocabulary of $G$, this means that $G$ generates a terminal array of non-$\#$'s (the first terms of $\Sigma$) iff $A$ accepts this array (from some starting point). ∎

We next show that the languages generated by monotonic array grammars are the same as the languages accepted by tape-bounded array acceptors.

**Proof.** In the first part of the proof just above, note that at any step of a derivation of $\Sigma$ in the monotonic array grammar $G$, the non-$\#$'s are always a subset of $\Sigma$, since $\#$'s can never be created by $G$. Thus, we can simulate $G$ using a tape-bounded $A$ that always remains on $\Sigma$. (A problem arises with this simulation if a rule $\alpha \rightarrow \beta$ of $G$ uses $\#$'s as context (i.e. there are $\#$'s in $\alpha$ that are also in the corresponding positions in $\beta$); these $\#$'s may be outside $\Sigma$, but $A$ must verify their presence in order to apply the rule. This can be done using an array scanning process. Suppose that $A$ is located at position $(i, j)$ and wants to verify that there is a $\#$ in position $(i', j')$, where the differences $i - i'$ and $j - j'$ are known to $A$. To do this, $A$ marks $(i, j)$, finds the outer border of $\Sigma$, and scans $\Sigma$ row by row. When $A$ reaches the row with the marked point, it returns to the outer border and follows it, using the positions of markers to keep track of its net up and down moves. If the outer border never reaches row $i'$, $\Sigma$ cannot intersect that row, so the position $(i', j')$ is certainly $\#$. Otherwise, $A$ marks the points of the outer border that are on row $i'$ and scans these rows of $\Sigma$, marking their points. Analogously, using a column-by-column scan, $A$ finds the marked point and checks whether the outer border reaches column $j'$. If not, $(i', j')$ is $\#$, and $A$ can rescan $\Sigma$, erase the marks on row $i'$ and column $j'$, rescan $\Sigma$, and return to the marked point $(i, j)$. In this way, $A$

can verify that #'s exist in given positions relative to some non-# point of $\alpha$, and thus check that all of $\alpha$ is present, without having to leave $\Sigma$. Note that a similar process may be necessary for the rewriting of $\alpha$, since the non-#'s of $\alpha$ may be separated by #'s, and $A$ may have to compute the positions of these non-#'s in order to locate them and rewrite them.) After any step of the simulation, $A$ can scan $\Sigma$ and check that the first and second terms are all the same (and all in $V_T$). If so, $A$ accepts; otherwise, it continues the simulation. Thus $A$ accepts exactly $L(G)$.

In the second part of the proof, note that the only rules of $G$ that can create #'s are the terminating rules (3a) and (3b); and these create #'s only if triples with # first terms were created by the simulation rule (2c). But if $A$ is tape-bounded, we can modify (2c) to have the form

$$(x, y, (q, d))(d')\# \rightarrow (x, z, (q'', d'^{-1}))(d')\#$$

where $q''$ is a possible state of $A$ after it has bounced back off the #. Thus when $A$ is tape-bounded, $G$ need never create #'s, so that $G$ can be monotonic. ∎

It does not seem possible to define a natural class of array grammars whose languages are the same as those of the finite-state array acceptors. In one dimension, the linear grammars generate more than the finite-state languages (e.g. Ex. (2) in Sec. 2.1 is linear but not finite-state); whereas the "right linear" grammars, in which (until the last step) the sole non-terminal symbol is always at the right end of the string, generate exactly the finite-state languages. In two dimensions, there is no natural analog of "right linear". Moreover, we shall now show that the languages of linear array grammars are incomparable with the finite-state array languages.

We first exhibit a finite-state array language that cannot be generated by a linear array grammar. Consider the set of thin upright T-shaped arrays of $x$'s on a background of #'s. This set is accepted by a deterministic tape-bounded finite-state array acceptor that operates as follows: It moves up until it hits a #, then moves left until it hits a # again. It then verifies that it is on a row of $x$'s that have #'s above and below them, with exactly one exception that has an $x$ below it and that is not at either end of the row. Finally, it moves back to the exceptional $x$ and moves downward, verifying that it is on a column of $x$'s that have #'s on their left and right. When it reaches the bottom of this column, if all these verifications have been carried out successfully, it accepts.

We now show that the set of such T's cannot be generated by a linear array grammar. Suppose $G$ were such a grammar; let the greatest diameter of any right-hand side of a rule of $G$ be $k$. Since the T's can be arbitrarily large, it is clear that $G$ must generate the ends of the arms of a large T at different steps in the derivation of that T. Let these arm ends be $P_1, P_2$, and $P_3$. One of them, say $P_1$, can be generated before the point $P$ at the T junction but $P_2$ and $P_3$ must be generated afterwards. After $P$ is generated, if the non-terminal moves sufficiently far ($> k$) down the $P_2$ arm, it can never generate the $P_3$ arm since it cannot return down the $P_2$ arm (which now consists of terminals) or cross the #'s (which, once rewritten, would destroy the shape of the desired thin T).

Conversely, we can exhibit a language that is generated by a linear array grammar but is not accepted by a tape-bounded finite-state array acceptor. Let $G$ be the array grammar whose rules are

$$S\# \to xS \qquad S\# \to xW$$

$$\begin{matrix} W \\ \# \end{matrix} \to \begin{matrix} x \\ W \end{matrix} \qquad \begin{matrix} W \\ \# \end{matrix} \to \begin{matrix} x \\ X \end{matrix}$$

$$\#X \to Xx \qquad \#X \to Yx$$

$$\begin{matrix} \# \\ Y \end{matrix} \to \begin{matrix} Y \\ x \end{matrix} \qquad Y \to x$$

Informally, the $S$ moves to the right, leaving a trail of $x$'s, until it changes to a $W$; the $W$ moves down, trailing $x$'s, until it changes to an $X$; the $X$ moves left, leaving $x$'s behind it, until it changes to a $Y$; and the $Y$ moves up, trailing $x$'s until it changes to an $x$. Thus the language of this grammar consists of four-sided upright rectangular arcs, composed of $x$'s, that may touch themselves, but cannot cross themselves. In particular, all the hollow, thin upright rectangles of $x$'s are in this language. But it is not hard to show that any tape-bounded finite-state array acceptor that accepts all such rectangles must also accept various sufficiently large rectangular spirals (having many more than four sides). Hence the language of $G$ is not a tape-bounded finite-state array language.

## 6.3. Graph Acceptors

A *graph acceptor* is placed on a node of its input labeled graph in a special starting state; it moves from node to neighboring node, changing state and rewriting symbols in accordance with its transition function, and is said to accept the input graph if it enters a special accepting state. (Note that there is no such thing here as a distinguished starting node; graphs have no "northwest corners.") This definition is analogous to those in the string and array cases, but there are some significant differences, which we will now discuss.

Since a node in an arbitrary graph can have any number of neighbors, we cannot define the moves of a graph acceptor in terms of a fixed set of directions such as left, right, up, or down. In fact, there is no way, in general, for the acceptor to distinguish the neighboring nodes from one another. We could allow it to move to any one of them, chosen at random; but this means that it would have no way to move back to its previous position, since this would now be indistinguishable from the other neighbors of its new position. Systematic exploration of the graph would thus be impossible. To avoid this difficulty, we can give the acceptor the ability to sense the labels of the nodes adjacent to its current position, and allow it to choose moves that depend on these labels. It can now get back to its starting point by marking it in a special way before moving; this makes the starting point a uniquely marked neighbor of the new position.

Another problem with graph acceptors is how to permit them to add (non-#) nodes to their input graphs. For strings and arrays, we handled this by starting with an infinite string or array, a finite, connected piece which consisted of non-#'s, and rewriting #'s as non-#'s when necessary. The analogous idea for graphs is to start with an infinite complete graph, of which a finite, connected piece has non-# node labels. Every node now has infinitely many neighbors labeled #, so that the acceptor can always move to one of them, from any position, if it wants to add to the non-# part of its input. This approach, unfortunately, has the disadvantage that every node is a neighbor of every other node, so that the acceptor can see the entire graph from any position; it is no longer "myopic." (An alternative approach can be defined in which the acceptor is allowed to merge two neighboring nodes or to split a node in two; this approach allows the graph on which the acceptor moves to remain always finite. We will not give the details of this approach here.)

We can define various types of "monotonicity" and "tape-boundedness" for graph acceptors, according to whether or not they can rewrite #'s as non-#'s. It is not hard to show that the classes of graphs accepted by graph acceptors are the same as the languages of graph grammars. Similarly, it can be shown that acceptors that cannot change the graph structure of their input graphs are equivalent to graph grammars that satisfy the same restriction. Central to the proofs is the fact that such an acceptor can systematically traverse its input graph, and return to its starting point, without leaving any marks behind it. One can also define "finite state" graph acceptors that cannot relabel their input graphs at all, but such acceptors are very weak, as seen in the second paragraph of this section.

If we restrict ourselves to trees rather than arbitrary graphs, this discussion can be modified appropriately; we will not give the details here. Tree grammars can be shown to be equivalent to a class of acceptors called tree automata; for the details see Ref. 3. Another way to restrict graph acceptors is to require that all graphs have bounded degree, say $r$, and that the arcs at each node have unique labels chosen from the set $d_1, \ldots, d_r$, representing the possible "move directions." This approach generalizes the cases of strings and arrays (where at each node there are two or four move directions, respectively); but it allows only a restricted class of graph languages, and so will not be treated here.

## 7. PROGRAMMED GRAMMARS AND PARAMETERIZED GRAMMARS

This final section introduces some generalizations of grammars that are important in practical applications. For simplicity, we define them here for string grammars, but they can also be defined for all the other types of grammars introduced in this chapter.

### 7.1. Programmed Grammars

In an ordinary grammar $G$, at any given step in a derivation, more than one rule of $G$ may be applicable. We have not specified up to now how to choose which rule to apply; the language of $G$ is defined by allowing all possible choices.

A *programmed grammar* specifies which rules are allowed at a given step after a given rule has just been successfully applied or unsuccessfully tried. To illustrate how programmed grammars work, consider the following set of rules:

$$
\begin{aligned}
&(1)\ S \to AB \\
&(2)\ A \to aA \quad (3)\ A \to bA \quad (4)\ A \to a \quad (5)\ A \to b \\
&(6)\ B \to aB \quad (7)\ B \to bB \quad (8)\ B \to a \quad (9)\ B \to b
\end{aligned}
$$

Initially we use rule (1), and after it, one of rules (2), (3), (4), or (5). Subsequently, the next rule to be applied is chosen according to the following table:

| Rule just used | Next rule |
|:---:|:---:|
| (2) | (6) |
| (3) | (7) |
| (4) | (8) |
| (5) | (9) |
| (6) or (7) | (2), (3), (4), or (5) |
| (8) or (9) | None |

It is easily seen that the language of this grammar is the set of all strings of the form $\sigma\sigma$, where $\sigma$ is any non-null string of $a$'s and $b$'s, i.e. the same language as in Ex. (3) of Sec. 2.1. Note that in the present grammar the rules are all context-free. Note also that in this example we had no need to specify which rules to use if a rule is tried and found not to apply.

More generally, a programmed grammar consists of a grammar $G$, say with rules numbered $1, \dots, n$, and a set of $n$ triples $(i, U_i, V_i), 1 \leq i \leq n$, where $i$ is a rule number and $U_i, V_i$ are sets of rule numbers. Here $U_i$ is the set of rules that we are allowed to apply if rule $i$ has just been successfully applied, and $V_i$ is the set of rules that we are allowed to apply if application of rule $i$ has just been attempted but was not successful. Initially, any rule of the form $S \to \beta$ can be applied. A derivation is called *admissible* if it begins with a rule of the form $S \to \beta$, and also satisfies the following property: Let the strings at three successive steps of the derivation be $\lambda \Rightarrow \mu \Rightarrow \nu$, where $\mu$ is obtained from $\lambda$ by applying rule $i$ and $\nu$ is obtained from $\mu$ by applying rule $j$. Then there exists a sequence of rules $i_1, i_2, \dots, i_m = j, m \geq 1$, such that $i_1 \in U_i, i_2 \in V_{i_1}, i_3 \in V_{i_2}, \dots, i_m \in V_{i_{m-1}}$. The language of a programmed grammar is the set of terminal strings obtainable from $S$ by an admissible derivation.

## 7.2. Parameterized Grammars

A powerful extension of the grammar concept is obtained by associating numerical-valued parameters with the symbols. In such a *parameterized grammar* (usually called an "attributed grammar"), we assign a set of initial parameter values to the initial symbol $S$; and we associate with each rule $\alpha \to \beta$ a set of functions that allow us to compute the values for the symbols in $\beta$ from the values for the symbols in $\alpha$.

An important special class of parameterized grammars are *coordinate grammars*, in which position coordinates ($d$-tuples of numbers in $d$ dimensions) are associated with each symbol. We can model spatial arrangements of symbols using coordinate grammars in which, in any rule $\alpha \rightarrow \beta$, $\alpha$ and $\beta$ are tuples of symbols, say $\alpha = (A_1, \ldots, A_m)$, $\beta = (B_1, \ldots, B_n)$, and we associate with the rule a $dn$-tuple of functions, each of $dm$ variables, that specify the coordinates of the $B$'s in terms of those of the $A$'s. The language is the set of patterns of terminal symbols derivable in this way from a single $S$, say at the origin.

## REFERENCES

1. A. Rosenfeld, *Picture Languages: Formal Models for Picture Recognition* (Academic Press, NY, 1979).
2. M. Nagl, *Graph-Grammatiken – Theorie, Anwendungen, Implementierung* (Vieweg, Braunschweigh, FRG, 1979).
3. K.S. Fu, *Syntactic Pattern Recognition and Applications* (Prentice-Hall, Englewood Cliffs, NJ, 1982).
4. V. Claus, H. Ehrig, and G. Rozenberg, eds., *Graph-Grammars and Their Application to Computer Science and Biology* (Springer, Berlin, 1979).
5. H. Ehrig, M. Nagl, and G. Rozenberg, eds., *Graph-Grammars and their Application to Computer Science* (Springer, Berlin, 1983).
6. H. Ehrig, M. Nagl, G. Rozenberg and A. Rosenfeld, eds., *Graph Grammars and Their Application to Computer Science* (Springer, Berlin, 1987).

# Structural Representation and Matching

# 5

---

# STRING MATCHING FOR STRUCTURAL PATTERN RECOGNITION

H. BUNKE

*Universität Bern*
*Institut für Informatik und angewandte Mathematik*
*Länggass-Strasse 51, CH-3012 Bern*
*Switzerland*

Many approaches to pattern recognition are based on distance or similarity measures, i.e. an unknown input pattern is compared, or matched, with a number of prototypes in order to find the prototype most similar to the unknown input. The data structures most commonly used in the structural approach are strings, trees and graphs. Thus a formal measure of distance between those data structures is required. In this chapter we review fundamental concepts for the matching of strings and discuss how they can be applied to pattern recognition.

## 1. INTRODUCTION

There is one idea common to many different approaches to pattern recognition no matter whether they are statistical, syntactic or structural. It is the comparison of an unknown pattern with a number of sample, or prototype, patterns using a distance or similarity measure. Given a number of prototypes where the respective classes of these prototypes are known, the classification of an unknown pattern is achieved by determining the most similar prototype and deciding for its class.

In a statistical classifier, samples are represented by the coefficients of a decision function, parameters of a probability distribution, or points in a feature space, and the concept of similarity is based on distance or decision functions in the $n$-dimensional space of real numbers[1]. Formal grammars are a useful concept if pattern structure is essential. The usual procedure is to infer — either manually or automatically, as described in Chapters 9 and 10 in this book — a grammar from a sample set. Then, an unknown input pattern is fed into a parser and analyzed according to this grammar. In this way not only a classification but also a structural description of the unknown pattern can be obtained. Syntactic analysis can be interpreted as a particular procedure for determining structural similarity. All important details of this approach are explained in Chapters 2 and 3 in this book. According to the different data structures which are used for pattern recognition, not only string grammars but also tree, graph and array grammars play an important role in pattern recognition, as is described in Chapters 4 and 10 of this book.

There are cases where the number of the available samples is too small for grammatical inference or where the full power of a grammatical approach is not required. If pattern structure is essential, nevertheless, a structural matching technique could perhaps be useful. The basic idea of structural matching is to directly represent the prototypes as well as the unknown input patterns by means of a suitable data structure and to compare these structures in order to find the prototype which is most similar to an unknown input pattern. This approach requires a formal measure of similarity between two structural representations. Many of such measures have been proposed in the literature. They can be divided into major categories according to the data structures used for pattern representation. The most important data structures are strings, trees, graphs and arrays. Depending on the particular problem domain, all of these data structures can be augmented by attributes, as explained in Chapters 1 and 2.

With respect to computational complexity, strings are very efficient since similarity measures between strings can be computed quite fast. However, strings are limited in their representational power. At the other extreme, graphs are the most powerful approach to structural pattern representation. However, graph matching is conceptually rather complicated and expensive with respect to computational cost. So there is a trade-off between representational power and efforts required for matching. A similar trade-off can be observed if we use a grammar for pattern class representation.

In the present chapter, we review the most important approaches to string matching. The very important fields of matching trees, graphs and relational structures are treated in Chapters 6, 7 and 8. From a theoretical point of view, structural matching can be considered as a special case of a syntactic, i.e. grammar based, approach. A more detailed discussion of this topic is included in Chapter 11.

Applications of string matching in pattern recognition include speech recognition[2], 2-D shape recognition and machine parts identification[3] and character recognition[4]. Other applications are described in Ref. 5.

## 2. THE BASIC ALGORITHM

In this section, we introduce a string distance and give an algorithm for its computation. Let $T$ be an alphabet of (terminal) symbols and $x = x_1 \ldots x_n \in T^*$, $y = y_1 \ldots y_m \in T^*$; $n, m \geq 0$.

The distance between $x$ and $y$ is defined in terms of elementary *edit operations* which are required in order to transform $x$ into $y$. In this section, we consider three different types of edit operations:

(a) *substitution* of a symbol $a \in T$ in $x$ by a symbol $b \in T$ in $y, a \neq b$,

(b) *insertion* of a symbol $a \in T$ in $y$,

(c) *deletion* of a symbol $a \in T$ in $x$.

Symbolically, we write $a \rightarrow b$ for a substitution, $\varepsilon \rightarrow a$ for an insertion and $a \rightarrow \varepsilon$ for a deletion where $\varepsilon$ denotes the empty string[a]. Obviously, by repeated application of these edit operations, any given string $x$ can be transformed into any other sequence of symbols $y$.

---

[a]This notation must not be confused with a production or a derivation in a grammar!

Consider, for example, $T = \{a, b, c\}$ and

$$x = x_1 \ldots x_6 = ababcb$$
$$y = y_1 \ldots y_7 = aabcbcc \qquad (1)$$

The application of the following sequence of edit operations transforms $x$ into $y$.

1. Delete $b$;   result: $aabcb$.
2. Insert $c$;   result: $aabcbc$.   (2)
3. Insert $c$;   result: $aabcbcc = y$.

Given two strings $x$ and $y$, there is usually more than one sequence of edit operations for transforming $x$ into $y$. First, it is easy to see that the result of a sequence of edit operations is invariant with respect to the order of the individual operations in this sequence. Besides changing the order, however, one can usually find other completely different sequences of elementary operations that yield, when applied to a string $x$, the same result $y$.

As an alternative to the sequence in (2), one also gets $y$ from $x$ by means of the following operations:

1. Insert $a$;   result: $aababcb$.
2. Substitute $a$ by $c$;   result: $aabcbcb$.   (3)
3. Substitute $b$ by $c$;   result: $aabcbcc = y$.

When inserting $a$ in step 1, there are two alternatives, namely, the insertion of $a$ in front of $x$, or the insertion between the first and second symbol. In either case the result is $aababcb$.

The edit operations are used for modelling variations which may change an ideal prototype string into its actual, noisy version. Depending on the particular application, certain distortions, i.e. edit operations, may be more likely than others. In order to take account of this observation, it makes sense to introduce *costs* of edit operations. The smaller (larger) the costs of an edit operation are, the more likely (unlikely) is the corresponding distortion to occur. Symbolically, we write $c(a \rightarrow b)$ for the costs of the substitution $a \rightarrow b$, $c(\varepsilon \rightarrow a)$ for the costs of the insertion $\varepsilon \rightarrow a$ and $c(a \rightarrow \varepsilon)$ for the costs of the deletion $a \rightarrow \varepsilon$. The costs of any edit operation are assumed to be a real number greater or equal to zero.

Let $s = e_1, e_2, \ldots, e_n$ be a sequence of edit operations for transforming a string $x$ into another string $y$. The costs $c(s)$ of this sequence are given by

$$c(s) = \sum_{i=1}^{n} c(e_i) \; . \tag{4}$$

Consider the example in (1) and assume costs equal to one for any edit operation. Then the costs of both sequences in (2) and (3) are equal to 3.

Given two strings $x$ and $y$ and given the costs of any edit operation which may be required for transforming $x$ into $y$, we define the *distance* $d(x, y)$ between $x$ and $y$ by

$$d(x, y) = \min\{c(s) : s \text{ is a sequence of edit operations}$$
$$\text{which transforms } x \text{ into } y\} \; . \tag{5}$$

So the distance between $x$ and $y$ is obtained by summing up the costs of all elementary operations of the sequence with minimum total costs among all sequences which transform $x$ into $y$.

At first glance it is not obvious how the minimum in (5) can be found efficiently since there may be many sequences of edit operations which transform $x$ into $y$. A solution to the problem is provided by the algorithm in Fig. 1. This algorithm is commonly used today for the calculation of $d(x, y)$ according to the definition in (5). Basically, it is a dynamic programming procedure, i.e. a particular breadth-first search.

The algorithm in Fig. 1 computes the elements of the $(n + 1) \times (m + 1)$ matrix $D(i, j)$ row by row from left to right. The first row and first column of $D(i, j)$ is separately computed in an initial phase. The symbols $x_i$ and $y_j$ in $x$ and $y$ are denoted by $x(i)$ and $y(i)$, respectively; $i = 1, \ldots, n; j = 1, \ldots, m$. The basic idea of the algorithm in Fig. 1 is to find a minimum cost path from $D(0, 0)$ to $D(n, m)$. This path corresponds to the minimum cost sequence of edit operations for transforming $x$ into $y$. In each element $D(i, j)$ of the path, the minimum accumulative costs are stored for transforming $x' = x \ldots x_i$ into $y' = y_1 \ldots y_j$, i.e. $D(i, j) = d(x', y')$. Arriving thus at the lower right corner of the matrix, $D(n, m)$ holds the value of $d(x, y)$. For any path element $D(i, j)$ there exist three potential predecessors, namely, $D(i, j - 1), D(i - 1, j - 1)$, and $D(i - 1, j), i = 1, \ldots, n; j = 1, \ldots, m$. Going from $D(i, j - 1)$ to $D(i, j)$ corresponds to the insertion of $y_j$. A step from $D(i - 1, j - 1)$ to $D(i, j)$ represents the substitution of $x_i$ by $y_j$. Finally, a transition from $D(i - 1, j)$ to $D(i, j)$ corresponds to the deletion of $x_i$. A graphical illustration is shown in Fig. 2. Lines 7 to 10 in Fig. 1 ensure that $D(i, j)$ actually holds the min-

input:

$x = x_1 \ldots x_n \in T^*, y = y_1 \ldots y_m \in T^*$, costs$(a \to b); a, b \in T \cup \{\varepsilon\}$

output:

$d(x, y)$

method:

0  begin

1  $D(0,0) := 0;$

2  for $i = 1$ to $n$ do  $D(i, 0) := D(i - 1, 0) + c(x(i) \to \varepsilon);$

3  for $j = 1$ to $m$ do  $D(0, j) := D(0, j - 1) + c(\varepsilon \to y(j));$

4  for $i = 1$ to $n$ do

5      for $j = 1$ to $m$ do

6          begin

7              $m_1 := D(i - 1, j - 1) + c(x(i) \to y(j));$

8              $m_2 := D(i - 1, j) + c(x(i) \to \varepsilon);$

9              $m_3 := D(i, j - 1) + c(\varepsilon \to y(j));$

10             $D(i, j) := \min(m_1, m_2, m_3);$

11             if $m_1 = D(i, j)$ then set pointer from $(i, j)$ to $(i - 1, j - 1);$

12             if $m_2 = D(i, j)$ then set pointer from $(i, j)$ to $(i - 1, j);$

13             if $m_3 = D(i, j)$ then set pointer from $(i, j)$ to $(i, j - 1);$

14          end;

15  $d(x, y) := D(n, m);$

16  end

Fig. 1. Algorithm for the computation of $d(x, y)$.

imum costs for transforming $x_1 \ldots x_i$ into $y_1 \ldots y_j$. The pointers in lines 11 to 13 can be used in order to find, in a backward trace starting at $D(n, m)$ and proceeding to $D(1, 1)$, the actual sequence of edit operations. A proof of the correctness of the algorithm in Fig. 1 can be found in Ref. 6.

As an example, consider the strings $x$ and $y$ in (1) and costs $c(a \to b) = c(\varepsilon \to a) = c(a \to \varepsilon) = 1, c(a \to a) = 0$ for any $a, b \in T; a \neq b$. The corresponding matrix $D(i, j)$ is shown in Fig. 3. The distance is $d(x, y) = 3$. There are different paths which can be traced back from $D(n, m)$ to $D(1, 1)$ since $D(n, m)$ and other matrix elements have more than one pointer. In total we get three paths as shown in Fig. 4. As discussed before, a diagonal step in the matrix corresponds to a substitution (where the substitution of any symbol $a \in T$ by itself is considered as a particular edit operation with costs equal to zero), while horizontal and vertical transitions represent insertions and deletions, respectively. So the

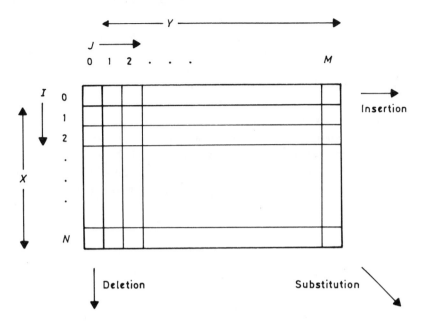

Fig. 2. Graphical illustration of the algorithm in Fig. 1.

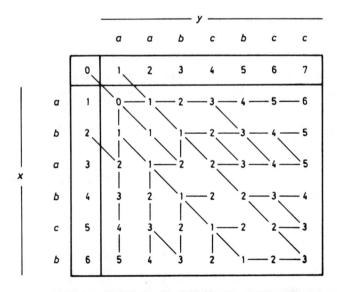

Fig. 3. An example of string distance computation.

path in Fig. 4a exactly corresponds to the sequence of edit operations given in (2), while the paths in Figs. 4b and 4c both represent the sequence in (3). Notice that the paths in Figs. 4b and 4c differ only with respect to the place where an additional symbol is inserted.

As another example consider $x$ and $y$ in (1) again but with different costs this time, namely, $c(a \rightarrow b) = 1, c(a \rightarrow a) = 0, c(\varepsilon \rightarrow a) = c(a \rightarrow \varepsilon) = 2$ for any $a, b \in T; a \neq b$. The corresponding matrix $D(i, j)$ is given in Fig. 5 and the corresponding minimum cost paths in Fig. 6.

In the foregoing discussion we have used the term "distance" for $d(x, y)$. Depending on the costs of edit operations, $d(x, y)$ is not a metric in general. It can easily be proven, however, that under the conditions

$$
\begin{aligned}
&\text{(a)}\ c(a \rightarrow b) \geq 0 \text{ for any } a, b \in T \cup \{\varepsilon\} , \\
&\text{(b)}\ c(a \rightarrow b) = 0 \text{ if and only if } a = b \text{ for any } a, b \in T , \\
&\text{(c)}\ c(a \rightarrow b) \leq c(a \rightarrow \varepsilon) + c(\varepsilon \rightarrow b) \text{ for any } a, b \in T , \\
&\text{(d)}\ c(a \rightarrow b) = c(b \rightarrow a) \text{ for any } a, b \in T \cup \{\varepsilon\}^{\text{b}},
\end{aligned}
\tag{6}
$$

$d(x, y)$ is effectively a metric, i.e.

$$
\begin{aligned}
&\text{(a)}\ d(x, y) \geq 0 \text{ for any } x, y \in T^* , \\
&\text{(b)}\ d(x, y) = 0 \text{ if and only if } x = y \text{ for any } x, y \in T^* , \\
&\text{(c)}\ d(x, z) \leq d(x, y) + d(y, z) \text{ for any } x, y, z \in T^* , \\
&\text{(d)}\ d(x, y) = d(y, x) \text{ for any } x, y \in T^* .
\end{aligned}
\tag{7}
$$

For most practical applications, it is too restrictive to require all conditions (6a) to (6d) to be fulfilled. Nevertheless, we will always use the term "distance" for $d(x, y)$, regardless whether the metric properties (7a) to (7d) hold true or not.

It is obvious from Fig. 1 that the computational complexity of the string distance computation is $O(nm)$ with respect to both time and space. The algorithm in Fig. 1 is also known as the *Levenshtein distance*, or *weighted* Levenshtein distance and has been reported in a number of papers, see e.g. Refs. 6 and 7.

---

[b] For the purpose of a coherent notation, we let $a$, $b$, $c \in T \cup \{\varepsilon\}$. This covers substitutions, insertions and deletions in one formula. Notice, however, that the edit operation $\varepsilon \rightarrow \varepsilon$ is not defined. Therefore, it is excluded from our considerations.

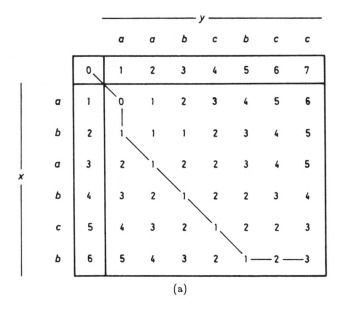

(a)

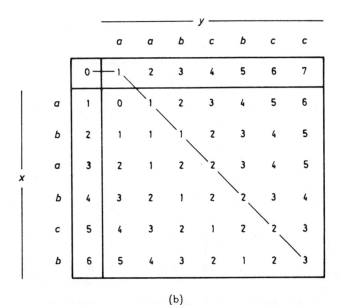

(b)

Fig. 4(a)-(c). Three different paths corresponding to the minimum cost edit operations in Fig. 3.

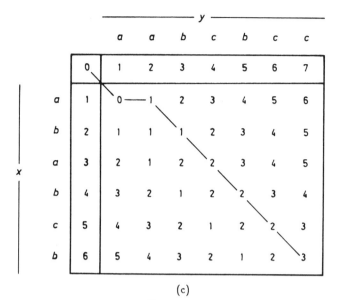

(c)

Fig. 4. Cont'd.

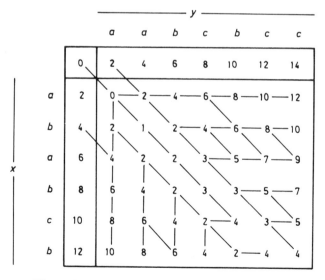

Fig. 5. Another example of string distance computation.

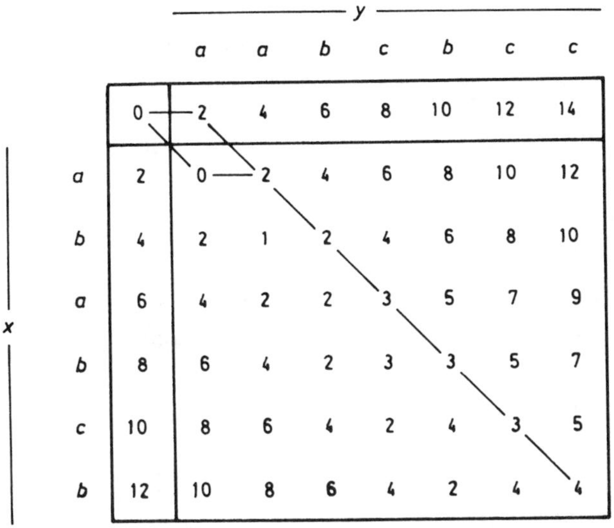

Fig. 6. Two different paths corresponding to the minimum cost edit operations in Fig. 5.

## 3. PATTERN RECOGNITION CONCEPTS BASED ON STRING DISTANCES

In the last section a distance measure for strings was introduced and an algorithm for its computation was given. In the present section, it will be shown how these concepts can be applied in pattern recognition. Let

$$P_1 = \{x_1^1, x_2^1, \ldots, x_N^1\}, \quad N \geq 1, \quad \text{and}$$
$$P_2 = \{x_1^2, x_2^2, \ldots, x_M^2\}, \quad M \geq 1 \tag{8}$$

be sets of prototype strings representing pattern classes $C_1$ and $C_2$ respectively, and let $x$ be a string representing an unknown pattern. We are interested in developing a decision procedure for the classification of $x$, i.e. we want to know whether $x \in C_1$ or $x \in C_2$.

A well-known concept from statistical decision theory is *nearest-neighbor classification* (NN-classification)[1]. Using the distance measure defined in (5) and the algorithm in Fig. 1, this concept can easily be adopted for the classification of the unknown string $x$. Let $D_1(x)$ be the distance between $x$ and that element in $C_1$ which is closest to $x$, i.e.

$$D_1(x) = \min\{d(x_i^1, x) : i = 1, \ldots, N\}. \tag{9}$$

Similarly, we define

$$D_2(x) = \min\{d(x_i^2, x) : i = 1, \dots, M\} . \tag{10}$$

Now the *NN decision rule* is given by

$$x \in \begin{cases} C_1, & \text{if and only if } D_1(x) \le D_2(x) \\ C_2, & \text{otherwise} \end{cases} . \tag{11}$$

This decision procedure can easily be modified by introducing a threshold $t$ for rejection.

$$x \in \begin{cases} C_1, & \text{if and only if } D_1(x) \le D_2(x) \text{ and } D_1(x) \le t \\ C_2, & \text{if and only if } D_2(x) < D_1(x) \text{ and } D_2(x) \le t \\ \text{REJECT}, & \text{otherwise} . \end{cases} \tag{12}$$

Notice that (11) results from (12) as a special case if $t = \infty$.

A straightforward extension of (11) is obtained if the decision is not only based on the nearest neighbor, i.e. on one prototype element, but on the $K$ nearest neighbors.

Let $x_1^1, \dots, x_K^1$ be the $K$ elements in $C_1$ which are closest to $x$, i.e.

$$d(x_i^1, x) \le d(x_j^1, x) \text{ for } i = 1, \dots, K; \quad j = K+1, \dots, N \tag{13}$$

and let

$$D_1^K(x) = \frac{1}{K} \sum_{i=1}^{K} d(x_i^1, x) , \tag{14}$$

$$D_2^K(x) = \frac{1}{K} \sum_{i=1}^{K} d(x_i^2, x) , \tag{15}$$

where $x_1^2, \dots, x_K^2$ are, analogous to (13), the $K$ elements in $C_2$ with smallest distance to $x$. The *K-NN classification rule* is given by

$$x \in \begin{cases} C_1, & \text{if and only if } D_1^K(x) \le D_2^K(x) \\ C_2, & \text{otherwise} . \end{cases} \tag{16}$$

Using a threshold $t$ we obtain, similar to (12), the K-NN classification procedure with rejection

$$x \in \begin{cases} C_1, & \text{if and only if } D_1^K(x) \le D_2^K(x) \text{ and } D_1^K(x) \le t \\ C_2, & \text{if and only if } D_2^K(x) < D_1^K(x) \text{ and } D_2^K(x) \le t \\ \text{REJECT}, \text{otherwise} . \end{cases} \tag{17}$$

If the number of prototype strings according to (8) is large and if we implement the computation of the $K$ nearest neighbors, $K \geq 1$, in a straightforward way by exhaustively searching through the complete sets $P_1$ and $P_2$, the classification method given by one of the decision rules (11), (12), (16), or (17) can be very time consuming. There are several ways to overcome this problem. First, we will discuss the possibility of reducing the size of the sample set. For this reason, we eliminate certain elements from the sample sets $P_1$ and $P_2$ in such a way that the principal information contained in $P_1$ and $P_2$ is preserved. One way to achieve such a sample size reduction is to keep only the "typical" elements. In order to measure the degree of typicalness of an element $x_i^l$ contained in $P_l$, one can calculate the average distance $A_i^l$ of this element to all other members in $P_l(l = 1, 2)$, i.e.

$$
\begin{aligned}
A_i^1 &= \frac{1}{N} \sum_{k=1}^{N} d(x_i^1, x_k^1), \quad i = 1, \dots, N \ . \\
A_j^2 &= \frac{1}{M} \sum_{l=1}^{M} d(x_j^2, x_l^2), \quad j = 1, \dots, M \ .
\end{aligned}
\tag{18}
$$

The smaller $A_i^1$ is, the more typical is $x_i^1$ with respect to class $C_1$. For achieving the desired reduction, only a certain number of elements $x_1^1, \dots, x_n^1$ and $x_1^2, \dots, x_m^2$ are kept in $P_1$ and $P_2$ respectively, such that

$$
\begin{aligned}
A_i^1 &\leq A_k^1; \quad i = 1, \dots, n; \quad k = n+1, \dots, N \ , \\
A_j^2 &\leq A_l^2; \quad j = 1, \dots, m; \quad l = m+1, \dots, M \ .
\end{aligned}
\tag{19}
$$

The methods based on (18) and (19) tend to retain elements which are near to the centre of a class. There are other techniques known from the literature which are inclined to keeping the elements close to the border of neighboring classes. More details can be found in Refs. 1 and 8.

Another way of speeding up the computation of the $K$ nearest neighbors according to one of the equations (11), (12), (16), or (17) is to avoid an exhaustive search through all samples. There are smart search techniques which examine — in the usual cases — only a part of the elements in $P_1$ and $P_2$. Nevertheless, these algorithms are guaranteed to find the $K$ prototype elements, $K \geq 1$, with minimum distance to $x$. Two examples of such search techniques are reported in Refs. 9 and 10.

In the foregoing discussion only two pattern classes $C_1$ and $C_2$ with their respective sets of prototypes $P_1$ and $P_2$ were considered. It should be obvious, however, that all decision procedures discussed in this section can be generalized to more than two classes in a straightforward way.

Clustering is another important concept in pattern recognition. The application of the string distance, according to (5), to the *clustering of strings* is treated in Ref. 4.

The main focus of attention in this section was on pattern classification. Notice, however, that a sequence of edit operations, obtained as a result of the algorithm in Fig. 1 in addition to the value of $d(x, y)$ can be interpreted as a structural description of the input pattern $y$ with respect to the most similar prototype $x$. This topic is discussed in greater detail in Chapter 11 in this book.

## 4. MODIFICATIONS OF THE BASIC ALGORITHM

There is a great number of modifications of the algorithm given in Fig. 1 known from the literature. We will review some of them in this section.

### 4.1. A Simplified Approach[11]

Given $x = x_1 \ldots x_n$ and $y = y_1 \ldots y_m$ we say there is an identity at position $i$ if and only if $x_i = y_i, i = 1, \ldots, \min(n, m)$. Let $I$ be the number of identities. We define

$$
\begin{aligned}
N &= \max(n, m) - I \ , \\
s(x, y) &= I/N \ , \\
d'(x, y) &= N/I \ .
\end{aligned}
\tag{20}
$$

Obviously, $s(x, y)$ is a measure of similarity while $d'(x, y)$ can be interpreted as a distance between $x$ and $y$. One can easily prove the following relations

(1) $s(x, y) = \infty, d'(x, y) = 0$   if $x_i = y_i$ for $i = 1, \ldots, n$ and $n = m$
(2) $s(x, y) = 0, d'(x, y) = \infty$   if $x_i \neq y_i$ for $i = 1, \ldots, \min(n, m)$
(3) $0 < s(x, y), d'(x, y) < \infty$   otherwise .

$$\tag{21}$$

The distance measure according to (20) is superior to the distance $d(x, y)$ discussed in Sec. 2 with regard to its computational complexity, which is only of order $O(\max(n, m))$. However, its application is restricted to those cases where a proper alignment of $x$ and $y$ with respect to their beginnings can be guaranteed and where there are no insertions and deletions.

### 4.2. Similarity in Terms of Common Subsequences[6]

A *subsequence* of a string $x = x_1 \ldots x_n$ is defined as any string $x_{i1} x_{i2} \ldots x_{il}$ where $1 \leq i1 \leq i2 \leq \ldots \leq il \leq n$. Given two strings $x$ and $y, z$ is a *common subsequence* of $x$ and $y$ if $z$ is a subsequence of both $x$ and $y$. Let $l(x, y)$ be the length of the longest common subsequence of $x$ and $y$. Then $l(x, y)$ can be used as a similarity measure between $x$ and $y$. The larger $l(x, y)$ is, the greater is the degree of similarity, or equivalently, the smaller is the distance between $x$ and $y$. For the purpose of normalization, $l(x, y)$ can be divided by the sum or the maximum of the lengths of $x$ and $y$.

It is interesting to notice that $l(x, y)$ can be computed using the algorithm in Fig. 1 if we define $c(a \rightarrow b) = 2, c(a \rightarrow a) = 0, c(\varepsilon \rightarrow a) = c(a \rightarrow \varepsilon) = 1$ for any $a, b \in T; a \neq b$. In this case, we get

$$d(x, y) = n + m - 2l(x, y)$$

and, therefore,

$$l(x, y) = (n + m - d(x, y))/2 \qquad (22)$$

where $n$ and $m$ denote the length of $x$ and $y$ respectively. Obviously, the computational complexity of the similarity measure $l(x, y)$ is $O(nm)$ with respect to both time and space.

## 4.3. Warping and Elastic Matching[12]

For some applications, like processing of continuous human speech where strings represent sound waves sampled at certain time intervals, it is desirable to allow the stretching, or expansion, of a single symbol $a$ into $k$ consecutive symbols $a_1 \ldots a_k$ as well as the compression of $a_1 \ldots a_k$ into $a$ without any costs, where $a_1 = a_2 = \ldots = a_k = a, k \geq 1$. This problem is often referred to as *elastic matching, warping,* or *time warping* if the strings to be compared represent discrete functions of time.

The desired property can be achieved by a slight modification of the algorithm in Fig. 1. We replace lines 7 to 9 in Fig. 1 by lines $7'$ to $9'$ in Fig. 7 and define

$$c((i - 1, j - 1) \rightarrow (i, j)) = c(x(i) \rightarrow y(j))$$

$$c((i - 1, j) \rightarrow (i, j)) = \begin{cases} 0 & \text{if } x(i - 1) = x(i) = y(j) \\ c(x(i) \rightarrow \varepsilon) & \text{otherwise} \end{cases} \qquad (23)$$

$$c((i, j - 1) \rightarrow (i, j)) = \begin{cases} 0 & \text{if } x(i) = y(j - 1) = y(i) \\ c(\varepsilon \rightarrow y(j)) & \text{otherwise} \end{cases}$$

Consider, for example, $T = \{a, b, c\}, x = aabcbc$ and $y = abbbcc$. Let the costs be given by $c(a \rightarrow b) = c(\varepsilon \rightarrow a) = c(a \rightarrow \varepsilon) = 1, c(a \rightarrow a) = 0$ for any $a, b \in T$. The matrix $D(i, j)$ computed by the modified algorithm

$$7' \quad m_1 := D(i-1, j-1) + c((i-1, j-1) \rightarrow (i,j)) ;$$
$$8' \quad m_2 := D(i-1, j) + c((i-1, j) \rightarrow (i,j)) ;$$
$$9' \quad m_3 := D(i, j-1) + c((i, j-1) \rightarrow (i,j)) ;$$

**Fig. 7.** A modification of the algorithm in **Fig. 1** for elastic matching.

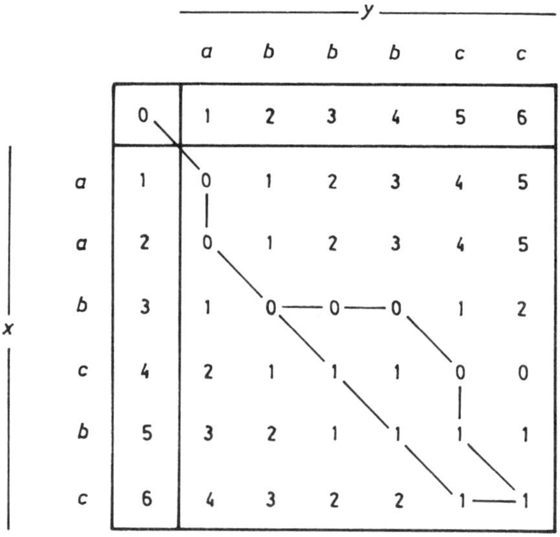

**Fig. 8.** An example of elastic matching.

according to Fig. 7 is given in Fig. 8. We conclude from $D(6,6)$ that the two strings have a distance of one under the elastic matching procedure. There are two minimum cost paths outlined in Fig. 8. Thus there are two minimum cost edit operation sequences, namely,

1. Delete $a$; result: $abcbc$; accumulative costs $= 0$.
2. Insert $b$; result: $abbcbc$; accumulative costs $= 0$.
3. Insert $b$; result: $abbbcbc$; accumulative costs $= 0$.
4. Delete $b$; result: $abbbcc$; accumulative costs $= 1$,

and

1. Same as above.
2. Substitute $c$ by $b$; result: $abbbc$; accumulative costs $= 1$.
3. Insert $c$; result: $abbbcc$; accumulative costs $= 1$.

Again, the computational complexity of the method is $O(nm)$ with respect to both time and space. There are other versions of warping and elastic matching known from the literature. More details and references can be found in Refs. 13 and 14.

## 4.4. String Distance Based on Generalized Substitutions[15]

The edit operations considered in Sec. 2 can be understood, from a general point of view, as elementary transformations which

- substitute a string of length 1 by another string of length 1 (edit operation $a \rightarrow b$)
- substitute a string of length 0 by another string of length 1 (edit operation $\varepsilon \rightarrow a$)
- substitute a string of length 1 by another string of length 0 (edit operation $a \rightarrow \varepsilon$).

So an obvious generalization of the approach discussed in Sec. 2 is to introduce, as elementary edit operations, substitutions $u \rightarrow v$ where both $u$ and $v$ are arbitrary strings of any length greater than or equal to zero. Let $c(u \rightarrow v)$ denote the costs of the generalized substitution $u \rightarrow v$. Notice that $c(u \rightarrow v)$ will usually be different from $d(u, v)$. In the following we always assume $c(u \rightarrow v) = 0$ if $u = v$ for any two strings $u, v \in T^*$. For a fixed alphabet $T$, we assume furthermore that there is only a finite number of generalized substitutions $u \rightarrow v$. Let $S$ be the set of these generalized substitutions. If $S$ contains the basic edit operations of Sec. 2, namely, substitution of any symbol by any other symbol, insertion of any symbol, and deletion of any symbol, then it is possible to compare any two strings. Otherwise, a comparison, i.e. the distance based on the concept of generalized substitution, may not exist for certain pairs of strings, $x$ and $y$. In the following $d(x, y)$ denotes the distance between the strings $x$ and $y$ based on a given set $S$ of generalized substitutions with respective costs.

The calculation of $d(x, y)$ can be performed similarly to the algorithm in Fig. 1. Again, we use an $(n + 1) \times (m + 1)$ array $D(i, j)$ where $n$ and $m$ are the lengths of $x$ and $y$, respectively. We fill the elements of the array row by row from left to right. $D(i, j)$ is equal to $d(x_1 \ldots x_i, y_1 \ldots y_j)$ for $i = 1, \ldots, n$ and $j = 1, \ldots, m$. Arriving thus finally at $D(n, m)$, we get $d(x, y) = D(n, m)$. In close correspondence with the algorithm in Fig. 1, the basic idea of the generalized substitution based distance calculation is to find a minimum cost path from $D(0, 0)$ to $D(n, m)$.

The only difference to Fig. 1 is that there are more general transitions possible from one matrix position, i.e. one element on the path, to the next. While in Fig. 1 there are only one-step transitions in diagonal, horizontal and vertical directions, the generalized substitution approach allows us to pass $l$ elements vertically downwards and $k$ elements horizontally to the right in one step on the path if there is a suitable generalized substitution in $S$ of the form $u \rightarrow v$ with length of $u$ and $v$ equal to $l$ and $k$, respectively.

The idea, on which the computation of $d(x,y)$ for generalized substitution relies, is illustrated in Fig. 9. Computing $D(i,j)$ requires searching for a matrix element $D(r,s)$ with $r \leq i, s \leq j, x' = x_1 \ldots x_r, y' = y_1 \ldots y_s, x'' = x_{r+1} \ldots x_i, y'' = y_{s+1} \ldots y_j$, such that the value of $D(r,s)$ plus the costs for the transition from $D(r,s)$ to $D(i,j)$, i.e. $c(x'' \rightarrow y'')$, is minimal, provided that there is a generalized transition $x'' \rightarrow y''$ in $S$. Formally, the computation of $D(i,j)$ is based on the formulae

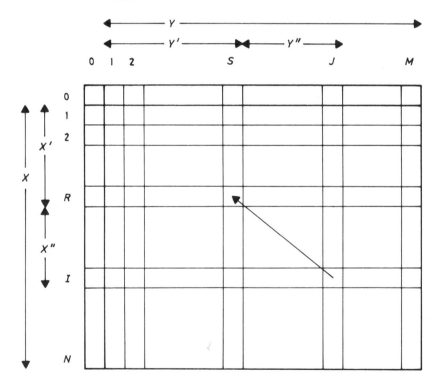

Fig. 9. Graphical illustration of the string distance computation based on generalized substitutions.

$$D(i,j) = \min\{d(x',y') + c(x'',y'') :$$
$$x'' \to y'' \in S, x_1 \ldots x_i = x'x'', y_1 \ldots y_j = y'y''\} ,$$
$$i = 0, \ldots, n; \; j = 0, \ldots, m .$$

$$d(x,y) = D(n,m) .$$

(24)

There are two different approaches to the implementation of formulae (24). First, one can search for the minimum using two nested loops. In this case, $d(x',y') + c(x'' + y'')$ in (24) is computed for every possibility of splitting $x_1 \ldots x_i$ into $x' = x_1 \ldots x_r$ and $x'' = x_{r+1} \ldots x_i$, and splitting $y_1 \ldots y_j$ into $y' = y_1 \ldots y_s$ and $y'' = y_{s+1} \ldots y_j$ provided that the set $S$ of generalized substitutions contains an element $x'' \to y''$. It can be easily seen that this implementation results in a computational complexity of $O(n^2 m^2)$ with respect to time.

The second approach is based on a main loop which goes through the set $S$ of generalized substitutions. For each element $u \to v$, it is checked whether $x_1 \ldots x_i$ and $y_1 \ldots y_j$ can be partitioned into $x'x''$ and $y'y''$, respectively, such that $x' = u$ and $y' = v$. If such a partition exists then the value of $d(x',y') + c(x'',y'')$ is computed. It is clear that the required number of operations for the calculation of $D(i,j)$ is independent of the length of the input and, therefore, depends only on the cardinality of the set $S$. Thus the computational complexity of this implementation with respect to time is still of order $O(nm)$. Clearly, depending on the size of $S$ and the length of the input, the one or the other implementation will run faster.

As an example, consider the strings, the edit operations and the costs in Figs. 3 and 4. Assume as an additional generalized substitution $b \to bc$ with costs $c(b \to bc) = 1$. Applying the algorithm which is based on (24), we get $d(x,y) = 3$. Besides the three sequences of edit operations corresponding to Fig. 4, we find a fourth sequence with costs equal to 3, namely,

1. Delete $b$; result: $aabcb$; accumulative costs $= 1$.
2. Substitute $b$ by $bc$; result: $aabcbc$; accumulative costs $= 2$.
3. Insert $c$; result: $aabcbcc$; accumulative costs $= 3$.

From an application oriented point of view it may be difficult
(a) to find appropriate basic edit operations $u \to v$, and
(b) to establish suitable costs $c(u \to v)$.

Likely, it is perhaps not easy to decide which type of distance or similarity measure discussed so far is most convenient for a particular problem. The only general statement which can be made is that

(a) the basic edit operations, i.e. steps on the minimum cost path in $D(i,j)$ should model, as naturally as possible, elementary deformations that may corrupt an ideal prototype pattern, resulting in a noisy version of it, and

(b) the more likely/unlikely a distortion is to occur, the lower/higher its associated costs should be. Automatic procedures for the inference of basic edit operations and their respective costs from sample sets are beyond the present state of the art and possibly subject to future research.

## 4.5. Context Dependent Costs[16]

All cost functions considered so far are based on the assumption of context independence. This means that the costs of insertion, deletion and substitution of a symbol, or more generally a block of symbols, are independent of the symbols in the neighborhood. There are applications, however, where the likelihood of whether a symbol is changed or not depends on its context. An example is the recognition of fluently spoken natural language where the pronounciation of a word often depends on the context.

Let $x = x_1 \ldots x_n \in T^*$ be a string. $K(x_i)$ denotes a context of $x_i$, i.e. a substring of $x$ containing $x_i$. Thus $K(x_i) = x' x_i x''$ for some $x', x'' \in T^*$. More precisely, for any nonempty $x$ we have $x' = \varepsilon$ if $i = 1$ and $x'' = \varepsilon$ if $i = n$. If it is desired to denote the context, i.e. the neighborhood, of $x_i$ explicitly we write $x' \underline{x}_i x''$.

Let $c(a \rightarrow b : K(a))$ denote the costs to substitute $a$ by $b$ under the condition that the symbol $a$ occurs in $x$ within the context $K(a), a \neq b$. Similarly, $c(a \rightarrow \varepsilon : K(a))$ and $c(\varepsilon \rightarrow a : K(a))$ denote context dependent costs for deletion and insertion, respectively. It is assumed that the substitution of a symbol by itself is independent of the context and has costs equal to zero; thus we have $c(a \rightarrow a : \varepsilon) = 0$ for any $a \in T$. Only edit operations affecting one symbol have been considered in Ref. 16. However, the idea of context dependent costs can be applied to generalized substitutions in a straightforward manner as well.

Consider for example the strings $x = x_1 x_2 x_3 x_4 x_5$ and $y = y_1 y_2 y_3 y_4$. Let the costs of the possible edit operations be

$$c_1 = c(x_1, y_1 : \underline{x}_1 x_2); \qquad c_4 = (x_4, y_4 : x_3 \underline{x}_4 x_5);$$
$$c_2 = c(x_2, y_3 : x_1 \underline{x}_2 x_3); \qquad c_5 = (x_5, \varepsilon : x_4 \underline{x}_5);$$
$$c_3 = c(x_3, \varepsilon : x_2 \underline{x}_3 x_4); \qquad c_6 = (\varepsilon, y_2 : x_1 \underline{\varepsilon} x_2) \ .$$

Then the following set of edit operations transforms $x$ into $y$ with accumulative costs equal to $c_1 + c_2 + c_3 + c_4 + c_5 + c_6$:

- substitute $x_1$ by $y_1$,
- substitute $x_2$ by $y_3$,
- substitute $x_4$ by $y_4$,
- delete $x_3$,
- delete $x_5$,
- insert $y_2$.

Notice that in this example we can no longer think of the edit operations as being sequentially performed on $x$. Instead, all edit operations are simultaneously applied.

Given two strings $x, y$ and context dependent costs, we can compute the *context dependent distance* $d(x, y)$ by the algorithm in Fig. 1. The only modification required is that we have to use context dependent costs $c(a \rightarrow b : K(a))$ instead of $c(a \rightarrow b)$.

Consider, as an example, $T = \{a, b, c\}$, $x = abca$ and $y = acc$. Let the context dependent costs be

$c(a, d : \underline{a}b) = 1$; $c(a, d : c\underline{a}) = 2$;
$c(b, d : a\underline{b}c) = 2$;
$c(c, d : b\underline{c}a) = 1$;
$c(a, \varepsilon : \underline{a}b) = 0.5$; $c(a, \varepsilon : c\underline{a}) = 3$;
$c(b, \varepsilon : a\underline{b}c) = 0.5$;
$c(c, \varepsilon : b\underline{c}a) = 0.5$;
$c(\varepsilon, d : \underline{\varepsilon}ab) = 2$; $c(\varepsilon, d : a\underline{\varepsilon}b) = 1$; $c(\varepsilon, d : b\underline{\varepsilon}c) = 1$;
$c(\varepsilon, d : c\underline{\varepsilon}a) = 1$; $c(\varepsilon, d : ca\underline{\varepsilon}) = 2$ ,

for any $d \in T$. The correspondence matrix $D(i, j)$ with the minimum cost path outlined is shown in Fig. 10. We conclude that the context dependent distance $d(x, y)$ is equal to 2.5. The minimum cost edit operations are the deletion of $b$ in the context $a\underline{b}c$ and the substitution of $a$ by $c$ in the context $c\underline{a}$.

Obviously, if the context to be taken into account in the cost coefficients $c(a \rightarrow b : K(a))$ is bound in its length, the algorithm for the computation of the context dependent distance $d(x, y)$ has a computational complexity of $O(nm)$ with respect to both time and space where $n$ and $m$ is the length of $x$ and $y$, respectively.

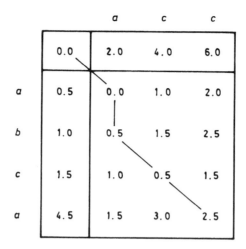

Fig. 10. An example of context dependent string distance.

### 4.6. A Faster Method[17]

There is an alternative to the algorithm given in Fig. 1 which has a computational complexity of only $O(nm/\min(m, \log n))$ with respect to time, where $n$ and $m$ are the lengths of the two strings to be compared and $m \leq n$. This algorithm is based on the idea of splitting the matrix $D(i, j)$ into submatrices and precomputing all operations to be performed on these submatrices. The algorithm can be applied whenever the alphabet $T$ is finite — as it is assumed throughout this chapter — and the costs are rational numbers. This method is asymptotically the fastest currently available for string edit computation. However, on a particular input it may run longer than the algorithm in Fig. 1, especially if the strings to be compared are relatively short. For a more detailed analysis and discussion the reader is referred to the original paper[17].

## 5. MATCHING OF ATTRIBUTED STRINGS

It was already explained in Chapters 1 and 2 of this book that the augmentation of the symbols in a string by *attributes* can be a very useful concept for particular pattern recognition problems. In this section we consider an alphabet $T$ and strings $x = x_1 \ldots x_n \in T^*$ where each symbol

$x_i \in T$ has an associated attribute vector

$$\underline{a}(x_i) = (a_1^i, a_2^i, \ldots, a_k^i) \in R^k; \quad i = 1, \ldots, n \ . \tag{25}$$

The attribute values of a symbol are real numbers representing numerical quantities like length of a line, size of region, or orientation of a surface. For the purpose of simplification, we assume the attribute vectors of all symbols as having identical lengths.

If one wants to determine the similarity, or distance, of two strings, not only the differences between the symbols but also the variations between the attribute vectors must be taken into account. The following approach to this problem was proposed in Ref. 18.

Let $x = x_1 \ldots x_n$ and $y = y_1 \ldots y_m$ be two strings with attribute vectors $\underline{a}(x_i)$ according to (25) and

$$\underline{b}(y_j) = (b_1^j, b_2^j, \ldots, b_k^j) \in R^k; \quad j = 1, \ldots, m \ . \tag{26}$$

One possibility of defining the distance $\delta(x, y)$ between $x$ and $y$ is

$$\delta(x, y) = d(x, y) + d_a(x, y) \tag{27}$$

where $d(x, y)$ is any of the string distances considered in Secs. 2 and 4 taking into account only differences between symbols, and $d_a(x, y)$ is the attribute distance. Since each attribute vector has real numbers as components, it is straightforward to define

$$d_a(x, y) = \sum_{(r,s)} \sum_{l=1}^{k} w_l |a_l^r - b_l^s| \tag{28}$$

where $w_l$ are suitably chosen weight coefficients and the outer sum is over all pairs $(r, s)$ such that symbol $x_r$ is substituted by symbol $y_s$ where $x_r = y_s$. In other words, the attribute distance $d_a(x, y)$ is calculated only for those symbols that are not changed when $x$ is transformed into $y$.

Consider, for example, strings $x$ and $y$ in (1) and the minimum cost edit operations path in Fig. 3 corresponding to (2). Assume attribute vectors according to (25) and (26). Then the attribute distance is given by (28) where $(r, s)$ in the outer sum assumes values $(1, 1)$, $(3, 2)$, $(4, 3)$, $(5, 4)$, and $(6, 5)$.

Notice that the calculation of $d_a(x, y)$ can be embedded, as a subprocedure, in lines 2, 3, 7, 8, 9 in Fig. 1. Therefore, the distance measure $\delta(x, y)$ according to (27) can be calculated using a procedure similar to Fig. 1.

As a particular application of attributed string matching, shape recognition of 2-D objects in images is reported in Ref. 3. A shape is represented by a sequence of boundary elements i.e. line segments. There is one symbol $b$ for representing line segments of any type. The variations that may exist among different boundary elements are captured by the attributes.

There are two attributes for any line segment $b$, namely length $l_b$ and orientation $o_b$ where the orientation is with respect to a line of reference. The task considered in Ref. 3 is shape classification using a nearest neighbor approach according to (8)–(12).

The edit operations affecting single symbols are insertion, deletion, and substitution with respective costs

$$c(\varepsilon \rightarrow b) = I_b + (l_b/m)(nm)^{\frac{1}{2}} \tag{29}$$

$$c(b \rightarrow \varepsilon) = D_b + (l_b/n)(nm)^{\frac{1}{2}} \tag{30}$$

$$c(b_1 \rightarrow b_2) = f(o_{b1}, o_{b2}) + |l_{b1}/n - l_{b2}/m|(nm)^{\frac{1}{2}} \tag{31}$$

where $n$ and $m$ denote the length of strings $x$ and $y$, respectively. In (29) $I_b$ denotes the costs for the non-attribute part of the operation, i.e. the costs for inserting symbol $b$, while the second term in the sum takes into account attribute costs. This is a generalization over (27) and (28) where no attribute costs are considered for insertions and deletions. The division of the length of the inserted symbol by the total length of string $y$ as well as the multiplication by $(nm)^{\frac{1}{2}}$ is for the purpose of normalization and weighting. The costs in (30) correspond to (29) for the case of deletion. In (31) $b_1$ denotes a symbol $b$ in string $x$ while $b_2$ represents its corresponding symbol in string $y$. Since there is only one symbol $b$, i.e. all symbols are identical, we have only costs concerning attribute differences but no symbol substitution costs in (31). The function $f(o_{b1}, o_{b2})$ evaluates the angular differences while the second term in the sum represents the difference in length, using again suitable normalization and weighting factors. Notice the correspondence between (31) and (28).

It is shown in Ref. 3 that edit operations affecting single symbols are not powerful enough to cope with the problem of shape recognition. Therefore, generalized substitutions according to Sec. 4.4 are proposed. The costs for the generalized edit operations are a straightforward extension of (29) to (31) and the algorithm for the computation of the resulting attributed string distance is based on (24) integrating attribute differences. The resulting shape recognition method has been tested and found suitable for the recognition of simple 2-D machine parts.

## 6. CONCLUSIONS

Matching of syntactic structures is a very important concept which may be a viable alternative to syntactic methods in a great variety of structural pattern recognition tasks. An important class of matching procedures is based on strings for pattern representation. String matching is conceptually simple and has the advantage of a low computational complexity. There is a broad spectrum of different versions of the basic string matching algorithm which may be suitable for many applications. However, strings are limited in their representational power due to their one-dimensional nature. For intrinsically higher-dimensional applications, pattern representations based on trees or graphs are perhaps more natural, and finally more efficient despite a greater computational complexity.

## REFERENCES

1. P.A. Devijver and J. Kittler, *Pattern Recognition: A Statistical Approach* (Prentice Hall, London, 1982).
2. D. Sankoff and J.R. Kruskal, *Time Warps, String Edits, and Macromolecules: The Theory and Practice of Sequence Comparison* (Addison Wesley, Reading, MA, 1983) Part. II, pp. 121-209.
3. W.H. Tsai and S.S. Yu, "Attributed string matching with merging for shape recognition", *IEEE Trans. PAMI* 7 (1985) 453-462.
4. K.S. Fu and S.Y. Lu, "A clustering procedure for syntactic patterns", *IEEE Trans. SMC* 7 (1977) 734-742.
5. D. Sankoff and J.R. Kruskal, *Time Warps, String Edits, and Macromolecules: The Theory and Practice of Sequence Comparison* (Addison Wesley, Reading, MA, 1983).
6. R.A. Wagner and M.J. Fischer, "The string-to-string correction problem", *J. ACM* 21 (1974) 168-173.
7. P.A.V. Hall and G.R. Dowling, "Approximate string matching", *Computing Surveys* 12 (1980) 381-402.
8. L.G. Shapiro, "The use of numerical relational distance and symbolic differences for organizing models and for matching", in *Techniques for 3-D Machine Perception*, ed. A. Rosenfeld (Elsevier Science Publ., 1986) pp. 255-270.
9. J.H. Friedman. *et al.*, "An algorithm for finding nearest neighbors", *IEEE Trans. Computers* 24 (1975) 1000-1006.
10. K. Fukunaga and P.M. Narendra, "A branch and bound algorithm for computing *k*-nearest neighbors", *IEEE Trans. Computers* 24 (1975) 750-753.
11. T.W. Sze and Y.H. Yang, "A simple contour matching algorithm", *IEEE Trans. PAMI* 3 (1981) 676-678.
12. K. Abe and N. Sugita, "Distances between strings of symbols – review and remarks", *Proc. 6th ICPR*, Munich, 1982, pp. 172-174.
13. J.B. Kruskal and M. Liberman, "The symmetric time-warping problem: From continuous to discrete", in Ref. 5, pp. 125-161.

14. M.J. Hung, M. Lennig and P. Mermelstein, "Use of dynamic programming in a syllable-based continuous speech recognition system", in Ref. 5, pp. 163-187.

15. J.B. Kruskal and D. Sankoff, "An anthology of algorithms and concepts for sequence comparison", in Ref. 5, pp. 265-310.

16. E. Tanaka, "A string correction method based on the context-dependent similarity", in *Syntactic and Structural Pattern Recognition, NATO ASI Series*, eds. G. Ferrate, T. Pavlidis, A. Sanfeliu and H. Bunke, (Springer, 1987) pp. 3-17.

17. W.J. Masek and M.S. Paterson, "A faster algorithm for computing string-edit distances", *J. Computer and System Sciences* **20** (1980)18-31.

18. K.S. Fu, "A step towards unification of syntactic and statistical pattern recognition", *IEEE Trans. PAMI* **5** (1983) 200-205.

# 6

---

# MATCHING TREE STRUCTURES

ALBERTO SANFELIU

*Instituto de Cibernética*
*Diagonal 647, 08028 Barcelona*
*Spain*

## 1. INTRODUCTION

One of the important elemental structures for describing complex objects for pattern recognition, for example, in scene recognition, speech understanding or ECG interpretation are trees. The description of structures by trees is more powerful than strings. This is useful in many cases where strings cannot be used to describe a complete structure, and from the point of view of analysis, trees are less expensive in time and space complexity than graphs. With respect to applications, trees have been used for character recognition[1], waveform correlation[2], 3-D object recognition[3], in areas such as behavioral science[4] and in other areas[5-8].

Tree structures are intermediate between strings and graphs, and a string or a graph can be transformed into a tree if some assumptions are taken into account. The string case is trivial as there is no need to consider any assumption, since a string is a tree with only one branch where the depth is the length of the string. The graph case is more complex, and basically two assumptions have to be taken into account in order to avoid generation of all possible combinations of graph nodes which lead to a combinatorial number of trees. The first assumption is to consider only planar graphs, which implies an order in the relative position of the nodes. The second assumption is to consider that one of the nodes of the graph can be always recognized for purposes of matching. Then the transformation of a graph into a tree can be done easily following a series of steps.

Since we can transform a graph into a tree, all algorithms to match trees are useful for graphs, although there is an important consideration to be borne in mind: if the root of the tree cannot be determined in the matching process, then all possible trees generated from the graph have to be considered. In this case, the interest of transforming a graph into a tree does not make sense.

In this chapter we will describe several techniques to match distorted trees by means of similarity measures between trees. For pattern recognition, these methods are of interest for classifying structures described by trees since the similarity measure is used as the decision rule in classification problems.

## 2. BASIC RESEARCH LINES IN TREE MATCHING

The description of an object or a family of objects (the meaning of an object is used in the broad sense) by tree structures can be done through the description of the direct relations between the primitive elements or by means of a generic tool which can generate or derive the relations between the elements. An example of the first group is shown in Fig. 1b, where the tree structure is constructed from the primitives which describe essential parts of the object and the relations between them. The second group can be generalized by a formal grammar, the production rules of which are used to derive the different tree structures of the object family (Fig. 1c). An interesting and important issue of the last group is the power to generate an infinite number of tree structures by using a reduced number of production rules.

For the purpose of recognition, the main issue is to find a similarity measure to match objects described by tree structures, in order to have a value which will be used for making the classification decision of the input object into one of the reference classes or into the rejected class. This matching process can be done by comparing the input tree (the object to be recognized) to the reference trees by means of the following methods:

1. Matching the input tree to each one of the trees of the other classes, that is, a tree to tree matching.

2. Computing the similarity measure between the input tree and the grammar of each one of the reference classes.

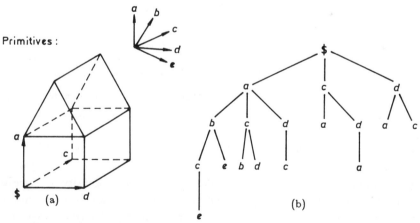

$$G_t = (V, r, P, s) \text{ over } \langle \Sigma, r \rangle$$
$$V = \{s, A_1, A_2, A_3, A_4, A_5, A_6, A_7, A_8, \$, a, b, c, d, e\}, \Sigma = \{\$, a, b, c, d, e\}$$
$$r(\$) = \{3\}, r(a) = \{3\}, r(b) = \{2\}, r(c) = \{1, 2\}, r(d) = \{1, 2\}$$

Fig. 1. (a) A house and the primitive structures; (b) the tree structure which describes the house.

P:

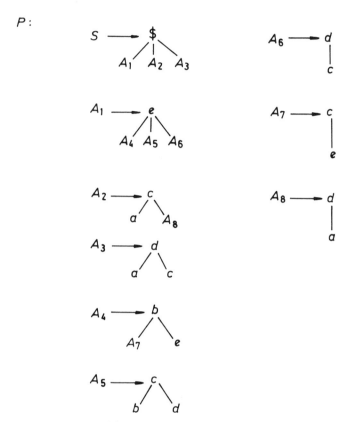

Fig. 1. Cont'd. (c) The tree grammar which generates the house.

The first group of techniques, tree to tree matching, has been studied by several researchers from the point of view of perfect matching (the isomorphism of tree to tree matching — from the general perspective of graph matching[9]), partial matching (finding the subtree matching — from the general perspective of graph matching[10]) and a generic matching between two different trees[4,11−19]. Perfect matching is used to identify if a tree is isomorphic to another tree of one of the reference classes. This type of matching can only be used to decide if a tree is isomorphic to another one, but we cannot obtain any numeric information about the similarity between the input tree and the references. Partial matching is used to know if a tree is a subtree of one of the reference classes or the reverse, which is useful for classification purposes, but cannot be applied to find out how similar they are.

Generic matching between two trees is used to compute a similarity value between the trees in order to know how similar one tree is with respect to the other tree. There are several ways of doing the matching and, moreover, for purposes of efficiency in time and space complexity, several restrictions are taken into account to reduce the time and space complexity. We will show some of these algorithms and the related complexity, in the following sections.

The second group of techniques, which computes the similarity measure between the input tree and the grammar of each one of the reference classes, is also used to obtain the similarity value between the input tree and the references, but in this case, instead of computing the similarity with each one of the structures of the reference classes, the only computation with the reference class is through the grammar[1]. This means that the number of computations for each class is always the same and it does not depend on the quantity of samples of the class, as for example, when there are many samples.

## 3. TREE TO TREE MATCHING

As we have commented in Sec. 1, we are going to describe only methods to match generic trees, that is, we will not describe the techniques for tree isomorphism or subtree matching, since we want to obtain similarity measures, which can be used as decision rules. The reason is that the similarity measure will be useful to classify the input tree into one of the reference classes or into the reject class, although the input class does not fit exactly with any of the reference models. This kind of matching implies that the similarity measure must distinguish between tree which are distorted with respect to any of the reference models.

The distortions of a tree structure have been divided into two groups of categories in order to obtain efficient algorithms from the point of view of time and space complexity. These two categories correspond to local and structural distortions. The first category includes the trees which differ only in the labels of the subtrees, but which preserve the structure with respect to the reference trees. The second category includes any modification in the structure and/or in the labels of the subtrees with respect to the reference structures.

### 3.1. Matching Trees with Local Distortions

Figure 2 shows the matching of two trees which preserve the structure, but which have different node labels. In this case the matching is reduced to find the subtrees which have different labels and to compute a similarity measure based on the weight or the probability associated to each one of the labels of the subtrees. The first step, the matching of the structure, is trivial, since the structure of the tree is not changed (Fig. 2), and there is an exact correspondence between the position of every subtree.

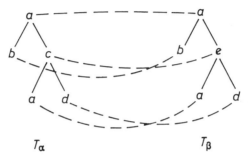

Fig. 2. Mapping two trees with local distortions.

Then, the problem is reduced to find the labels that do not match the ones of the reference tree and to apply a similarity measure. There are different ways to do this matching, but basically this is a typical problem of the theoretic decision methods in pattern recognition[20]. Before proceeding with the similarity measure we are going to define some terms.

Let $T_\alpha$ be a tree and $x_i \in T_\alpha$ ($1 \leq i \leq n$, where $n$ is the number of nodes of $T_\alpha$) the components or labels of the $T_\alpha$ subtrees $(T_\alpha(i))$. Let $y_i$ be the components of the $T_\beta$ tree. The cost of substituting the label $x_i$ with $y_i$ is defined as $c(x_i \rightarrow y_i) \geq 0$. Since the structure is preserved, the preorder of the nodes of trees $T_\alpha$ and $T_\beta$ is the same, which implies that $i = j$ and $c(x_i \rightarrow y_i)$. Then the cost of label substitution is

$$c(x_i \rightarrow y_i) \geq 0 \qquad (1)$$

in all cases except when $x_i = y_i$. In this case $c(x_i \rightarrow y_i) = 0$. Usually the values of $c(x_i \rightarrow y_i)$ are taken to be in the interval $[0,1]$ for normalizing purposes.

Following the same idea applied to the string case, we can define a similarity measure as a distance measure as follows,

$$d(T_\alpha, T_\beta) = \sum_{i=1}^{n} w_i c(x_i \to y_i) \qquad (2)$$

where $w_i$ is the weight of the cost of substituting the element $i$. This distance measure is a metric when the weight $w_i$ is constant, independent of any value of $i$ (the typical value is $\frac{1}{n}$). In order to normalize this distance measure, the cost of substitution $c$ must be in the interval $[0,1]$, and

$$\sum_{i=1}^{n} w_i = 1 .$$

This distance measure can be used to decide to which class the input tree belongs. A classical classification technique is the K-NN (K-nearest neighbor) classifier, which has been presented for the string case. Let $D_k(T_I)$ be the minimum distance between the input tree and the trees of the class $C_k$, i.e.

$$D_k(T_I) = \min\{d(T_I, T_i)\} \quad (i = 1, \dots, N) . \qquad (3)$$

If there are only two classes $C_1$ and $C_2$ the decision rule for the input tree $T_I$ is:

$$T_I \in \begin{cases} C_1, & \text{if and only if } D_1(T_I) \leq D_2(T_I) \\ C_2, & \text{otherwise} \end{cases} . \qquad (4)$$

Following some criterion of the previous distance measure, we can define another similarity measure based on the product of probabilities. In this case, the cost of substitution is defined as

$$c(x_i \to y_i) = P(x_i \to y_i) \qquad (5)$$

where $P(x_i \to y_i)$ is the probability of substituting $x_i$ with $y_i$. This probability over the different symbols of $y_i$ must be equal to 1, that is $\sum_{j=1}^{m} P(x_i \to y_i) = 1$, where $m$ indicates the number of different symbols which belong to the element $y_i$. For example, let $a, b, c$ be the possible symbols of $y_i$, and let $x_i$ be equal to the symbol $a$, then $P(a \to a) = 0.8$, $P(a \to b) = 0.1, P(a \to c) = 0.1$.

With this cost definition, the distance measure can be defined as

$$d(T_\alpha, T_\beta) = \prod_{i=1}^{n} P(x_i \to y_i) . \qquad (6)$$

The value obtained in this distance measure has the reverse meaning of the aforementioned measure since the highest value corresponds to the best matching between the input tree and the reference one. The difference with respect to classification is that the input tree will belong to the class with higher probability.

Both distance measures only depend on the number of symbols of one of the trees, since both trees always have the same structure. Therefore, the time complexity is proportional to the number of nodes of the tree, i.e. $O_T(N)$.

## 4. THE TREE TO TREE MATCHING PROBLEM BASED ON EDIT OPERATIONS

There have been several studies in matching trees, but basically the methods which became most popular are those based on edit operations, because it is a natural way of comparing two structures[21]. The idea of these methods is to compute a distance measure by means of calculating the number of modifications to transform the input tree into a reference tree. The computation is done on a node to node basis, where there is no *a priori* knowledge about the substructures of the trees, therefore the mapping between both tree does not need any special function.

The tree correction problem which is based on edit operations to transform a tree into another tree needs five basic operations, namely: node insertion, node deletion, node label substitution, node merging and node splitting. The five operations can be seen as illustrated by examples in Fig. 3. The notations are: $c(t(i) \rightarrow t(j))$ for node label substitution $(t(i)$ into $t(j))$; $c(t(i) \rightarrow \wedge)$ for node deletion; $c(\wedge \rightarrow t(j))$ for node insertion; $c(t(i) \rightarrow \text{split } t(i))$ for node splitting; and $c(t(i), t(i) \rightarrow \text{merge into } t(i))$ for merging two nodes, where $t(i)$ and $t(j)$ are the node labels of a tree and $\wedge$ is the empty symbol. With these operations we can define a distance measure which is formulated as follows:

$$d(T_\alpha, T_\beta) = \min\{r(s)|s \text{ is a sequence of edit}$$
$$\text{operations which transform } T_\alpha \text{ into } T_\beta\} \qquad (7)$$

where $r(s)$ is the edit operation (Fig. 3). This distance measure is defined as the minimum number of applied operations to transform a tree into another tree, where the minimum is taken since there could be many different paths to reach the reference tree from the input tree by using those operations.

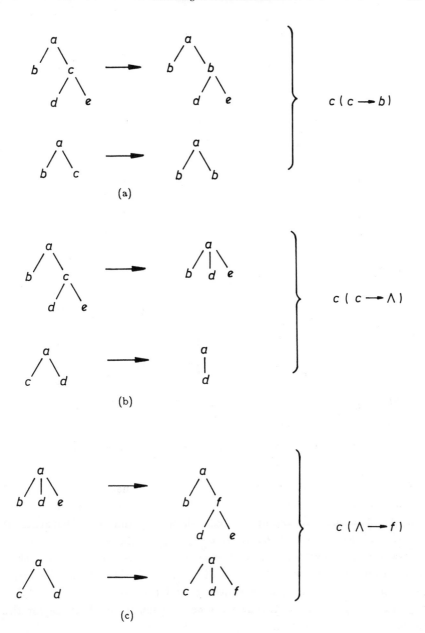

Fig. 3. Examples of the five edit operations. (a) Substitution of a node label; (b) deletion of a node; (c) insertion of a node.

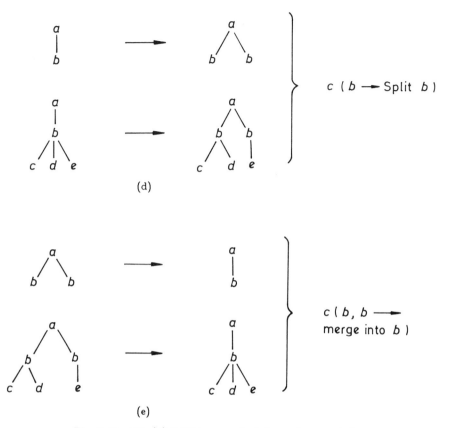

(d)

(e)

Fig. 3. Cont'd. (d) Splitting a node; (e) merging two nodes.

Indeed, the number of paths is infinite, but by eliminating the paths which reach a known state and including some restrictions, there are only a finite number of paths. For example, Fig. 4 shows two different derivations to transform tree $T_\alpha$ into $T_\beta$ by applying the operations of Fig. 3. The first derivation needs five consecutive operations, two node deletions and three node insertions, and the distance is $d(T_\alpha, T_\beta) = 5$. The second derivation only uses one operation, node splitting, and the distance is $d(T_\alpha, T_\beta) = 1$. Although there are other derivations, the minimum distance for this example is the second one.

The distance measure defined before always exists since a tree can be transformed into any other by means of a finite number of operations, and

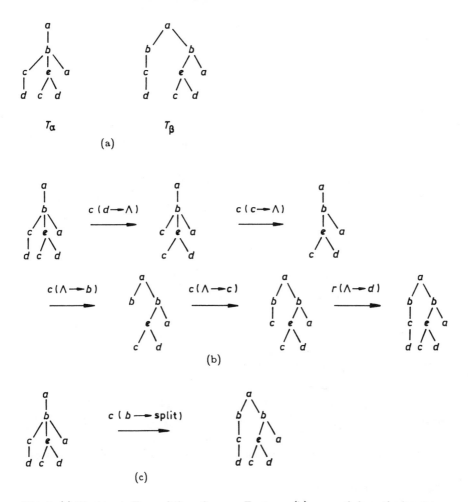

Fig. 4. (a) The input, $T_\alpha$, and the reference, $T_\beta$, trees; (b) one path from the input tree to the reference tree by applying insertion and deletion edit operations $d(T_\alpha, T_\beta) = 5$; (c) the minimum cost solution through a split edit operation, $d(T_\alpha, T_\beta) = 1$.

as we will see later, in some cases, this distance measure is a metric. An important problem of these techniques is that the time complexity and space complexity could be very high. In general, this computation can be formulated as a state-space search problem, where the input tree $(T_\alpha)$ is the initial state, the reference tree $(T_\beta)$ is the final state, and the five operations defined before are the operators. The upper bound of the time complexity can be computed as follows. If the size of $T_\alpha$ is $N$, and the distance between both trees is $d$, then a breath-first search will take approximately $O((5N)^d)$ operations to reach the optimal path. This result leads to the conclusion that the time complexity is too high and that it cannot be used if there are no other algorithms to compute the similarity measure.

In the next sections, we will describe two groups of methods which reduce significantly the time and space complexity, although they are restricted versions of the general one. The first group of techniques only considers the first three operations (node deletion, node insertion and node label substitution). We will describe the method developed by Tai[15], and an improved method of the Tai distance developed by Tanaka[17]. The second group is applied to unlabeled trees and only takes into account the splitting and merge node operations, although these are split into two additional operations[12].

## 4.1. A Tree to Tree Matching Method by Node Deletion, Node Insertion and Node Label Substitution

### 4.1.1. Basic idea

One of the basic methods for tree matching was developed by Tai[15], where the three edit operations were considered: node deletion, node insertion, and node label substitution. The distance measure $D(T_\alpha, T_\beta)$ is defined as the minimum sequence of edit operations needed to transform the input tree $(T_\alpha)$ into the reference one $(T_\beta)$. The algorithm has a time complexity of $O_T(N_\alpha N_\beta D_\alpha^2 D_\beta^2)$, where $N_\alpha$ and $N_\beta$ are the number of nodes of the trees, and $D_\alpha$ and $D_\beta$, the depths of the trees.

Before we proceed to explain the algorithm, let us define our notation which will be used in the rest of the chapter, although later on, some new notation will be introduced.

From now onwards, all trees are labeled ordered trees, where $T_\alpha$ is the input tree, and $T_\beta$ is the reference tree or the tree to match. A direct descendant of a node (the son) is denoted by $s(i)$, and a direct ancestor of a node (the father) is denoted by $f(i)$ ($f^2(i)$ is equivalent to $f(f(i))$). The number of nodes of a subtree with root $i$ is denoted by $N(i)$. The label of the node $i$ is $t(i)$. The leftmost leaf of subtree $i$ is denoted by $el(i)$, the number of leaves of a subtree $i$ by $L(i)$ ($L$ is the abbreviation of $L(1)$), and a leaf is denoted by *leaf(i)*. Finally, the depth of the tree $T$ is $D(i)$. Any of these symbols with a subscript $\alpha$ or $\beta$ relates to the symbol of the trees $T_\alpha$ or $T_\beta$ respectively.

The edit operations and cost are the following

Insertion:     $c(\wedge \rightarrow t(i)) = q$
Deletion:      $c(t(i) \rightarrow \wedge) = p$
Substitution: $c(t(i) \rightarrow t(j)) = r$

For example, in Fig. 5, $N(1) = 10, L(3) = 2, s(2) = \{3,6\}, f(3) = \{2\}, t(5) = \{C\}, leaf(6) = \{8,9\}$ and $el(2) = \{4\}.$

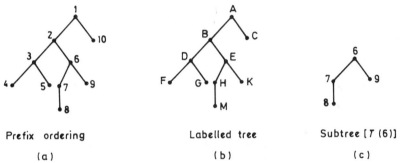

Prefix ordering                    Labelled tree                    Subtree [T (6)]

(a)                                (b)                              (c)

Fig. 5. Tree notations: (a) Prefix ordering; (b) labeled tree; (c) subtree $T(6)$.

Let us now define the mapping conditions of the Tai distance. A mapping in the tree correction problem is a description of how a sequence of edit operations transform $T_\alpha$ into $T_\beta$ without considering the order of the applied edit operations. For example, Fig. 6 shows a mapping which can be described as follows.

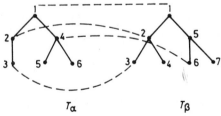

$T_\alpha$                    $T_\beta$

Fig. 6. The mapping $M$ between trees.

A line connecting $t_\alpha(i)$ to $t_\beta(j)$ means that $t_\alpha(i)$ should be changed to $t_\beta(j)$ if $t_\alpha(i) \neq t_\beta(j)$, but $t_\alpha(i)$ remains unchanged as $t_\beta(j)$, if $t_\alpha(i) = t_\beta(j)$. Nodes of $T_\alpha$ which are not connected by a line must be deleted, and nodes of $T_\beta$ not touched must be inserted. We define a mapping from $T_\alpha$ to $T_\beta$ as $M : T_\alpha \rightarrow T_\beta$ where $M$ is the set of pairs of integers $(i,j)$ which satisfy:

1. $1 \leq i \leq N_\alpha, 1 \leq j \leq N_\beta$

2. For any two pairs $(i_1, j_1)$ and $(i_2, j_2) \in M$
   (a) $i_1 = i_2$ iff $j_1 = j_2$
   (b) $i_1 < i_2$ iff $j_1 = j_2$
   (c) $t_\alpha(i_1)$ is an ancestor (descendant) of $t_\alpha(i_2)$ iff $t_\beta(j_1)$ is an ancestor (descendant) of $t_\beta(j_2)$.

With these definitions we can describe the method which is explained in depth in Ref. 15.

As we have previously defined

$$d(T_\alpha, T_\beta) = \min\{\text{cost}(s) | s \text{ is a sequence of}$$
$$\text{edit operations which transforms } T_\alpha \text{ into } T_\beta\}. \qquad (8)$$

Then, because of our definition of a mapping:

$$d(T_\alpha, T_\beta) = \min\{\text{cost}(M) | M \text{ is a mapping from } T_\alpha \text{ to } T_\beta\}. \qquad (9)$$

The Tai distance measure is a metric if the cost of insertion and deletion have the same weight, i.e. $p = q$. Let $D(i, j) = d(T_\alpha(i), T_\beta(j))$, then at least one of the following three cases must hold:

1. $T_\beta(j)$ is substituted by $T_\alpha(i)$.
2. One subtree of $T_\beta(j)$ is substituted by $T_\alpha(i)$.
3. $T_\beta(j)$ is substituted by one subtree of $T_\alpha(i)$.

The three cases are shown in Fig. 7. The first case means that $T_\beta(j)$ must be substituted by $T_\alpha(i)$, that is $T_\beta(j)$ will be substituted by the minimum number of edit operations from the subtree $T_\alpha(i)$ which will be denoted by $MIN\_M(i, j)$. The computation of this value consists in the cost of substituting node $j$ by node $i, c(t_\alpha(i) \to t_\beta(j))$, and the cost of mapping the rest of the subtrees $T_\alpha(i)$ into $T_\beta(j)$.

The last cost can be divided into the following three parts:

(i) The cost of matching nodes from $T_\alpha(1)$ to $T_\alpha(s)$, into $T_\beta(1)$ to $T_\beta(t)$.
(ii) The cost of matching the nodes from $T_\alpha(s)$ to $T_\alpha(i-1)$, into $T_\beta(t)$ to $T_\beta(j-1)$, where any descendant of $T_\alpha(s)(T_\beta(t)$ to $T_\alpha(f(i)))(T_\beta(f(j)))$ is not connected by a line of a mapping.
(iii) The cost of substituting the nodes $s$ and $t, c(t_\alpha(s) \to t_\beta(t))$.

The minimum cost between these three parts plus the substitution of the label of $i, j$ is the solution of $MIN\_M(i, j)$. For more details refer to Ref. 15.

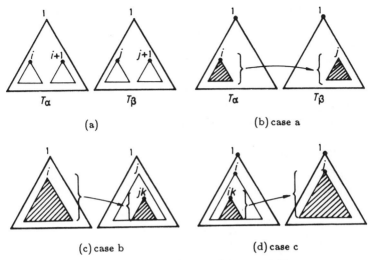

(a)                              (b) case a

(c) case b                    (d) case c

Fig. 7. The three main steps in tree matching.

The second case means that a subtree $T_\beta(j_k)$ is substituted by a subtree $T_\alpha(i)$ which implies insertion of the nodes from the subtree $T_\beta(j)$ and computation of the distance $D(i, j - 1)$. Then the computation can be formulated as follows:

$$D(i, j - 1) + c(\wedge \rightarrow t_\beta(j)) . \qquad (10)$$

The third case means that the subtree $T_\beta(j)$ is substituted by a subtree $T_\alpha(i_k)$, which is nothing but to delete the nodes from the subtree $T_\alpha(i)$ and to compute the distance $D(i - 1, j)$. This can be formulated as follows:

$$D(i - 1, j) + c(t_\alpha(i) \rightarrow \wedge) . \qquad (11)$$

These three cases are the basic ones to compute the distance measure between trees. The algorithm is shown below.

### 4.1.2. The algorithm

The Tai distance measure is computed in three steps:

1. Compute $E[s : u : i, t : v : j]$ for all $s, u, i, t, v, j$, where $E[s : u : i, t : v : j]$ is defined as:

   $\min\{\text{cost}(M) | M$ is a mapping from nodes $T_\alpha(s)$ to $T_\alpha(i)$, with $T_\beta(t)$ to $T_\beta(j)$ such that $(s, t) \in M$ and no descendant of $T_\alpha(s)(T_\beta(t))$ on the path from $T_\alpha(s)(T_\beta(t))$ to $T_\alpha(u)(T_\beta(v))$ is connected by a line $M$}.

2. Compute $MIN\_M(i,j)$ for all $i,j$.

3. Compute $D(i,j)$ for all $i,j$.

where $1 \leq i \leq N_\alpha, 1 \leq j \leq N\beta$.

The detailed algorithm is as follows

Step 1 has the following form:

**for** $i = 1, 2, \ldots, N_\alpha$
**for** $j = 1, 2, \ldots, N_\beta$
**for** $u = i, f(i), f^2(i), \ldots, 1$ **do**
**for** $s = u, f(u), f^2(u), \ldots, 1$ **do**
**for** $v = j, f(j), f^2(j), \ldots, 1$ **do**
**for** $t = v, f(v), f^2(v), \ldots, 1$ **do**
**if** $s = u = i$ and $t = v = j$ **then** $E[s : u : i, t : v : j] = c(t_\alpha(i) \rightarrow t_\beta(j))$
**else if** $s = u = i$ **or** $t < v = j$ **then** $E[s : u : i, t : v : j]$
    $= E[s : u : i, t : f(j) : j - 1] + c(\wedge \rightarrow t\beta(j))$
**else if** $s < u = i$ **or** $t = v = j$ **then** $E[s : u : i, t : v : j]$
    $= E[s : f(i) : i - 1, t : v : j] + c(t_\alpha(i) \rightarrow \wedge)$
**else if** $E[s : u : i, t : v : j] = \min\{E[s : x : i, t : v : j],$
    $E[s : u : i, t : y : j], E[s : u : x - 1, t : v : j - 1] + E[x : x : i, y : y : j]$

Step 2 is the following

**for** $i = 2, 3, \ldots, N_\alpha$ **do**
  **for** $j = 2, 3, \ldots, N_\beta$ **do**
  **begin**
    $MIN\_M(i,j) \leftarrow$ INFINITE
    **for** $s = f(i), f^2(i), \ldots, 1$ **do**
      **for** $t = f(j), f^2(j), \ldots, 1$ **do**
      **begin**
        $temp \leftarrow MIN\_M(s,t) + E[s : f(i) : i - 1, t : f(j) : j - 1]$
          $-c(t_\alpha(s) \rightarrow t_\beta(t));$
        $MIN\_M(i,j) \leftarrow \min(temp, MIN\_M(i,j))$
      **end**
      $MIN\_M(i,j) \leftarrow MIN_M(i,j) + c(t_\alpha(i) \rightarrow t_\beta(j))$
  **end;**

The last step is given below:

$$D(1,1) \leftarrow 0$$
$$D(i,1) \leftarrow D(i-1,1) + c(t_\alpha(i) \rightarrow \wedge) \text{ for } i = 2, 3, \ldots, N_\alpha;$$
$$D(1,j) \leftarrow D(1,j-1) + c(\wedge \leftarrow t_\beta(j)) \text{ for } j = 2, 3, \ldots, N_\beta;$$
**for** $i = 2, 3, \ldots, N_\alpha$ **do**
**for** $j = 2, 3, \ldots, N_\beta$ **do**
$$D(i,j) \leftarrow \min\{D(i,j-1) + c(\wedge \rightarrow t_\beta(j)), D(i-1,j) + c(t_\alpha(i) \rightarrow \wedge),$$
$$MIN_M(i,j)\};$$

This algorithm has a time complexity of $O_T(N_\alpha N_\beta D_\alpha^2 D_\beta^2)$, and a space complexity of $O_S(N_\alpha N_\beta D_\alpha^2 D_\beta^2)$.

## 4.2. An Efficient Tree to Tree Correction Method

### 4.2.1. Basic idea

There have been other words improving the time and space complexity of the Tai metric. Aoki[22] developed a top-down method which has a time complexity of $O_T(N_\alpha N_\beta D_\alpha D_\beta)$, and recently Tanaka[17] designed a method which has a time complexity of $O_T(N_\alpha N_\beta L_\alpha^2)$ or $O_T(N_\alpha N_\beta L_\beta^2)$ and a space complexity of $O_s(N_\alpha N_\beta L_\alpha)$ or $O_S(N_\alpha N_\beta L_\beta)$, where $D_\alpha$ and $D_\beta$ are the depth of the trees, and $L_\alpha$ and $L_\beta$, the number of leaves of the trees. We are going to explain the last method.

The Tanaka approach is a bottom-up method applied to rooted, ordered and labeled trees. The method follows the same ideas explained in the Tai metric but rearranges the operations applied to subtrees in order to profit from the restrictions due to the leaves of one of the trees.

The main disadvantage of Tai's method is that all possible distances between subtrees must be computed when $T_\beta(j)$ is substituted by $T_\alpha(i)$. This implies calculation of a huge number of distance values between subtrees which are not necessary since they are included in other computations.

Tanaka's method used two strategies to reduce the number of computed subtree distances. The first one is to rearrange the algorithm using dynamic programming from the leaves to the root, and the second one is to use the restrictions imposed by the leaves of one of the trees. In this way, the method starts from bottom to the top computing the distance values between the leaves of one tree and the subtrees of the other tree, and then from the subtrees of the first tree to the other subtrees of the second tree, until $D(1,1)$ is reached. The search of the minimum cost is improved by arranging the computed distances as a matrix where the highest leftmost coordinates are $(m+1, z+1)$ and the lowest rightmost coordinates are $(0, 1)$. In this way, the computation of the distance from $T_\alpha(i)$ to the forest $F_\beta(j, z)$ (a forest is a subgraph which contains only the nodes between the limits $j$ and $z$ (Fig. 8)) is equivalent to the computation of the shortest route from $m+1, z+1)$ to $(0, j)$.

(a) $T_\alpha$          (b) Forest $F(3, 9)$

Fig. 8. (a) Prefix ordering; (b) the forest $F(3,9)$.

The method consists of four parts (see Fig. 9 for clarification of the method):

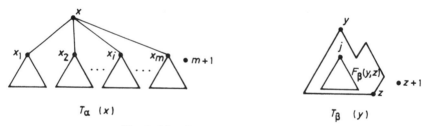

$T_\alpha(x)$          $T_\beta(y)$

Fig. 9. Mapping subtrees to a forest.

1. Computation of the boundaries $(1 \le i \le m; 1 \le j \le z + 1)$

    (a) $d(m+1, j) = (z + 1 - j)*q$
    (b) $d(i, z+1) = d(i + 1, z + 1) + N_\alpha(x_i)*p$
    (c) $d(0, z+1) = d(1, z+1) + p$

    The first formula, (a), computes the number of insertions to be made to insert all nodes that are missing from $z + 1$ to $j$. The second formula, (b), computes the nodes which cannot be matched from $T_\alpha(x_i)$ to $T_\beta(y)$.

2. Computation of $d(i, j)$ where $1 \leq i \leq m, 1 \leq j \leq z$.

$$d(i, j) = \min \begin{cases} d(i, j + 1) + q \\ d(i + 1, j) + N_\alpha(x_i) * p \\ d(i + 1, l_1 + 1) + D(x_i; j, l_1) \\ d(i + 1, l_2 + 1) + D(x_i; j, l_2) \\ \quad\vdots \\ d(i + 1, l_s + 1) + D(x_i; j, l_s) \end{cases}$$

where $l_1 < l_2 < \ldots < l_s \leq z$ and each $l_i$ is a leaf.

The computation of $d(i, j)$ is obtained from the minimum value of the following three groups of computations:

• $d(i, j+1)+q$ is the insertion of node $j$ plus the value of the distance from $i$ to $j + 1$.

• $d(i + 1, j) + N_\alpha(x_i) * r$ is the deletion of the nodes of the subtree $N_\alpha(x_i)$ plus the distance from $i + 1$ to $j$.

• $d(i + 1, l_k + 1) + D(x_i; j, l_k)$ where $1 \leq k \leq s$, is the computation of the distance between the subtree $T_\alpha(x_i)$ and the forest $F(x_i; j, l_k)$ plus the distance from $i + 1$ to $l_k + 1$.

3. Computation of $d(0, j)(1 \leq j \leq z + 1)$

$$d(0, j) = \min \begin{cases} d(0, j + 1) + q \\ d(1, j) + p \\ d(1, j + 1) + \delta(x, j) \end{cases}$$

where

$$\delta(x, j) = \begin{cases} 0 \text{ if } j \in An(z + 1) \text{ and } t_\alpha(x) = t_\beta(j) \\ p \text{ if } j \in An(z + 1) \text{ and } t_\alpha(x) \neq t_\beta(j) \\ \inf \text{ if } j \neq An(z + 1) \end{cases}$$

where $\inf > q + r$ and $An(z + 1)$ are all the ancestors of $z + 1$.

The computation of $d(0, j)$ is just to consider the three edit operations of insertion, deletion or substitution.

4. Computation of $D(x; y, z)(1 \leq y \leq z)$

$$D(x; y, z) = d(0, y) .$$

### 4.2.2. The algorithm

The Tanaka algorithm is described below in detail

**for** $k := 1$ **to** $L_\beta$ **do**
**begin**
 $z := leaf_\beta$;
  **for** $x := N_\alpha$ **downto** 1 **do**
  $D1(x, 1, z, D(x; 1, z))$;
**end**;
$D(T_\alpha, T_\beta) := D(1 : 1, N_\beta)$;

where $D1(x, z, D(x; 1, z))$ is computed as follows:

**for** $j := z + 1$ **downto** 1 **do** $d(m + 1, j) := (z + 1 - j) * q$;
**if** $m \neq 0$ **then do**
**begin**
 **for** $i : m$ **downto** 1 **do**
 $d(i, z + 1) := d(i + 1, z + 1) + N_\alpha(x_i) * r$;
 **for** $i := m$ **downto** 1 **do**
 **for** $j : z$ **downto** 1 **do**
 **begin**
 $\delta(1) := d(i, j + 1) + q$;
 $\delta(2) := d(i + 1, j) + N_\alpha(x_i) * r$;
 $\delta(3) := d(i + 1, l_1 + 1) + D(x_i; j, l_1)$;
 $\delta(4) := d(i + 1, l_2 + 1) + D(x_i; j, l_2)$;
 $\vdots$
 $\delta(s + 2) := d(i + 1, l_s + 1) + D(x_i; j, l_s)$;
 $d(i, j) := \min(\delta(1), \delta(2), \ldots, \delta(s + 2))$;
 **end**
**end**
**for** $j := z$ **downto** 1 **do**
**begin**
 $\delta(1) := d(0, j + 1) + q$;
 $\delta(2) := d(1, j) + r$;
  **if** $j \in An(z + 1)$ **then**
   **if** $t_\alpha(x) = t_\alpha$ **then** $\gamma(x, j) := 0$
   **else** $\gamma(x, j) := p$
  **if** $j \neq An(z + 1)$ **then** $\gamma(x, j) := \inf$
 $\delta(3) := d(1, j + 1) + \gamma(x, j)$;

**end;**

**for** $j := z$ **downto** 1 **do**
$D(x; j, z) := d(0, j);$

The time complexity of the algorithm is $O_T(N_\alpha N_\beta L_\alpha^2)$ if we take the leaves from tree $T_\alpha$, and $O_T(N_\alpha N_\beta L_\beta^2)$ in the other case, and the space complexity is $O_T(N_\alpha N_\beta L_\alpha)$ or $O_T(N_\alpha N_\beta L_\beta)$, respectively.

### 4.3. A Tree Matching Algorithm Based on Node Splitting and Merging

#### 4.3.1. Basic idea

The three basic operations insertion, deletion and substitution of a node are not sufficient for the general case of the correction problem since in some situations two additional operations must be taken into account. These operations have been previously commented on and they are node splitting and node merging. Figure 4 shows the result of computing the distance measure between two trees by considering only the first three edit operations (Fig. 4b) and the five operations (Fig. 4c). As it is shown in Fig. 4, the distance $d(T_\alpha, T_\beta)$ obtained in the first case is equal to 5, while in the second case it is equal to 1. Then, we can conclude that including the two additional edit operations allows us to obtain better results for some problems.

A method which considers four of these operations on unlabeled trees has been proposed by Lu[12]. This method includes the general operations except the substitution of the node labels. The method is explained below.

The method uses four edit operations which are described in Fig. 10. Looking carefully at these operations we can observe that they include node insertion and deletion for unlabeled trees, which can be seen as a generalization of the method proposed by Tai.

The idea of the method is that in order to establish a match between the trees $T_\alpha$ and $T_\beta$, first we have to study the matches of each subtree rooted at a son of $a$ (we will denote the subtree of $T_\alpha$ as $a/T_\alpha$ where $a$ is the root of the subtree). Then, we combine the $n$ matches of the $n$ sons of $a$, and we compute the minimum cost of matching for the subtree rooted at $a$.

Before explaining the method let us go on to introduce some new concepts. A region in $T_\alpha$ is denoted by $\tau_T(a, b)$ where $a \leq b$ is a set of nodes of $T$ such that $x \in \tau_T(a, b)$ if $a \leq x \leq b$. The nearest common predecessor (NCP) of all nodes in $\tau_T(a, b)$, is the root of a subtree $s/T$ such that, $s$ is the

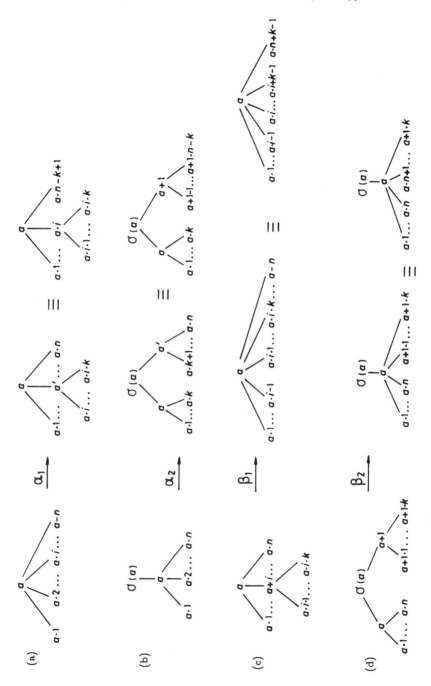

Fig. 10. The four edit operations in the splitting and merging tree matching.

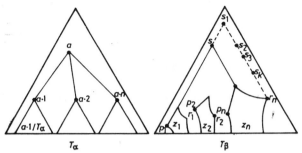

Fig. 11. Mapping subtrees to regions.

common predecessor of all nodes in $\tau_T(a,b)$. Finally, a region is *consistent* if the following holds true:

1. $\tau_T(p_i, r_i)$ and $\tau_T(p_i, r_i)$ do not overlap for $1 \le i; j \le n, i \ne j$.
2. Any node in $\tau_T(p_i, r_i)$ does not have predecessor-descendant relations with any node in $\tau_T(p_j, r_j), i \ne j$.

The algorithm developed by Lu performs the operations in an efficient way by means of a divide-and-conquer strategy.

The divide strategy is used to match a subtree of $T_\alpha$ to a region in $T_\beta$. In this process two cases can happen: the match is between the subtree of $T_\alpha$ and a region $\tau_{T_\beta}(p, r)$ or the match is between the subtree and an empty region as a result of splitting and merging. To compute the distance measure, the divide strategy means that the matching between a subtree of $T_\alpha$ and a region of $T_\beta$ is reduced to matching the sons of the subtree of $T_\alpha$ to each one of the regions of $T_\beta$ which match them and are consistent.

This concept is illustrated in Fig. 11 where the $n$ regions are consistent. With all the possible matchings between subtrees of $T_\alpha$ and regions of $T_\beta$ the last problem is to find the minimum region which covers all the $n$ regions in $T_\beta$, for each subtree.

The conquer strategy resolves this last step; computing the distance between a subtree and the minimum cover for the $n$ regions in $T_\beta$. The first step is to find the NCP, $s$, for the $n$ regions, and the second is to compute the minimum number of operations to match $a/T_\alpha$ into the region $\tau_{T_\beta}(p_1, r_n)$ (Fig. 11). Then the distance measure for $\tau_{T_\beta}(p_1, T_j), j = 1, \ldots, J$ is:

$$d = \sum_{i=1}^{n} d_i + (|\tau_{T_\beta}(p_1, r_n)| - \sum_{i=1}^{n} |\tau_{T_\beta}(p_i, r_i)|) + 2 * J - 1 . \qquad (12)$$

In this equation, the first term is the total distance of mapping $n$ subtrees $a/T_\alpha$, to $n$ regions $\tau_{T_\beta}(p_i, r_i)$. The second term is the cost for merging needed to remove the nodes which do not belong to the $n$ regions in the cover region. Finally, the third term is the number of splitting and merging operations used to shift $n-1$ regions from being the sons of $s$ to being the sons of $s_j, j = 1, \ldots, J$ or of $r_n$.

With these two strategies the matching can be calculated in polynomial time.

### 4.3.2. The algorithm

The implementation of the algorithm has been done in a recursive way and follows the strategy described previously. The algorithm has a time complexity of $O_T(NM^2)$, where $N$ and $M$ are the respective sizes of both trees.

The steps of the algorithm are the following:

1. Compute all the distances between a leaf of $T_\alpha$ and a subtree of $T_\beta$, i.e. $d(a, b/T_\beta)$. The result is stored in a $K$-stack with three values, the limits of the region in $T_\beta$ and the value of the distance. For example, if the region is a leaf of $T_\beta$, $b$, then the distance is zero and will be described as $(b, b, 0)$, but if the region is a subtree $c/T_\beta$, the distance will be

$$d = |c/T_\beta| - 1$$

   and its description will be $(c, e, d)$ where $e$ is the end of the region.

2. Compute the distance between a subtree of $T_\alpha$, $ai/T_\alpha$ and a subtree of $T_\beta$, $b/T_\beta$. The results are incorporated in the $K$-stack. This step is recursively computed where Step 1 is called, when necessary.

3. Check the regions for consistency and discard all the regions where an inconsistency is found. Moreover, arrange the $K$-stack with the lowest cost at the top.

4. Find the NCP which covers the regions.

5. Given the region $W = (p_1, r_n, d)$ that covers the $n$ sons, and the NCP of these regions, $s$, compute the number of mergings needed to make $(p_i, s_j, d_j)$ be a cover for the $n$ sons. This step finds the minimum cover subtree of the $n$ regions, that is the minimum distance for that cover.

6. Until no more subtrees on $T_\beta$ exist, go to Step 2.

7. Obtain the minimum cost.

The detailed algorithm is described in Ref. 12.

## 5. A TREE TO TREE-GRAMMAR MATCHING

The methods explained above were applied to tree to tree matching. Now, we are going to extend the matching to the case of tree to tree-grammar matching, where the tree grammar generates a language, the terminal structures of which are trees. This technique is more powerful that tree to tree matching as far as pattern recognition is concerned, since it allows us to compute the distance measure between the input tree and a family of trees generated by a formal grammar. If a class is identified by a grammar, then this technique does not require looking for the distance measure between every tree that belongs to the class, but to the grammar which generates them.

### 5.1. Error-Correcting Tree Automata

#### 5.1.1. Basic idea

Lu and Fu[1] developed a technique for tree to tree-automata matching based on edit operations. They used the following: substitution, stretch, branch, split and deletion of nodes. The definition of these operations is as follows (Fig. 12):

1. Substitution: the substitution of the label of a node by another terminal symbol $(c(a_i \rightarrow y))$.
2. Stretch: the insertion of an extraneous labeled node between a node and its immediate predecessor $(c(a \rightarrow y \text{ over } a))$.
3. Branch: the insertion of an extraneous labeled node to the left of all the immediate successors of a node $(c(a \rightarrow y \text{ leftmost } a))$.
4. Split: the insertion of an extraneous labeled node to the right of a node $(c(a \rightarrow y \text{ right } a))$.
5. Deletion: the deletion of a node of rank 1 or 0 $(c(a \rightarrow \wedge))$.

The method uses the same idea shown in the previous processes although the edit operations are now incorporated in the grammar rules. The edit operations are included as new rules with some modifications as we will see later on. With these rules, the grammar can generate not only trees of its language, but also other trees where all the possible errors (we call errors the differences between the input tree and the trees generated by the

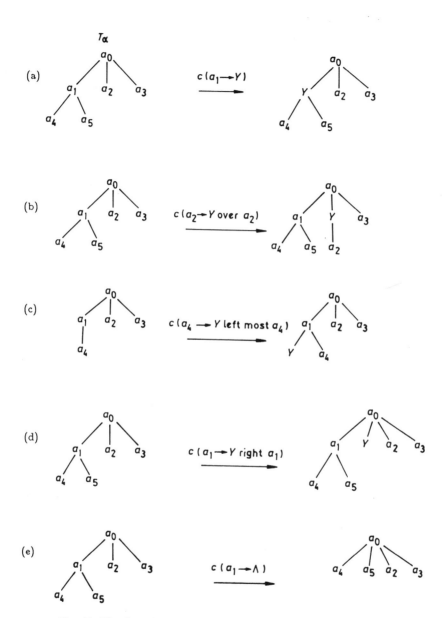

Fig. 12. The five edit operations in the error-correcting tree automata.

grammar) are included. In this way, the distance measure is defined as the minimum cost of generating the input tree from the grammar.

A more formal way of defining the distance measure is the following. Let $L$ be the language of a grammar $G$, and let $T_\beta$ be the input tree, then a distance measure between $T_\beta$ and $L$ is:

$$d(L, T_\beta) = \min\{d(w, T_\beta)|w \in L\} \ .$$

The method to compute the distance measure uses a modified tree grammar where the five edit operations have been incorporated. A grammar transformed by including the edit operations is called an expanded grammar. However, the expansion of the grammar cannot be done in a direct way, since it would imply transforming the tree grammar into the general type of grammar in the Chomsky hierarchy. For this reason, instead of incorporating the *pure* edit operations, the grammar (or automata in this case) includes only the specific errors which can occur. This restriction is strong, but it is necessary for maintaining the simplicity of the problem and the efficiency of the parser.

The method proposed by Lu and Fu to expand the tree grammar uses an intermediate grammar description in order to make the processes more efficient. The intermediate grammar is called *binary tree grammar* and the definition is as follows:

**Binary tree grammar**: A tree grammar $G_b = (V_b, r_b, P_b, S)$ over $\langle \Sigma_b, r_b \rangle$ (where $V_b$ is the alphabet of nonterminals, $\Sigma_b$ is the alphabet of terminals, $P_b$ are the production rules and $S$ the start symbol) is said to be in binary form if:

1. A pseudosymbol $*$ is in $\Sigma_b$.
2. $r_b = \{0, 1, 2\}(r_b : \Sigma \rightarrow N, r_b$ is the rank of symbols in $\Sigma$, where $r(a/T_\alpha = $ maximum number of sons of the subtree $a/T_\alpha))$.
3. Each production rule in $P_b$ is in one of the following forms:
   (a) $U_1 \rightarrow X_1*$
   (b) $U_2 \rightarrow U_1 X_1*$
   (c) $X_0 \rightarrow U_1 X_1 x$
   (d) $X_0 \rightarrow X_1 x$
   (e) $X_0 \rightarrow x$

where $U_1, U_2, X_0, X_1 \in \{V_b - \Sigma_b\}$ and $x \in \{\Sigma_b - (*)\}$.

The transformation of a tree grammar into a binary tree grammar can be done by applying a sequence of operations which are described in Ref. 1.

Figure 13d shows a tree grammar which describes the letter E (Fig. 13a,b), and Fig. 13e shows the binary version.

Once a tree grammar has been transformed into its binary form, the grammar can be expanded with the five edit operations described as before. In the transformation process, all possible terminals which can be in the input tree are included in the grammar rules, which means that every new rule which incorporates terminals will be repeated as many times as the terminals exist. The algorithm to expand the grammar is described in detail in Ref. 1.

The method to compute the similarity measure is reduced to parse the input tree by using the expanded grammar, and then selecting the derivation which generates the input tree with the minimum cost. The cost of every derivation depends on the production rules applied in the derivation, and the cost is nothing but the sum of the individual costs of those rules. As we can imagine, a rule of the non-expanded grammar, i.e. a rule of the primitive grammar, has cost equal to zero, and the rules incorporated by the expansion (due to one of the five edit operations) has a cost equal to the assigned cost.

### 5.1.2. *The algorithm*

The algorithm has the following steps:

1. Transform the tree grammar into binary form.
2. From the binary form grammar, construct a tree automaton which expands the grammar in order to accept all possible erroneous trees.
3. Compute the minimum distance between the input tree and the language generated by the tree automaton.

The details of the method can be seen in Ref. 1 or in the book by Fu (1982)[5].

## 6. APPLICATIONS

Tree matching has been applied to different kinds of problems, for example, character recognition, airplane identification, waveform correlation and 3-D object recognition. In this section we will give a short review of some of these applications.

One of the applications of tree matching has been on handprinted character recognition, where the characters are described by means of several primitives. Figure 14a, b shows character A described through primitives

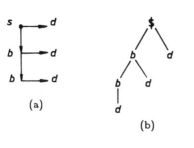

(a)

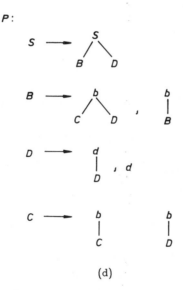

(b)

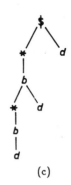

(c)

$$G_t = (V, r, P, s) \text{ over } \langle \Sigma, r \rangle$$
$$V = \{S, B, C, D, \$, b, d\} \quad \Sigma = \{\$, b, d\}$$
$$r(\$) = 2, r(b) = \{1, 2\}, r(d) = \{0, 1\}$$

P:

$$S \longrightarrow \begin{array}{c} S \\ B \quad D \end{array}$$

$$B \longrightarrow \begin{array}{c} b \\ C \quad D \end{array}, \quad \begin{array}{c} b \\ B \end{array}$$

$$D \longrightarrow \begin{array}{c} d \\ D \end{array}, \quad d$$

$$C \longrightarrow \begin{array}{c} b \\ C \end{array} \quad \begin{array}{c} b \\ D \end{array}$$

(d)

$$G_b = (V_b, r_b, P_b, S) \text{ over } \langle \Sigma_b, r_b \rangle$$
$$V_b = \{S, U_s, B, U_B, D, C, \$, b, d, *\}, \quad \Sigma_b = \Sigma \cup \{*\}$$
$$r_b(\$) = \{2\}, r_b(b)\{1, 2\}, r_b(d) = \{0.1\}, r_b(*) = \{1\}$$

**Fig. 13.** Description of a letter E. (a) Original character with the primitives; (b) the tree structure of the character; (c) the binary tree; (d) the grammar which generates character E.

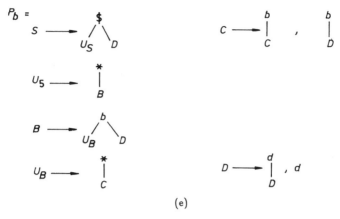

(e)

Fig. 13. Cont'd. (e) The binary grammar.

and the related tree is presented in Fig. 14d. The objective of the method is to classify the input characters in each one of the classes defined by the proper characters. In order to avoid the matching with each one of the trees of one class, every class is represented by a tree grammar. Figure 14c, shows the grammar which generates the character A, and Fig. 14e, f two distorted characters A.

The method used is that of error correcting between the input tree and a tree grammar of each one of the reference classes. The process of recognition is the following[1]: digitize and binarize the input character in a $16 \times 16$ format; extract the chain code and primitives; transform the input into a tree representation; apply the distance between the input tree and the language generated by the class grammar for each one of the reference classes, and classify the input patterns in the class where the minimum distance based on the nearest-neighbor syntactic recognition rule is obtained. For this case, the costs for substitution, insertion and deletion were assumed to be equal to 1, and the method was applied to 26 input patterns. All the patterns were well classified and the average time for recognition on a CDC 6500 was 4.5 seconds per character (the method was programmed in FORTRAN IV).

Another application has been on waveform correlation[2], where the waveforms are described by trees as it is shown in Fig. 15. The description of the waveform as a tree is made by quantizing the amplitude and sampling in time intervals. From both discretizations, the complete tree can be constructed in a similar way as if we overlay a grid on the waveform. Figure 15a

Character A:

$G_A = (V_A, r_A, P_A, A)$

where $V_A = \{A, A_1, A_2, N_a, N_d, N_e\}, \Sigma_A = \{\$, a, c, d\}$

$r_A(\$) = \{2\}, r_A(a) = \{0, 2\}, r_A(c) = \{0, 1\}, r_A(d) = \{0\}$

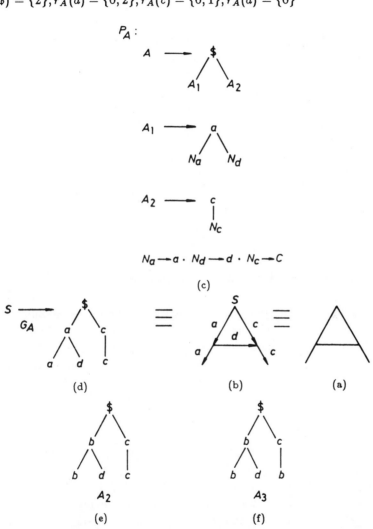

$P_A$:

$$A \longrightarrow \$ \atop A_1 \quad A_2$$

$$A_1 \longrightarrow a \atop N_a \quad N_d$$

$$A_2 \longrightarrow c \atop N_c$$

$$N_a \longrightarrow a \cdot N_d \longrightarrow d \cdot N_c \longrightarrow C$$

(c)

(d)  (b)  (a)

$A_2$

(e)

$A_3$

(f)

Fig. 14. (a) The input character A; (b) the representation through the primitives; (c) the tree grammar for character A; (d) the derived tree from the grammar; (e) and (f) distorted samples which have a distance cost of 2 and 3 respectively.

shows the grid and the waveform, and Fig. 15b shows the tree. The purpose of this application is to correlate a reference waveform over the input waveform.

The method used is tree to tree matching based on node splitting and merging. The process is the following: digitize the input waveform and overlay the selected grid to obtain the tree; correlate the input tree to the reference waveform and calculate the distance measure; the minimum cost of correlation is the best fit between the waveforms. The waveform correlation was applied to several complex waveforms, first by using only the amplitude quantizations and second by including the sampling discretization. In the first case, 16 quantizations were considered and about 150 nodes were obtained for both trees. The correlation showed very good results, better than in the string to string methods. The trade-off, however, was the computational complexity which was around 25 minutes of CPU time on a VAX 11/780 computer.

A third application has been on 3-D object recognition[23,24], where the objects can be partially occluded by other objects or by the limits of the vision field. The system is prepared for identifying the objects in a 2-D scene, from 3-D models of the reference objects, that is, the models are not described by a set of perspective projections. The system consists of the following modules: a CAD module to generate the 3-D models; a structure transformer module which converts the CAD format into several internal structures (one is the cyclic-tree[23]); an initial hypothesis module which by matching cyclic-trees[23], finds the best partial matchings between the scene objects and the reference models; a module to infer the 3-D position and orientation of the identified models; and a verification module which obtains the similarity values of the identified scene objects. The system has been applied for identifying workpieces in industrial scenes[24].

## 7. CONCLUSIONS

The tree matching techniques are much more powerful than the string matching techniques, and they look very promising, although the trade-off is the time complexity of the methods. At present, the techniques of tree matching allow more difficult problems than in the string case; moreover, they are also applied to objects which can only be described by graphs. These issues make tree matching a very attractive and powerful technique.

There are several research topics in this area which will make even more interesting the use of tree matching as a useful technique for the future.

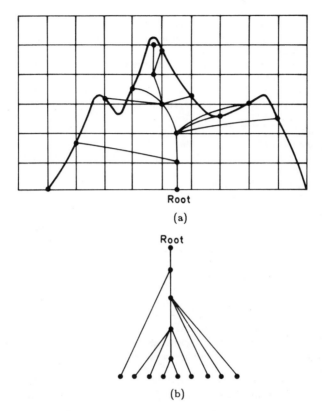

Fig. 15. (a) A waveform and the complete tree structure; (b) the tree representation.

The first one is the extension of tree matching to cyclic trees[3,23], which increases the power of description and allows representation of structures which are implicitly circular, for example, the representation of 3-D (volumetric) objects. The second one is the use of parallel computers for doing the matching process, which can reduce significantly the time complexity. Both issues will increase the use of tree matching in tasks of pattern recognition, artificial intelligence and in related fields.

## REFERENCES

1. S.Y. Lu and K.S. Fu, "Error-correcting tree automata for syntactic pattern recognition", *IEEE Trans. Computers*, **27** (1978) 1040-1053.
2. Y-C. Cheng and S-Y. Lu, "Waveform correlation by tree matching", *IEEE Trans. Pattern Analysis and Machine Intelligence* **7** (1985) 299-395.

3. A. Sanfeliu, Parallel Straight Segments In the Recognition of 3D Objects, Instituto de Cibernética, Technical Report IC-DT-1987.04, Sept. 1987.

4. S.A. Boorman and D. Oliver, "Metrics on spaces of finite trees", *J. Math. Psychology* **10** (1973) 172-178.

5. K.S. Fu, *Syntactic Pattern Recognition and Applications* (Prentice-Hall, 1982).

6. B.K. Bhargava and K.S. Fu, Application of Tree System Approach to Classification of Bubble Chamber Photographs, Purdue University TR-EE 72-30, Nov. 1972.

7. K.S. Fu and B.K. Bhargava, "Tree systems for syntactic pattern recognition", *IEEE Trans. Computers* **22** (1973) 1087-1099.

8. S.Y. Lu and K.S. Fu, "A syntactic approach to texture analysis", *Computer Graphics and Image Processing* **7** (1978) 303-330.

9. D.G. Corneil and C.C. Gotlieb, "An efficient algorithm for graph isomorphism", *J. ACM* **17** (1970) 51-64.

10. J.R. Ullman, *J. ACM* **23** (1976) 31-42.

11. S.Y. Lu, "A tree to tree distance and its applications to cluster analysis", *IEEE Trans. Pattern Analysis and Machine Intelligence* **1** (1979) 219-224.

12. S.Y. Lu, "A tree matching algorithm based on node splitting and merging", *IEEE Trans. Pattern Analysis and Machine Intelligence* **6** (1984) 249-256.

13. K. Ohmori and E. Tanaka, "A unified view on tree metrics", *Proc. NATO ARW on Syntactic and Structural Pattern Recognition, NATO ASI Series,* (Springer-Verlag, 1988).

14. S.M. Selkow, "The tree to tree editing problem", *Info. Process. Letters* **6** (1977) 184-186.

15. K.C. Tai, "The tree to tree correction problem", *J. ACM* **26** (1979) 422-433.

16. E. Tanaka, "A computing algorithm for the tree metric based on structure preserving mapping", *Trans. IECE* E68 (1985) 317-324.

17. E. Tanaka, "Efficient computing algorithms for the Tai metric", submitted to *Int. J. Pattern Recognition and Artificial Intelligence,* 1988.

18. J.W. Thacher, "Tree automata: an informal survey", n *Currents in the Theory of Computing,* ed. A.V. Aho, (Prentice Hall, Englewood Cliffs, NJ, 1973).

19. R. Wilhelm, "A modified tree to tree correction problem", *Info. Process. Letters* **12** (1981) 127-132.

20. K. Fukunaga, *Introduction to Statistical Pattern Recognition* (Academic Press, 1972).

21. A. Leveshtein, "Binary codes capable of correcting deletions, insertions and reversal", *Sov. Phys. Dokl.* **10** (1983) 707-710.

22. K. Aoki, "A top-down algorithm to compute the distance between trees," *Trans. IECE* **66** (1968) 157-158.

23. A. Sanfeliu, "Matching complex structures: The cyclic-tree representation scheme", submitted to *Proc. IAPR Int. Workshop on Structural and Syntactic Pattern Recognition,* Pont-á-Mousson, France, 12-14 Sept. 1988.

24. A Sanfeliu and M. Añaños, "A CAD based vision system for identifying industrial workpieces", submitted to 6th IFAC/IFIP/IFORS/IMACS Symposium on Information Control Problems in Manufacturing Technology, Madrid, Spain, 29 Sept.-1 Oct., 1989.

# 7

# MATCHING RELATIONAL STRUCTURES USING DISCRETE RELAXATION

LINDA G. SHAPIRO
and
ROBERT M. HARALICK
*Department of Electrical Engineering*
*University of Washington*
*Seattle, WA 98195*
*USA*

A relational description of an object describes the object in terms of its properties, its parts, and the interrelations among its parts. Relational matching is the process of comparing two relational descriptions to determine the correspondence between their part sets and to decide, based on this correspondence, how similar they are. Relational matching can be used for stereo vision, for object recognition, and for organizing a database of models. In this chapter, we describe several different kinds of relational matching and give algorithms that use discrete relaxation to solve the relational matching problem. An approach to relational matching using parallel hardware is briefly discussed.

## 1. INTRODUCTION

High-level vision processes perform matching and reasoning tasks. One important task that high-level vision performs is to identify objects in the scene from their projections on the image and to interpret the meaning of the scene as a whole. Although classification of many simple objects can be performed by statistical techniques, the recognition of complex objects having parts in various spatial relationships requires a different approach. When the objective is not only to recognize an object, but also to measure some critical angles or distances on the object, then again statistical techniques are not sufficient. When the scene is interpreted as a whole, the analysis depends on the interpretations of the various objects in the scene and on their spatial relationships. In all of these tasks, an approach called *relational matching* can be used to solve the problem. In this paper we define several kinds of relational matching, give sequential algorithms for solving relational matching problems using discrete relaxation, and briefly discuss a parallel approach to relational matching.

## 2. RELATIONAL DESCRIPTIONS AND MAPPINGS

How can a complex object or entity be described? The object or entity has global properties such as area, height and width. It also has a set of parts or important features. The parts each have properties of their own and there are spatial relationships that describe their interconnections. In order to define the process of relational matching, we need a unified context in which to express these properties and relationships. We call this context a *relational description*. A relational description is a set of relations that together describe a complex object or entity. The relation is the basic unit of a relational description, so we will start with relations.

### 2.1. Relations

Let $O_A$ be an object or entity and $A$ be the set of its parts or important features. An N-ary *relation* $R$ over $A$ is a subset of the Cartesian product $A^N = A \times \ldots \times A$ (N times). For example, suppose that $O_A$ is a chair and its part set $A$ consists of four legs, a back and a seat. A list of the parts is a unary relation $R_1 \subseteq A$. A list of the pairs of parts that connect together is a binary relation $R_2 \subseteq A \times A$. Other binary relations of interest include the list $R_3 \subseteq A \times A$ of pairs of parallel parts and the list $R_4 \subseteq A \times A$ of pairs of perpendicular parts. The set of triples of the form $(p_1, p_2, p_3)$ where parts

$p_1$ and $p_3$ both connect to part $p_2$ is a fifth relation $R_5 \subseteq A \times A \times A$. The set $D_A = \{R_1, R_2, R_3, R_4, R_5\}$ forms a relational description of the chair. This relational description describes only spatial relationships. Before we add properties to make the descriptions more robust, we discuss a method for comparing these simple relations.

## 2.2. Relational Homomorphisms

Let $A$ be the part set of object $O_A$, and $B$ be the part set of object $O_B$. Let $R \subseteq A^N$ be an N-ary relation over part set $A$. Let $f : A \to B$ be a function that maps elements of set $A$ into set $B$. We define the *composition* $R \circ f$ of $R$ with $f$ by

$$R \circ f = \{(b_1, \ldots, b_N) \in B | \text{ there exists}$$
$$(a_1, \ldots, a_N) \in R \text{ with } f(a_i) = b_i, i = 1, \ldots, N)\} \, .$$

Figure 1 illustrates the composition of a binary relation with a mapping.

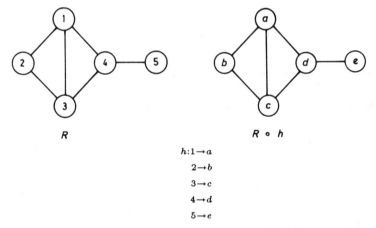

$$R \qquad\qquad\qquad R \circ h$$

$$h : 1 \to a$$
$$2 \to b$$
$$3 \to c$$
$$4 \to d$$
$$5 \to e$$

Fig. 1. The composition of binary relation $R$ with mapping $h$.

Let $S \subseteq B^N$ be a second N-ary relation. A *relational homomorphism* from $R$ to $S$ is a mapping $f : A \to B$ that satisfies $R \circ f \subseteq S$. That is, when a relational homomorphism is applied to each component of an N-tuple of $R$, the result is an N-tuple of $S$. Figure 2 illustrates the concept of a relational homomorphism.

A relational homomorphism maps the primitives of $A$ to a subset of the primitives of $R$ having all the same inter-relationships that the original

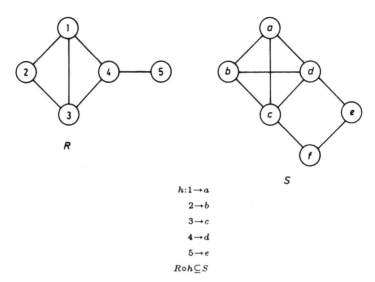

$$h:1 \rightarrow a$$
$$2 \rightarrow b$$
$$3 \rightarrow c$$
$$4 \rightarrow d$$
$$5 \rightarrow e$$
$$Roh \subseteq S$$

Fig. 2. A relational homomorphism $h$ from binary relation $R$ to binary relation $S$.

primitives of $A$ had. If $A$ is a much smaller set than $B$, then finding a one-one relational homomorphism is equivalent to finding a copy of a small object as part of a larger object. Finding a chair in an office scene is an example of such a task. If $A$ and $B$ are about the same size, then finding a relational homomorphism is equivalent to determining that the two objects are similar. A *relational monomorphism* is a relational homomorphism that is one-one. Such a function maps each primitive in $A$ to a unique primitive in $B$. A monomorphism indicates a stronger match than a homomorphism. Figure 3 illustrates a relational monomorphism.

Finally, a *relational isomorphism* $f$ from an N-ary relation $R$ to an N-ary relation $S$ is a one-one relational homomorphism from $R$ to $S$, and $f^{-1}$ is a relational homomorphism from $S$ to $R$. In this case, $A$ and $B$ have the same number of elements, each primitive in $A$ maps to a unique primitive in $B$, and every primitive in $A$ is mapped to by some primitive of $B$. Also, every tuple in $R$ has a corresponding tuple in $S$, and vice versa. An isomorphism is the strongest kind of match: a symmetric match. Figure 4 illustrates a relational isomorphism and Fig. 5 shows the difference between a relational isomorphism and a relational monomorphism.

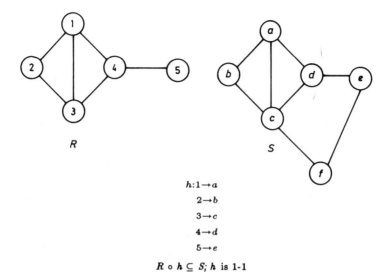

$$h:1 \rightarrow a$$
$$2 \rightarrow b$$
$$3 \rightarrow c$$
$$4 \rightarrow d$$
$$5 \rightarrow e$$

$$R \circ h \subseteq S;\ h \text{ is } 1\text{-}1$$

**Fig. 3.** A relational monomorphism $h$ from binary relation $R$ to binary relation $S$. There is a copy of $R$ in $S$.

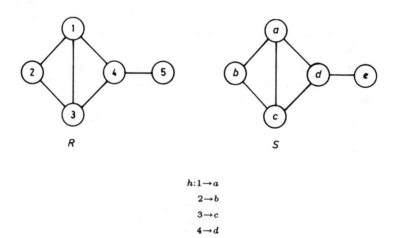

$$h:1 \rightarrow a$$
$$2 \rightarrow b$$
$$3 \rightarrow c$$
$$4 \rightarrow d$$
$$5 \rightarrow e$$

$$R \circ h = S \text{ and } h \text{ is } 1\text{-}1$$

or equivalently,

$$R \circ h \subseteq S,\ S \circ h^{-1} \subseteq R,\ \text{and } h \text{ is } 1\text{-}1$$

**Fig. 4.** A relational isomorphism $h$ from binary relation $R$ to binary relation $S$.

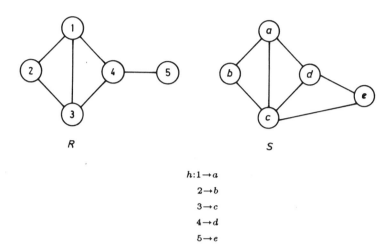

$$h: 1 \rightarrow a$$
$$2 \rightarrow b$$
$$3 \rightarrow c$$
$$4 \rightarrow d$$
$$5 \rightarrow e$$

$R \circ h \subseteq S$, $h$ is 1-1, and $h$ is onto.

Fig. 5. A relational monomorphism from binary relation $R$ onto binary relation $S$. This mapping $h$ is not a relational isomorphism since $h^{-1}$ is not a relational monomorphism from $S$ to $R$.

## 2.3. Relational Descriptions and Relational Distance

A *relational description* $D_X$ is a set of relations $D_X = \{R_1, \ldots, R_I\}$ where for each $i = 1, \ldots, I$, there exists a positive integer $n_i$ with $R_i \subseteq X^{n_i}$ for some set $X$. $X$ is a set of the parts of the entity being described and the relations $R_i$ indicate various relationships among the parts. A relational description may be used to describe an object model, a group of regions on an image, a two-dimensional shape, a Chinese character, or anything else having structure to it. In the spirit of the relational homomorphisms defined in the previous section, we wish to define a distance measure for pairs of relational descriptions.

Let $D_A = \{R_1, \ldots, R_I\}$ be a relational description with part set $A$. Let $D_B = \{S_1, \ldots, S_I\}$ be a second relational description with part set $B$. We will assume that $|A| = |B|$; if this is not the case, we will add enough dummy parts to the smaller set to make it the case.

Let $f$ be any one-one, onto mapping from $A$ to $B$. The *structural error* of $f$ for the $i$th pair of corresponding relations $(R_i$ and $S_i)$ in $D_A$ and $D_B$ is given by

$$E_s^i(f) = |R_i \circ f - S_i| + |S_i \circ f^{-1} - R_i| .$$

The structural error indicates how many tuples in $R_i$ are not mapped by $f$

to tuples in $S_i$ and how many tuples in $S_i$ are not mapped by $f^{-1}$ to tuples in $R_i$.

The *total error* of $f$ with respect to $D_A$ and $D_B$ is the sum of the structural errors for each pair of corresponding relations. That is,

$$E(f) = \sum_{i=1}^{I} E_s^i(f) \ .$$

The total error gives a quantitative idea of the difference between the two relational descriptions $D_A$ and $D_B$ with respect to the mapping $f$.

The *relational distance* between $D_A$ and $D_B$ is then given by

$$GD(D_A, D_B) = \min_{f : A \xrightarrow[\text{onto}]{1-1} B} E(f) \ .$$

That is, the relational distance is the minimal total error obtained for any one-one, onto mapping $f$ from $A$ to $B$. In Ref. 1 we proved that the relational distance is a metric over the space of relational descriptions. We call a mapping $f$ that minimizes total error a *best mapping* from $D_A$ to $D_B$. If there is more than one best mapping, we arbitrarily select one as the designated best mapping. More than one best mapping will occur when the relational descriptions involve certain kinds of symmetries.

*Examples*

Let $A = \{1, 2, 3, 4\}$ and $B = \{a, b, c, d\}$. Let $D_A = \{R_1 \subseteq A^2, R_2 \subseteq A^3\}$ and $D_B = \{S_1 \subseteq B^2, S_2 \subseteq B^3\}$. Let $R_1 = \{(1,2)(2,3)(3,4)(4,2)\}$ and $S_1 = \{(a,b)(b,c)(d,b)\}$. Let $R_2 = \{(1,2,3)\}$ and $S_2 = \{(a,b,c)\}$. Let $f$ be defined by $f(1) = a, f(2) = b, f(3) = c, f(4) = d$. These relations are illustrated in Fig. 6. Then we have

$$|R_1 \circ f - S_1| = |\{(a,b), (b,c), (c,d), (d,b)\} \\ - \{(a,b), (b,c), (d,b)\}| = 1$$

$$|S_1 \circ f^{-1} - R_1| = |\{(1,2), (2,3), (4,2)\} \\ - \{(1,2), (2,3), (3,4), (4,2)\}| = 0 \ ,$$

$$E_s^1(f) = 1 + 0 = 1$$
$$|R_2 \circ f - S_2| = |\{(a,b,c)\} - \{(a,b,c)\}| = 0$$
$$|S_2 \circ f^{-1} - R_2| = |\{(1,2,3)\} - \{(1,2,3)\}| = 0 \ ,$$

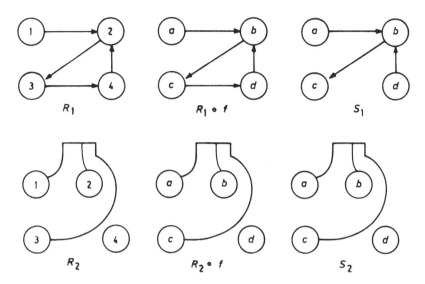

Fig. 6. The relations $R_1$, $R_1 \circ f$, $S_1$, $R_2$, $R_2 \circ f$ and $S_2$. The notation ⊓ indicates a hyperarc representing a triple.

$$E_s^2(f) = 0 + 0 = 0 \, ,$$
$$E(f) = E_s^1(f) + E_s^2(f) = 1 \, .$$

We note that $f$ is the best mapping and therefore $GD(D_A, D_B) = 1$.

For a simple but practical example, consider a set of object models constructed from simple parts with two binary relations: the connection relation and the parallel relation. Figure 7 illustrates a model (M1) and two other models (M2 and M3) that are each a relational distance of 1 from the first model. The model M4 shown in Fig. 8 is a variation of M3, but its relational distance from M3 is 6, due to several missing relationships induced by the additional two parts.

### 2.4. Attributed Relational Descriptions and Relational Distance

The relational descriptions defined in the previous section describe relationships among parts, but not properties of parts, properties of the whole, or properties of these relationships. However, it is easy to extend both the concept of relational description and the definition of relational distance to include them. Intuitively, an $m$-tuple of attributes added to an $n$-tuple of parts produces an $n + m$-tuple that specifies a relationship plus the properties of that relationship. If $n = 1$ and $m > 0$, each tuple lists a part and

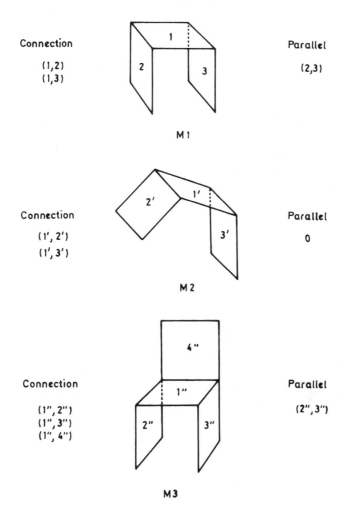

Connection

(1,2)
(1,3)

Parallel

(2,3)

**M 1**

Connection

(1', 2')
(1', 3')

Parallel

0

**M 2**

Connection

(1", 2")
(1", 3")
(1", 4")

Parallel

(2", 3")

**M 3**

Fig. 7. An object model M1 and two other models, M2 and M3, that are each a relational distance of 1 from M.

its properties. If $n = 0, m > 0$, and the relation has only one tuple, this is a property vector describing the global properties of the object. Formally, the definitions change to the following.

Let $X$ be a set of parts of object $O_X$ and $P$ be a set of property values. Generally, we can assume that $P$ is the set of real numbers. An *attributed relation* over part set $X$ with property value set $P$ is a subset of $X^n \times P^m$ for

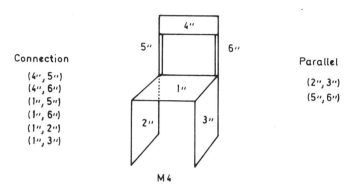

Fig. 8. A model M4 that differs from M3 by a relational distance of 6.

some non-negative integers $n$ and $m$. An *attributed relational description* $D_X$ is a sequence of attributed relations $D_X = \{R_1, \ldots, R_I\}$ where for each $i = 1, \ldots, I$, there exists a non-negative integer $n_i$, a non-negative integer $m_i$ (where $n_i + m_i > 0$), and a property value set $P_i$ with $R_i \subseteq X^{n_i} \times P_i^{m_i}$. For example, a binary parts connection relation $R \subseteq X^2$ can be extended to an attributed relation $R' \subseteq X^2 \times \mathcal{R}$, with $\mathcal{R}$ the set of real numbers, where an attributed pair $(x_1, x_2, a)$ specifies that part $x_1$ connects to part $x_2$ at angle $\mathbf{a}$.

Consider an attributed relation $R \subseteq A^n \times P^m$ over some part set $A$ and property value set $P$. Let $r \in R$ be an $n + m$-tuple having $n$ parts followed by $m$ property values. Let $S \subseteq B^n \times P^m$ be a second attributed relation over part set $B$ and property value set $P$. Let $f : A \to B$ by a one-one, onto mapping from $A$ to $B$. We define the composition $r \circ f$ of attributed tuple $r$ with $f$ by

$$r \circ f = \{(b_1, \ldots b_n, p_1, \ldots, p_m) \in B^n \times P^m$$
$$|\text{there exists } (a_1, \ldots, a_n, p_1, \ldots, p_m)$$
$$\in R \text{ with } f(a_i) = b_i, \ i = 1, \ldots, n\} \ .$$

Assume that if $(b_1, \ldots, b_n, p_1, \ldots, p_n) \in S$ and $(b_1, \ldots, b_n, q_1, \ldots, q_m) \in S$, then $p_1 = q_1, \ldots, p_m = q_m$. That is, each $n$-tuple of parts has only one $m$-tuple of properties. The error of a tuple $t = (b_1, \ldots, b_n, p_1, \ldots, p_m)$

with respect to a relation $S \subseteq B^n \times P^m$ is given by

$$
e(t, s) = \begin{cases} \text{norm\_dis}((p_1, \dots, p_m), (q_1, \dots, q_m)) & \text{if } (b_1, \dots, b_n, q_1, \dots, q_m) \\ & \in S \\ 1 & \text{otherwise} \end{cases}
$$

where norm_dis returns the Euclidean distance (or any other desired distance) between two vectors, normalized by dividing by some maximum possible distance. Thus $e(t, s)$ is a quantity between 0 and 1. Now we can extend the definition of the structural error of $f$ for the $i$th pair of corresponding relations $(R_i$ and $S_i)$ to

$$
E_s^i(f) = \sum_{r \in R_i} e(r \circ f, S_i) + \sum_{s \in S_i} e(s \circ f^{-1}, R_i) .
$$

Total error and relational distance are defined as in Sec. 2.3.

## 3. ALGORITHMS FOR RELATIONAL MATCHING

In Sec. 2 we explored several ways of defining relational matching. One can demand that two relational descriptions be isomorphic in order to say they match, or one can be more lenient and say that there must be a relational homomorphism from the first to the second. Furthermore, it may be desirable to find the best match between an unknown relational description and a set of stored relational models. In this case, the stored model that has the least relational distance to the unknown description is the best match. Whether the object is to detect relational isomorphisms, monomorphisms, or homomorphisms or to compute relational distance, the only known algorithms that can solve arbitrary matching problems employ a tree search. In this section we describe the standard backtracking tree search and one of its variants, and we make some comments on parallel algorithms. For more details and other variants, see Refs. 2-7. To simplify the discussion, the algorithms presented will be to determine all relational homomorphisms from a relation $R$ to a relation $S$. The algorithms for monomorphisms, isomorphisms and relational distance are straightforward variations of the homomorphism algorithms.

### 3.1. Backtracking Tree Search

Let $R$ be an N-ary relation over part set $A$ and let $S$ be an N-ary relation over part set $B$. We will refer to the elements of set $A$ as *units* and the elements of set $B$ as *labels*. We wish to find the set of all mappings

$f : A \rightarrow B$ that satisfy $R \circ f \subseteq S$. Of course the set may be empty, in which case the algorithm should fail. The backtracking tree search begins with the first unit of $A$. This unit can potentially match each label in set $B$. Each of these potential assignments is a node at level 1 of the tree. The algorithm selects one of these nodes, makes the assignment, selects the second unit of $A$, and begins to construct the children of the first node, which are nodes that map the second unit of $A$ to each possible label of $B$. At this level, some of the nodes may be ruled out because they violate the constraint $R \circ f \subseteq S$. The process continues to level $|A|$ of the tree. The paths from the root node to any successful nodes at level $|A|$ are the relational homomorphisms. Figure 9 illustrates a portion of the backtracking tree search for a simple digraph matching problem. The algorithm for a backtracking tree search is as follows.

```
procedure treesearch (A, B, f, R, S)
a:= first (A);
for each b ∈ B
      {
      f' := f ∪ {(a, b)};
      OK:= true;
      for each N-tuple r in R containing component a
         and whose other components are all in domain( f )
               if r∘f' is not in S
               then {OK := false; break } endif;
      if OK then
            {
            A' = remainder (A);
            if isempty(A')
            then output(f')
            else treesearch(A', B, f', R, S);
            }
      endif
      }
end treesearch;
```

## 3.2. Backtracking with Forward Checking

The backtracking tree search has exponential time complexity. Although there are no known polynomial algorithms in the general case, there

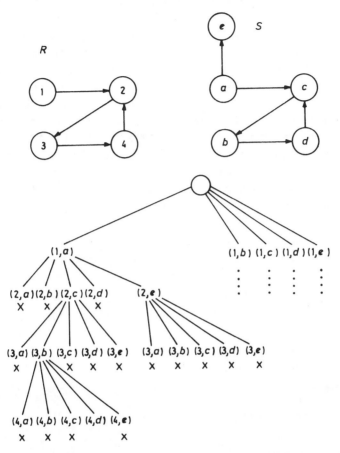

Fig. 9. The backtracking treesearch to find a homomorphism from $R = \{(1,2), (2,3), (3,4), (4,2)\}$ to $S = \{(a,c), (c, b), (b, d), (d, c), (a, e)\}$. An "X" under a node indicates failure. The only homomorphism found is $f = \{(1, a), (2, c), (3, b), (4, d)\}$.

are a number of discrete relaxation algorithms that can cut down search time by reducing the size of the tree that is searched. Forward checking is one such method. It is based on the idea that once a unit-label pair $(a, b)$ is instantiated at a node in the tree, the constraints imposed by the relations cause instantiation of some future unit-label pairs $(a', b')$ to become impossible. Suppose that $(a, b)$ is instantiated high in the tree and that the subtree beneath that node contains nodes with first components $a_1, a_2, \ldots, a_n, a'$. Although $(a', b')$ is impossible for any instantiations of

$(a_1, a_2, \ldots, a_n)$ it will be tried in every path that reaches its level in the tree. The principle of forward checking is to rule out $(a', b')$ at the time that $(a, b)$ is instantiated and keep a record of that information.

The data structure used to store the information is called a future error table (FTAB). There is one future error table for each level of recursion in the tree search. Each table is a matrix having one row for each element of $A$ and one column for each element of $B$. For any uninstantiated or *future unit* $a' \in A$ and potential label $b' \in B$, FTAB $(a', b') = 1$ if it is still possible to instantiate $(a', b')$ given the history of instantiations already made. FTAB$(a', b') = 0$ if $(a', b')$ has already been ruled out due to some previous assignment. When a pair $(a, b)$ is instantiated by the backtracking tree search, an updating procedure is called to examine all pairs $(a', b')$ of future units and their possible labels. For each pair $(a', b')$ that is incompatible with the assignment of $(a, b)$ and the previous instantiations, FTAB$(a', b')$ has become 0. If for any future unit $a'$, FTAB$(a', b')$ becomes 0 for all labels $b' \in B$, then instantiation of $(a, b)$ fails immediately. The backtracking tree search with forward checking is as follows.

```
procedure forward_checking_treesearch (a, b, f, FTAB, R, S)
a := first (A);
for each b ∈ B
    if (FTAB(a, b) == 1)
    then
            {
            f' := f ∪ {(a, b)};
            A' := remainder(A);
            if isempty(A')
            then output(f')
            else
                    {
                    NEWFTAB := copy(FTAB);
                    OK := update(NEWFTAB, a, b, A', B, R, S, f');
                    if (OK) forward_checking_treesearch
                            (A', B, f', NEWFTAB, R, S);
                    }
            endif
            }
    endif
```

**procedure** update(FTAB, $a, b$, future_ units, $B, R, S, f'$)
update := false;
**for** each $a' \in$ future_ units
    **for** each $b' \in B$ with FTAB$(a', b') == 1$
        **if** compatible$(a, b, a', b', R, S, f')$
        **then** update := true
        **else** FTAB$(a', b') := 0$
        **endif**;
**end** update

For binary relations $R$ and $S$, the utility function *compatible*, which determines whether an instantiation of $(a', b')$ is possible given instantiation $(a, b)$, is very simple. Units $a$ and $a'$ only constrain one another when either $(a, a')$ or $(a', a)$ is in $R$. Thus, the algorithm for function *compatible* for binary relations $R$ and $S$ is as follows.

**procedure** b_ compatible$(a, b, a', b', R, S, f')$
**if** $((a, a') \in R$ **and not** $((b, b') \in S))$ or
   $((a', a) \in R$ **and not** $((b', b) \in S))$
**then** b_ compatible := false
**else** b_ compatible := true **endif**;
**end** b_ compatible;

Note that for binary functions, the last argument $f'$ to function b_ compatible is not used, but is included here for consistency.

For N-ary relations $R$ and $S$, $N > 2$, those N-tuples of $R$ where $a$ and $a'$ are among the components and all other components that are already instantiated must be examined. The code for N-ary relations $R$ and $S$ is as follows:

**procedure** compatible$(a, b, a', b', R, S, f')$
$f'' := f' \cup \{(a', b')\}$;
compatible := true;
**for** each $r \in R$ containing $a$ and $a'$ whose other components
  are in domain $(f'')$
        **if** $r \circ f''$ is not in $S$
        **then** { compatible := false; break} **endif**;
**end** compatible;

The binary procedure is very fast, since its time complexity is constant.

The general procedure, if implemented as stated here, would have to examine each N-tuple of $R$. For a software implementation, it would be desirable to design the data structures for $R, S$, and $f$ so that only the appropriate N-tuples of $R$ are tested. A hardware implementation could offer even more flexibility.

### 3.3. Parallel Algorithms

To make the relational matching algorithm parallel, one needs to be able to make the backtracking tree search parallel. It is not difficult to understand how to parallelize the tree search in a computational network of parallel processors[8]. The whole tree is given to one processor within the network and this processor begins to work on the tree search. All processors in the network which are not working on the tree search and therefore idle, interrupt, in turn, all processors to which they can directly communicate. The interrupt essentially is a message indicating "idleness". Any processor which is working and receives an "idleness" interrupt, takes the tree it is working on and splits the tree into two subtrees. It keeps one subtree and it gives the other to the interrupting processor to work on.

So long as there is some communication path, however indirect, between every pair of processors in the network, the above approach to parallelizing the tree search will guarantee that every processor gets some work to do after it becomes idle. The communication overhead of passing a subtree to another processor can be minimal if the basic data for the entire problem is broadcast to each of the processors before tree search computation begins. Thus, specifying a subtree consists merely of specifying a simple list of all the instantiations already made above the subtree. For example, if the root of the subtree is at a level $N$ from the root node of the entire tree, then a list of $N$ ordered pairs of the already instantiated units and their corresponding labels specifies the subtree.

In so far as parallelizing the forward checking procedure, a parallel array processor SIMD implementation can be readily formulated[9]. The unit label table can be represented as a bit matrix with the labels indexing the columns and the units indexing the rows. The updating procedure essentially amounts to ORing over each row and then ANDing those results. This kind of updating must be done for each unit-label pair.

## 4. SUMMARY

We have introduced the concepts of relational descriptions, relational homomorphisms and isomorphisms and relational distance. We have generalized these concepts to attributed relational descriptions and attributed relational distance. We have given procedures for finding relational homomorphisms that use discrete relaxation and operate on sequential computers and briefly discussed parallel algorithms for multiprocessor systems. We feel that the current trend toward massively parallel architectures will produce a number of new algorithms that can rapidly solve any relational matching problem. Such algorithms will be important in the solution of complex vision problems.

## REFERENCES

1. L.G. Shapiro and R.M. Haralick, "A metric for comparing relational descriptions", *IEEE Trans. PAMI* **7** (1985) 90-94.
2. R.M. Haralick and L.G. Shapiro, "The consistent labeling problem — Part I", *IEEE Trans. PAMI* **1** (1979) 173-184.
3. R.M. Haralick and L.G. Shapiro, "The consistent labeling problem — Part II", *IEEE Trans. PAMI* **2** (1980) 193-203.
4. A. Rosenfeld, R.A. Hummel and S.W. Zucker, "Scene labeling by relaxation operations", *IEEE Trans. SMC* June (1976) 420-433.
5. L.G. Shapiro and R.M. Haralick, "Structural descriptions and inexact matching", *IEEE Trans. PAMI* **3** (1981) 504-519.
6. L.G. Shapiro and R.M. Haralick, "Organization of relational models for scene analysis", *IEEE Trans. PAMI* **4** (1982) 595-602.
7. L.G. Shapiro, "The use of numeric relational distance and symbolic differences for organizing models and for matching", in *Techniques for 3D Machine Perception* (North Holland, 1985).
8. J.T. McCall, J. Tront, F. Gray, R.M. Haralick and W.M. McCormick, "The effects of combinatorial problem parameters on the design of multi parallel architecture", *IEEE Trans. Comput.* **34** (1985) 973-980.
9. J.R. Ullman, R.M. Haralick and L.G. Shapiro, "Computer architecture for solving consistent labeling problems", *The Computer Journal* **28** (1985) 105-111.

# 8

---

# RANDOM GRAPHS

A.K.C. WONG, J. CONSTANT and M.L. YOU
*Department of Systems Design Engineering*
*University of Waterloo,*
*Waterloo, Ontario*
*Canada N2L 3G1*

This chapter introduces the concept of a random graph and its application to structural pattern recognition. A random graph can be considered a mapping (analogous to a random variable) from a sample space onto a range space consisting of all possible outcomes in the form of attributed graphs. To depict the probabilistic characteristics of an ensemble of attributed graphs, we introduce a low order probability distribution and an associated random graph obtained by synthesis from the ensemble. To reflect the variability of the outcomes of a random graph, we introduce a special entropy measure. The synthesis process is based on an optimal graph monomorphism algorithm. It uses a distance measure which is the minimum change in entropy of the distributions before and after the merging of two random graphs. The optimal morphism, in turn, determines how they should be merged. When the ensemble contains more than one class of pattern graphs, the synthesis process yields subensembles (clusters) together with their associated probability distributions. This process resembles unsupervised learning (or clustering) in pattern classification. Using the maximum likelihood rule and the probability computed for a pattern graph with respect to various classes, we can assign the pattern graph to a class. The usefulness of the method is demonstrated by a character recognition problem and a string alignment problem.

## 1. INTRODUCTION

In classical pattern recognition, a pattern is generally represented by a pattern vector. In structural pattern recognition, a pattern can be represented explicitly by a set of primitives and the relations among them in the form of an attributed graph[1-3]. The picture description language (PDL) and picture languages developed by Shaw[4,5] were early graph representations of structural patterns. Later, Pavlidis[6,7] proposed primary graphs and region adjacency graphs (RAG). More recently, attributed relational graphs (ARG) were introduced by Tsai and Fu[2,8], while attributed graphs and hypergraphs were proposed by Wong *et al.*[9,10]. To account for the variations of structural patterns in an ensemble, a probabilistic description of the ensemble is desirable. The random graph approach[3,11] is presented here for such a description.

By random graph we mean a mapping (analogous to a random variable) from a sample space onto a range space consisting of all possible attributed graph outcomes of the random graph. We call the union attributed graph (an attributed graph whose vertex and arc attributes can assume a set (union) of values according to a graph synthesis process) of all attributed graphs in the range space, together with its associated probability distribution, a *random graph representation* of the ensemble. In this manner, a structural pattern can be explicitly represented in the form of an attributed graph and an ensemble of such representations can be considered as outcomes of a random graph.

When estimating the probability distribution of the structural patterns from an ensemble, it is impractical to consider the high order probability distribution where all components and their relations in the structural patterns are taken jointly. A more practical approach is to propose an approximating (first order) distribution which takes into account the incidence relations between attributed arcs and vertices and relates both the vertices and arcs of the structural patterns to a common ordering scheme which is obtained through an optimal graph mapping process called random graph synthesis.

For the random graph synthesis process, a special entropy measure, defined for the probability distribution of a random graph, is introduced[3]. This measure is used to reflect the structural and attribute value variation of the attributed graphs in an ensemble. Since an attributed graph itself can be treated as a unique outcome of a random graph, it can be considered also as a random graph representation. The synthesis process can be realized by merging random graph representations using an optimal graph monomorphism algorithm[3,11−15] that minimizes the change of entropy for the distributions before and after the merging process. A hierarchical graph synthesis algorithm[3] is used for the synthesis of a random graph representation from an ensemble of attributed graphs.

The increment of entropy in the synthesis of two random graph representations possesses properties that render it a distance measure between random graph representations[3]. Since an attributed graph can be treated as a special case of a random graph representation, the distance can be defined for (1) two attributed graphs, (2) an attributed graph and a random graph distribution and (3) two random graph distributions. Such distance measures are used to formulate various tasks for structural pattern recognition.

In general, a random graph representation can be derived as a synthesis of a cluster of individual attributed graphs. If the class memberships for a given set of graphs are not known *a priori*, the synthesis process which can generate more than one random graph representation, is considered to be unsupervised learning (or clustering). Because there is a cluster of attributed graphs corresponding to each random graph representation, the probability distribution associated with each random graph can be referred to as the structural probability distribution of the cluster (or pattern class). If all the graphs in the input set belong to a single pattern class, we could obtain a single random graph representation. Such a synthesis process is considered supervised learning. When classifying an attributed graph which represents a structural pattern, into one of several classes of patterns represented by random graphs, we can apply either the minimum distance rule or the maximum likelihood rule. When using the distance rule, we place an unknown pattern in a given class if the distance between the attributed graph of that pattern and the random graph distribution of the class is minimized. When the maximum likelihood decision rule is used, an unknown pattern is assigned to a class when the likelihood of the attributed graph of the pattern being an outcome of the random graph of that class is the maximum.

## 2. ATTRIBUTED GRAPHS AND RANDOM GRAPHS

In the attributed graph representation of a structural pattern, a vertex with attribute values is used to represent a primitive and an attributed arc is used to represent a relationship between primitives.

Let $Z = \{z_i | i = 1, 2, \ldots, I\}$ be a nonempty, finite set of possible attributes for describing pattern primitives and $S_i = \{s_{ij} | j = 1, 2, \ldots, J_i\}$ be the set of possible attribute values associated with $z_i$ for each $i$. (These values could be nominal, ordinal, continuous, logical, etc.) Let $L_v = \{(z_i, s_{ij}) | i = 1, \ldots, I; j = 1, \ldots, J_i\}$ be the set of legal attribute-value pairs. A pattern primitive $\pi$ is simply a specification of (unique) values for some attributes. Thus, $\pi$ is a subset of $L_v$ having at most one ordered pair for any particular $z_i$. Let $\Pi$ be the set of all possible pattern primitives.

Similarly, let $F = \{f_i | i = 1, 2, \ldots, I'\}$ be a nonempty, finite set of possible relational attributes between primitives and $T_i = \{t_{ij}\}$ be a set of possible values of $f_i$. Let $L_a = \{(f_i, t_{ij}) | i = 1, \ldots, I'; j = 1, \ldots, T_i\}$. A relation $w$ is a specification of a set of (unique) values for some relational attributes. It is a subset of $L_a$. Let $\theta$ be the set of all relations.

**Definition 2.1.** Let $H = (N, E)$ be a graph. An *attributed graph* $G$ over $L = (L_v, L_a)$, with an *underlying graph structure* $H$, is defined to be a pair $(V, A)$, where $V = (N, \nu)$ is called an *attributed vertex set* and $A = (E, \delta)$ is called an *attributed arc set*. The mappings $\nu : N \to \Pi$ and $\delta : E \to \theta$ are called *vertex interpreter* and *arc interpreter* respectively.

Attributed graphs inherit in the obvious way all the structural properties and concepts (such as order and completeness) that are definable in terms of the underlying graph structure.

For example, to compare attributed graphs, we can use graph morphisms. In general, a graph morphism is an incidence preserving vertex to vertex mapping. It is referred to as a monomorphism if the mapping is one-to-one, as an epimorphism if the mapping is onto and as an isomorphism if the mapping is one-to-one and onto. These definitions can be extended to attributed graphs by making an attributed graph morphism simply a morphism of underlying graphs (i.e. a structural morphism). An attributed graph morphism is called complete if it preserves attributes and values. A special case is complete isomorphism.

**Definition 2.2.** Two attributed graphs $G_1 = (V_1, A_1)$ and $G_2 = (V_2, A_2)$ are said to be *structurally isomorphic* if there exists an isomorphism $\eta : H_1 \to H_2$ where $H_1$ and $H_2$ are the underlying graph structures of $G_1$ and $G_2$ respectively. $G_1$ and $G_2$ are said to be *completely isomorphic*, written $G_1 = G_2$, if there exists an attribute value preserving structural isomorphism $\mu$ between $G_1$ and $G_2$.

Epi- and monomorphisms are defined similarly.

It will be useful, for matching graphs of different orders, to introduce the notion of extension of a graph to a given order.

**Definition 2.3.** A graph $G = (V, A)$ of order $n$ can be *extended* to form a complete graph $G' = (V', A')$ of order $k$, $k \geq n$, by adding vertices and arcs with null attribute values (see below). We call $G'$ the *k-extension* of $G$, and $G$ an *n-reduction* of $G'$.

We next proceed to the definition of random graphs. This definition is adapted from Refs. 3 and 11. An alternative but equivalent approach is discussed in Note 2 below.

A random graph is simply a graph structure with randomly varying vertex and arc attribute values. Put another way, it is a graph, together with a set of jointly distributed random variables, some (one for each vertex) ranging over pattern primitives and some (one for each arc) ranging over relations. More precisely we have the following definition.

**Definition 2.4.** Let $H = (N, E)$ be a graph. A *random graph $R$* over $L = (L_v, L_a)$ with an underlying graph structure $H$ is defined to be a pair $(W, B)$ where $W = (N, \nu)$, $B = (E, \delta)$, $\nu : N \to \Pi'$, $\delta : E \to \theta'$, $\Pi'$ is a set of random variables with values in $\Pi \cup \{\phi\}$ and $\theta'$ is a set of random variables with values in $\theta \cup \{\phi\}$. In addition, a joint distribution is assumed for all the random variables in the ranges of $\nu$ and $\delta$. These are called random vertices and random arcs respectively. The head and tail functions $\sigma$ and $\tau$ will be applied to random arcs to yield the random vertices associated with the head and the tail, respectively, of the underlying arc.

Any attributed graph obtained in the obvious way by instantiating all random vertices and random arcs is called an outcome graph of the random graph. It is sometimes convenient to order the random vertices $(\alpha_1, \alpha_2, \ldots, \alpha_n)$ and the random arcs $(\beta_1, \beta_2, \ldots, \beta_m)$ of a random graph. The null outcomes, $\phi$, are described later (after Def. 2.5).

**Note 1.** If we let $C$ denote the set of all outcome graphs of a random graph $R$, then the joint distribution $P$ of random vertices and arcs of $R$ induces a probability measure on $C$ in the following way. Let $G \in C$. Then define the probability of $G$ to be the sum of the joint probabilities of the random vertices and arcs over all instantiations which produce $G$. (Note that it is possible for the *same* outcome graph to arise in several different ways by instantiating random vertices and arcs, so the probability of an outcome graph must include all possible orientations). It is trivial to show that this yields a probability measure on $C$. Hence, the joint distribution of random vertices and arcs determines a probability measure on the set of all outcome graphs.

**Note 2.** Conversely, any (structural) isomorphism $\mu$ from an outcome graph $G$ to the random graph $R$ determines outcomes (in $G$) for all random vertices and arcs of $R$ and hence a joint probability of these outcomes. This will be called the *probability of G according to $\mu$* and denoted by $P(G, \mu)$. This generalizes to any monomorphism $\mu$ from any attributed graph $G$ to $R$. The monomorphism can be thought of as labelling, orienting or ordering the vertices and arcs of the outcome graph according to those of $R$. If all outcome graphs $G$ and all possible isomorphisms of each graph to $R$ are considered, the $P(G, \mu)$ do not give a probability measure since an outcome graph may have several different isomorphisms to $R$ giving the same joint outcome for all random arcs and vertices so the probabilities will sum to more than 1. However, if two such isomorphisms are considered equivalent whenever one composed with the inverse of the other yields a complete automorphism of $G$, then the *probability of G according to an equivalence class $[\mu]$ of isomorphisms* can be defined to be the probability of $G$ according to any member $\mu$ of the class.

It is routine to show that the resulting measure on the set of pairs of outcome graphs and isomorphism classes is both well-defined (with respect to the equivalence relation) and a true probability measure summing to 1. This provides an alternative way of defining random graphs without referring to the random variables associated with individual vertices and arcs. A random graph simply becomes a space of (outcome graph, isomorphism class) pairs (where the isomorphisms are now to the common underlying graph structure) with a probability measure. Such a pair will be called a labelled outcome graph, since the isomorphism class $[\mu]$ determines a labelling of vertices and arcs of $G$ by those of $R$ which is unique "up to complete automorphism of $G$"; i.e. if we label the vertices and arcs of $R$, then the labelled outcome graphs are in one-to-one correspondence with the labelled outcomes of $R$ obtained by instantiating the labelled vertices and arcs. The random variables and joint distribution of Def. 2.4 follow easily from this definition. Thus, we see that a probability measure on a suitably structured set of outcome graphs determines the joint distribution of random vertices and arcs of a random graph.

Although this approach may seem less intuitive, it has the advantage of defining random graphs in terms of their possible (unordered, unlabelled) outcome graphs which are the observable entities in any practical application and which provide the samples from which the random graph structure must be inferred. It is easily verified that the two approaches are equivalent.

Random graphs, like attributed graphs, inherit structurally defined concepts from the underlying graph structure. As with the attributed graphs, the various types of morphism between random graphs, and between random and attributed graphs, can be defined in terms of underlying graph structures (i.e. a morphism means a morphism of underlying graph structures). If a random graph morphism preserves the joint probability distribution of random arcs and vertices it will be called complete. Note that, inasmuch as an attributed graph can be considered a random graph with certain outcomes, this nomenclature agrees with that for attributed graph morphisms. For example, extending the concept of attributed graph isomorphism to random graphs we arrive at the following definition.

**Definition 2.5.** Two random graphs $R_1 = (W_1, B_1)$ and $R_2 = (W_2, B_2)$ are *completely isomorphic* if and only if there exists a structural isomorphism $\eta : R_1 \rightarrow R_2$, such that the probability distributions of their corresponding random vertices and random arcs are identical. $R_1$ and $R_2$ are also said to be *equivalent*, denoted by $R_1 = R_2$.

To simplify the definition of probability and entropy of random graphs we introduce the term *random element* to refer to either a random vertex or a random arc, or both, whenever a distinction between them is unnecessary. $\gamma$ will denote a random element. Hence, a random graph with $n$ vertices and $m$ arcs ordered arbitrarily for convenience can also be associated with an ordered $(n + m)$-tuple of random elements

$$\underline{\gamma} = (\gamma_1, \gamma_2, \ldots, \gamma_n, \gamma_{n+1}, \ldots, \gamma_{n+m}) = (\alpha_1, \ldots, \alpha_n, \beta_1, \ldots, \beta_m) \, ,$$

called a random element vector. Instantiating $\underline{\gamma}$ gives an *outcome vector* $\underline{g} = (a_1, \ldots, a_n, b_1, \ldots, b_m)$. The outcome vectors are in one-to-one correspondence with the labelled outcome graphs and inherit the probability measure from the random graph in the obvious way.

As defined above, the range of each element includes the *null attribute* $\phi$. This attribute will be used to signify a missing structural vertex or arc without actually having to modify the underlying graph structure. In this way, structural subgraphs can be represented simply as outcomes of the random graph. To maintain the proper incidence structure in the subgraphs we require that the outcome of a random arc be null whenever either endpoint has a null outcome, i.e.

$$Pr\{\beta = \phi | \sigma(\beta) = \phi \text{ or } \tau(\beta) = \phi\} = 1$$

where $\sigma(\beta)$ and $\tau(\beta)$ are the initial and terminal endpoints of $\beta$ respectively.

A further simplification and unification is effected by replacing each random graph by an equivalent complete graph with (possibly) some null vertices and arcs. A random graph $R = (W, b) = ((N, \nu), (E, \delta))$ of order $n$ is replaced by a complete random graph $R' = (W, B')$ where $B' = (E', \delta')$,

$$E' = \{(n_1, n_2) \in N \times N | n_1 \neq n_2\} \text{ and } \delta'(\beta) = \left\{ \begin{array}{ll} \delta(\beta) & \text{for } \beta \in E \\ \Phi & \text{for } \beta \notin E \end{array} \right\}$$

Here $\Phi$ is a random variable which takes the value $\phi$ with probability 1. $R'$ is called the $n$-extension of R.

Any outcome graph $G = (V, A)$ "oriented" with respect to $R$ by an isomorphism $\mu : G \to R$ can likewise be replaced by its $n$-extension $G' = (V', A')$ and $\mu$ extended to an isomorphism $\mu' : G' \to R'$ with $P(G, \mu) = P(G', \mu')$. Although $\mu'$ is not necessarily unique, $P(G', \mu')$ is determined uniquely by this equation.

Thus, without loss of generality, any random graph $R$, and any outcome graph oriented with respect to $R$ by an isomorphism can be considered complete whenever convenient.

The definitions of attributed graphs and random graphs introduced here are sufficiently general to handle cases where different vertices have different numbers of attributes and no order is imposed on the attributes (and similarly for arcs). It will be convenient in the subsequent discussion and examples to focus our attention on the special case of *homogeneous* attributed and random graphs in which all vertices have the same attributes (possibly with different values) and likewise for arcs. In this case, the (attribute, value) pairs can be listed always in the same order and the attribute names suppressed so that $n$-tuples of attribute values replace pattern primitives and relations. In the examples, $n$ will usually be taken to be 1. Thus, for example, a random vertex will often be indicated as having a distribution of real numbers as values. The extension of all concepts introduced to the general case is straightforward.

Figure 1 gives an example of a random graph $R$ and its outcomes. $R$

consists of random vertices $(A, B, C, D)$ and random arcs $(U, V, W, X, Y, Z)$. The ranges of $A, B, C$ and $D$ are $\{a, b, \phi\}, \{f, \phi\}, \{c, e\}$ and $\{b, \phi\}$ respectively, and those of $U, V, W, X, Y$ and $Z$ are $\{\phi\}, \{v\}, \{\phi\}, \{u, \phi\}, \{y, z\}$ and $\{x\}$ respectively. Figure 1b is an extension of a graph of order 3 to one of order 4 by adding null elements. Figure 1c is an outcome of order 4 whereas Fig. 1d is an infeasible outcome since non-null arcs cannot be incident to a null vertex.

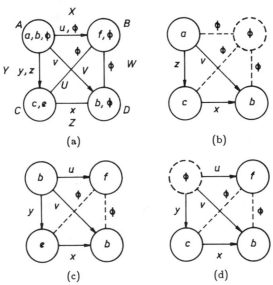

Fig. 1. An example of a random graph and its outcomes. (a) A random graph $R$ of order 4. (b) An outcome graph of order 3 and its extension to order 4. (c) An outcome graph of order 4. (d) An infeasible outcome of $R$.

## 3. PROBABILITY AND ENTROPY OF FIRST ORDER RANDOM GRAPHS

Let $R$ be a random graph, $G$ an outcome graph oriented with respect to $R$ by isomorphism $\mu$, $G'$ the extension of $G$ to the order of $R$ and $(a_1, \ldots, a_n, b_1, \ldots, b_m)$ the attribute values of the vertices and arcs of $G$ corresponding to the random elements $(\alpha_1, \ldots, \alpha_n, \beta_1, \ldots, \beta_m)$ which comprise $R$. Then, as explained in Note 1 to Def. 2.4,

$$P(G, \mu) = P(G', \mu') = Pr\left(\bigwedge_{i=1}^{n}(\alpha_i = a_i) \wedge \bigwedge_{j=1}^{m}(\beta_j = b_j)\right). \qquad (1)$$

As discussed in the introduction, the estimation of such high order joint probabilities for a random graph is impractical. We thus introduce a lower order model which can be used as an approximation in the general case. It will allow probability estimation which takes into consideration both structural (relational) and contextual information in the random graph representation.

We introduce the following assumptions:

(1) The random vertices $\{\alpha_i\}$ are mutually independent.

(2) Given values for the random vertices $\{\alpha_i\}$, the random arcs $\{\beta_j\}$ are independent.

(3) A random arc $\beta$ is independent of any random vertex other than its endpoints $\sigma(\beta)$ and $\tau(\beta)$.

Random graphs satisfying these assumptions will be called *first order random graphs*. The rest of the discussion will focus on their estimation and use in pattern classification and analysis. Even though, in first order random graphs, the random arcs are independent *given the random vertex values*, they are not necessarily independent in the joint distribution of all random elements. This is because the outcome of an arc in general affects probabilities for its head and tail vertices, which in turn affect probabilities for adjacent arcs. Thus the arcs are related through their common structural vertices.

Based on the above assumptions, (1) becomes

$$P(G,\mu) = \prod_{i=1}^{n} Pr(\alpha_i = a_i)$$
$$\times \prod_{j=1}^{m} Pr(\beta_j = b_j | \sigma(\beta_j) = a_{j1}, \tau(\beta_j) = a_{j2}) \qquad (2)$$

where $\sigma(\beta_j) = \alpha_{j1}$ and $\tau(\beta_j) = \alpha_{j2}$ are the head and tail of $\beta_j$ and $a_{j1}$ and $a_{j2}$, their values assigned by $\mu$.

By putting $p_i(a) \triangleq Pr(\alpha_i = a)$ and

$$p_j(b|a_1, a_2) \triangleq Pr(\beta_j = b | \sigma(\beta_j) = a_1, \tau(\beta_j) = a_2) ,$$

(2) may be rewritten:

$$p(G,\mu) = \prod_{i=1}^{n} p_i(a_i) \prod_{j=1}^{m} p_j(b_j | a_{j1}, a_{j2}) . \qquad (3)$$

Next, we introduce a special entropy measure to reflect the variability of the outcomes of a random graph.

**Definition 3.1.** The *entropy* $H(R)$ of a random graph $R = (W, B)$ is defined by

$$H(R) = -\sum_{(G,[\mu])} p(G,\mu) \log p(G,\mu) \tag{4}$$

where the summation is taken over all labelled outcome graphs of $R$. It is the same as the Shannon entropy of the joint distribution of the random elements of $R$. Using (3), we can write (4) in a form which is more useful for calculation purposes:

$$H(R) = -\sum_{g} p(g) \left[ \sum_{i=1}^{n} \log p(a_i) + \sum_{j=1}^{m} \log p(b_j | a_{j1}, a_{j2}) \right]$$

where the outer sum is over all possible outcome vectors $g = (a_1, \ldots, a_n, b_1, \ldots, b_m)$ of the random element vector $\gamma = (\alpha_1, \ldots, \alpha_n, \beta_1, \ldots, \beta_m)$ and $p(g)$ denotes $p(\gamma = g)$. Note that the order of the elements of $g$ is important.

By splitting up $p(g)$ into separate vertex and conditional arc probabilities, rearranging the sums and adding joint probabilities to get marginal ones, this can be further simplified to:

$$H(R) = -\sum_{i=1}^{n} \sum_{a \in R(\alpha_i)} p_i(a) \log p_i(a)$$

$$-\sum_{j=1}^{m} \sum_{b \in R(\beta_j)} \sum_{a_k \in R(\alpha_{jk})} p_{j1}(a_1) p_{j2}(a_2) p_j(b|a_1, a_2) \log p_j(b|a_1, a_2)$$

$$\tag{5}$$

where $k = 1, 2$ and, for any random element $\gamma$, $R(\gamma)$ ("range of $\gamma$") denotes the set of possible outcomes of $\gamma$, $\sigma(\beta_j) = \alpha_{j1}$ and $\tau(\beta_j) = \alpha_{j_2}$ as before.

Equation (5) indicates that the entropy of a first order random graph $R$ can be found in a straightforward way from the marginal distributions of the random vertices and of the random arcs conditioned on their endpoints. The term contributing to the overall entropy in (5) by the random element $\gamma$ will be denoted by $H(\gamma)$, i.e.

$$H(\alpha_i) \overset{\Delta}{=} -\sum_{a \in R(\alpha_i)} p_i(a) \log p_i(a)$$

and

$$H(\beta_j) \triangleq - \sum_{b \in R(\beta_j)} \sum_{a_k \in R(\alpha_{jk})} p_{j1}(a_1)p_{j2}(a_2)p_j(b|a_1, a_2) \log p_j(b|a_1, a_2),$$

$$(k = 1, 2) \ .$$

Using this notation, (5) becomes

$$H(R) = \sum_{i=1}^{n} H(\alpha_i) + \sum_{j=1}^{m} H(\beta_j) = \sum_{i=1}^{n+m} H(\gamma_i) \qquad (6)$$

**Example 3.2.** Figure 2 is a random graph with its vertex distributions listed inside the vertices and its conditional probability distributions of the random arcs given in Fig. 2b. Figures 2c and 2d are two labelled outcome graphs, $G_1$ and $G_2$ with $\mu_1$ and $\mu_2$ determined by the explicit labels in capital letters. Based on (3), the probabilities of $G_1$ and $G_2$ are:

$$p(G_1, \mu_1) = [p(a)p(c)p(e)][p(u|a, c)p(x|a, e)p(z|c, e)]$$
$$= 0.104 \ .$$
$$p(G_2, \mu_2) = [p(a)p(d)p(f)][p(v|a, d)p(w|a, f)p(y|d, f)]$$
$$= 0.022.$$

The entropy of $R$ is:

$$H(R) = [H(A) + H(B) + H(C)] + [H(X) + H(Y) + H(Z)]$$
$$= [0.7219 + 0.8813 + 0.9710] + [0.7960 + 0.5726 + 0.3281] = 4.271$$

## 4. SYNTHESIS OF RANDOM GRAPHS FROM GRAPHS WITH A COMMON LABELLING

### 4.1. Synthesis from Labelled Attributed Graphs

From a set of attributed graphs with commonly labelled vertices and arcs (extended to isomorphic complete graphs of the largest order necessary) we can derive a labelled random graph with the attributed graphs as labelled outcome graphs in a straightforward way by using outcome frequencies to estimate the probabilities required. More precisely, let $C = \{G^1, G^2, \ldots, G^m\}$ be a class of complete attributed graphs of order $r$, partitioned into equivalence classes $\{C_1, C_2, \ldots, C_n\}$ by the equivalence relation

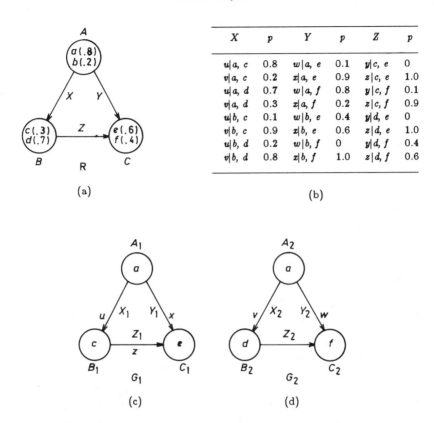

| X | p | Y | p | Z | p |
|---|---|---|---|---|---|
| $u\|a, c$ | 0.8 | $w\|a, e$ | 0.1 | $y\|c, e$ | 0 |
| $v\|a, c$ | 0.2 | $z\|a, e$ | 0.9 | $z\|c, e$ | 1.0 |
| $u\|a, d$ | 0.7 | $w\|a, f$ | 0.8 | $y\|c, f$ | 0.1 |
| $v\|a, d$ | 0.3 | $z\|a, f$ | 0.2 | $z\|c, f$ | 0.9 |
| $u\|b, c$ | 0.1 | $w\|b, e$ | 0.4 | $y\|d, e$ | 0 |
| $v\|b, c$ | 0.9 | $z\|b, e$ | 0.6 | $z\|d, e$ | 1.0 |
| $u\|b, d$ | 0.2 | $w\|b, f$ | 0 | $y\|d, f$ | 0.4 |
| $v\|b, d$ | 0.8 | $z\|b, f$ | 1.0 | $z\|d, f$ | 0.6 |

(a)  (b)

(c)  (d)

Fig. 2. A first order random graph and two of its labelled outcomes. (a) The random graph $R$. (b) The probability distributions of random arcs in $R$. (c), (d) Two labelled outcomes $G_1$ and $G_2$.

"completely isomorphic" and let each equivalence class $C_i$ be represented by a graph $G_i \in C_i$. We can represent $C$ by the set of distinct graphs $D = \{G_1, G_2, \ldots, G_n\}$, together with, for each $G_i$ in $D$, frequency $f_i$ indicating the size of the class $C_i$. Assume that there are given "labelling schemes" $\Psi_i = (\Psi_{iV} : V_i \to L_V, \Psi_{iA} : A_i \to L_A), i = 1, \ldots, n$, where $\Psi_{iV}$ is a bijection from the underlying structural vertex set of $G_i$ to a common set of vertex labels $L_V = \{1, 2, \ldots, r\}$ and $\Psi_{iA}$ similarly labels arcs with labels from $L_A = \{1, \ldots, r(r-1)\}$. We further assume that the arc labellings are consistent across all graphs in $D$ in the sense that the arc from vertex (labelled) $i$ to vertex (labelled) $j$ has the same label in all graphs.

From $D$ and its associated frequencies and labellings we can derive a random graph $R$ satisfying the following conditions:

1. There is a labelling scheme $\phi = (\phi_N : N \to L_N, \phi_E : E \to L_E)$ on $R$, where $\phi_N$ and $\phi_E$ are injections labelling the underlying vertices (in $N$) and arcs (in $E$) of $R$.

2. There are isomorphisms $\mu_i = (\mu_{iV}, \mu_{iA}) : G_i \to R, i = 1, \ldots, n$, which preserve these labels, i.e. such that $\Psi_{iV} = \phi_N \circ \mu_{iV}$ and $\Psi_{iA} = \phi_E \circ \mu_{iA}$.

3. $P(G_i, \mu_i) = f_i \sum_{i=1}^{n} f_i$.

In fact, condition 3 uniquely determines a probability distribution on the labelled outcome graphs defined by 1 and 2, and hence, as pointed out in Note 2 to Def. 2.4, a random graph.

The resulting joint distribution of random elements of $R$ exactly describes the variation observed in $C$ and assigns zero probability to the outcome graphs of $R$ which do not belong to $C$ (these are obtained by instantiating the random elements of $R$ to *combinations* not occurring in $C$). If the samples in $C$ do not constitute the entire population, then we would like $R$ to be more inclusive so as to model graphs similar to those in $C$ as well. This can be effected by allowing the attribute values observed for vertices and arcs to occur independently, constrained only by the assumptions for first order random graphs. This means estimating separately distributions of individual random vertices and conditional distributions of individual random arcs given endpoint values.

Denote the (structural) vertex (labelled) $j$ and arc (labelled) $k$ of attributed graph $G_i$ by $v_{ij}$ and $a_{ik}$, respectively, and its interpreters by $\nu_i$ and $\delta_i$. Then a complete, first order random graph $R$ of order $r$ representing graphs similar to those in $C$ is defined as follows.

Let the underlying graph structure of $R$ be complete, of order $r$, and labelled as the underlying graphs of $G_i$. For example, take it to be the underlying labelled graph of $G_1$. To define $\nu$ and $\delta$ for $R$, associate with vertex $i$ a random variable (random vertex) $\alpha_i$ which has as range space the set containing the attribute values of $v_{ki}$ for all $k$ and with arc $j$ a random variable $\beta_j$ which has as range space the set containing the attribute values of the $a_{kj}$ for all $k$, and define

$$p_i(a) = Pr(\alpha_i = a) = \left[ \sum_{k:\nu_k(v_{ki})=a} f_k \right] \Big/ \left[ \sum_j f_j \right] \qquad (7)$$

for all possible values $a$ of $\alpha_i$ (including $\phi$).

Similarly, define

$$p_j(b|a_1, a_2) = Pr(\beta_j = b | \sigma(\beta_j) = a_1 , \ \tau(\beta_j) = a_2)$$

$$= \sum_{\substack{i:\nu_i(\sigma(a_{ij}))=a_1 \\ \nu_i(\tau(a_{ij}))=a_2 \\ \delta_i(a_{ij})=b}} f_i \Big/ \sum_{\substack{i:\nu_i(\sigma(a_{ij}))=a_1 \\ \nu_i(\tau(a_{ij}))=a_2}} f_i \qquad (8)$$

for all possible values $b$ of $\beta_j$, $a_1$ of $\nu_i(\sigma(a_{ij}))$ and $a_2$ of $\nu_i(\tau(a_{ij}))$.

Now (7) and (8), together with assumptions (1)–(3) defining first order random graphs, define the joint probability distribution of $R$. The first order random graph $R$ so defined, which is more inclusive than that determined by (6) (having more possible outcome graphs in general), is called the *random graph synthesis* of the attributed graphs in $C$ or $D$), or simply the *synthesis* of $C$ (or $D$). The procedure applies, without change to a set of $C$ of non-isomorphic labelled attributed graphs, simply by first replacing each by its $r$-extension where $r$ is the largest vertex label in $C$.

## 4.2. Synthesis from Labelled First Order Random Graphs

Suppose that $F = \{R_1, R_2, \ldots, R_m\}$ is a set of first order random graphs independently synthesized from disjoint subsets of a class of attributed pattern graphs. Let $n_i$ be the number of graphs in the $i$th subset $i = 1, \ldots, m$. Assume, without loss of generality, that all the $R_i$ are (structurally) isomorphic with order $r$. Let the underlying graph of $R_i$ be $(N_i, E_i)$, with interpreters $\nu_i$ and $\delta_i$. Suppose further that there exists a set of labelling schemes $\phi_i = (\phi_{iN} : N_i \rightarrow L_N, \phi_{iE} : E_i \rightarrow L_E), i = 1, \ldots, n$, mapping the vertices and arcs of the $R_i$ into common label sets $L_N$ and $L_E$ with consistent arc labellings just as for the attributed graphs above. Then we can obtain for $F$ a synthesis which is a "super" random graph encompassing all $R_i, i = 1, \ldots, m$.

Let $\alpha_{ij}$ and $\beta_{ik}$ denote the $j$th random vertex and the $k$th random arc of $R_i$ "according to $\phi_i''$, $i = 1, \ldots , r$; $k = 1, \ldots , r(r - 1)$. Let

$$p_{ij}(a) = Pr(\alpha_{ij} = a)$$

and

$$p_{ik}(b|a_1, a_2) = Pr(\beta_{ik} = b|\sigma(\beta_{ik}) = a_1, \ \tau(\beta_{ik}) = a_2)$$

be the given probability distributions of the random vertices and arcs of $R_i$. Then the synthesis of $\{R_i\}$ is a random graph $R$ with the same complete labelled underlying graph structure as any of $R_i$ and $\nu, \delta$ and the joint distribution of random vertices and arcs defined as follows. With vertex $k$, we associate a random vertex $\alpha_k$ having the union of the range spaces of the $\alpha_{ik}$ over $i$ as its range space. Similarly, with arc $k$, we associate a random arc $\beta_k$ having the union of the range spaces of the $\beta_{ik}$ as its range space. We then define the probabilities.

**Definition 4.1.**

$$p_k(a) = Pr(\alpha_k = a) = \sum_{i=1}^{m} q_i p_{ik}(a) \tag{9}$$

with

$$q_i = n_i \left/ \sum_{i=1}^{m} n_i \right. . \tag{10}$$

**Definition 4.2.**

$$p_k(b|a_1, a_2) = Pr(\beta_k = b|\sigma(\beta_k) = a_1, \tau(\beta_k) = a_2)$$
$$= \sum_{i=1}^{m} q_i r_{ik} p_{ik}(b|a_1, a_2)/r_k \tag{11}$$

where

(1)  $\sigma(\beta_{ik}) = \alpha_{ih}, \tau(\beta_{ik}) = \alpha_{it}$

(2)  $\tau_{ik} = Pr(\sigma(\beta_{ik}) \neq \emptyset, \tau(\beta_{ik}) \neq \emptyset)$
$$= 1 - [P(\alpha_{ih} = \emptyset) + P(\alpha_{it} = \emptyset)]$$

(3)  $r_k = Pr(\sigma(\beta_k) \neq \emptyset, \tau(\beta_k) \neq \emptyset) = \sum_{i=1}^{m} q_i r_{ik}$

Note that $q_i$ represents the priori probability of $R_i$ in the original class of graphs which produced the $R_j; j = 1, 2, \ldots, m$. $r_{ik}$ and $r_k$ are introduced into (11) to reflect the assumption of the 1st order random graph (to get an appropriate probability space under the 1st order random assumption).

Now (9), (10) and (11), together with assumptions (1)-(3) for first order random graphs, define the joint distribution of (random vertices and arcs of) $R$. The random vertices and arcs obtained in this way will be called random elements *synthesized* from their corresponding (by label) random elements in the graphs $R_j; j = 1, \ldots, m$. The new random graph $R$ will be called a *synthesis of (the random graphs in) F according to the given labellings*. In the case of the synthesis of a pair of graphs with common labelling induced by isomorphism $\mu$, $R$ will be called a synthesis *according to $\mu$*.

Figure 3 shows two random graphs $R_1$ and $R_2$ to be synthesized under a given morphism $\mu$ which defines a common labelling once one is chosen arbitrarily for $R_1$. Here $R_1$ and $R_2$ are supposed to have equal *a priori* probabilities $q_1 = q_2$. Figure 4 shows the result of the synthesis.

So far, a common labelling of graphs is assumed to be known in the synthesis. When this is not the case, an optimal isomorphism between the random graphs will be used to establish a common labelling. This involves a consideration of increment of entropy in the synthesis of random graphs. The increment of entropy will be used in the definition of distance and similarity measures for attributed graphs and random graphs.

## 5. DISTANCE MEASURE BETWEEN RANDOM GRAPHS

### 5.1. Increment of Entropy

Let $+(R_1, R_2, \mu)$ denote the synthesis of the random graphs $R_1$ and $R_2$ under a common labelling established by a given morphism $\mu$, and $+(\gamma_1, \gamma_2, \mu)$ denote the synthesis of the random elements $\gamma_1$ and $\gamma_2$ in $R_1$ and $R_2$, respectively, corresponding according to $\mu$. Then we have the following definition.

**Definition 5.1.** Let $q_1$ and $q_2$ be *a priori* probabilities associated with $R_1$ and $R_2$ respectively. The *increment of entropy* in $\gamma$ after $R_1$ and $R_2$ are synthesized is defined as:

$$H'(\gamma) = H(\gamma) - [q_1 H(\gamma_1) + q_2 H(\gamma_2)] . \qquad (12)$$

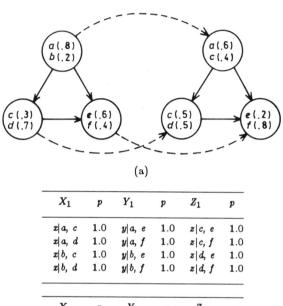

(a)

| $X_1$ | $p$ | $Y_1$ | $p$ | $Z_1$ | $p$ |
|---|---|---|---|---|---|
| $x\vert a, c$ | 1.0 | $y\vert a, e$ | 1.0 | $z\vert c, e$ | 1.0 |
| $x\vert a, d$ | 1.0 | $y\vert a, f$ | 1.0 | $z\vert c, f$ | 1.0 |
| $x\vert b, c$ | 1.0 | $y\vert b, e$ | 1.0 | $z\vert d, e$ | 1.0 |
| $x\vert b, d$ | 1.0 | $y\vert b, f$ | 1.0 | $z\vert d, f$ | 1.0 |

| $X_2$ | $p$ | $Y_2$ | $p$ | $Z_2$ | $p$ |
|---|---|---|---|---|---|
| $x\vert a, c$ | 1.0 | $y\vert a, e$ | 1.0 | $z\vert c, e$ | 1.0 |
| $x\vert a, d$ | 1.0 | $y\vert a, f$ | 1.0 | $y\vert c, f$ | 1.0 |
| $y\vert c, c$ | 1.0 | $x\vert c, e$ | 1.0 | $z\vert d, e$ | 1.0 |
| $y\vert c, d$ | 1.0 | $x\vert c, f$ | 1.0 | $z\vert d, f$ | 1.0 |

(b)

Fig. 3. **Example of random graph synthesis.** (a) $\mu$: $R_1 \rightarrow R_2$. (b) The probability distributions of random arcs in $R_1$ and $R_2$.

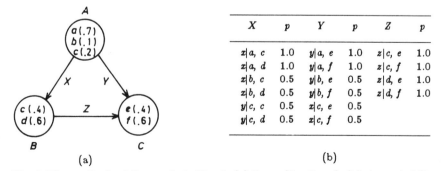

(a)

| $X$ | $p$ | $Y$ | $p$ | $Z$ | $p$ |
|---|---|---|---|---|---|
| $x\vert a, c$ | 1.0 | $y\vert a, e$ | 1.0 | $z\vert c, e$ | 1.0 |
| $x\vert a, d$ | 1.0 | $y\vert a, f$ | 1.0 | $z\vert c, f$ | 1.0 |
| $x\vert b, c$ | 0.5 | $y\vert b, e$ | 0.5 | $z\vert d, e$ | 1.0 |
| $x\vert b, d$ | 0.5 | $y\vert b, f$ | 0.5 | $z\vert d, f$ | 1.0 |
| $y\vert c, c$ | 0.5 | $x\vert c, e$ | 0.5 | | |
| $y\vert c, d$ | 0.5 | $x\vert c, f$ | 0.5 | | |

(b)

Fig. 4. **The synthesis of the graphs in Fig. 3.** (a) $R = +(R_1, R_2, \mu)$; (b) the probability distribution of random arcs in $R$.

Analogously, the *increment of entropy* in $R = +(R_1, R_2, \mu)$ is defined as

$$H'(R) = H(R) - [q_1 H(R_1) + q_2 H(R_2)] . \tag{13}$$

**Property 1.** The increment of entropy in $\gamma = +(\gamma_1, \gamma_2, \mu)$ is bounded:

$$0 \leq H'(\gamma) \leq 1 .$$

**Proof.** Let the probability distributions associated with $\gamma_1$ and $\gamma_2$ be $(p_{11}, p_{12}, \ldots, p_{1n})$ and $(p_{21}, p_{22}, \ldots, p_{2n})$ respectively. Then the probability distribution of the synthesized random element associated with the synthesized graph will be

$$(q_1 p_{11} + q_2 p_{21}, q_1 p_{12} + q_2 p_{22}, \ldots, q_1 p_{1n} + q_2 p_{2n}) .$$

Thus,

$$
\begin{aligned}
H'(\gamma) &= H(\gamma) - q_1 H(\gamma_1) - q_2 H(\gamma_2) \\
&= q_1 \sum_{k=1}^{n} p_{1k} \log p_{1k} + q_2 \sum_{k=1}^{n} p_{2k} \log p_{2k} \\
&\quad - \sum_{k=1}^{n} (q_1 p_{1k} + q_2 p_{2k}) \log(q_1 p_{1k} + q_2 p_{2k}) \\
&= \sum_{k=1}^{n} q_1 p_{1k} \log[p_{1k}/(q_1 p_{1k} + q_2 p_{2k})] \\
&\quad + \sum_{k=1}^{n} q_2 p_{2k} \log[p_{2k}/(q_1 p_{1k} + q_2 p_{2k})] \\
&= \sum_{j=1}^{2} \sum_{k=1}^{n} q_j p_{jk} \log[p_{jk}/(q_1 p_{1k} + q_2 p_{2k})] .
\end{aligned}
$$

The above expression can be interpreted as the mutual information associated with a channel of two symbols[16]. Thus

$$H'(\gamma) \leq -q_1 \log_2 q_1 - q_2 \log_2 q_2 \leq \log_2 2 = 1 .$$

**Property 2.** If R is of order $N$, then

$$0 \leq H'(R) \leq N^2 .$$

The proof of this property is similar to the one above.

## 5.2. Weighted Increment of Entropy

In addition to determining an increase in the entropies of the resulting synthesized random graph elements, the choice of correspondence $\mu$ between two random graphs may entail other important costs. For example, it may be relevant to consider some measure of the distance (or difference) between the values taken by the random elements being merged, as a cost incurred in synthesizing a new one from them. The idea is that we would like, in general, to avoid merging elements with very different values. This difference in values is not taken into account by the unweighted entropy measure (except when discriminating identical from non-identical values). For example, values that differ by half the possible range of the attribute in question, are handled in the same way as values that differ by only $1/1000$ of the possible range, in calculating the increment of entropy.

One way of taking the difference into account is to compound the loss of information cost, as reflected in the increase in entropy in a synthesized random element, with another cost varying directly with the (normalized) distance between (vector) values of the component random elements being merged. The resulting measure of cost will be called the *weighted increment of entropy* in the synthesized graph.

Let $s$ and $t$ be possible outcomes of $\gamma_1$ and $\gamma_2$, respectively. Define the weighted distance between $s$ and $t$ as follows:

**Definition 5.2.** The weighted distance from $s$ to $t$ is

$$
d(s,t) = \begin{cases}
0 & \text{if } s = t = \phi \\
k & \text{if exactly one of } s \text{ and } t \text{ is } \phi \\
\displaystyle\sum_{i=1}^{n} w_i |s_i - t_i| & \text{if } s = (s_1, \ldots, s_n) \in \mathbb{R}^n \text{ and} \\
& \qquad t = (t_1, \ldots, t_n) \in \mathbb{R}^n
\end{cases}
\tag{14}
$$

where $k$ is set to some (large) value reflecting the cost of matching a null element with a non-null one and $w_i$ is a weighting factor associated with the $i$ th attribute $C_i$. Typically, $w_i$ might be a normalization factor such as $\frac{1}{r_i}$ where $r_i$ is the range of values of $C_i$. Attributes $C_j$ with nominal values can also be included by replacing $|s_j - t_j|$ in (14) by 0 or 1 according to whether $s_j = t_j$ or $s_j \neq t_j$.

Now the distance from random element $\gamma_1$ to random element $\gamma_2$ can be defined as the average distance of their outcomes:

**Definition 5.3.** The distance from $\gamma_1$ to $\gamma_2$ is defined as

$$d(\gamma_1, \gamma_2) = \sum_{s \in \gamma_1} \sum_{t \in \gamma_2} Pr(\gamma_1 = s) Pr(\gamma_2 = t) d(s, t) \tag{15}$$

where $s \in \gamma_1$ and $t \in \gamma_2$ have the obvious meaning.

We note that $d(\gamma_1, \gamma_2) \geq 0$ and $d(\gamma_1, \gamma_2) = 0$ if and only if there is a value $e$ such that $Pr(\gamma_1 = e) = Pr(\gamma_2 = e) = 1$. In other words, when $\gamma_1$ and $\gamma_2$ always (with probability 1) have the same value the distance between them is 0.

**Definition 5.4.** The weighted increment of entropy $H''(\gamma)$ in the synthesis of random element $\gamma$ from random elements $\gamma_1$ and $\gamma_2$ is defined as

$$H''(\gamma) = d(\gamma_1, \gamma_2) H'(\gamma) \tag{16}$$

where $d(\gamma_1, \gamma_2)$ is defined by (15) and $H'(\gamma)$ by (12).

**Definition 5.5.** The weighted increment of entropy $H''(R)$ in the synthesis of random graph $R$ from $R_1$ and $R_2$ is defined to be the sum of the weighted increments of entropy in the synthesis of all the random elements of R, i.e.

$$H''(R) = \sum_{\gamma \in R} H''(\gamma) \tag{17}$$

where $\gamma \in R$ has the obvious meaning.

**Property 3.** If $d(s, t) \in [0, 1]$ (for example by taking $k = 1$ and $w_i = \frac{1}{r_i}$ in (14)), then the weighted increment of entropy in the synthesis $\gamma$ of random elements $\gamma_1$ and $\gamma_2$ is bounded:

$$0 \leq H''(\gamma) \leq 1$$

**Property 4.** If $d(s, t) \in [0, 1]$ then the weighted increment of entropy in the synthesis $R$ of two random graphs, $R_1$ and $R_2$, of order $N$ is bounded:

$$0 \leq H''(R) \leq N^2 .$$

These properties follow from properties 1 and 2 above and the definitions of $H''(\gamma)$ and $H''(R)$.

## 5.3. Distance and Optimal Isomorphism

Since the weighted increment of entropy $H''(R)$ represents the loss of information and the value distance costs incurred in synthesizing R from $R_1$ and $R_2$ according to isomorphism $\mu$ when $\mu$ is unknown and $R_1$ and $R_2$ have no common labelling or orientation, we want to choose $\mu$ so as to minimize $H''(R)$ before carrying out the synthesis. The resulting optimal isomorphism will be denoted $\mu^*$. The resulting weighted increment of entropy can be used as a measure of distance between $R_1$ and $R_2$.

**Definition 5.6.** The distance between (unlabelled) random graphs $R_1$ and $R_2$ is defined to be

$$d(R_1, R_2) = \min_{\mu}(H''[+(R_1, R_2, \mu)])$$
$$= H''[+(R_1, R_2, \mu^*)] . \tag{18}$$

**Property 5.** Let the order of the synthesis of $R_1$ and $R_2$ be $N$. The distance measure $d(R_1, R_2)$ has the following properties:

1. $0 \le d(R_1, R_2) \le N^2$,
2. $d(R_1, R_2) = 0$ iff $R_1 = R_2$ (complete isomorphism); and
3. $d(R_1, R_2) = d(R_2, R_1)$.

Unfortunately, this distance measure generally does not satisfy the triangle inequality of a metric due to the presence of the probabilities in (15) and hence in (18).

In order to compare distances between random graphs of different orders, it is desirable to normalize the absolute distance, making it a measure of relative similarity. Since the increment of entropy in a synthesis of two random graphs is bounded by 0 and $N^2$, we propose the following definition.

**Definition 5.7.** Let $R_1$ and $R_2$ be of order $N$. We define the *similarity* $s(R_1, R_2)$ between $R_1$ and $R_2$ to be:

$$s(R_1, R_2) = 1 - d(R_1, R_2)/N^2 . \tag{19}$$

**Property 6.** The similarity measure defined above has the following properties:

1. $0 \le s(R_1, R_2) \le 1$;
2. $s(R_1, R_2) = 1$ iff $R_1 = R_2$ (completely isomorphic); and
3. $s(R_1, R_2) = s(R_2, R_1)$.

Since an attributed graph can be treated as a special case of a random graph, the above distance (or similarity) can be applied to (1) two attributed graphs, (2) an attributed graph and a random graph, and (3) two random graphs.

## 6. SYNTHESIS OF RANDOM GRAPHS FROM UNLABELLED SAMPLE GRAPHS

When an ensemble of unlabelled attributed graphs is given, we do not, in general, have any way of synthesizing a random graph to represent the ensemble unless we can first establish a common labelling. Given any common labelling, or equivalently any set of isomorphisms to a common underlying graph structure, a random graph $R$ can be synthesized from the ensemble and the entropy $H(R)$ of $R$ can be calculated. Since the entropy reflects the variability of the labelled outcome graphs of $R$, we would like to choose the common labelling so as to minimize $H(R)$. This global optimization problem[3] does not lead to a computationally practical method for choosing the labelling, because there are too many possible orientations to consider, especially when the number and order of the graphs is high. Therefore, we propose a hierarchical method for approximating the solution by first finding local optima and then selecting the best.

Besides simplicity in computation, the hierarchical approximation has another advantage. It is capable of detecting subclasses in the ensemble. Without such a capability, the synthesis process may lead to unnatural and misleading results.

### 6.1. A Hierarchical Synthesis Process

As alluded to earlier, a common labelling can be established for a pair of graphs, $R_1$ and $R_2$, by using the weighted entropy $H''(R)$ of $R$ synthesized from them under isomorphism $\mu$ as an objective function and optimizing (minimizing $H''(R)$) with respect to $\mu$. This yields an optimal isomorphism $\mu^*$ which defines a common (arbitrary) labelling on $R_1$ and $R_2$. The use of $H''(R)$ as an objective function is motivated by the desire to minimize both the differences in the resulting labelled graphs and the loss of information incurred by merging them.

Let $D = \{G_1, G_2, \dots, G_n\}$ be an ensemble of attributed graphs. Without loss of generality, each $G_i$ in $D$ can be treated as a random graph $R_i$. We can thus replace $D$ by a set $F = \{R_1, R_2, \dots, R_n\}$, where each $R_i$ in $F$ is a random graph. Let $R_{ij}$ denote the synthesis of $R_i$ and $R_j$ under the optimal isomorphism $\mu_{ij}^*$. Then the distance $d_{ij}$ between them is $H''(R_{ij})$. We use two $n \times n$ arrays $L = [\mu_{ij}]$ and $M = [d_{ij}]$, to direct the synthesis of $F$. Obviously, $M$ is a symmetric matrix with diagonal elements $d_{ii} = 0$ for all $i$. In the iterative process, those pairs of distinct graphs in $F$ with a minimum distance in $M$ are combined and replaced by the synthesis. After re-indexing, $F$ is reduced to $F = \{R_1, R_2, \dots, R_m\}, m < n$. This procedure is repeated until one random graph, the synthesis of the set, remains or until it is terminated by a thresholding criterion. The final remaining first order random graph(s) represent(s) the class pattern (or subclass patterns), encompassing and generalizing its outcomes in $D$.

## 6.2. Thresholding

In a structural pattern recognition task, when a class of patterns is composed of several subclasses, we can introduce a similarity threshold to determine the splitting condition. If the criterion function value between two random graphs exceeds the threshold, instead of synthesizing them into one random graph, we allow them to coexist as tentative representations of separate pattern subclasses of the same class.

A criterion which immediately suggests itself for thresholding is the normalized similarity measure $s_{ij}$ between graphs $R_i$ and $R_j$. If an appropriate point $t \in [0, 1]$ could be chosen, then only those pairs of random graphs with $s_{ij} \geq t$ would be synthesized.

However, since it is difficult to prescribe a good value for $t$ reliably in advance, a dynamic thresholding criterion is proposed. Let $S_i$ and $S_j$ be the lists of all the similarity measures encountered in the stepwise synthesis processes producing $R_i$ and $R_j$, respectively. We define the *average similarity measure of $R_i$ and $R_j$* to be

$$s^* = \left( \sum_{s \in S_i} s + \sum_{s \in S_j} s \right) \Big/ (|S_i| + |S_j|) \tag{20}$$

where $|S|$ denotes the number of entries in the list S. The dynamic threshold $t^*$ can then be defined as:

$$t^* = r \times s^* \tag{21}$$

where $r$ again is a prescribed rate with a value in $[0,1]$.

In the synthesis process, $R_i$ and $R_j$ will be synthesized only if $s_{ij} \geq t^*$. Obviously, $t^*$ becomes tighter (larger) when the set of graphs shows increasing similarity as more and more similar graphs are put together in the set. This variability characteristic of $t^*$ makes it flexible and useful when no *a priori* knowledge of the class of graphs is available, even though the determination of $r$ in (21) depends on knowledge of the problem domain.

6.3. The Graph Synthesis Algorithm

In this section, we present the Hierarchical Graph Synthesis algorithm (HGS) in pseudo-code.

Input:
(1)    A class of graphs $D = \{G_1, G_2, \dots, G_n\}$;
(2)    (a) A prescribed number of classes, $n_k$; or
       (b) (i) A prescribed graph similarity threshold $t$; and/or
           (ii) A prescribed rate for average similarity $r$.

Output:
(1)    A reduced set of random graphs, $F = \{R_1, R_2, \dots, R_m\}, 1 \leq m \leq n$;
(2)    The labellings of the outcome graphs in $D$.

Steps:

```
begin {HGS}
  begin {initiation}
    F := D;
    define all Rᵢ in F to be "new";
    current_number := number of entries in D;
    for i := 1 to n do Sᵢ := empty;
    L := n × n empty matrix;
    M : = n × n empty matrix;
  end; {initiation}
  if current_number ≥ 2 then repeat
    for each pair of graphs Rᵢ and Rⱼ in F do
      if Rᵢ = "new" or Rⱼ = "new" then begin
        find optimal isomorphism μᵢⱼ and save μᵢⱼ in L;
        compute distance dᵢⱼ and save dᵢⱼ in M;
        define Rᵢ and Rⱼ to be "old";
      end; {for-if}
      min_diff : = minimum distance value in M;
      for each dᵢⱼ in M do begin
        if dᵢⱼ ≤ min_diff and Rᵢ, Rⱼ not synthesized then
```

```
    begin
      compute s_ij;
      if S_i = empty and S_j = empty then s* := s_ij
      else begin
        compute s* from S_i and S_j; {see (20)}
        t* := r × s*;
      end; {else}
      if s_ij ≥ t and s_ij ≥ t* then begin
        R_ij := +(R_i, R_j, μ_ij); {synthesize R_i, R_j}
        F := F - R_j; {deletion}
        label G_k, the original graph in D
          corresponding to R_i according to μ_ij;
        R_j := R_ij;
        reset R_j to be "new";
        S_j := S_i, S_j, s_ij; {concatenation}
      end; { if s_ij}
    end; { if d_ij}
  end; {for}
  re_index all remaining graphs {R_1, R_2, ... , R_m} in F;
  re_index elements in M corresponding to F;
  previous_number := current_number;
  current_number := number of graphs remaining in F;
  until current_number = previous_number, or n_k, or 1;
end.  {HGS}
```

The time complexity of the above algorithm is of order $O(n^3)$ times the order of the average time complexity of the optimal graph isomorphism search.

## 7. APPLICATIONS OF RANDOM GRAPHS IN PATTERN RECOGNITION

The application of random graphs in structural pattern recognition can be illustrated by two simple examples. First, we use an English character recognition problem to illustrate both unsupervised and supervised classification. Next, we use a string mutation and alignment problem to show how the random graph approach can be used to model a class of strings and detect their underlying pattern of variation.

## 7.1. Characterization of Structural Pattern Classes

A random graph, synthesized from a cluster of attributed graphs, reflects the probabilistic configuration of the cluster. If the graphs are designated as pertaining to the same pattern class, the synthesis process is referred to as *supervised* construction of a class pattern. If the class memberships for a given set of graphs are not known, the synthesis, which generates more than one random graph, is considered an *unsupervised* classification or *clustering*.

The probability distribution of a random graph can be considered the *structural probability distribution* of a pattern class. One of the advantages of such a distribution is that it can be used as a base graph in graph matching for classification purposes[3]. Major advantages of this representation are:

1. The distribution describes the statistical variation in both the structural and the attribute value information of the entire class of graphs. It is a more informative representation of the class than, say, the cluster prototypes.
2. The first order random graph allows varied or deformed patterns as members of the class even though they were not included in the training set.
3. A pattern can be classified by comparing it successively to each random graph in a set representing the possible classes.

## 7.2. Classification of Structural Patterns

Suppose that $R_1, R_2, \ldots, R_n$ represent $n$ different classes (or subclasses) of structural patterns. Let $G$ be an attributed graph representing an unknown pattern. To classify $G$, we can use either the minimum distance rule or the maximum likelihood rule. In both cases, we first find optimal isomorphisms $\mu_i : G \rightarrow R_i, i = 1, \ldots, n$. Depending on the criterion used, we then obtain the distance $d(G, R_i)$ between $G$ and $R_i$ or the probabilities $p(G, \mu_i)$ of $G$ being an outcome of $R_i$. Next, using the minimum distance rule, we classify $G$ in class $i$, if and only if

$$d(G, R_i) < d(G, R_j), \text{ for all } j, \ i \neq j.$$

Using the maximum likelihood rule, we classify $G$ in class $i$ if and only if

$$p(R_i)p(G, \mu_i) > p(R_j)p(G, \mu_j), \ i \neq j, \quad \text{ for all } j$$

where $p(R_j)$ is the *a priori* probability of class $j$ (characterized by $R_j$) and $p(G, \mu_j)$, is the probability of $G$ being an outcome of $R_j$ according to $\mu_j$.

### 7.3. An Illustrative Example in Character Recognition

In this example, an English character recognition problem is used to illustrate the application of random graphs to structural pattern recognition. A pseudo random number generator is used to generate strokes with various orientations in representations of the handwritten English letters F, H, and E. Of the 60 characters generated, 20 for each letter, all 47 distinct variations are listed in Fig. 5, where the numbers to the left and right of ":" denote the character index and its frequency of occurrence respectively. Attribute codes for character primitives and primitive relations are defined in Fig. 6 and each variation is represented accordingly as an attributed graph (see Fig. 8).

With the graph synthesis procedure HGS, pairwise distances among the attributed graphs are first computed and tabulated. The pair(s) with the shortest distance are then merged. Next, new distances between the merged graphs and the remaining graphs are computed. The closest pair(s) are merged again. The process continues as indicated in the hierarchical tree (Fig. 7a) from which we observe that all 47 distinct characters are successfully clustered into their respective letter classes.

Fig. 5. Variations of handwritten English letters F, H, and E.

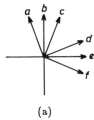

(a)

| Code | Description | Diagram |
|------|-------------|---------|
| u | above | ▭ (above) |
| v | bending | ⌐ or L |
| w | branching | ⊢ or ⊣ |
| x | crossing | + |
| y | near (gap) | ⌐ or ⊢ or L |
| z | left of | ‖ |

(b)

Fig. 6. Attribute codes for primitives and relations. (a) Primitive codes. (b) Relation codes.

Using the three estimated probability distributions representing variations of letters F, H, and E in Fig. 7b, we can classify the attributed graph of an unknown sample into one of the pattern classes. For three unknown patterns (Fig. 8) not used in the training process, correct

## 7.4. The String Mutation and Alignment Problem

The string mutation and alignment problem is of great importance in the study of mutation of biomolecules[17,18], as well as in syntactic pattern

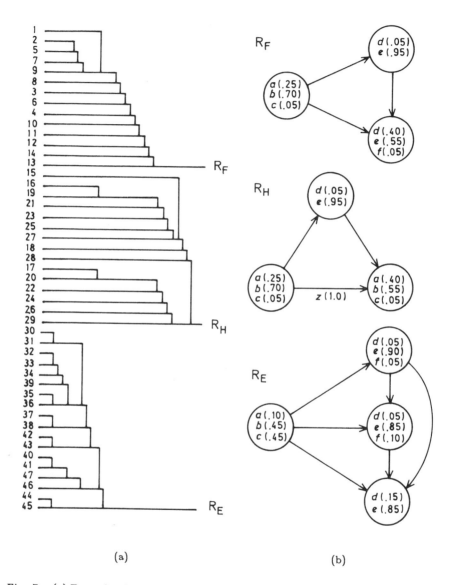

Fig. 7.   (a) Example of hierarchical clustering process for random graph synthesis.
(b) The synthesized random graphs represent the ensembles of F's, H's and E's respectively. The conditional probabilities of the edge attribute values conditioned on those of the incident vertices are not shown here.

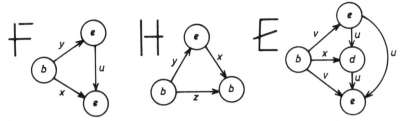

Fig. 8. Three unknown patterns and their attributed graphs.

recognition[19-21]. To date, most of the distance or similarity measures used for comparing or aligning strings have been based on criterion functions defined for the two strings under comparison. The characteristics of the ensemble or subensembles of strings are not taken into consideration in the comparison process. As a result, it is extremely difficult to resolve ambiguity when two strings are compared in order to reveal or extract the characteristics of the ensemble or subensembles. By treating a string as a special case of an attributed graph, we can use random graph synthesis to integrate an ensemble of strings and reveal explicitly its statistical pattern of variation[22]. This pattern, expressed in terms of a probability distribution, enables us to recover a common labelling scheme (common alignment), using which, individual strings can be compared with the distribution of the random string or with each other.

A string is an ordered sequence of symbols. Let $\{x_i\}$ be a set of strings generated from the same source (or belonging to the same class). Let us suppose that, due to variations, mutations or deformations, the individual $x_i$ may be different in their corresponding symbols, or even in length. Given $\{x_i\}$, we are interested in the synthesis of a random string R which aligns and labels the individual symbols in all $x_i$ with a sequence of random elements. The random elements describe the statistical variation of the corresponding symbols in the strings. Therefore, each symbol in $x_i$ can be described as an outcome of its corresponding random element in R with an associated probability. The synthesis can be considered a supervised learning process.

To create test data with which to study the variation of strings in an ensemble, we consider that a string could be mutated or deformed into another through certain local changes of symbols, including deletion, insertion and replacement of one symbol by another. Suppose that the

Table 1. Substitution and deletion probabilities of symbols.

$$p(j|i) \text{ and } p(\phi|i)$$

| | $a_j$: $a$ | $b$ | $c$ | $d$ | $e$ | $f$ | $g$ | $h$ | $\phi$ |
|---|---|---|---|---|---|---|---|---|---|
| $a_i$: $a$ | 0.8 | 0.1 | 0 | 0 | 0 | 0 | 0 | 0 | 0.1 |
| $b$ | 0 | 0.8 | 0.1 | 0 | 0 | 0 | 0 | 0 | 0.1 |
| $c$ | 0 | 0 | 0.8 | 0.1 | 0 | 0 | 0 | 0 | 0.1 |
| $d$ | 0 | 0 | 0 | 0.8 | 0.1 | 0 | 0 | 0 | 0.1 |
| $e$ | 0 | 0 | 0 | 0 | 0.8 | 0.1 | 0 | 0 | 0.1 |
| $f$ | 0 | 0 | 0 | 0 | 0 | 0.8 | 0.1 | 0 | 0.1 |
| $g$ | 0 | 0 | 0 | 0 | 0 | 0 | 0.8 | 0.1 | 0.1 |
| $i$ | 0.1 | 0 | 0 | 0 | 0 | 0 | 0 | 0.8 | 0.1 |

Table 2. Insertion probabilities next to $S_4$ and $S_8$.

$$r(j|\ 4) \text{ and } r(j|\ 8)$$

| $a_j$: | $a$ | $b$ | $c$ | $d$ | $e$ | $f$ | $g$ | $h$ | $\phi$ |
|---|---|---|---|---|---|---|---|---|---|
| $S_4$ | 0.1 | 0.1 | 0 | 0 | 0 | 0 | 0 | 0 | 0.8 |
| $S_8$ | 0 | 0.1 | 0.1 | 0 | 0 | 0 | 0 | 0 | 0.8 |

strings are made from an alphabet $A = \{a_1, a_2, \ldots, a_n\}$ of $n$ symbols. Let $s = s_1 s_2 \ldots s_m (s_i \in A)$ be a "source" string composed of $m$ symbols from $A$. Let $p(j|i)$ denote the (substitution) probability that symbol $a_i$ is deformed into symbol $a_j (a_i, a_j \in A)$, and $q(\phi|i)$ denote the (deletion) probability that $a_i$ is deleted. Furthermore, let $r(j|i)$ denote the (insertion) probability that the symbol $a_j$ is inserted right after $s_i$ in the string $s$.

In this illustration, we let $A = \{a_1, a_2, \ldots, a_8\} = \{a, b, \ldots, h\}$ and $s = s_1 s_2 \ldots s_8 = gahcagba$. Assume that the substitution and deletion probabilities are as shown in Table 1 and the insertion probabilities following $s_4$ and $s_8$ as listed in Table 2. The other insertion probabilities not listed in Table 2 are 0. Using the mutation and deformation probabilities tabulated in Tables 1 and 2 and the source string $s = gahcagba$, we generate a set of strings which are mutations or variations of $s$. In this example, 150 strings are generated and then sorted, first according to their lengths and then in alphabetic order, yielding a total of 112 distinct strings with their corresponding frequencies f as listed in Table 3.

Each string is now represented by an attributed graph with the symbols of the string as attributed nodes and arcs joining consecutive symbols in the obvious way. The arcs will be considered to have the same (arbitrary) attribute value, thus playing a trivial role in the synthesis process.

The set of 112 strings is now used as input to our hierarchical graph synthesis algorithm. For each pair of input strings, the similarity is computed. Though various definitions of similarity of strings have been proposed[17-20], the one adopted here is based on (15)–(19), with

$$d(a_i, a_j) = \begin{Bmatrix} 0 & \text{if} & i = j \\ 1 & \text{if} & i \neq j \end{Bmatrix}, \quad d(a_i, \phi) = 0 \quad \text{and} \quad d(\phi, \phi) = 1 \quad \text{in} \quad (15) \ .$$

A random string is first synthesized from the pair of strings with the closest resemblance. The process then repeats, as described earlier, until the synthesized random string for the entire ensemble is obtained. This random string then characterizes the ensemble. Note that after the first synthesis, the random "strings" will in general have more than one arc leading from some vertices.

Table 4 shows the probability distributions of the 10 random elements in the final random string. For instance, the first random element has a probability distribution $p(g) = 0.787, p(h) = 0.087$, and $p(\phi) = 0.126$, where $\phi$ represents the null outcome. We note that the probabilities of the outcome symbols in the random elements are slightly different from the variation probabilities of symbols defined in Tables 1 and 2. This can be attributed mainly to the effect of the small sample size (150) generated by the pseudo random number generator. We would expect a closer match in the corresponding probabilities if a larger sample size were adopted.

Table 5 illustrates the alignment of the individual strings according to the common labelling scheme (or the optimal matching between the input string and the random string) resulting from the synthesis. Here a null symbol is represented by "*". We note that since the hierarchical synthesis algorithm merges the most similar pairs of strings iteratively, the strings in Table 5 are no longer in ascending order by ID number as in Table 3.

## 8. CONCLUSION

We have shown in this chapter that structural patterns can be represented effectively by attributed graphs and random graphs. After introducing the basic concepts and notation, we have provided formal definitions of

Table 3. Variations of the given string $s = gahcagba$.

| ID | f | String | ID | f | String | ID | f | String |
|---|---|---|---|---|---|---|---|---|
| 1 | 1 | ahcab | 39 | 1 | gahcagb | 77 | 4 | gahcbgba |
| 2 | 1 | ahcba | 40 | 1 | gahcahb | 78 | 1 | gahcbgbb |
| 3 | 1 | ahchb | 41 | 1 | gahcgba | 79 | 1 | gahcbgca |
| 4 | 1 | gaagb | 42 | 1 | gahdbab | 80 | 1 | gahcbhba |
| 5 | 1 | gagba | 43 | 1 | gahdbga | 81 | 1 | gahdaagb |
| 6 | 1 | gcagb | 44 | 1 | gahdbgb | 82 | 3 | gahdagba |
| 7 | 1 | ghcab | 45 | 1 | gahgbab | 83 | 1 | gbacagba |
| 8 | 1 | hahba | 46 | 1 | gbcagba | 84 | 1 | gbacahba |
| 9 | 1 | aacgba | 47 | 1 | gbhaaca | 85 | 1 | gbhbagba |
| 10 | 1 | acbgba | 48 | 2 | gbhagba | 86 | 2 | gbhcagba |
| 11 | 1 | gahaga | 49 | 1 | gbhcaha | 87 | 1 | gbhcagca |
| 12 | 1 | gahcaa | 50 | 4 | ghcagba | 88 | 1 | gbhcahcb |
| 13 | 1 | gahcab | 51 | 1 | haacgbb | 89 | 1 | ghcagcab |
| 14 | 1 | gahcga | 52 | 1 | hadagba | 90 | 1 | ghcbgcab |
| 15 | 1 | gahdba | 53 | 1 | hahcaba | 91 | 5 | hahcagba |
| 16 | 1 | gbagba | 54 | 1 | hcbgbab | 92 | 1 | hahcagca |
| 17 | 1 | gbcabb | 55 | 1 | acbagbac | 93 | 1 | hahcbgba |
| 18 | 1 | hcagba | 56 | 1 | ahcagbab | 94 | 1 | hbacagbc |
| 19 | 1 | aacaaha | 57 | 1 | ahcagbac | 95 | 1 | hbhdagbb |
| 20 | 1 | ahcagba | 58 | 1 | ahcbagba | 96 | 1 | bacaahbbb |
| 21 | 1 | ahcbgca | 59 | 1 | gaacabab | 97 | 1 | gaacagbac |
| 22 | 1 | ahcbhba | 60 | 1 | gaacagba | 98 | 1 | gaadaagba |
| 23 | 1 | bhcagba | 61 | 1 | gaacagbb | 99 | 1 | gahcaagba |
| 24 | 1 | bhcbgba | 62 | 1 | gaacbaga | 100 | 1 | gahcaagca |
| 25 | 1 | gaaagbb | 63 | 1 | gaacbgbb | 101 | 1 | gahcaahbb |
| 26 | 1 | gaacaga | 64 | 1 | gacaagba | 102 | 2 | gahcagbab |
| 27 | 1 | gabhcac | 65 | 1 | gacbagba | 103 | 1 | gahcahbac |
| 28 | 1 | gacagba | 66 | 1 | gacbbgbb | 104 | 1 | gahcbahba |
| 29 | 1 | gacagca | 67 | 1 | gahaagbb | 105 | 1 | gahcbgbab |
| 30 | 1 | gacahba | 68 | 1 | gahagbab | 106 | 1 | gahdaagba |
| 31 | 2 | gacbgba | 69 | 2 | gahcaaba | 107 | 1 | gahdagbab |
| 32 | 1 | gacbhba | 70 | 1 | gahcabab | 108 | 1 | gbcbahbab |
| 33 | 1 | gadagba | 71 | 19 | gahcagba | 109 | 1 | gbhcaagba |
| 34 | 2 | gahagba | 72 | 1 | gahcagbb | 110 | 1 | gbhcahbab |
| 35 | 1 | gahagbb | 73 | 2 | gahcagca | 111 | 1 | hahbbgbac |
| 36 | 1 | gahagcb | 74 | 1 | gahcahac | 112 | 1 | gahcaagbab |
| 37 | 1 | gahcaba | 75 | 1 | gahcahba | | | |
| 38 | 2 | gahcaga | 76 | 1 | gahcbaba | | | |

Table 4. Probability distributions of the random elements.

| R.E. | | P.D. | R.E. | | P.D. | R.E. | | P.D. |
|---|---|---|---|---|---|---|---|---|
| 1 | $g$ | 0.787 | 5 | $a$ | 0.133 | 9 | $a$ | 0.827 |
| | $h$ | 0.087 | | $b$ | 0.140 | | $b$ | 0.087 |
| | $\phi$ | 0.126 | | $\phi$ | 0.727 | | $\phi$ | 0.086 |
| 2 | $a$ | 0.767 | 6 | $a$ | 0.747 | 10 | $b$ | 0.140 |
| | $b$ | 0.147 | | $b$ | 0.093 | | $c$ | 0.053 |
| | $\phi$ | 0.086 | | $\phi$ | 0.160 | | $\phi$ | 0.807 |
| 3 | $a$ | 0.113 | 7 | $g$ | 0.760 | | | |
| | $h$ | 0.753 | | $h$ | 0.132 | | | |
| | $\phi$ | 0.134 | | $\phi$ | 0.108 | | | |
| 4 | $c$ | 0.780 | 8 | $b$ | 0.813 | | | |
| | $d$ | 0.093 | | $c$ | 0.093 | | | |
| | $\phi$ | 0.127 | | $\phi$ | 0.094 | | | |

Remark: R.E. denotes "Random Elements",
P.D. denotes "Probability Distribution".

attributed graphs, random graphs and various types of graph morphism. We have also described the estimation of the probability distribution and entropy of a random graph and introduced an entropy increment measure as a distance measure between random graphs. With this measure, we derive a normalized similarity measure applicable to attributed graphs and random graphs. Further, we have shown that, using this measure, unsupervised classification of structural patterns can be carried out by a hierarchical random graph synthesis procedure. Using an appropriate threshold, a set of attributed graphs can be synthesized into several random graph representations, each of which corresponds to a cluster. The resulting probability distributions of the random graphs then reflect the statistical variation of the contextual and structural characteristics of each cluster. We have also shown that, when classes of structural patterns are given, the random graph synthesis process can be used to estimate a probability distribution for each class. Unknown pattern graphs can then be classified by using the proposed distance or by applying the maximum likelihood rule.

Table 5. The alignment of strings after synthesis.

| ID | f | String | ID | f | String | ID | f | String |
|---|---|---|---|---|---|---|---|---|
| 96 | 1 | *bacaahbbb | 110 | 1 | gbhc*ahbab | 11 | 1 | gah**ag*a* |
| 19 | 1 | *aacaah*a* | 3 | 1 | *ahc**hb** | 45 | 1 | gah***gbab |
| 47 | 1 | gbh*aa*ca* | 32 | 1 | ga*c*bhba* | 68 | 1 | gah**agbab |
| 101 | 1 | gahcaahbb* | 22 | 1 | *ahc*bhba* | 107 | 1 | gahd*agbab |
| 98 | 1 | gaadaagba* | 80 | 1 | gahc*bhba* | 65 | 1 | ga*cbagba* |
| 27 | 1 | ga***bhcac | 30 | 1 | g*ac*ahba* | 58 | 1 | *ahcbagba* |
| 111 | 1 | hah*bbgbac | 84 | 1 | gbac*ahba* | 14 | 1 | gahc**g*a* |
| 52 | 1 | ha*da*gba* | 24 | 1 | *bhc*bgba* | 10 | 1 | *a*cb*gba* |
| 43 | 1 | gahd*bg*a* | 6 | 1 | g**c*agb** | 41 | 1 | gahc**gba* |
| 44 | 1 | gahd*bgb** | 46 | 1 | gb*c*agba* | 31 | 2 | ga*cb*gba* |
| 33 | 1 | ga*da*gba* | 83 | 1 | gbac*agba* | 77 | 4 | gahcb*gba* |
| 82 | 3 | gahda*gba* | 5 | 1 | g****agba* | 105 | 1 | gahcb*gbab |
| 81 | 1 | gahdaagb** | 16 | 1 | gb***agba* | 13 | 1 | gahc*a*b** |
| 106 | 1 | gahdaagba* | 48 | 2 | gbh**agba* | 40 | 1 | gahc*ahb** |
| 90 | 1 | g*hc*bgcab | 85 | 1 | gbh*bagba* | 76 | 1 | gahcba*ba* |
| 94 | 1 | hbac*agb*c | 23 | 1 | *bhc*agba* | 75 | 1 | gahc*ahba* |
| 54 | 1 | **hc*bgbab | 86 | 2 | gbhc*agba* | 104 | 1 | gahcbahba* |
| 95 | 1 | hbhd*agbb* | 109 | 1 | gbhcaagba* | 12 | 1 | gahc*a**a* |
| 66 | 1 | ga*cbbgbb* | 78 | 1 | gahc*bgbb* | 18 | 1 | **hc*agba* |
| 51 | 1 | haac**gbb* | 74 | 1 | gahc*ah*ac | 37 | 1 | gahc*a*ba* |
| 35 | 1 | gah**agbb* | 103 | 1 | gahc*ahbac | 69 | 2 | gahcaa*ba* |
| 67 | 1 | gah*aagbb* | 2 | 1 | *ahcb***a* | 28 | 1 | ga*c*agba* |
| 55 | 1 | *a*cbagbac | 21 | 1 | *ahcb*gca* | 64 | 1 | ga*caagba* |
| 63 | 1 | gaac*bgbb* | 79 | 1 | gahcb*gca* | 20 | 1 | *ahc*agba* |
| 4 | 1 | ga***ag*b* | 9 | 1 | *aac**gba* | 57 | 1 | *ahc*agbac |
| 36 | 1 | gah**agcb* | 1 | 1 | *ahc*a*b** | 39 | 1 | gahc*agb** |
| 15 | 1 | gahd***ba* | 93 | 1 | hahc*bgba* | 72 | 1 | gahc*agb*b |
| 42 | 1 | gahd***bab | 53 | 1 | hahc*a*ba* | 70 | 1 | gahc*a*bab |
| 89 | 1 | g*hc*agcab | 91 | 5 | hahc*agba* | 56 | 1 | *ahc*agbab |
| 17 | 1 | gb*c*a*b*b | 87 | 1 | gbhc*agca* | 102 | 2 | gahc*agbab |
| 108 | 1 | gb*cbahbab | 92 | 1 | hahc*agca* | 50 | 4 | g*hc*agba* |
| 59 | 1 | gaac*a*bab | 26 | 1 | gaac*ag*a* | 38 | 2 | gahc*ag*a* |
| 25 | 1 | gaa**agbb* | 62 | 1 | gaacbag*a* | 34 | 1 | gah**agba* |
| 61 | 1 | gaac*agbb* | 29 | 1 | ga*c*agca* | 71 | 19 | gahc*agba* |
| 8 | 1 | **h**ahba* | 73 | 2 | gahc*agca* | 99 | 1 | gahcaagba* |
| 7 | 1 | g*hc*a***b | 100 | 1 | gahcaagca* | 112 | 1 | gahcaagbab |
| 88 | 1 | gbhc*ahc*b | 60 | 1 | gaac*agba* | | | |
| 49 | 1 | gbhc*ah*a* | 97 | 1 | gaac*agbac | | | |

Remark: * denotes a null symbol.

The random graph synthesis process relies on optimal graph isomorphism or monomorphism algorithms. To provide good algorithms, various techniques have been developed for matching attributed graphs[2,12−14]. Recently, based on a branch-and-bound tree searching technique, we have developed an efficient algorithm for finding optimal graph isomorphisms and monomorphisms[15] using a heuristic function for consistent lower bound cost estimation.

Finally, we note that the proposed method can be extended to cover more complex structural patterns by modelling $n$-ary relations as hyperedges in hypergraphs. It would also be desirable to include the notion of hierarchical graph[1,23]. Attributed hypergraphs and hierarchical graphs can be generalized to random hypergraphs and random hierarchical graphs for use in more complex structural pattern recognition problems.

## REFERENCES

1. A.K.C. Wong and L. Goldfarb, "Modelling systems and multilevel hierarchical relational structures", in *Large Engineering Systems 2*, eds. G.J. Savage and P.H. Roe (Sanford Educational Press, Waterloo, Ontario, 1978) pp. 37-44.
2. W.H. Tsai and K.S. Fu, "Error-correcting isomorphism of attributed relational graphs for pattern analysis", *IEEE Trans. Systems, Man and Cybernetics* 13 (1979) 353-362.
3. A.K.C. Wong and M.L. You, "Entropy and distance of random graphs with application to structural pattern recognition". *IEEE Trans. Pattern Analysis and Machine Intelligence* 7 (1986) 599-609.
4. A.C. Shaw, "A formal picture description scheme as a basis for picture processing systems", *Info. and Control* 14 (1969) 9-52.
5. A.C. Shaw, "Parsing of graph-representable pictures", *J. ACM*, 17 (1970) 453-481.
6. T. Pavlidis, *Structural Pattern Recognition* (Springer-Verlag, New York, 1977).
7. T. Pavlidis, "Structural description and graph grammars", in *Pictorial Information Systems*, eds. S.K. Chang and K.S. Fu, (Springer-Verlag, 1980) pp. 86-103.
8. A. Sanfeliu and K.S. Fu, "A distance measure between attributed relational graphs for pattern recognition", *IEEE Trans. Systems, Man, and Cybernetics* 13 (1983) 353-362.
9. F.A. Akinniyi, A.K.C. Wong and D. Stacey, "A new algorithm for graph monomorphism based on the projections of product graph", *IEEE Trans. Systems, Man and Cybernetics* 16 (1986) 740-751.
10. A.K.C. Wong, "Knowledge representation for robot vision and path planning using attributed graphs and hypergraphs", *NATO ASI: Machine Intelligence and Knowledge Engineering for Robotic Applications*, eds. A.K.C. Wong and A. Pugh (1987).
11. A.K.C. Wong and D.E. Ghahraman, "Random graphs: structural-contextual dichotomy", *IEEE Trans. Pattern Analysis and Machine Intelligence* 2 (1980) 341-348.
12. D.E. Ghahraman, A.K.C. Wong and T. Au, "Graph optimal monomorphism algorithms", *IEEE Trans. Systems, Man and Cybernetics* 10 (1980) 189-196.
13. L.G. Shapiro and R.M. Haralick, "Structural descriptions and inexact matching", *IEEE Trans. Pattern Analysis and Machine Intelligence* 3 (1981) 504-519.

14. D.E. Ghahraman, A.K.C. Wong and T. Au., "Graph monomorphism algorithm", *IEEE Trans. Systems, Man and Cybernetics* 10 (1980) 181-196.

15. M.L. You and A.K.C. Wong, "An algorithm for graph optimal isomorphism", *Proc. Seventh Int. Conf. on Pattern Recognition*, 1984, pp. 316-319.

16. R. Gallagar, *Information Theory and Reliable Communication* (Wiley, New York, 1968).

17. A.K.C. Wong, T.A. Reichert, D.N. Cohen and B.O. Aygun, "A generalized method for matching informational macromolecular code sequences", *Comput. Biol. Med.* 4 (1974) 43-57.

18. D.N. Cohen, T.A. Reichert and A.K.C. Wong, "Matching code sequences utilizing context free quality measures", *Mathematical Biosciences* 24 (1975) 25-30.

19. K.S. Fu, "A step towards unification of syntactic and statistic pattern recognition", *IEEE Trans. Pattern Analysis and Machine Intelligence* 5 (1983) 200-205.

20. K. Abe and N. Sugita, "Distance between strings of symbols – Review and remarks" *Proc. 1982 Int. Conf. on Pattern Recognition*, Vol. 1 (1982) pp. 172-174.

21. K.S. Fu, *Syntactic Pattern Recognition and Application* (Prentice-Hall, New Jersey, 1982).

22. M. You, A Random Graph Approach to Pattern Recognition, Ph.D. Thesis, Dept. of Systems Design Engineering, University of Waterloo, Waterloo, Ontario (1983) pp. 37-44.

23. H. Niemann, "Hierarchical graphs in pattern analysis", *Proc. 1980 Int. Conf. on Pattern Recognition*, 1980, pp. 213-216.

24. A.E. Masumi, Picture Analysis of Graph Transformation, Ph.D. Thesis, Dept. of Computer Science, University of Illinois at Urbana-Champaign (1978).

25. K.S. Fu, "Picture Syntax", in *Pictorial Information Systems*, eds. S.K. Chang and K.S. Fu (Springer-Verlag, 1980) pp. 104-127.

# Learning

# 9

---

# GRAMMATICAL INFERENCE

LAURENT MICLET

*Centre National Etudes Telecommunications*
*LAA Dept. TSS-RCP*
*B.P. 40, F-22301 Lannion Cedez*
*France*

This chapter deals with the problem of learning syntactic structures from examples, which has been called "grammatical inference". Apart from its fascinating (and phoney) linguistic challenge (could a computer, like the young Tarzan of the Apes, learn a language by simply reading books written in it?), it has an interesting position in syntactic pattern recognition. Its goal is to discover the hidden grammatical rules assumed in describing the structure of string patterns. Of course, only a finite number of such examples are known and grammatical inference must lead to some generalization, therefore arbitrary heuristics must be introduced.

Grammatical inference is a necessary part of syntactic and structural pattern recognition, and it has produced useful tools and methodologies for structural learning. Its future may rely on combining its techniques with statistical tools (hidden Markov models, for example), or other formal systems (symbolic learning). Automatic learning from examples is a necessity for pattern recognition, and grammatical inference has made some positive steps in this direction. This is what we intend to show in this chapter.

## 1. INTRODUCTION

### 1.1. What is Grammatical Inference?

The first algorithms in the field of grammatical inference are older than the creation of the "machine learning" concept; nevertheless, we can consider that this discipline is a part of the large field of automatic learning. More precisely, it belongs to what D. Angluin calls "inductive inference"[1], namely "systems which try to guess general rules from examples". Concerning grammatical inference, the rules to be guessed are rewriting rules in the Formal Language Theory sense (as developed by Chomsky), or a natural extension of these; the examples are sentences extracted from the languages that these rules can produce (inference samples). Let us take as an example the following grammar:

$$G = \{S \longrightarrow aS | aA, \; A \longrightarrow bA | b\} \; .$$

It produces the language

$$L(G) = \{a^n b^m | n \geq 1, \; m \geq 1\} \; ,$$

containing for example the subset of sentences

$$I = \{aab, \; aaab, \; aabbb\} \; .$$

If we consider $I$ as an inference sample, then trying to find a grammar $G'$ such that

$$I \subset L(G)$$

is a grammatical inference problem. An algorithm designed for this purpose may find $G$ as the solution, but could also infer the grammar

$$G' = \{S \longrightarrow aA, \; A \longrightarrow aB, \; B \longrightarrow aC | bD | b,$$
$$C \longrightarrow bD | b, \; D \longrightarrow bE, \; E \longrightarrow bD | b\}$$

which generates the language

$$L(G') = \{a^n \; b^{2p+1} | n = 2 \text{ or } 3, \; p \geq 0\}$$

which would be another good answer to the problem as stated.

We can propose a methodological definition for grammatical inference such as: "automatic learning of formal grammars from finite subsets of the language they generate".

Of course, as a definition which needs to be concise, it is both too precise and too loose. It is too precise because some useful algorithms that we can find in the literature under the name of "grammatical inference" do not fit exactly this definition. It is too loose because it excludes a very important aspect of the topic: grammatical inference has not been developed only for the sake of solving a nice problem, but has almost constantly been in close relationship with pattern recognition purpose. This is more a historical than a methodological aspect, but it is very important for understanding the limits of the field. This explains some weaknesses in the domain: some methods have been developed only for specific data, with no generalization purpose. But it gives to the topic a great interest, at the intersection of symbolic learning and engineering problems.

## 1.2. Grammatical Inference and Pattern Recognition

In principle, the interest of grammatical inference is obvious in the basic model of syntactic pattern recognition: it gives automatic methods for learning the models of the pattern classes; this is quite similar to applying the formulae giving the estimation of the parameters of a Gaussian distribution in $\mathbb{R}$ from the coordinates of the learning sample of the corresponding class. The inference sample is the partial information on what a grammar is able to generate: inference should merely be an estimation of the "parameters" of the grammar, i.e. the discovery of its rules. In the pure paradigm of syntactic pattern recognition, the situation of grammatical inference is quite clear.

But in practice things are severely different. First of all, the pure syntactic hypothesis is an ideal situation: one knows now that real patterns are not context-free or regular, and it is not realistic to hope to have good performances in real situations with strictly classical models. Secondly, even if the strict syntactic case were realistic, the inference problem would be very difficult. We shall see that its theoretical formulation is not of great help to practitioners, and that even in the simplest case of regular grammars, the programmer has in practice to deal with a highly combinatorial problem, with no real clues to help his search. These two basic considerations explain why grammatical inference has many difficulties in being really used in operational pattern recognition programs, and that its applications are really disappointing, with regards to its obvious methodological interest.

Historically, grammatical inference has always been closely related to pattern recognition, except for a pure theoretical branch, which is not yet really connected to algorithms. It is clear now that the interest of researchers in this domain is decreasing, the publications are less and less numerous; the years 1970-80 were the most fruitful, but since the early eighties, articles or congress communications on the topic have been rare. The reasons are probably the two which have been quoted earlier: difficulty even in a clear formulation, and application to real pattern recognition problems which makes the situation even worse. The result is that in most cases of syntactic pattern recognition systems, grammars are manually designed for better accuracy[2].

The evolution of pure syntactic pattern recognition to structural modelling lets one think that grammatical inference has to be transformed to become a more useful tool; it is probably in connection with artificial intelligence models, namely, "machine learning", that this discipline will evolve, and produce algorithms that will be more useful for a number of practical problems[3]. Nevertheless, grammatical inference, as it is presented here, has already proved its interest, and is one among the set of tools that the designer of a pattern recognition system must know.

### 1.3. Different Approaches to Grammatical Inference

To describe the concepts and the algorithms of the field of grammatical inference (or simply to sort a bibliography of the domain), several axes can be chosen. Firstly, there exists a border between researchers interested in the theoretical possibility of learning a grammar, and those who want to write an algorithm for solving their practical problem of finding a grammar for modelling a class of patterns. The former, as we shall see later, are interested in an abstract learning process, and its convergence on an infinite sample of sentences; the latter are involved in a precise problem: they have the learning data in a given format, they know what kind of rules they want to generate, and sometimes they restrict the problem even more by giving extra information (guiding the algorithm by a teacher, or imposing a structure to the grammar).

Another classification concerns the type of grammar one is looking for (and that is how we shall organize this chapter). Is it context-free or regular? Is it a more complex model, like a probabilistic automaton, or a two-dimensional generalization of classical models, etc.?

A third point of view[1] concerns the type of algorithm which is designed, with no reference to the class of grammars or to the data. Is it a search in a state space whose structure may be used to avoid a brute force enumeration? Is it an optimization of parameters by a gradient method? Is it a direct access to a solution with an *ad hoc* heuristic? This last classification shows clearly that the main problem to which the designer of an algorithm is confronted with in grammatical inference is to avoid the over exponential complexity of the problem (with regards to the size of the sample), by explicit or implicit heuristics.

We shall first make allusions to the theoretical problem of inference, according to Gold's concepts. Then we shall describe algorithms, with a special emphasis on the regular grammar inference problem which has a solid background, and has produced many heuristic solutions. We shall see its extension to probabilistic automata and the special case of "hidden Markov models". Then we shall treat context-free and "multidimensional" grammars. Finally, examples of application in pattern recognition will be given. For other surveys of grammatical inference see Refs. 1, 4–7.

## 2. GRAMMATICAL INFERENCE FROM A THEORETICAL POINT OF VIEW

The basic references of the formal frame of grammatical inference are the works by Gold[8] and Feldman[9]. Though not constructive, they give the landmarks of the domain where the practical algorithms will lie. In the particular field of learning for pattern recognition, they are not very useful, demanding learning samples of increasing size which the practitioner cannot handle. That is the reason why we quote them only in a short paragraph, though they are of obvious importance for anybody who is interested in automatic learning. Other references in the field of theoretical grammatical inference are Refs. 1, 10 and 11.

Gold is interested in grammars in a class $C$, called "admissible". Such a class is defined as follows. Given an alphabet $X$:

(1) $C$ is denumerable.
(2) For $x \in X^*$, it is decidable whether or not $x \in L(G)$ for any $G \in C$.

(The classes of grammars defined by Chomsky as regular, context-free and context-sensitive are admissible.)

Now, we suppose that it is possible to give a "complete information sequence" $I(L(G))$ to an inference algorithm. For a given grammar $G$, generating the language $L(G), I(L(G))$ is an ordered presentation of all the sentences in $L(G)$ ("positive" information sequence), and all the sentences in $X^*-L(G)$. The problem is to know whether, when this information sequence is given, there exist algorithms able to find out $G$. This information sequence is ordered along an index $t$. We have the following definition: A class of languages $C$ is said to be "identifiable in the limit" if there exists an algorithm $D$ (that will be called an "inference algorithm") such that for every grammar $G \in C$ and any complete information sequence $I(L(G))$, there exists a $\tau$ such that:

$$\forall t > \tau \qquad (1) \ G_t = G_\tau$$
$$(2) \ L(Gt) = L(G)$$

where $G$ is the result of $D$ with the data consisting of the first sentences in $I(L(G))$.

Gold gives the following results: When $C$ is an admissible class of grammars, there is an algorithm such that for every $G \in C, L(G)$ is identifiable in the limit, through a complete information sequence $I(L(G))$.

If we are limited to only giving to the algorithm a positive information sequence, then we have the following property: Let $C$ be an admissible class of grammars that generates all finite languages and one infinite language $L$. Then $L$ is not identifiable in the limit through a complete positive information sequence of $L$.

Since it includes regular and context-free languages this is not a very encouraging result for the designer of an inference algorithm: he then knows *a priori* that Gold's requirements of identification in the limit will not be fulfilled if he tries to infer a non-trivial grammar from a positive sequence. But, since no practical finite value is given on the parameter anyway, it would not have been a constructive result to have had the reverse property.

In theory, one may design an algorithm inside Gold's requirements, and identify in the limit a non-trivial grammar through an infinite sequence. But in working from finite samples, and if there may be interest in convergence properties, one will never have the possibility of verifying them. The conclusion is that it is impossible to evaluate a practical inference algorithm with Gold's criteria; the designer has to find himself a heuristic method for this evaluation, which is a paradoxical situation. This leads to a very different type of algorithms in the field of grammatical inference: some look for generality, while others are designed *ad hoc* for a practical pattern recognition problem, and would not fit other data.

It has to be noticed that a lot of work is still in progress in this fundamental field; a survey of earlier works and recent advances may be found in the book by Osherson, Straub and Weinstein[12]. It is quite possible that this so-called "formal learning theory" will be of more help in the future for pattern recognition and artificial intelligence learning problems.

## 3. INFERENCE OF REGULAR GRAMMARS

Regular grammars are the simplest model in Chomsky's hierarchy; they have been used in several ways in pattern recognition. We study in this section how to infer such models — notice that it is more convenient to represent them not in the form of rewriting rules, but as "finite-state machines", or "finite automata". We shall first give a few necessary definitions, and also a theorem on the enumeration of solutions to an inference problem in regular grammars; finally, we shall describe several algorithms which can be seen as different heuristics to make a choice in the large space of possible solutions.

### 3.1. Finite Automata and Regular Grammars

A regular grammar has rewriting rules in the general form:

$$A \rightarrow a\,B|c$$

An equivalent and more useful representation is that of finite automata, defined as follows:

A finite automaton is a 5-tuple:

$$A = (X,\ Q,\ \delta,\ q_0,\ F)$$

where $X$ is the alphabet, $Q$ is the set of "states", $\delta$ is the transition function, $q_0$ is the initial state, $F$ is a subset of final states.

The function can be extended to the domain $\delta : Q \times X^* \longrightarrow Q$ with the following rule:

$$\delta(q,\ x) = \delta(\ldots\delta(\delta(q,\ a_1),\ a_2)\ldots)a_n$$

where $x = a_1 a_2 \ldots a_n$.

A sentence $x$ in $X^*$ is accepted (and is in the language generated by the equivalent grammar) if

$$\delta(q_0,\ x) \in F \ .$$

The language accepted by $A$ is henceforth

$$L(A) = \{x \in X^* | \delta(q_0,\ x) \in F\} \ .$$

If we graphically represent the transition $\delta(q, a) = q'$ by

Fig. 1.

and mark the initial state by "$-$" and the final ones by "$+$", we obtain, for example, an automaton like the following graph:

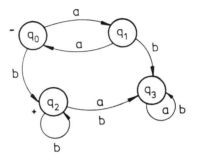

Fig. 2.

It accepts the language:

$$L = \{a^{2n}b^m \,|\, n \geq 0, \; m \geq 1\}$$

which can also be written as a "regular expression":

$$L = (aa)^* bb^* \; .$$

### 3.1.1. Non-deterministic automata

    The definition of a finite automaton can be extended to include the case in which the transition function $\delta$ has values in $P(Q)$, the set of all subsets of $Q$, i.e. to the case in which $\delta$ is a one-to-many mapping. The automaton is then said to be *non-deterministic*, and a pair $(a, q) \in X \times Q$ can correspond to a number of different states; expressed graphically:

$$\delta(q, a) = (q_1, q_2)$$

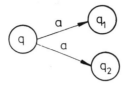

Fig. 3.

Such an automaton can generate a language in the same manner as a deterministic one; a sentence $x$ will be a part of it if there exists a string of letters on the transitions between $q_0$ and a state of $F$.

**Theorem 3.1.** Let $L$ be a language such that $L = L(A)$ where $A$ is a nondeterministic finite automaton. Then there is a deterministic automaton $A'$ such that $L = L(A')$.

This is proved by considering

$$A^1 = (X,\ Q^1,\ \delta^1,\ q_0^1,\ F^1)$$

where $Q^1 = P(Q)$, the set of all subsets of $Q$, $q_0^1 = \{q_0\}$, $F^1$ is the set of those subsets $S$ of $Q$ such that $S \cap F \neq \emptyset$, $\delta^1$ is defined for $R \in P(Q)$ and

$$\delta^1(R,\ a) = \bigcup_{q \in R} \delta(q,\ a)\ .$$

It is easily shown that

$$L(A^1) = L(A)\ .$$

A practical algorithm for constructing a finite automaton consists simply of the construction of the transition function $\delta^1$, starting with the definition of $A^1$. However, some states in $Q^1$ are inaccessible to $A^1$ and therefore need not be generated; consequently only such states as are necessary are generated, using the definition of $\delta^1$. In most cases, the number of such states is less than $2^{|Q|}$.

With non-deterministic automata the analysis of a string of $X^*$ can lead to ambiguities, and we have the following.

**Definition 3.2.** A string of $X^*$ is said to be ambiguous for an automaton if it can be accepted by the latter in at least two different ways.

Note that no string of $X^*$ is ambiguous for a deterministc automaton.

### 3.1.2. Finite automata and regular grammar

There is a direct correspondence between a regular grammar and a finite automaton: the initial state of the automaton corresponds to the axioms of the grammar, the two alphabets are identical and the transition function corresponds to the production rules, as follows:

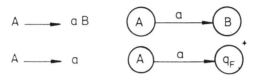

Fig. 4.

where $q_F \in Q'$.

**Example 3.3.** The regular grammar

$$G \begin{cases} S \longrightarrow aS|bA \\ A \longrightarrow bA|a \end{cases}$$

corresponds to the automaton of Fig. 5.

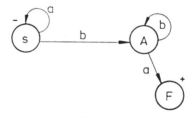

Fig. 5.

Further, the transition function $\delta$ may be specified completely by the introduction of a "garbage" state. In general, an automaton derived from a regular grammar is not deterministic.

The following result follows directly: the family of languages over an alphabet $X$ that is recognized by a finite automaton is identical with that of the languages over $X$, generated by a regular grammar.

*3.1.3. Derived automata*

Let $A = (X, Q, \delta, q_0, F)$ be a finite automaton and let $P = (P_1, P_2, \ldots, P_r)$ be a partition of $Q$. Then we have the following.

**Definition 3.4.** The automaton $A' = (X, P, \gamma, P_0, R)$ where
  (i) $P_0 \in P$ is such that $q_0 \in P_0$
  (ii) $R = \{P_i \in P : \exists q_j \in F, \; q_j \in P_i\}$
  (iii) $\gamma(P_i, a) = P_j$ if $\exists q_k \in P_i$ and $q_e \in P_j$ such that $\delta(q_k, a) = q_e$
is called the *automaton derived from A for the partition P*.

Thus a derived automaton is constructed by *merging* the states of the original automaton; this operation forms the basis of methods of regular inference (cf. Sec. 5.2). The following important property follows directly from the definition.

**Property 3.5.** If $A$ is a finite automaton and $A'$ is an automaton derived from $A$ for an arbitrary partition of the states of $A$, then

$$L(A) \subset L(A') .$$

*3.1.4. Representation of languages by regular expressions*

The formalism of regular expressions defined below enables us to define the *rational parts* of a set $X^*$, i.e. the set of "rational" languages over $X$. Kleene's theorem guarantees that this is identical with the set of regular languages.

*Regular expressions*

Let $X = \{a, b, c, \ldots\}$ and $X' = \{+, {}^*, \emptyset, (,)\}$ be two disjoint alphabets. Then we have the following.

**Definition 3.6.** A string $\alpha$ on $X \cup X'$ is a regular expression if and only if either

  (i) $\alpha \in X$ or $\alpha = \emptyset$, or
  (ii) $\alpha$ can be written in one of the forms $(\beta + \gamma), (\beta\gamma)$ or $(\beta^*)$ where $\beta$ and $\gamma$ are regular expressions on $X$.

A regular expression $\alpha$ represents a language $L\alpha$ over $X$ provided that the following conditions are satisfied:

  (a) The language written $\emptyset$ is the empty language
  (b) The language written $a$ is the language $\{a\}$

(c) $L_{(\beta+\gamma)} = L_\beta \cup L_\gamma$
$L_{(\beta\gamma)} = L_\beta L_\gamma$
$L_{\beta^*} = (L_\beta)^*.$

In order to reduce the number of pairs of parentheses, and thus to simplify the writing of regular expressions the operations are given relative priorities; in decreasing order these are

1   star   2   product   3   union .

Further, some liberties can be taken with the notation and the same symbol can be used to denote the regular expression $\alpha$ and the language $L\alpha$ which it represents.

**Example 3.7.**

$$(a + b^*)c = \{ac,\ c,\ bc,\ bbc, \dots, b \dots bc, \dots\}$$
$$(a + bb)^* + c = \{c,\ \lambda,\ a,\ bb,\ bba,\ abb,\ abba,\ aabb,\ bbaa, \dots\} .$$

Thus a regular expression defines a family of languages, and we call a language so defined over $X$ a *rational language* over $X$, or a *rational subset* of $X^*$. Such languages, which may be infinite, can thus be represented in a condensed notation, which is not the same as the rewriting system of representation by a grammar.

The algebraic properties of this family of languages can be summarized in the following property which follows directly from the definition.

> **The family of rational languages is the smallest family that is closed under the operations of product, union and star.**

*Kleene's theorem*

A comparison of the properties of rational and regular languages shows that every rational language is regular. This follows from the fact that, given any regular expression whatever, a series of automata can be constructed that will lead to a finite automaton that will accept the language represented by that expression. The fundamental theorem of the theory of regular languages states that the converse is true. This is **Kleene's theorem**[13].

> **Every regular language is rational.**

The existence of two different types of representation of a regular language, on the one hand by a regular grammar or a finite automaton and on the other by a regular expression, leads us to raise the question of how to go from one type to the other. We shall not go into this question, which is not quite simple, and is not necessary for our purpose. All we need to know here is that regular expressions, regular grammars and finite automaton are distinct representations of the same languages.

### 3.1.5. *Some properties of finite automata*

#### *Set of k-tails, k-equivalence of states and minimization*

Our aim here is to demonstrate a minimizing algorithm, i.e. to give a method for finding the automaton with a minimum number of states that will recognize a given language $L$, starting from any automaton that recognizes this language. We assume that such a minimal algorithm exists and that it is unique to within an isomorphism.

Let $A = (X, Q, \delta, q_0, Q')$ be a finite automaton and $L = L(A)$ be a regular language. We say that an element $x$ of $X^*$ is a *terminal string* or simply a *tail* of $q \in Q$ if

$$\delta(q, x) \in Q'$$

and is a $k$-tail of $q \in Q$ if

$$\delta(q, x) \in Q' \qquad \text{and} \qquad |x| \leq k .$$

The set of $k$-tails of $q$ is written $\Psi_q^k$.

We say that two distinct states $q$, $q'$ of $A$ are distinguishable by $x \in X^*$ if either

$$(q, x) \in Q' \qquad \text{and} \qquad \delta(q', x) \notin Q'$$

or

$$\delta(q, x) \notin Q' \qquad \text{and} \qquad \delta(q' x) \in Q' ,$$

and that these states are *k-equivalents* if they are not distinguishable by any word $x$ such that $|x| \leq k$.

We denote $k$-equivalence by $\overset{k}{\equiv}$; it is easily shown to be a true equivalence relation on $Q$.

It follows from the definitions that two states $q$, $q'$ are $k$-equivalent if and only if they have the same set of $k$-tails, i.e. for $q$, $q' \in Q$,

$$q \overset{k}{\equiv} q' \iff \Psi_q^k = \Psi_{q'}^k .$$

Two states, $q$, $q'$ of an automaton are *equivalent* if $q \overset{\infty}{\equiv} q'$, written simply as $q \equiv q'$; thus two such states have the same set of terminals.

**Proposition 3.8.** Let $P$ be the partition of the states of an automaton $A$ resulting from the relation $\equiv$ and $A_n$ the derived automaton of $A$ for $P$; then $A_n$ is the minimal automaton that recognizes the language $L(A)$.

This shows how the minimizing algorithm can be found. That equivalence relation on the states of the automaton has to be found which corresponds to the minimal automaton; the search for $\equiv$ is performed by means of a recurrence on the $k$-equivalent relations $\overset{k}{\equiv}$, starting from $\overset{0}{\equiv}$.

A simply property of the $k$-equivalence is at the basis of the Moore's algorithm for minimization[14].

**Property 3.9.**

$$q \overset{k+1}{\equiv} q' \iff \begin{cases} q \overset{k}{\equiv} q' \\ a \in X : \delta(q, a) \overset{k}{\equiv} \delta(q', a) . \end{cases}$$

We can now give this minimization algorithm.

*Moore's algorithm*[14]

(i) $k := 0$; compute $\overset{0}{\equiv}$

(ii) *while $k \leq N - 2$ and $\overset{k}{\equiv} \neq \overset{k-1}{\equiv}$ do*

    (a) $k := k + 1$

    (b) compute $\overset{k}{\equiv}$ as a function of $\overset{k-1}{\equiv}$ using 3.9

(iii) merge the $k$-equivalent states, i.e. compute the derived automaton for the equivalence relation $\overset{k}{\equiv}$.

**Example 3.10.** Suppose that we wish to minimize the automaton represented by Fig. 6 which recognizes a set of phrases for which the number of $b$s is a multiple of 3. The application of Moore's algorithm gives Table 1.

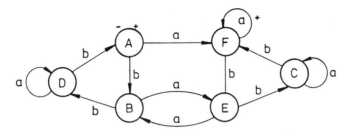

Fig. 6.

Table 1.

| | $k = 0$ | $k = 1$ | $k = 2$ |
|---|---|---|---|
| *A* | $\lambda$ | $\lambda, a$ | $\lambda, a, aa$ |
| *B* | $\emptyset$ | $\emptyset$ | $bb$ |
| *C* | $\emptyset$ | $b$ | $b, ba, ab$ |
| *D* | $\emptyset$ | $b$ | $b, ba, ab$ |
| *E* | $\emptyset$ | $\emptyset$ | $bb$ |
| *F* | $\lambda$ | $\lambda, a$ | $\lambda, a, aa$ |
| Classes of $\overset{k}{\equiv}$ | $\{A, F\}$ $\{B, C, D, E\}$ | $\{A, F\}$ $\{C, D\}$ $\{B, E\}$ | $\{A, F\}$ $\{C, D\}$ $\{B, E\}$ |

The minimal automaton, obtained from the last partition $(k = 2)$, is as follows:

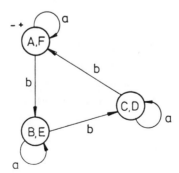

Fig. 7.

### 3.1.6. More properties of finite automata

We now state several properties of regular languages and finite automata to conclude the presentation section, and to give the last concepts necessary to present regular grammatical inference.

**Property 3.11.**

Every finite language is regular; the language $L = X^*$ is regular.

**Property 3.12.**

A finite automaton can be characterized by the set of its $(|Q| - 1)$-tails instead of its transition function.

**Property 3.13.** ("pumping lemma")

If $L$ is a regular language on $X$, then $\exists p \in \mathbb{N}$ such that $\forall x \in L$, with $|x| > p$, $x$ can be written

$$x = uvw$$

where $v > 1$, so that:

$$\forall k \geq 0, \ uv^k w \in L .$$

**Property 3.14.**

The language $L = \{a^n \, b^n | n \geq 0\}$ is not regular.

## 3.2. The Theory of Regular Inference

In the formal frame of regular languages, the grammatical inference problem can be clearly stated and solved, though it will not give constructive algorithms; these will be heuristics based on the algebraic properties that we have developed in the last section. But let us first rigorously state the regular inference problem.

First of all, we shall be interested in finite identification sequences, called "samples", finite sets of sentences on an alphabet $X$. We shall not consider here negative samples. We therefore are asking the following question:

Given a sample $I$ of sentences, is it possible to find a regular grammar $G$ such that $I \subset L(G)$?

### 3.2.1. Complete sample

As stated, the inference problem has an infinity of solutions, among which is the trivial one of the universal grammar $G_u$ for which the language accepted is $X^*$, where $X$ is the alphabet in which $I$ is written. This is expressed in the form of an automaton by

Fig. 8

Here we can add to $X$ as many letters as we wish and still retain the universal grammar.

Another solution is what is called the *maximal canonical grammar* MCG $(I)$, one of the grammars for which the language generated is identical with $I$. For example, if

$$I = \{a, \ bc, \ abc, \ ababc\} \ ,$$

then $\text{MCG}(I)$ is represented by the automaton which we call $\text{MCA}(I)$.

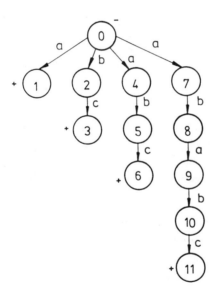

Fig. 9.

Similarly we can add to $\text{MCG}(I)$ whatever transitions we wish, involving letters which may or may not belong to $X$, without departing from the set of solutions. This would allow an infinity of possibilities of no importance, and so to avoid this we impose the condition that the sample is *complete* with respect to the grammar proposed as a solution. The definition of completeness is as follows.

**Definition 3.15.** A sample $I$ is said to be *structurally complete* (or simply *complete*) with respect to a grammar $G = (X, \ V, \ P, S)$ if

(a) $I \subset L(G)$

(b) the alphabet in which $I$ is written is $X$

(c) every rule of $P$ is used at least once in the generation of the strings in $I$.

Given this condition, the problem of grammatical inference becomes the following:

For a sample $I$, find a grammar (or all possible grammars) such that

(a) $I \subset L(G)$

(b) $I$ is complete with respect to $G$.

With this natural restriction we can construct algorithms for enumerating solutions, in particular for the regular case; but the number of solutions will always be very great in relation to the size of the sample.

*3.2.2. A theorem for regular inference*

If we accept the assumptions expressing the completeness of the sample and use the concept of derived automaton, we can develop a method for enumerating the regular solutions of the inference problem; since we are concerned here with regular grammars we can choose representations either by means of grammars or by means of finite automata.

**Theorem 3.16.**[15] A necessary and sufficient condition for an automaton $A$ to be a solution of the inference problem

$I \subset L(A)$

$I$ is complete with respect to $A$

is that $A$ is derived from the maximal canonical automaton $\text{MCA}(I)$.

If $I$ consists of $N$ letters, the number of states of $\text{MCA}(I)$ is of the order of $N$ and the number of solutions is of the order of the number of partitions of this set of $N$ elements, because a derived automaton is associated with each partition of the states of $\text{MCA}(I)$. This number is given by the recurrence relation

$$E(0) = 1$$

$$E(N) = \sum_{j=0}^{N} \binom{N}{j} E_j$$

and the order of magnitude is

$$E(10) \approx 10^5 \qquad E(20) \approx 10^{15} .$$

Since the set of partitions of a finite set forms a lattice, so too does this set of solutions; furthermore, the set has a largest element, here $G_u$, and a smallest, $\text{MCG}(I)$.

Thus we have a theoretical solution to the inference problem in terms of regular grammars: we have found a set of grammars that solves the problem and for which the sample is complete, and we have also shown the simple structure of this set. However, in any real application to the recognition of a pattern, it is not practical to work with this set of potential solutions; we need instead to select a single solution and to explicitly know it, so as to be able to make use of it in working algorithms.

We are thus faced with the problem of choosing between a very large number of possibilities. Since all the grammars of the set are candidates, we must apply some criterion applicable to every potential solution. The criterion will be an external condition and its form will be determined by further constraints that we decide to impose on the solution. It will not necessarily take the form of a function of the grammar that can be computed explicitly but may be given as an algorithm expressing how the choice between the various possibilities is made.

Actually, the use of an explicit criterion would be defeated by the large number of cases to which it would have to be applied, because even for a sample of modest size this rapidly becomes too great for the calculations to be made in a reasonable time. Thus we have to turn to heuristic methods, first to reduce the number of solutions to be considered, and second to choose a single solution from this reduced set. Such methods are provided by algorithms that search in the lattice of solutions, select a number of these to which to apply the criterion (which may be explicit or otherwise) and as a result decide whether to choose one as the final solution or to continue the search. The name heuristic is given because there is no certainty that such a procedure will find the grammar that optimizes the criterion. The optimality of the solution cannot be checked by individual computation when the criterion is not given in explicit form, but with experience a global estimate can be made of the efficiency of the heuristic method.

## 3.3. A List of Practical Methods for Regular Inference

As stated in the last paragraph, a practical regular inference method is but an algorithm for choosing one grammar among the huge set of solutions, and the evaluation of its qualities is quite subjective. This explains why many different methods have been proposed, which are difficult to compare. We now present five algorithms. The potential user has no other solution than to try them on his data, and choose the "best" one, according to the results he desires. As an example of such an evaluation, see Ref. 16 where an "objective" comparison of three of them has been tried.

### *3.3.1. The "successor" method*

Vernadat and Richetin[17] have proposed a simple algorithm, that seems to have been independently found by Rodger and Rosebrugh[18] for a quite different application. The basic idea is to create a state for each letter of the alphabet that occurs in the sample. Starting from this very heavy constraint, the algorithm goes as described in the following example:

Sample: $I = (caab, \ bbaab, \ caab, \ bbab, \ cab, \ bbb, \ cb)$

"Successors" of $\lambda$ in $I$ : $(c, \ b)$. Create state $q_0$.
"Successors" of $a$ in $I$ : $(a, \ b)$. Create state $q_1$.
"Successors" of $b$ in $I$ : $(a, )$. Create state $q_2$.
"Successors" of $c$ in $I$ : $(a, \ b)$. Create state $q_3$.

The resulting automaton would be in a first step:

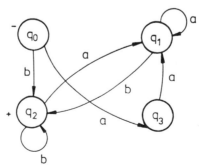

Fig. 10.

But considering that $q_1$ and $q_3$ have the same set of successors, they may be merged, leading to the following minimized automaton.

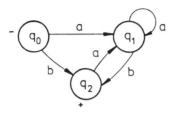

Fig. 11.

### 3.3.2. The Pao-Carr method

Pao and Carr[19] use a different paradigm for finding a finite-state machine from an inference sample: they assume that there exist some "teacher", who knows the grammar to be inferred, and to whom the program asks questions during its computing process. According to the answers, this process will generate a grammar that is shown to be the correct one (if the answers are correct). The algorithm uses the information from the teacher to construct a trajectory in the lattice of the solutions, starting from the canonical automaton and merging states according to the answers. These are made in the following way:

At a node in the lattice, the program has to choose between different possible mergings of states. It constructs a sentence and asks the teacher whether or not it is in the language to be found. According to the answer, the states to be merged can be selected.

As a comment on this method, we can say that it is not a very realistic one (in terms of computation time: the number of questions asked to the teacher must be huge), but it introduces an interesting teacher-pupil dialogue, instead of using an internal heuristic . There is no example (as far as we know) of the application of such a methodology in a pattern recognition problem though it can be quite interesting.

### 3.3.3. The $uv^k w$ algorithm

This is a procedure designed to search the sample for signs of the recursive rules that will characterize the grammar being sought. The assumption that this can in fact be done is equivalent to assuming, in the case of regular grammars, that the sample contains strings that are long in relation to the number of states of this grammar; we know that if this is so we can apply the pumping lemma and therefore that such recursions will manifest themselves in the sample by repetitions of substrings. Thus the algorithm first searches in the sample for repeated substrings and then makes the assumption that these are generated by successive passages through the same loops in the representative automaton. This assumption is subsequently checked so as to isolate the case in which the loop was not cycled several times in the course of generating the phrase. When a possible recursion has been identified, a step in the inference is completed by rewriting the sample, this being made possible by the formalism of regular expressions. A succession of such inferential steps can be made, and the termination stage is decided automatically. The sample is thus rewritten several times, each time giving a regular expression that includes its predecessor, and the final result is therefore a regular expression representing a regular language that has been found by inference. A regular grammar that accepts this language can then be constructed, thus completing the inference process.

The execution of the algorithm is shown by the following example. We shall omit the details, which are given by Ref. 16. The sample $I$ is

$$x_1 = aabaaababcabc.$$
$$x_2 = abcabaabcbc$$
$$x_3 = aaaaabc$$

*Step 1*

We look for repetitions in the phrases of $I$ (in the form $u(v)^k w$).

$$x_1 = (a)^2 baaababcabc$$
$$x_1 = aab(a)^3 babcabc$$
$$x_1 = aabaa(ab)^2 cabc$$
$$x_1 = aabaab(abc)^2$$
$$x_2 = abcab(a)^2 bcbc$$
$$x_2 = abcabaa(bc)^2$$
$$x_3 = (a)^5 bc$$

Recursion hypotheses: $a$, $ab$, $abc$, $bc$
Best hypothesis: $a$
Rewriting of $I$ for $z = a^+$:

$$x_1 = zbzbzbczbc$$

$$x_2 = zbczbzbcbc$$
$$x_3 = zbc$$

## Step 2

$$x_1 = (zb)^3 czbc$$
$$x_1 = zbzb(zbc)^2$$
$$x_2 = zbc(zb)^2 cbc$$
$$x_2 = zbczbz(bc)^2$$

Recursion hypotheses: $zb$, $bc$, $zbc$

Best hypothesis: $zb$

Rewriting of $I$ for $y = (zb)^+$:

$$x_1 = ycyc$$
$$x_2 = ycycbc$$
$$x_3 = yc$$

## Step 3

Only hypothesis: $yc$

Rewriting of $I$ for $x = (yc)^+$:

$$x_1 = x$$
$$x_2 = xbc$$
$$x_3 = x$$

Regular expression inferred:

$$x + xbc = ((a^+b)^+c) + ((a^+b)^+c)^+ bc$$

The corresponding automaton, which is non-deterministic, is shown below.

This method is well adapted to repetitive structures; at the cost of adjusting the several parameters it can be used for preprocessing a sample and after preliminary study of the repetitions another inference procedure can be used in order to find more complex structures.

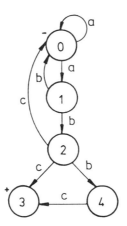

Fig. 12.

This $uv^k w$ method is similar to the Chomsky and Miller earlier method (as cited in Ref. 20). The main difference is that it does not need a teacher, and leads to some realistic program, in terms of computational time. We shall meet again methods with teachers in the context-free inference section, where the method by Solomonoff extends the Chomsky and Miller's.

### 3.3.4. The k-tails method[4,63]

This method, which uses a simple heuristic state-merging process, underlies much work on inference; it consists in finding the $k$-equivalence relation among the states of the maximal canonical grammar, or any canonical grammar. Whilst the authors of the method do not say so, a particularly simple way to find this relation is to use the minimization algorithm for regular grammars but to halt the process at an arbitrary value of $k$; the partitioning of the states of the canonical grammar brought about by the $k$-equivalence gives a derived grammar which is the solution sought.

It can be seen that this algorithm may give a solution for every value of $k$ between 0 and $(|Q| - 2)$, where $Q$ is the set of states of the canonical grammar that is used; thus it can find only a very limited number of solutions, which means that the heuristic process for scanning the lattice of potential solutions offers little freedom of choice. The following is a typical example of the use of the method.

With

$$X = \{a\ b,\ c\}$$

and

$$I = \{bcbca,\ aaabca,\ aabcbca,\ aaa\}$$

the minimal canonical automaton is as shown in Fig. 12. Applying the method of $k$-tails we have the following.

$K = 0$: the partition of the states defining the derived automaton is

$$(\{1, 2, 3, 4, 5, 6, 7, 8\},\ \{6, 9\})$$

and the language accepted by the derived automaton is

$$L_0 = (a + b + c)^*a \ (\text{a set of strings, in } X^* \text{ ending in } a)$$

$K = 1$: partition $(\{1, 2, 3, 4, 7\}, \{5, 8\},\ \{6, 9\})$

language $L_1 = (a + b + c)^*(c + a)a$

$K = 2$: partition $(\{1\},\ \{2\},\ \{3\},\ \{4\},\ \{5, 8\},\ \{6\},\ \{7\},\ \{9\})$

language $L_2 = [(b + c) + (bc + aa)(abc)^*b]^*(bc + aa)(abc)^*a$

$K = 3$: partition $(\{1\},\ \{2\},\ \{3\},\ \{4\},\ \{5, 8\},\ \{6\},\ \{9\})$

language $L_3 = (bcbc + aa)(abc + bcbc)^*a$

$K \geq 4$: language $L_K = I$

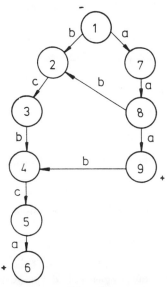

Fig. 13.

As $K$ increases, a set of nested languages is obtained, the largest for $K = 0$ and the smallest for $K \leq |Q| - 2$, in this case for $K = 4$. Notice that the result is very sensitive to the value of $K$, i.e. the change from one value to the next can result in a very great change in the language. The results of experiments made with this method show that in general the best results are obtained with samples consisting of short strings and with values of $K$ close to its maximum. However, it seems that the method seldom gives the results that can be considered to be satisfactory, largely because of the great sensitivity to the parameter $K$. It is particularly ill adapted to problems of pattern recognition, because here the grammar that is sought provides some generalization of the overall properties of the sample, whilst the method is concerned primarily with the ways in which the strings end and gives great weight to the terminations in selecting the rules for the grammar. Nevertheless it is much used in practice, probably because it is easy to operate.

### 3.3.5. The tail-clustering method[15]

This is a generalization of the method of $k$-tails based on the property that an automaton can be reconstructed from the sets of $|Q| - 1$ terminals of its states. The process is thus one of grouping the states of the maximal canonical grammar as a result of comparisons between their sets of terminals, using measures of distance between phrases and between sets of phrases and a hierarchical classification algorithm. The method gives better results than the two previous algorithms, but at the cost of more complex computations.

An example of a non-trivial regular structure inferred by this algorithm is the following:

$$I = \{bbaba,\ aba,\ bbaaabbab,\ bbbbb,\ babbbaaab,\ bbaab,$$
$$abaabab,\ bbb,\ ababb,\ abbab,\ baabbbbbaba\}$$

and the automaton inferred is shown below. (The language consists of strings having an even number of $a$s and an odd number of $b$s.)

### 3.3.6. Inference of "reversible" languages

D. Angluin has more recently proposed a family of algorithms for inferring subclasses of regular languages, called "$k$-reversible" languages[21]. It is impossible here to give details about the whole matter of this reference.

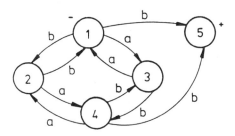

Fig. 14.

But it is important to note that both theoretical and practical results are given about the inference of such languages. In particular, we can quote the following properties and results. If we informally define the "reverse" of a finite automaton as the automaton obtained in reversing the transitions, and interchanging the initial and final states, we can define a "zero-reversible" automaton in the following way: it is such that it and its reverse are both deterministic. A zero-reversible language will be a regular language such that the corresponding minimal automaton is zero-reversible.

Now let us define a "characteristic sample" of a zero-reversible language $L$ as a finite sample $I \subset L$ such that $L$ is the smallest zero-reversible language containing $I$. The author demonstrates that any zero-reversible language has such a characteristic sample.

Then an inference algorithm is given, which starts from a canonical automaton of the sample, and iteratively merges some states according to simple rules; it is shown that it infers the smallest zero-reversible language containing the sample. Moreover, a connection is made with Gold's concept of "inference in the limit", based on the existence of characteristic samples for such languages. Finally, the complexity of the inference process is evaluated and shown to be quasi-linear in $n$, where $n$ is the number of letters of the sample.

All these results are extended to "$k$-reversible" languages which are a generalization of zero-reversible ones, and properties of "reversible" languages ($k$-reversible for some $k$) are also given.

A comparison is made with the $k$-tails and tail-clustering algorithms, and it is claimed that, on the examples which are zero-reversible, the proposed algorithm is better than the two other heuristics.

This method seems particularly interesting; first, because it provides a "missing link" between theoretical works on inductive inference, and a practical inference algorithm, and second because it gives a quick method for inferring in a non-heuristic manner a well-defined automaton from a given sample. The limitation to the subset of zero or $k$-reversible languages does not seem to be an important drawback, since most of the examples given by other authors have this characteristic. Unfortunately, no example of its application has yet been tried on an actual pattern recognition learning situation.

### 3.3.7. Some more methods and results

Other methods have been devised to infer regular structures. We can briefly quote as well Ref. 22, which extends the $k$-tails algorithm, and Ref. 23, which describes an interactive procedure with a teacher using both a positive and a negative sample based also on $k$-tails. In Ref. 24, some results can be found about the theoretical complexity of the inference of finite-state languages, such as the NP-completeness of the problem — "find a regular expression of limited size fitting a positive inference sample". The work by Vidal *et al.* must also be mentioned[25]. They develop a methodology based on algebraic properties of "local languages", a subset of regular languages, and are able to infer general regular languages from a positive inference set. A quite interesting application to speech recognition is given in Ref. 65.

### 3.4. INFERENCE OF SEQUENTIAL MACHINES

A slightly more complex model than finite automata is that of "sequential machine", which includes an output function in parallel with the transition function. In a finite automaton a sentence on $X$ is only accepted or is not, meaning it leads or does not lead from the initial state to a final one. In sequential machines, every transition will generate an "output" in an alphabet $Y$. At the end, the sentence $x$ in $X$ will have produced a sentence $y$ in $Y$. An inference sample is there made of a set of "input-output" couples $(x, y)$.

A more rigorous definition of such a "sequential machine" (or finite automaton with outputs) can be given.

A sequential machine is defined by:

$$M = (X, \ Y, \ Q, \ \delta, \ \lambda, \ q_0)$$

where $X$ is the input alphabet,

$Y$ is the output alphabet,

$Q$ is the set of states,

$\delta : Q \times X \longrightarrow Q$ is the transition function,

$\lambda : Q \times X \longrightarrow Y$ is the output function,

$q_0$ is the initial state.

(Note that $\lambda$ could be defined as well as a function: $\lambda : Q \longrightarrow Y$. There is an equivalence between these two models of sequential machines).

The functions $\delta$ and $\lambda$ can be extended to the domains:

$$\delta : Q \times X^* \longrightarrow Q$$
$$\lambda : Q \times X^* \longrightarrow X^* \ .$$

In this way, given an input sentence $x$ in $X^*$ one can associate to $x$ an output sentence $y$ in $Y^*$. Thus, in this case, an inference sample will be a set of couples $(x, \ y)$ of the input-output behaviour of the sequential machine.

At least two authors have recently studied this problem. The first is Veelenturf[26], who gives an algorithm with the following property: "when the number $n$ of states of the machine to be identified is known, and the sample contains all input-output pairs of length $2n - 1$, the machine found will be equivalent to the original machine, and will be minimal". It constructs a succession of machines with an increasing number of states, based on the examination of increasing prefix strings of the sample. Luneau, Richetin and Cayla[27] have extended and ameliorated the method. They infer a minimal machine, with the same property of convergence to the actual model when the sample is composed of all input-output sequences of sufficient length (assuming that the number of states of the model is known, which is an information out of the sample itself).

## 4. INFERENCE OF STOCHASTIC AUTOMATA AND HIDDEN MARKOV MODELS

We present in this section an extension of classical grammatical models to the case where the production rules are supposed to be associated with a "probability" of rewriting. This gives "stochastic" grammars and automata, which have been used in pattern recognition. Their inference has been studied a little; we present also the parallel "fuzzy" extension of automata. But the most successful case in the learning of such structural models comes from a slightly different probabilistic structure, called "hidden Markov model" which can also produce sentences, and has good learning algorithms. Though it is not exactly grammatical inference, we shall still give a short introduction to these techniques.

## 4.1. Stochastic Grammars

The extension of a formal grammar so as to provide a probabilistic model can be accomplished by introducing the idea of the probability that a given phrase has been generated by the grammar. Alternatively, it would be possible to start from the automaton associated with the grammar. For the regular case a theorem states that the languages associated with the grammar and the automaton are equivalent.

We shall assume that in general the probability of applying a given rule at a given stage is independent of the sequence of rules that have been applied up to that stage. Given this, a stochastic grammar $G_S$ is defined as follows.

$$G_S = (V,\ X,\ P,\ Z)$$

where $P$ is a set of rules of the form

$$\alpha \xrightarrow{P} \beta \quad p \in [0,\ 1]$$

where

$$\alpha \in (V \cup X)^* V (V \cup X)^*$$
$$\beta \in (V \cup X)^* \ .$$

In the regular case $\alpha \in V$ and $\beta \in X \times V$ or $X$.

We write

$$q(x) = \prod_{i=1}^{n} p_i$$

to denote that the string $x$ has been generated by $G_S$ as a result of applying the sequence of rules $P_1 \ldots P_n$ with probabilities $p_1 \ldots p_n$ respectively. If the grammar is ambiguous then, by definition, some phrases can be generated in several different ways, and for such phrases the probability of occurrence is defined by summing this expression over all the possible sequences by which it could be generated. If the number of possibilities is $n_x$

and to the $j$th of these corresponds a probability $q_j(x)$ the total probability is

$$p(x|G_S) = \sum_{j=1}^{n_x} q_j(x) \ .$$

When no confusion is possible this is written simply as $p(x)$.

The non-stochastic grammar $G$ obtained by removing from $G_S$ the probabilities assigned to the rules is called the *characteristic grammar* of $G_S$ and the *stochastic language* generated by $G_S$ is defined by

$$L(G_S) = \{(x, \ p(x)) \text{ where } x \in L(G)\} \ .$$

A property that is natural to require of a stochastic grammar is that the sum of the probabilities of all rules having the same left-hand side is 1; the grammar is then said to be "proper".

## 4.2. Stochastic Finite Automata

Just as the generation of strings in a stochastic language corresponds to a probabilistic grammar, so their analysis corresponds to a stochastic form of an automaton. For the regular case a stochastic finite automaton is defined as follows.

$$\mathcal{A}_S = (X, \ Q, \ M, \ \pi_0, \ F)$$

where $X$ is the alphabet, $Q$ is the set of $n$ states, $M$ is a mapping of $X$ in the set of $n \times n$ stochastic matrices, $\pi_0$ is a vector of $n$ components representing the initial distribution and $F$ is a set of final states. The element $M_{ij}(a)$ of $M$ is the probability of transition from state $q_i$ to state $q_j$ on receiving the letter $a \in X$. We extend the domain of $M$ from $X$ to $X^*$ as follows:

$$M(\lambda) = I_n$$
$$M(a_1 \ldots a_p) = M(a_1) \ldots M(a_p) \quad \text{for} \quad a_1 \ldots a_p \in X^* \ .$$

The stochastic language accepted by $\mathcal{A}_S$ is defined by

$$L(\mathcal{A}_S) = \{(x, \ p(x)) : x \in X^* \quad \text{and} \quad p(x) = \pi_0 M(x)\pi_F > 0\}$$

where $\pi_F$ is a column vector of $n$ components, those corresponding to $F$ having the value 1 and the others 0.

With every string $x \in X^*$ there is the associated probability

$$p(x) = \pi_0 M(x)\pi_F$$

which is also the probability that the string can be generated by the stochastic grammar from which the automaton is derived.

A fundamental result here is the following:

**With every stochastic regular grammar there can be associated a stochastic finite automaton that accepts the same stochastic language.**

The passage from one to the other is entirely natural, but two states must be added, deduced directly from the non-terminal elements of the grammar.

(a) a final state, corresponding to productions of the form $A \longrightarrow a$;

(b) a garbage state, the probabilities of which are adjusted so that the matrices are stochastic, i.e. have unit row sums.

### 4.3. Inference of Stochastic Automata

The problem of inference is both more complex and better stated in the case of stochastic grammar than in the classical case, for not only do the rules of the grammar have to be determined but also their associated probabilities; extra information is available in the form of the probabilities assigned to the phrases constituting the sample of the stochastic language that is provided.

The inference process consists in starting from samples where the sentences are coupled with a probability of occurrence. Then regular inference algorithms can be generalized. In this way, for example, Fu describes an application of the $k$-tails algorithm to the inference of probabilistic automata[6]. Only a few examples of this type of method can be found in the inference literature, the reason being that inference of non-stochastic automata, as seen before, is generally a complex process, and cannot be run on large samples: the precision with which rules probabilities are computed in probabilistic versions is then quite low.

### 4.4. Fuzzy Automata and their Inference

An alternative model to stochastic grammars and languages consists in introducing a "fuzzy" (instead of probabilistic) weighting on the rules. The fuzzy sets theory is, more generally, presented as an alternative to probability theory. It has been used in pattern recognition in many different subjects[28,29]. Concerning what we are interested in, namely, grammatical inference, some publications have been made about learning of fuzzy grammars. We shall only give the references, without entering at all into details. They are Refs. 28, 30 and 31.

## 4.5. Hidden Markov Models

The basic concept of Markov chains can be described as follows. Let $Q = (q_1, \ldots, q_s)$ be a set of states; we assume that a random process in discrete time is characterized by the probability of being in one of these states, and that it is a first order Markov process; namely, that the probability of being in a state $q_i$ at time $n$ depends only on the state in which the process was at time $n - 1$. Hence, the basic equation of such a process is:

$$P_{ij} \overset{A}{=} P(q^n = q_j | q^1 = q_{i_1}, \ldots, q^{n-1} = q_{i_{n-1}}) = P(q^n = q_j | q^{n-1} = q_i) \ .$$

We can characterize the whole process by a transition matrix $P$, which has elements $P_{ij}$. We have to assume that $P$ is normalized, such that:

$$\forall_i \in [1, \ s] \quad \sum_{j=1}^{s} P_{ij} = 1 \ ,$$

and that we know the initial probabilistic at time $1 : P(q^1 = q_i)$ for $i \in [1, \ s]$ with their sum equal to 1.

We have to produce sentences on an alphabet $X$ with such a process. This is done by assuming that being in a state $q_i$ allows the process to emit a letter from $X$. If we suppose that $X = (a_1, \ldots, a_n)$, we have to know another matrix $B = (b_{ij})$, where $b_{ij}$ is the probability of emitting the letter $a_i$ when the process is in the state $q_j$.

Note that another model very commonly relies on assuming that a state emits a vector in $R_n$ with a parametric distribution of probabilities, and that this set of parameters characterizes the output process, instead of matrix $B$. Since we are interested in grammatical inference, we shall only assume the first case. Nevertheless, the second one is quite important in pattern recognition applications, and it should not be ignored when dealing with this type of probabilistic model. The associated algorithms of string generation, and of the learning of its parameters on a set of examples are not very different from those of our discrete case.

Firstly, we have to describe how such a model can produce sentences, and how to associate a "probability" for such a sentence to be emitted by this model. Secondly, we shall be interested in the learning of $P$ and $B$ from an "inference" sample. This means that, assuming one knows the underlying structure of the automaton and a sample of the sentences that they have produced, we shall look for a method of computing the parameters $P$ and $B$ of the model.

### 4.5.1. Recognition

Two different ways have been described for estimation with which confidence value a given sentence $x$ can be produced by such a model.

The first consists in computing the sum of the probabilities of the emission of $x$ in all different possible manners. It is in fact the actual probability that $x$ has been produced by the model. The second gives an approximation of this value: it computes the most probable way of emitting $x$.

Let $x = x_1 \ldots x_n$ be the sentence, and $\alpha_j^n$ the probability that the process is in state $q_j$ at time $n$, after the emission of $x_1, \ldots x_n$. Then we can write the following recurrence, assuming that $x_{n+1} = a_k$

$$\forall j \in [1, \ s] : \alpha_j^{n+1} = \left( \sum_{i=1}^{s} \alpha_i^n P_{ij} \right) b_{jk} \ .$$

And, starting from the initial values

$$\forall j \in [1, \ s] : \alpha_j^1 = \sum_{i=1}^{s} P_{ij} b_{jk_0} \ ,$$

we can compute the $\alpha_j^M$ for all $ji$ n $[1, \ s]$.

If we suppose there is a distinguishing final state of the index $F \in [1, \ s]$, then the probability of emitting $x$ is $\alpha_F^M$ in the first case.

Direct computation by this equation leads to an exponential number of multiplications (of order $MS^M$). But a quicker procedure ("forward-backward" method) exists, and decreases the computation to a $O(S^2 M)$ calculation, which is quite feasible.

If we now consider the recurrence

$$\alpha_j^{n+1} = \max_{i \in [1, \ s]} \alpha_i^n P_{ij} b_{jk}$$

the value $\alpha_F^M$ will be the result in the second case. It may be computed by a dynamic programming Viterbi algorithm.

### 4.5.2. Learning

Matrices $P$ and $B$ must be evaluated from a sample of sentences, if one wants to learn the "hidden" Markov model generating this sample and generalizing it. We do not quite have a problem of inference of stochastic automata, since the size and the structure of $P$ and $B$ must be given. By structure, we mean that some transitions will be fixed to 0 in $P$ or in $B$, implying forbidden changing of states or emission of letters in a state. As an example, it is common in speech recognition to use the following structure for $P$ ("Bakis model"):

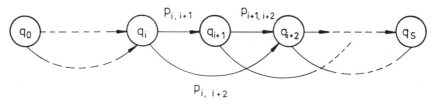

Fig. 15

and to arbitrarily set the number of states to a number between 5 to 10 (only probabilities corresponding to the arrows of the graph are not set to zero). This kind of structure has proved itself very efficient in the recognition of words[32].

The learning problem can be stated as follows: given a sample $I$ and the structure of the underlying automaton, we are looking for matrices $P$ and $B$ such that.

$$\prod_{x \in I} p(x,\ P,\ B) \quad \text{is maximum}$$

(where $p(x,\ P,\ B)$ stands for the probability of $x$ to be generated by the process characterized by $P$ and $B$). This can be realised by an iterative algorithm (the "Baum-Welch" formulae), which starts from randomly (or more accurately) initialized matrices $P$ and $B$, and re-estimates their value with each sentence of the sample. The convergence of this algorithm ensures that at the end, the model is optimized to best match the training sample. From a practical point of view, we have to note that the convergence of $P$ and $B$ have to be realized on rather large samples, and that it may take a very long learning time, but the solution is mathematically (at least locally) optimal. The principle is to use the forward-backward procedure, and to modify the parameters according to the way that the sentence of the sample is generated by the current model. One has to note that, as in the recognition process, an approximation of these values can be obtained by using the Viterbi algorithm. We do not intend here to go into the details of this learning procedure, which is rather complex and raises severe programming problems. References 32–35 will give precise details on both their theory and application. Examples of their use in speech recognition are given in the section about practical applications of grammatical inference.

## 5. INFERENCE OF CONTEXT-FREE GRAMMARS

Context-free grammars were originally studied for modelling natural language; later on, they were intensively used as models or programming languages, and are used also in structural pattern recognition. The corresponding inference algorithms have been successively devised with the same purposes. For example, one of the first papers on grammatical inference[20] makes explicit reference to linguistic studies and automatic translation. Later, ambitions decreased and the more recent papers deal with subfamilies of context-free grammars such as "non-recursive"[36], or "programmed"[27] in a goal of pattern recognition learning algorithms.

Among the whole bibliography, which is much smaller than the one on regular grammars we have chosen to describe two methods: one assumes that the sample contains information about how its sentences have been generated; the other infers probabilistic context-free grammars and introduces interesting concepts about "convergence" of an inference procedure. We shall at the end make short references to some other papers.

### 5.1. Crespi-Reghizzi Algorithm[37]

The principle of this algorithm (which has been refined in the following), is to use "structured" inference samples, namely, a set of sentences where the order of letters generation is indicated by brackets. This information reduces considerably the combinatorial scale of the problem by giving an *a priori* indication of the structure of the derivation tree associated with the string, but the corresponding derivation rules have still to be found.

The algorithm is based on the concept of the *terminal profile* of a string in $(X \cup V)^*$. If $\alpha$ is a string and $G$ a grammar

$$G = (X, \ V, \ S, \ P)$$

then the terminal profile of $\alpha$ is defined as

$$P(\alpha) = (L_t(\alpha), \ R_t(\alpha))$$

where

$$L_t(\alpha) = \{a : \alpha \stackrel{*}{\Longrightarrow} A a \gamma\}$$
$$R_t(\alpha) = \{a : \alpha \stackrel{*}{\Longrightarrow} \gamma a A\}$$

and

$$a \in X \qquad A \in V \cup \{\lambda\} \qquad \gamma \in (V \cup X)^* .$$

Thus $L_t(\alpha)$ is the set of elements $a$ of the alphabet $X$ which can appear in positions $Aa\gamma$ or $a\gamma$ in the strings that can be derived from $a$ by applying the rules of $G$. The algorithm is as follows.

(a) For each string of the structure sample, extract a canonical context-free grammar $G_i$; given the information on the structure, this can be done very simply.

(b) For each grammar $G_i$ calculate the terminal profile of the right-hand parts of the rules of $G_i$.

(c) Equate those elements of $V$ associated with the left-hand parts of the rules of $G_i$ with those right-hand parts having the same terminal profile.

(d) Combine all the rules thus obtained from the set of strings and simplify the resulting grammar.

The author of the algorithm has shown that it produces algebraic grammars of special form, and does not cover all possible forms.

**Example 5.1.**
$$I = \{((a) + ((a) + ((a))))\} .$$

(a) Extraction of a canonical grammar from the structured sample deepest terminal: $a$

rule: $N_t \longrightarrow a$

rewriting of the string: $(N_1 + (N_1 + N_1))$

deepest string: $N_1 + N_1$

rule: $N_2 \longrightarrow N_1 + N_1$

rewriting of the string: $(N_1 + N_2)$

rule: $N_3 \longrightarrow N_1 + N_2$

canonical grammar inferred: 
$$S \longrightarrow N_3$$
$$N_3 \longrightarrow N_1 + N_2$$
$$N_2 \longrightarrow N_1 + N_1$$
$$N_1 \longrightarrow a$$

(b) Terminal profile of $N_1 : (\{a\}, \{a\})$

Terminal profile of $N_2 : (\{a+\}, \{a+\})$

Terminal profile of $N_3$ : $(\{a+\}, \{a+\})$

(c), (d), Equating $N_2$ and $N_3$

Grammar inferred, after simplification:

$$S \longrightarrow a + S | a + a \ .$$

### 5.2. Cook's Method

The inference method developed by Cook[38] deals with stochastic context-free grammars. Their rules are in the form:

$$A_j \longrightarrow \alpha_{j1} | \ldots | \alpha_{jl_j} \quad (p_{j1}, \ldots, p_{jl_j}) \ ,$$

where the $A_j$ are the set $V$ of non-terminals and $\alpha_{ji}$ are in $(V \cup X)^*$. The basic rewriting rule

$$A_j \longrightarrow \alpha_{ji} (p_{ij}) \ ,$$

means that $A_j$ can be rewritten in $\alpha_{ji}$ with probability $p_{ji}$. Now, with a string $x$ in $X^*$ generated by such a grammar, there is associated with it a probability $p(x)$, computed as the sum over all possible derivations leading to $x$ of the products of the probabilities of the rules used in one of these derivations.

The method is based on two measures defined for the grammar sought, which intuitively are seen to be mutually contradictory: *complexity*, derived from information theory concepts, and *discrepancy*, an indication of the plausibility of the sample's coming from the language generated by the grammar. These somewhat arbitrary measures are used to find a path through a network of grammars set up by manipulating the production rules, a heuristic search being conducted for an optimum, if possible global, among their local values.

More precisely, let $I$ be a stochastic sample and suppose that at a certain stage a provisional inference of a grammar $G$ has been reached. The complexity $C(G)$ is calculated as follows:

(a) If $\alpha$ is a string in $(V \cup X)^*$ with $|\alpha| = n$, in which the symbols $X_1, X_2, \ldots X_m$ appear $k_1, k_2 \ldots, k_m$ times respectively, then

$$C(\alpha) = (n+1) \log(n+1) - \sum_{i=1}^{m} k_i \log k_i \ .$$

(b) If the rules of $G$ are written

$$A_1 \longrightarrow \alpha_{11}|\ldots|\alpha_{1l_1}(p_{11},\ldots,p_{1l_1})$$
$$A_r \longrightarrow \alpha_{r1}|\ldots|\alpha_{rl_r}(p_{r1},\ldots,p_{rl_r})$$

then

$$C(G) = \sum_{i=1}^{r}\sum_{j=1}^{l}[-\log p_{ij} + C(\alpha_{ij})] \ .$$

Thus the complexity, as defined here, does not involve the language generated by $G$ as such but only the information carried by the production rules.

The discrepancy of $L(G)$ relative to $I$ is given by

$$D(L(G), I) = \sum_{|x|<N} |P_{L(G)}(x)[-\log P_{L(G)}(x) + C(x)]$$
$$- P_I(X)[-\log P_I(x) + C(x)]|$$

where $N$ is the length of the longest string in the sample and $P_I(x)$ and $P_{L(G)}(x)$ are the probabilities of $x$ in $I$ and $L(G)$ respectively. This evaluation therefore requires a knowledge of all possible strings of $L(G)$ up to a certain length.

To find the optimal grammar, the global criterion $D(L(G), I) + C(G)$ is evaluated and the grammar is modified in successive stages so that this decreases at each state. The modifications are formal manipulations of the rules which comply with the grammar of the set of solutions to the stochastic inference problem. They are as follows.

(a) **Substitution:** An element of $V$ is replaced by a string $\alpha \in (V \cup X)^*$ which repeats itself. This reduces $C(G)$.

(b) **Disjunction:** If two symbols $X, Y$ appear several times in similar positions they can both be replaced by a non-terminal symbol $B$ and the rule $B \longrightarrow X|Y$ added. The associated probabilities must be calculated so as to reduce $D(L(G), I)$.

(c) **Reduction:** Unused or inaccessible rules are discarded.

The algorithm works as follows.

(a) The canonical grammar is assumed as the starting point.

(b) Let $G$ be the grammar at the current stage. Applying substitutions to $G$ a grammar is constructed and $G'$, the one for which the criterion is least, is selected. If the value is less than that for $G$ the step is repeated for $G'$, and so on.

(c) Otherwise, disjunctions are applied to $G'$ and the $G''$ of minimum criterion selected. If the value is less than that for $G'$, step 2 is performed with $G''$.

(d) Otherwise, the same procedure is performed with deletions. If no grammar can be found for which the criterion is less than that of $G$, then $G$ is the solution.

Cook gives the following example.

*Sample with alphabet $X = \{(, +, ), a, b\}$*

| | | | |
|---|---|---|---|
| $((a))$ | 0.02 | $((b))$ | 0.02 |
| $a + a$ | 0.02 | $a + b$ | 0.02 |
| $b + b$ | 0.02 | $(a + a)$ | 0.005 |
| $(a + b)$ | 0.005 | $a + (a)$ | 0.005 |
| $a + (b)$ | 0.005 | $(b + a)$ | 0.005 |
| $b + (b)$ | 0.005 | $(a) + b$ | 0.005 |
| $(b) + a$ | 0.005 | $b + a + a$ | 0.0025 |
| $b + a + b$ | 0.0025 | $b + b + b$ | 0.0025 |
| $a + a + b$ | 0.0025 | $a + b + a$ | 0.0025 |
| $a + b + b$ | 0.0025 | | |

from which the grammar inferred is

$$A \longrightarrow (A)|A + A|a|b .$$

The complexity of the method is very great, but this seems inevitable when dealing with such rich structures.

## 5.3. Some Other Methods for Context-Free Grammars

Gips[39], as quoted in Ref. 6, infers "pivot" grammars which form a class between linear and context-free grammars. Solomonoff[20] uses a teacher, supposed to be able to answer the following question: "does sentence $x$ belong to the language of the grammar to be inferred?" Like in Pao and Carr's algorithm for regular grammars, this is a help for discovering embeddings in the rules. Lu and Fu make an analoguous "recursive structure hunting"[40] in the sentences of the sample, and discover the basic nestings in a context-free programmed grammar (a context-free programmed grammar is a variation on a basic model of sophisticated rewriting rules, as developed by Rozenkrantz[41]). They ensure that their algorithm can infer grammars generating languages "sufficient for string pattern representation in syntactic pattern recognition", but do not give any such example. Chirathamjaree[36] gives an algorithm for non-recursive context-free grammars, and an example of application to speech recognition (in an elliptic paragraph). We can quote here as well, through it does not concern context-free models, an article by Angluin[42], aiming at finding "patterns" in a string; it is quite relevant to grammatical inference though not formalized in terms of rewriting rules. The complexity and possibilities of the method are carefully described.

## 6. INFERENCE OF "MULTIDIMENSIONAL" GRAMMARS

We mean by "multidimensional grammar" a rewriting system of the Chomsky basic form, but whose terminal alphabet is not composed of letters: it will be, for example, a set of primitive trees, or a set of small two-dimensional pictures. Then the rewriting system will produce not strings, but trees or pictures, by assembling the primitive elements with its extended concatenation rules. The interest of such models for pattern recognition is quite great, since they can represent more complex structures than strings. Here, their inference is a relevant problem as well.

We present here a method for inferring tree grammars, which is, as far as we know, the more recent and comprehensive one. Then, we briefly give a bibliography on the rest of the topic. A bibliographic summary on the same subject is found in Ref. 43.

### 6.1. Inferring a Tree Grammar

As with the classical grammars already considered, learning methods can be developed for tree grammars[44], and inference procedures have been developed whose principles have been suggested by the study of regular syntactic structures. The methods aim either to detect regularities in the teaching sample as in the $uv^k w$ method or to generalize the concept of $k$-tails. The algorithms of Bhargava and Fu[45] and those of Gonzales and Thomason[44] are associated with the first of these aims, and that of Levine with the second. Levine's algorithm has good theoretical support and also has the advantage of generalizing the other algorithms, and for these reasons it is given here[46].

The trees are regarded as forming a *tree domain D*, i.e. a list of words on $\mathbb{N}^*$ describing the unique structure associated with a given labelling, thus a tree is a mapping $t$ of $D$ in the set $A$ of labels (cf. Ref. 62). We write $D = \text{dom}(t)$.

The tree $t$ can be represented by

$$t = \{(x,\ a) : x \in \text{dom}(t) \quad \text{and} \quad a = t(x)\}\ .$$

We write $b/a = b \iff b = ab'$, for $a,\ b,\ b'/ \in \mathbb{N}^*$. The *subtree* of $t$ in $y$, where $y \in \text{dom}(t)$, is defined by

$$t/y = \{(x,\ b) : (y,\ x,\ b) \in t\}\ .$$

The operation or *replacement* of the subtree of $t$ in $y$ by a tree $u$ results in the tree $t'$ defined by

$$t' = t(y \longleftarrow u) = \{(x,\ b) \in t : t(x) = b,\ y \le x\} \cup (y.z,\ u(z)) : z \in \text{dom}(u)\}$$

with the convention $y.0 = y$.

**Example 6.1.** With the notation on the left for the tree $t$ on the right, $t = \{(0,\ a), (1,\ a), (2,\ a), (1.1,\ a), (2.1,\ a), (2.2,\ a)\}$

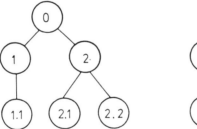
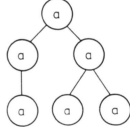

Fig. 16.

$u = \{(0,\ d), (1,\ c), (2,\ b)\}$

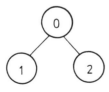
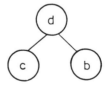

Fig. 17.

The replacement of the subtree of $t$ in 1 by $u$ is written

$$t(1 \longleftarrow u) = \{(0,\ a), (2,\ a), (2.1,\ a), (2.2,\ a)\} \cup \{(1,\ d), (1.1,\ c), (1.2,\ b)\}$$

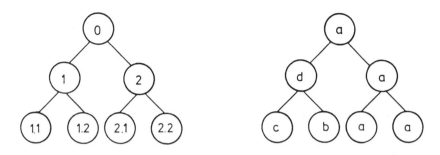

Fig. 18.

An equivalence relation $R$ between trees is said to be *invariant* (meaning invariant under subtree replacement) when

$$tRu \iff v(x \longleftarrow t)Rv(x \longleftarrow u)$$

for all $x \in \text{dom}(v)$ and all trees $t, u$ and $v$.

The $m$th order derivative of a set $S$ of trees with respect to a tree $t$ is the set $D_t^m(S)$ defined recursively by

$$D_t^1(S) = \{u(b \longleftarrow \$) \quad \text{where} \quad u \in S \quad \text{and} \quad u/b = t\}$$
$$D_t^{i+1}(S) = D_t^1(D_t^i(S)) \quad \text{for} \quad i > 1$$

where $\$$ is a particular character belonging to the set $A$ of labels. The derivative has the property

$$D_t^1(S) = D_u^1(S) \implies D_t^j(S) = D_u^j(S) \quad \text{for all} \quad j > 1 .$$

With the aid of a tree automaton an invariant equivalence relation can be defined and related to these derivatives. If $M$ is a tree automaton and $T(M)$ the set of trees that it will accept, we have the following two theorems.

**Theorem 6.2.** The following three propositions are equivalent:
  (a) $S$ is a set of trees accepted by $M$.
  (b) $S$ is the union of the classes between which there is an invariant equivalence relation of finite index.
  (c) If the equivalence $R^M$ is defined by

$$tR^M u \iff \forall \text{ trees } v \text{ and } \forall x \in \text{dom}(v)$$
$$v(x \longleftarrow t) \in S \iff v(x \longleftarrow u) \in S .$$

$R^M$ is of finite index.

**Theorem 6.3.** With $R^M$ as defined in Theorem 6.2

$$D_t^j(T(M)) = D_u^j(T(M)) \Longleftrightarrow t R^M u \quad \text{for all} \quad j \geq 1 .$$

These properties are generalizations of those of regular languages.

The above results can be used by a tree automaton in making inferences from a sample set of trees. Generalizing the concept of $k$-tails, the $m$th order derivative bounded at depth $K$ is defined by

$$D_t^{K,m}(S) = \{u : u \in D_t^m(S) \text{ with level } (u) \leq K\} .$$

Then

$$t R^M u \Longrightarrow D_t^{k,l}(T(M)) = D_u^{k,l}(T(M)) \text{ for all } k \geq 0, \ l \geq 1 .$$

The algorithm uses this property, as do the $k$-tails and tail clustering algorithms. A canonical automaton is constructed and if necessary certain states are made identical so as to generalize the language that it will accept, the identification being based on a study of the bounded derivatives of the corresponding set of trees.

*Levine's algorithm*

(a) $S$ is the sample, a set of finite trees.

(b) $R^M$ is the equivalence relation associated with the *canonical tree automaton*, i.e. the automaton having one state for each subtree of $S$.

(c) For all pairs of subtrees of $S(t_e, t_j)$ not belonging to the same class, do if $D_{t_j}^{k,i}(S) = D_{t_0}^{k,i}(S)$ and $D_{t_j}^{k,i} \neq \emptyset$ and $D_{t_j}^{k,i}(S) \neq \{\$\}$ then make the states of the automaton corresponding to the classes containing $t_e$ and $t_j$ identical.

(d) This gives an equivalence relation $R^M$, less detailed than $R^M$, corresponding to an automaton $M'$ that recognizes a tree language containing $S$; thus the inference problem is solved.

**Example 6.4.** The sample $S$ is

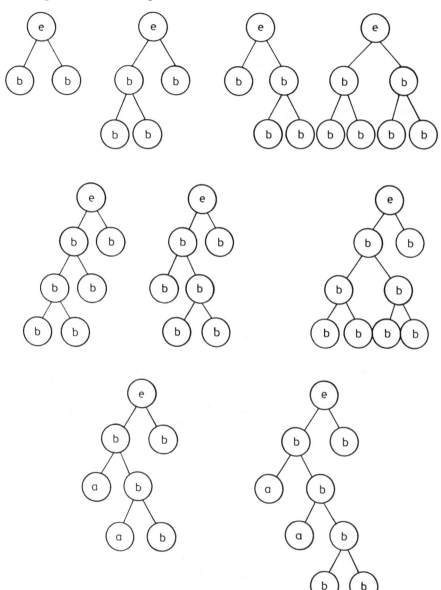

Fig. 19.

The inferred tree automaton is

$$M = (\{S,\ A,\ B,\ C\},\ \{e,\ a,\ b\},\ f, \{S\})$$

where

$$
\begin{array}{lll}
f_b = B & f_b(A,\ B) = C & f_b(B,\ B) = B \\
f_a = A & f_b(A,\ C) = B & f_e(B,\ B) = S \ .
\end{array}
$$

The corresponding tree grammar is

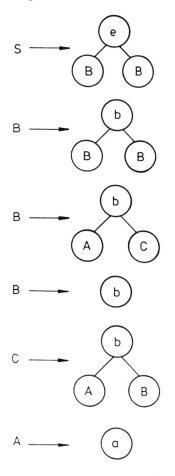

Fig. 20.

which generates an infinite language, containing for example the trees

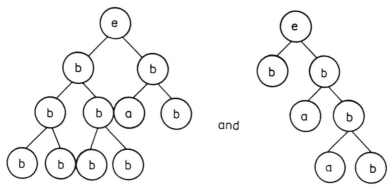

and

Fig. 21.

## 6.2. Some Other "Multidimensional" Inference Methods

### 6.2.1. Array grammars

This topic will be examined in detail in Chapter 10 of this book. The basic references are Refs. 47–51.

### 6.2.2. The Evan's approach

In a classical paper[52], Evans gives a general scheme for inferring rules from examples, these rules possibly being of a more complex form than rewriting grammatical ones. A very good summary is given for example in Ref. 61 (pp. 372–376). If we restrict this method to string grammars, we obtain a regular inference algorithm, producing a solution by a heuristic merging of states in the canonical grammar. A discussion on this method and a comparison with tree grammars inference is in Ref. 43.

### 6.2.3. Inference of ATN

Augmented transition networks (ATN) have been introduced by Woods for modelizing natural language, and used in particular in high levels of speech recognition systems[53]. They cannot really be defined as "multidimensional grammars" in the sense of this section, since they produce strings of letters in an alphabet. Nevertheless, they are derived from the Chomsky rewriting system, and we included them in this section as another extension of the classical models, with application to pattern recognition.

The basic model *basic transition network* is a directed graph of which the arcs and the nodes are labelled and in which an initial and a final state can be distinguished. It differs from a finite automaton in that the label on an arc can be not only a terminal symbol of the alphabet but also the name of a state, and selecting an arc thus labelled leads to the following actions. The node to which the arc leads is placed on a stack, a jump is made to the state with which the arc is labelled and the analysis is continued from there. When the final state is reached a return is made to the state at the top of the stack; if the stack is then empty the process has succeeded.

**Example 6.5.** Consider the network of Fig. 22. Such a machine could recognize, for example, the sentences

> Has the last bus gone?
> The man at the hotel took Mary to the next town.

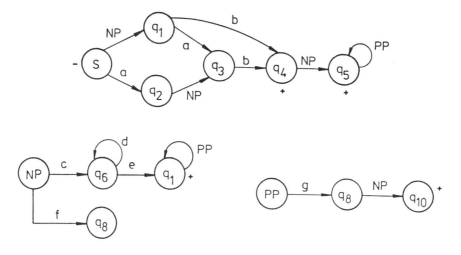

Fig. 22.

These correspond to the models *acdeb* and *cegcebfgcde* respectively, if we interpret

> *a* as an auxiliary,
> *b* as a verb,
> *c* as an article,
> *d* as an adjective,
> *e* as a noun,
> *f* as a proper noun,
> *g* as a preposition.

It will be seen that the method provides a tool for the syntactic description and analysis of a greatly simplified natural language; its complexity is that of a set of finite automata, controlled by a stack. It can be shown to have the power of a *stack automaton*, which means that for recognition its power is equivalent to that of a context-free grammar for generation.

What is most used in practice is a more general version — the *augmented transition network* — in which each arc carries also a condition that has to be satisfied before it can be selected and a group of instructions that are executed if it is selected. The power now is that of a Turing machine, meaning that this automaton can be used to simulate any algorithm whatsoever.

Chou and Fu[54] have discussed the matter of inferring such models from samples of sentences they can produce. They propose an extension of the $k$-tails method for basic transition networks and by this way extend this method to context-free languages. They give afterwards some indication of the possibilities of extension to ATN. As far as we know, their final hope that "more research will be stimulated on this subject" has not materialized.

## 7. A LIST OF PRACTICAL APPLICATIONS OF GRAMMATICAL INFERENCE

We present in this section a list of practical problems of pattern recognition where grammatical inference has been used. It is quite short and disappointing when compared to the conceptual importance of the subject and the amount of theoretical or methodological works on the topic, as seen before. This is certainly not a good point for the future of the domain: if no application can prove that grammatical inference is better than the "hand-made" designing of grammars, its practical interest will no longer encourage research. This may explain why the bibliography in grammatical inference is now decreasing. More flexible paradigms for learning have to be experienced: grammatical inference has not yet proved to really be a practical success in applications of pattern recognition.

Ouriachi[55] designs a pattern recognition system in robotics for the assembly of mechanical components. It detects the edges of the components, makes a polygonal approximation, and describes them in a sentence on an *ad hoc* vocabularly. The model of each class is computed by grammatical inference and the recognition is performed with a simple syntactic analysis on the inferred finite automata. In this way the assembly can be realised by the robot. The inference method is the $uv^kw$ algorithm, which describes classes of sentences as regular expressions, which are then transformed in deterministic finite automata for the syntactic analysis (recognition) process. The author reckons the inference method to be useful for his example, though a "hand-made" design of the grammars is presented as "still more precise and efficient".

Vernadat[17] studies the outputs of dynamic linear systems, and is interested in the design of an interactive software for helping to modelize dynamic linear systems. A module of his software has to describe the shape of the impulse reponse of the systems, and helps the operator choose the class of the system among several possible structures. This defines a pattern recognition procedure in which grammatical inference is used for the learning part. The different shapes are encoded as sentences on a five-letter alphabet, and the discrimination has to be done between eight classes. The algorithm, which has been designed for this problem, is the "successor" method. The author claims his results to be as good as those obtained by experts in such systems.

Winston[56], in a famous Ph.D. thesis, has described a learning system for structured patterns. Fu[6] states it again in terms of grammatical inference and gives an example of the learning of a grammar describing the structure of a pyramid. The terminal elements are high-level primitives, such as cubes, supposed to be extracted from an image.

Lu and Fu[40] propose stochastic tree grammars to modelize textures in images. For each cluster of windowed patterns of the same class, they want to infer a tree structure. This is done in fact by decomposing the tree in strings, and inferring a stochastic finite-state grammar for each class of such strings, with the Biermann and Feldman method. Then the tree grammar is recomposed from the inferred string grammars, and may be simplified. This inference procedure is included in a complex pattern recognition system of textures, by structural means; so it is difficult to give any advice on its practical efficiency without considering this context.

Lee and Fu[57] describe a general methodology to use inference methods in pattern recognition systems, with, in particular, the intervention of a teacher which selects the alphabet on which the patterns are to be written, and segments the patterns into subpatterns, in order to make the inference algorithms work in the best conditions. They give two examples, both on the coding of edges of images as chains of primitive segments.

The first uses the Freeman coding, and infers a grammar describing right triangles, including a certain amount of noise. The second is the coding of the edge of chromosomes on a more elaborate alphabet. The inferred grammar describes the family of "submedian" chromosomes.

Moayer and Fu[58] present a system of fingerprints classification, with a tree grammar modelling of pattern classes. Since they are dealing with a great number of classes, they want to avoid the manual design of the corresponding grammars. Therefore, they use an inference procedure, based on the following steps:

- selection of the picture components which have a high-repetitive occurrence,
- inference of a grammar for this substructure,
- merging of the grammars of the substructures.

Afterwards, to avoid the creation of one grammar for example, they use a classification procedure between the grammars, by combining their rules when they generate too similar patterns. The computer simulation on real data seems to prove that this inference scheme is very efficient.

Brauneg and Gonzalez[59] use the $k$-tails method for inferring models of classes in a goal of pattern recognition in pictures of industrial objects (bolts, screws, wire splices, wirenuts). The edges are detected, coded in Freeman alphabet, and finally described as a string of discrete angles between these primitives patterns. Then the inference process is realised. The interesting part of this work is that a study is made on the set of overlapping patterns between the inferred classes as they may cause ambiguities in the decision process. So, a "semantic" procedure is used to resolve them, which refers to a more general knowledge on the shapes of patterns to discriminate. The authors think that this interaction between pure syntactic techniques and use of higher level knowledge has proved efficient.

In Ref. 64, a proposition is made to use grammatical inference for the designing of programming languages. Reference 65, already quoted, gives an application to the inference of regular grammars for speech recognition of Spanish digits.

Finally, we have to insist on the fact that most of the research and applied results in the domain of (extended) grammatical inference is presently in the field of Markov models. The applications of these models, with many different technical variations in learning and recognition, has proved very efficient in the domain of word, connected words and syllable recognition in speech, and is also used now in pictures as well[60]. Let us quote a partial list of the laboratories or companies which work on the topic, and have obtained good results in speech recognition with this kind of automatic syntactic learning: IBM (USA, France), Bell Labs (USA), CNET (France), MATRA (France), Philips (Belgium), Dragon Systems (USA), RSRE (GB), CSELT (Italy), etc. A complete bibliography is beyond the scope of this paper, but may easily be extracted from the proceedings of the ICASSP Conferences, for example.

REFERENCES

1. D. Angluin and C.-H. Smith, "Introductive inference, theory and methods", *ACM Computing Surveys* **15** (1983) 741-765.
2. K.S. Fu, ed., *Syntactic Pattern Recognition and Applications*, (Springer Verlag, 1977).
3. J. Quinqueton and L. Miclet, "Learning from examples and grammatical inference", in *Syntactic and Structural Pattern Recognition*, eds. G. Ferrate *et al.* (Springer Verlag, 1986) pp. 153-171.
4. A.W. Biermann and J.A. Feldman, "A survey of results in grammatical inference", *Frontiers of Pattern Recognition*, ed. S. Watanabe (Academic Press, 1972).
5. K.S. Fu, *Syntactic Pattern Recognition and Applications*, (Prentice-Hall, 1982).
6. K.S. Fu, *Syntactic Pattern Recognition and Applications*, (Prentice-Hall, 1982).
7. L. Miclet, *Structural Methods in Pattern Recognition*, (North-Oxford Academic, 1986, and Springer-Verlag, 1986).
8. E.M. Gold, "Language identification in the limit", *Information and Control* **10** (1967) 447-474.
9. J. Feldman, "Some decidability results on grammatical inference and complexity", *Information and Control* **20** (1972) 244-262.
10. E.M. Gold, "Complexity of automaton identification from given data", *Information and Control* **37** (1978) 302-320.
11. J. Case and C. Smith, "Comparison of identification criteria for machine inductive inference", *Theoretical Computer Science* **25** (1983) 193-220.
12. D.N. Osherson, M. Straub and S. Weinstein, *Systems That Learn* (MIT Press, 1986).
13. S.C. Kleene, "Representation of events in nerve nets", in *Automata Studies*, eds. C.E. Shannon and J. McCarthy, (Princeton University Press, 1956) pp. 3-40.
14. A.V. Aho and J.D. Ullman, *The Theory of Parsing, Translation and Compiling*, Vol. 1, Chap. 2 (Prentice-Hall, 1972).
15. L. Miclet, "Regular inference with a tail-clustering method", *IEEE Trans. on SMC* **9** (1980) 737-743.
16. L. Miclet, "Inference de grammaires régulières", Thése de Docteur-Ingénieur, E.N.S.T., Paris, France, 1979.
17. F. Vernadat and M. Richetin, "Analyse assistée par ordinateur de systémes dynamiques", Thése de 3éme cycle, Université de Clermont II, France, 1981.
18. R.S. Rodger and R.D. Rosebrugh, "Computing a grammar for sequences of behavioural acts", *Animal behaviour* **27** (1979) 737-749.
19. T.W. Pao and J.W. Carr III, "A solution of the syntactical induction-inference problem for regular languages, *Computer Languages* **3** (1978) 53-64.
20. R. Solomonoff, "A new method for discovering the grammars of phrase structure languages", *Information Processing* (UNESCO New York, 1959).

21. D. Angluin, "Inference of reversible languages", *J. ACM* **29** (1982) 741-785.
22. S.Y. Itoga, "A new heuristic for inferring regular grammars", *IEEE Trans. on PAMI* **3** (1981) 191-197.
23. A.W. Biermann, "An interactive finite-state language learner", Report from the Computer Science Department, Stanford University, Feb. 1972.
24. D. Angluin, "On the complexity of minimum inference of regular sets", *Information and Control* **39** (1978) 337-350.
25. H. Rulot and E. Vidal, "An efficient algorithm for the inference of circuit-free automata", in *Syntactic and Structural Pattern Recognition*, eds. G. Ferrate *et al.*, (Springer Verlag, 1986) pp. 173-184.
26. L.P.J. Veelenturf, "Inference of sequential machines from sample computations", *IEEE Trans. on Computers* **27** (1978) 167-170.
27. P. Luneau, M. Richetin and C. Cayla, "Sequential learning from input-output behaviour", *Robotica* **1** (1984) 151-159.
28. D. Du Bois and H. Prade, *Fuzzy Sets and Systems: Theory and Applications* (Academic Press, 1980).
29. R. De Mori, *Computer Models of Speech Using Fuzzy Algorithms* (Plenum Press, 1983).
30. A.K. Majumdar and A.K. Roy, "Inference of fuzzy regular pattern grammar", *Pattern Recognition Letters* **2** (1983) 27-32.
31. S. Tamura and K. Tanaka, "Learning of fuzzy formal language", *IEEE Trans. on SMC* **3** (1974) 98-102.
32. L.R. Rabiner, S.E. Levinson and M.M. Sondhi, "On the application of vector quantization and hidden Markov models to speaker independent, isolated word recognition", *B.S.T.J.* **62**, No. 75 (1983) 1105.
33. L.R. Rabiner and B.H. Juang, "An introduction to hidden Markov models", *IEEE ASSP Magazine*, Jan 1986.
34. L.R. Bahl, F. Jelinek and R.L. Mercer, "A maximum likelihood approach to continuous speech recognition", *IEEE Trans. on PAMI* **5** (1983) 179-190.
35. H. Bourlard, Y. Kamp, H. Ney and C.J. Wellekens, "Speaker dependent connected speech recognition via dynamic programming and statistical methods", *Speech and Speaker Recognition*, ed. M. Schroeder (Karger, 1985) pp. 115-148.
36. C. Chirathamjaree, "A method for the inference of non-recursive context-free grammars", *Int. J. Man-Machine Studies*, **12**(1980) 379-387.
37. S. Crespi-Reghizzi, "An effective model for grammatical inference", *Proc. of IFIP Congress*, Ljubljana, 1971, pp. 524-529.
38. C.M. Cook and A. Rosenfeld, "Some experiments in grammatical inference", *NATO ASI on Computer Oriented Learning Processes*, Bonas, France, 1974 pp. 157-171.
39. J.A. Feldman, J. Gips, J.J. Horning and S. Reder, "Grammatical complexity and inference", Tech. Rep. CS-125, Stanford Univ., 1969.
40. S.Y. Lu and K:S. Fu, "Stochastic tree grammar inference for texture synthesis and discrimination *CGIP* **9** (1979) 234-245.
41. D.J. Rosenkrantz, Programmed grammars and classes of formal languages, *J. ACM* **16** (1969) 117-131.
42. D. Angluin, "Finding patterns common to a set of strings", *Journal of Computer and Systems Science* **21** (1980) 46-62.
43. J.M. Brayer and K.S. Fu, "Some multidimensional grammar inference methods", *Pattern Recognition and Artificial Intelligence*, ed. C.H. Chen (Academic Press, 1976).

44. R.C. Gonzalez and M.G. Thomason, "On the inference of tree patterns for syntactic pattern recognition", *Proc. of International Conference on Systems, Man and Cybernetics*, Dallas, 1974.

45. B.K. Bhargava and K.S. Fu, "Transformations and inference of tree grammars for syntactic pattern recognition", *Proc. of International Conference on Systems, Man and Cybernetics*, Dallas, 1974.

46. B. Levine, "Derivatives of tree sets with applications to grammatical inference", *IEEE Trans. on PAMI*, **3** (1981) 285-293.

47. A. Rosenfeld, *Picture Languages* (Academic Press, 1979).

48. P.S.P. Wang, "Hierarchical structures and complexities of isometric array patterns", *IEEE Trans. on PAMI* **5** (1983) 92-99.

49. P.S.P. Wang, "An application of array grammars to clustering analysis for syntactic patterns", *Pattern Recognition* **17** (1984) 441-451.

50. G. Biswas and R.C. Dubes, "Some experiments in two-dimensional grammatical inference, *Pattern Recognition Letters* **2** (1984) 173-177.

51. X.W. Dai and P.S.P. Wang, "An algorithm for inferring context-free array grammars", *Proc. of Int. Conf. on Pattern Recognition*, Paris, France, 1986, pp. 129-131.

52. T.G. Evans, "Grammatical inference techniques in pattern recognition", *Software Engineering*, Vol. 2, ed. J.T. Tou (Academic Press, 1969) pp. 183-202 .

53. W.A. Woods, "Transition networks grammars for natural language analysis", *C. ACM* **13** (1970) 591-606.

54. S.M. Chou and K.S. Fu, "Inference for transition network grammars", *Proc. of Int. Joint Conf. on Pattern Recognition 3*, CA, 1976, pp. 79-84.

55. K. Ouriachi, Processus de Reconnaissance des Formes applicable a un assemblage automatique", *Thése de 3éme cycle*, Universitè des Sciences et Techniques de Lille, 1980.

56. P.H. Winston, "Learning structural descriptions from examples", Ph.D. Thesis, TR-76, Dept. of Elect. Eng. MIT, Sept. 1970.

57. H.C. Lee and K.S. Fu, "A syntactic pattern recognition system with learning capability", *Proc. Int. Symp. Comput. Inf. Sci.*, *COINS-72*, Miami Beach, FL, Dec. 1972.

58. B. Moayer and K.S. Fu, "A tree system approach for fingerprint pattern recognition", *IEEE Trans. on Computers* **25** (1975).

59. D.J. Brauneg and R. Gonzalez, "An approach to industrial computer vision using syntactic/semantic learning techniques", *Proc. of Int. Conf. on Pattern Recognition 7*, Montreal, 1984, pp. 1366-1369.

60. M.G. Thomason and E. Granum, "Dynamic programming inference of Markov networks from finite sets of sample strings, *IEEE Trans. on PAMI* **8** (1986) 491-501.

61. R.C. Gonzalez and M.G. Thomason, *Syntactic Pattern Recognition: An Introduction*, Chap. 3, Sec. 2; Chap. 4, Sec. 6; Chap. 6, Sec. 4 (Addison-Wesley, 1978).

62. S. Gorn, "Explicit definition and linguistic domains", *Computer Science*, eds. Hart and Takasu (University of Toronto Press, Toronto, 1967).

63. A.W. Biermann and J.A. Feldman, "On the syntheses of finite-state machines from samples of their behavior", *IEEE Trans. on Computers* **21** (1971) 592-597.

64. S. Crespi-Reghizzi, M.A. Melkanoff and L. Lichten, "The use of grammatical inference for designing programming languages", *C. ACM* 16(1973) 83-90.

65. P. Garcia, E. Segarra, E. Vidal and I. Galiano, "On the use of the morphic generator grammatical inference algorithm methodology in an automatic speech recognition", to be published in *Int. J. of Patt. Recog. Art. Intell.*, 1989.

# 10

# AN ALGORITHM FOR INFERRING CONTEXT-FREE ARRAY GRAMMARS

P.S.P. WANG and X.W. DAI
*College of Computer Science*
*Northeastern University*
*Boston, MA 02115*
*USA*

Among various models employed in two-dimensional syntactic pattern recognition, isometric array grammar has emerged recently[4,5,9,11,13,16-19], and has several advantages over others in that it does not require encoding from two-dimensional patterns into one-dimensional strings, can avoid distortion, and can obtain more accurate solutions as opposed to some other models such as trees and graphs[1,20,21]. While the grammatical inference problems for trees have been investigated, the nature of such problems for arrays remains unknown. This chapter explores this open question for a special class of array grammars known as "context-free array grammars"[5,6,19]. An algorithm for inferring context-free array grammars using a 3×3 clockwise spiral window as neighborhood index is constructed. A sample set of arrays is tested using Pascal.

## 1. INTRODUCTION

In the syntactic approach to pattern recognition, a pattern is represented by a sentence in a language. The sentence could be a string, a tree, a graph of pattern primitives and relations or an array[1]. The grammars are employed to describe the syntax of these languages or the structural relations of these patterns. In addition to the structural description, a grammar can also be used to characterize a syntactic source that generates all the sentences in a language, or the patterns belonging to a particular class (or set). In order to model a language or to describe a class of patterns, it is hoped that the grammar used can be directly inferred from a set of sample sentences or a set of sample patterns. This problem of learning a grammar based on a set of sample sentences is called grammatical inference[2], and is discussed in greater detail in Chapter 9 of this book.

Array grammars, first proposed by Kirsch[3], is a kind of 2-dimensional grammar used for modeling 2-dimensional patterns. A survey of array grammars, its history and development can be found in Ref. 4 and Chapter 4 of this book. Recently an open problem has been raised (Ref. 5) concerning array grammatical inference. Given a set of array patterns, how can we infer an array grammar (say a CFAG) that characterizes that set?

This paper intends to explore this open question for a special class of array grammars known as "context-free array grammars" (CFAG) first proposed in Ref. 6. The reason we choose CFAGs is that on the one hand they are powerful enough to generate many interesting digital patterns and on the other hand they are not as complicated as monotonic array grammars (MAG) which are the two-dimensional counterparts of Chomsky's one-dimensional context-sensitive grammars[5,7-9].

It is conjectured that the role the CFAGs play in two-dimensional languages may be as significant and important as that of Chomsky's context-free string grammars in one-dimensional languages[9]. In Sec. 2, some basic definitions, terminologies and backgrounds are given. An inference algorithm which simulates the CFAG derivation process is constructed in Sec. 3, followed by an illustrative example. Finally, some discussions and topics for future research are discussed. We adapt the definitions and notations by Hopcroft and Ullman[7], Rosenfeld[4] and Wang[10,11]. A preliminary version of this chapter was presented in Ref. 12.

## 2. BACKGROUND

### 2.1. Array Grammars

**Definition 2.1.** An isometric array grammar[13] is a 5-tuple

$$G = (V_N, V_T, P, S, \#)$$

where

$V_N$ is the finite set of nonterminal symbols,
$V_T$ is the finite set of terminal symbols,

$$V_N \cup V_T = V$$
$$V_N \cap V_T = \emptyset \quad ,$$

$\# \notin (V_N \cup V_T)$ is the background or blank symbol,
$S \in V$ is the start symbol, and
$P$ is the productions of the form $\alpha \to \beta$, where arrays $\alpha$ and $\beta$ are geometrically identical over $V_N \cup V_T\{\#\}$; $\alpha$ is not all #s.

We say that array $X$ directly generates array $Y$, denoted by $X \Rightarrow Y$, if there is a rewriting rule $\alpha \to \beta$, $X$ contains $\alpha$ as a subarray and $Y$ is identical to $X$ except that the subarray $\alpha$ is replaced with the corresponding symbols of the array $\beta$. Let $\overset{*}{\Rightarrow}$ be the reflexive and transitive closure of $\Rightarrow$. The language generated by an array grammar $G$, denoted by $L(G)$, is the set of all arrays of terminal symbols and #s that can be generated from the starting symbol $S$ in a field of #s.

**Definition 2.2.** Let $G = (V_N, V_T, P, S, \#)$ be an isometric array grammar. If for every production $\alpha \to \beta$ in $P$, $\alpha$ and $\beta$ are connected, and the image of each left-side symbol in $V_N \cup V_T$ is in $V_N \cup V_T$, i.e. #s cannot be created, then $G$ is context-sensitive. In addition, if $\alpha$ contains exactly one nonterminal symbol in a field of #s, then $G$ is context-free.

Notice that the terminology "context-free" is borrowed from Chomsky. In an isometric environment, a context-free array grammar is not entirely free of context. It is still sensitive to #s.

If every $\alpha \to \beta$ in $P$ is of the form

$$\#A \to Ba, \qquad A\# \to aB, \qquad \begin{array}{cc} \# & B, \\ A & a \end{array} \qquad \begin{array}{cc} A & a, \\ \# & B \end{array}$$

$$\begin{array}{cc} A & a, \\ \# & B \end{array} \qquad \begin{array}{cc} \# & B, \\ A & a \end{array} \qquad \begin{array}{cc} A & a, \\ \# & B \end{array} \qquad \begin{array}{cc} \# & B, \\ A & a \end{array}$$

or $\quad A \to a$

where $A, B \in V_N, a \in V_T$, then $G$ is finite state or regular.

**Lemma 2.3.** (Chomsky normal form)[5,6]

Every context-free array language $L(G)$ can be generated by $G$,

$$G = (V_N, V_T, P, S, \#)$$

where every $\alpha \rightarrow \beta$ in $P$ is of the form

$$\#A \rightarrow CB, \qquad A\# \rightarrow BC, \qquad \begin{matrix} \# \\ A \end{matrix} \rightarrow \begin{matrix} C, \\ B \end{matrix} \qquad \begin{matrix} A \\ \# \end{matrix} \rightarrow \begin{matrix} B, \\ C \end{matrix}$$

$$\begin{matrix} A \\ \# \end{matrix} \rightarrow \begin{matrix} B, \\ C \end{matrix} \qquad \begin{matrix} A \\ \# \end{matrix} \rightarrow \begin{matrix} B, \\ C \end{matrix} \qquad \begin{matrix} A \\ \# \end{matrix} \rightarrow \begin{matrix} B, \\ C \end{matrix} \qquad \begin{matrix} A \\ \# \end{matrix} \rightarrow \begin{matrix} B, \\ C \end{matrix}$$

$$\text{or} \quad A \rightarrow a$$

where $A, B, C \in V_N, a \in V_T$.

In general, a production can be represented by a triple $(A, BC, d)$, where $0 \leq d \leq 7$. For instance $A\# \rightarrow BC$ can be represented by $(A, BC, 0)$, $\begin{smallmatrix} \# \\ A \end{smallmatrix} \rightarrow \begin{smallmatrix} C \\ B \end{smallmatrix}$ can be represented by $(A, BC, 1)$ etc. and $A \rightarrow a$ is represented by $(A, a, -)$. Notice that this representation coincides with the Freeman's chain code octal primitives shown in Fig. 1.

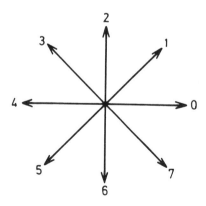

Fig. 1. Freeman's chain code primitives.

**Example 2.4.** Let $G = (\{S, S1, S2, S3\}, \{a\}, P, S, \#)$, where $P$ is

1. $(S \ , \ aS1, \ 6)$
2. $(S1, \ aS1, \ 6)$

$$
\begin{aligned}
&3.\ (S1,\ aS2,\ 0)\\
&4.\ (S2,\ aS2,\ 0)\\
&5.\ (S2,\ aS3,\ 2)\\
&6.\ (S3,\ aS3,\ 2)\\
&7.\ (S3,\ a\ \ \ ,\ \_)
\end{aligned}
$$

It can be seen that

$$
L(G) = \{\ \begin{matrix} & & & a & & & & a \\ a & a & a & & a & a & & a\ \dots \\ & a & a, & a & a & a, & a\ a\ a\ a, \end{matrix}\ \}
$$

$$
= \{\text{all digitized } \cup\text{'s with 3 sides of arbitrary lengths}\}\ .
$$

Obviously, $L(G)$ is an infinite set.

**Definition 2.5.** A parsing grammar is a quintuple $G = (V_N, V_T, P, S, \#)$, where each component has exactly the same meaning as an array grammar, except that all rules in $P$ have the form $\alpha \leftarrow \beta$. The language parsed by $G$ is defined as

$$
L(G) = \{\sigma\ |\ S \overset{*}{\underset{G}{\Rightarrow}} \sigma,\ \sigma \text{ corrected terminal array}\}\ .
$$

**Example 2.6.** Let $G$ be as in Ex. 2.4. The parsing grammar is

$$
G = (\{S, S1, S2, S3\}, \{a\}, P, S, \#)\ .
$$

where $P$ is

$$
1.\ \begin{matrix} S \\ \# \end{matrix} \leftarrow \begin{matrix} a \\ S1 \end{matrix} \qquad \text{or}\quad (S \leftarrow aS1, 6);
$$

$$
2.\ \begin{matrix} S1 \\ \# \end{matrix} \leftarrow \begin{matrix} a \\ S1 \end{matrix} \qquad \text{or}\quad (S1 \leftarrow aS1, 6);
$$

$$
3.\ S1\# \leftarrow aS2 \quad \text{or}\quad (S1 \leftarrow aS2, 0);
$$

$$
4.\ S2\# \leftarrow aS2 \quad \text{or}\quad (S2 \leftarrow aS2, 0);
$$

$$
5.\ \begin{matrix} \# \\ S2 \end{matrix} \leftarrow \begin{matrix} S3 \\ a \end{matrix} \qquad \text{or}\quad (S2 \leftarrow aS3, 2);
$$

$$
6.\ \begin{matrix} \# \\ S3 \end{matrix} \leftarrow \begin{matrix} S3 \\ a \end{matrix} \qquad \text{or}\quad (S3 \leftarrow aS3, 2);
$$

$$
7.\ S3 \leftarrow a \qquad\quad \text{or}\quad (S3 \leftarrow a,\ \_);
$$

For instance, to see if $\begin{matrix} & a & \\ a & & a \\ & aaa & \end{matrix} \in L(G)$

$$
\begin{matrix} a \\ a\ a \\ aaa \end{matrix}
\xRightarrow{7}
\begin{matrix} a \\ a\ S3 \\ aa\ a \end{matrix}
\xRightarrow{5}
\begin{matrix} a \\ a \\ aaS2 \end{matrix}
\xRightarrow{4}
\begin{matrix} a \\ a \\ aS2 \end{matrix}
\xRightarrow{3}
\begin{matrix} a \\ a \\ S1 \end{matrix}
\xRightarrow{2}
\begin{matrix} a \\ S1 \end{matrix}
\xRightarrow{1}
S
\quad \#
$$

Therefore, the parsing sequence is 7  5  4  3  2  1.

## 2.2. Grammatical Inference

As part of any inference process we must be given a set of sentences that are known to be in the language, and possibly a set of sentences that are known not to be in the language.

**Definition 2.7.** A set of sentences $S^+$ is a positive sample of a language $L(G)$, if $S^+ \subseteq L(G)$, and a set of sentences $S^-$ is a negative sample of a language $L(G)$ if $S^- \not\subseteq L(G)$, where

$$L(G) = \{x \mid S \overset{*}{\Rightarrow} x\}, \overline{L}(G) = \{x \mid x \notin L(G)\} \ .$$

A sample of a language $L(G)$ is any subset $\mathcal{L}$ of $(L(G) \times \overline{L}(G))$. In particular, $s = (s^+, s^-) \in \mathcal{L}$.

In any real inference problem we will always be dealing with samples $\mathcal{L}$ in which $S^+ \cup S^-$ has only a finite number of elements.

### Basic Inference Process

The inference process can be formulated in the following manner[2]. Assume that a finite sample $\mathcal{L} = \{(s^+, s^-) \mid s^+ \in S^+, s^- \in S^-\}$ is given. Find at least one grammar $G$ satisfying a given set of criteria, such that

$$s^+ \in L(G), \quad \text{and} \quad s^- \in \overline{L}(G) \ .$$

## 3. INFERRING ARRAY GRAMMARS

### 3.1. Basic Assumptions

In this inference process, the size of the array pattern is always finite, for example, $20 \times 20$ as in our experiment. Then we assume that

**A1:** Array language $L(G)$ generated within a fixed array frame is a finite set.

**Example 3.1.** Let $G$ be as in Ex. 2.4 with

$$L(G) = \left\{ \begin{array}{l} a \\ a \;\; a \;\; a \;\; a \;\; \ldots \\ a \;\; a, \;\; aaa, \end{array} \right\}$$

$$= \{\text{all digitized } \cup \text{'s with 3 sides of arbitrary length}\} \;.$$

If $L(G)$ is generated in a $20 \times 20$ array, then each side is not still arbitrary but is at most 20. Obviously, $L(G)$ is a finite set. ∎

**A2:** The array grammar being inferred is finite.

**A3:** The array patterns, such as $S^+$, must be parsed by the parsing grammar which has productions of the form

$$(A \leftarrow a, \; -) \;;$$
$$(A \leftarrow BC, \; d) \;;$$
$$(A \leftarrow aB, \; d) \;;$$

where $A, B, C \in V_N, a \in V_T, 0 \leq d \leq 7$.

In order to parse every element (terminal symbol) of the array pattern, we take a $3 \times 3$ window (Fig. 2)[14]

| $P9$<br>$(i-1, j-1)$ | $P2$<br>$(i-1, j)$ | $P3$<br>$(i-1, j+1)$ |
|---|---|---|
| $P8$<br>$(i, j-1)$ | $P1$<br>$(i, j)$ | $P4$<br>$(i, j+1)$ |
| $P7$<br>$(i+1, j-1)$ | $P6$<br>$(i+1, j)$ | $P5$<br>$(i+1, j+1)$ |

Fig. 2. A 3×3 window.

Each point being parsed is put into the center as $P1$. Its eight neighbors are included also (Fig. 2). Moving this window point by point from the bottom over the complete array, we can parse all pixels of the pattern.

Suppose the pattern is a binary digitized picture where each pixel is either 1 or 0 ('a' or ' '), then we have the following definition.

**Definition 3.2.**[14] $P1$ is the endpoint in the array pattern if $A(P1) \leq 1$, where $A(P1)$ is the number of the transition from 0 to 1 in the ordered set $P2, P3, P4, \ldots, P8, P9$, that is, the eight neighbors of $P1$. (Fig. 2 and Fig. 3).

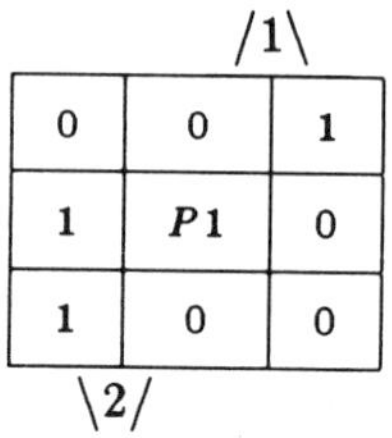

$$/1\backslash$$

| 0 | 0 | 1 |
|---|---|---|
| 1 | $P1$ | 0 |
| 1 | 0 | 0 |

$$\backslash 2 /$$

Fig. 3. Counting the 0 to 1 transition in the ordered set $P2, P3, \ldots, P8, P9$.

**Example 3.3.** If the patterns in the window are as in Fig. 3, then $A(P1) = 2$. So $P1$ in Fig. 3 is not the endpoint.

**Definition 3.4.** $Pi$ is the nextpoint of $P1$ if $Pi$ is the neighbor, is along the original parsing direction of $P1$ and is not blank (i.e. '0'). Otherwise, $P2$ is the first non-blank point met in the ordered set $P2, P3, \ldots, P8, P9$.

## 3.2. Grammatical Inference

Based on the above assumptions, the problem becomes that of looking for a parsing grammar of the array patterns. Once the parsing grammar is found, the generating grammar can be obtained by reversing all the arrows of the productions of the parsing grammar.

*Algorithm (Parsing-Grammar)*

Input : "Skeleton" of $20 \times 20$ array pattern (after being preprocessed).

Output : Generating or Parsing Grammar in Chomsky 2-point normal form.

Step1 : FOR $i := 1$ TO 20  DO
  FOR $j := 1$ TO 20  DO
  IF $T[i,j]$=endpoint THEN store $i,j$ into LIFO stack $L$;
  / * $T$ is a $20 \times 20$ array of terminal symbols in which an array pattern is kept.        */

Step2 : If $L\langle\rangle$ null THEN POP index $(m,n)$ of endpoint, $p \leftarrow m, q \leftarrow n$
  ELSE FOR $i := 20$ DOWNTO 1  DO
    FOR $j := 20$ DOWNTO 1  DO
    IF $T[i,j]\langle\rangle$ ' ' AND $S[i,j] = 0$ THEN

$$p \leftarrow i, \quad q \longleftarrow j, \quad \text{GOTO Step3}$$
ELSE IF $T[i,j]\langle\rangle$ ' ' AND $S[i,j]\langle\rangle$ 0 THEN
$\qquad$ GOTO Step4;
$\quad$ GOTO Step6;

/* $S$ is a 20×20 array of nonterminal symbols. (In this program, we only use integer subscription to express the nonterminal symbol. For example, $S[i,j] \leftarrow k$ means $S$ is moved into the location $(i,j)$.) $S[i,j] = 0$ means that the point $(i,j)$ is to be parsed the first time. $\qquad$ */

Step3 : $T[p,q] \leftarrow$ ' ', $k \leftarrow k+1$, $S[p,q] \leftarrow k$, return ('$S \leftarrow a$, _);

Step4 : Search for the next connected point from $T[p,q]$
$\qquad$ IF there does not exist such a point for $T[p,q]$ THEN
$\qquad\qquad$ GOTO Step6
$\qquad$ ELSE $p \leftarrow \text{next}P, q \leftarrow \text{next}Q$;
$\qquad$ Check $T[p,q]$ either new endpoint or not;
$\qquad$ / * $T[\text{next}p, \text{next}q]$ is nextpoint for $T[p,q]$ $\qquad$ */

Step5 : If endpoint=true THEN $T[p,q] \leftarrow$ ' ' ;
$\qquad$ If $S[p,q] = 0$ $\quad$ THEN $S[P,Q] \leftarrow K$; and
$\qquad\quad$ Return ('$S \leftarrow aS$,' $d$)
$\qquad$ ELSE $k \leftarrow k+1, i \leftarrow S[p,q], S[p,q] \leftarrow k$,
$\qquad\quad$ Return ('$S \leftarrow SS$, ' $d$);
$\qquad$ IF $T[p,q]=$ ' ' THEN GOTO Step4
$\qquad$ ELSE GOTO Step2

Step6 : IF $k = 0$ THEN Return (' The pattern is null.')
$\qquad$ ELSE Return ('$S$ is start symbol.');
$\qquad$ STOP.

## Time Complexity

Suppose the pattern has $n$ connected terminal symbols, $m$ intersections, $l$ endpoints, and $k$ circles. We see that each point except the intersection is parsed only once. How many times an intersection is parsed depends on how many lines intersect this point. For every circle we have to search the bottom-right point and start the parsing procedure from this point for each

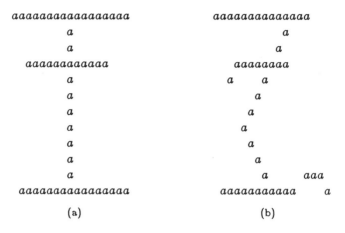

(a)                                    (b)

(c)

Fig. 4. Input patterns $S^+$. $(S^+ = \{(a), (b), (c),\})$ .

circle. Then we say

$$\text{Time Complexity} = a(n - m) + b(l \times m) + c(k)$$

where $a, b, c$ are constant coefficients.

**Example 3.5.** We did an experiment using Pascal. The input patterns $S^+$ are shown in Fig. 4.

The output result:

$$S1 \leftarrow a\ ,\ \_ \ \ ;$$
$$S1 \leftarrow aS1\ ,\ 0\ ;$$
$$S1 \leftarrow aS1\ ,\ 7\ ;$$

$$S2 \leftarrow a , \_ \quad ;$$
$$S2 \leftarrow aS2 , \quad 4 ;$$
$$S2 \leftarrow aS2 , \quad 5 ;$$

$$S3 \leftarrow a , \_ \quad ;$$
$$S3 \leftarrow aS3 , \quad 0 ;$$
$$S3 \leftarrow aS3 , \quad 1 ;$$

$$S4 \leftarrow a , \_ \quad ;$$
$$S4 \leftarrow aS3 , \quad 3 ;$$
$$S4 \leftarrow aS4 , \quad 4 ;$$
$$S4 \leftarrow aS4 , \quad 5 ;$$

$$S5 \leftarrow a , \_ \quad ;$$
$$S5 \leftarrow aS5 , \quad 0 ;$$
$$S5 \leftarrow aS5 , \quad 1 ;$$

$$S6 \leftarrow a , \_ \quad ;$$
$$S6 \leftarrow aS6 , \quad 4 ;$$

$$S7 \leftarrow S5S6 , \quad 2 ;$$
$$S7 \leftarrow aS7 , \quad 2 ;$$
$$S7 \leftarrow aS7 , \quad 1 ;$$

$$S8 \leftarrow S3S7 , \quad 2 ;$$
$$S8 \leftarrow S4S7 , \quad 2 ;$$

$$S9 \leftarrow a , \_ \quad ;$$
$$S9 \leftarrow aS9 , \quad 2 ;$$
$$S9 \leftarrow S3S8 , \quad 2 ;$$

$$S10 \leftarrow S2S9 , \quad 2 ;$$
$$S11 \leftarrow S1S10 , 2 ;$$

$S11$ is start symbol.

These are the productions of the parsing grammar of the pattern.

## 4. CONCLUSION

We have just proposed an algorithm to produce a context-free array grammar from 2-dimensional syntactic patterns. We find the following:

(1) A parsing or a generating grammar can be directly obtained from 2-dimensional patterns $S^+$. The method does not require a pattern to be encoded into a 1-dimensional string. No primitive extraction is needed and no semantic operators such as $+, *, -$, etc. are used[1,2,15].

(2) The algorithm is "unsupervised", that is, nothing else other than an input set of arrays is needed.

Our algorithm provides an alternative for implementing the 2-dimensional syntactic pattern recognition approach with context-free array grammars. This is also to try to answer how an array grammar (CFAG) that characterizes the set can be inferred. Similar work for other 2-dimensional languages has been done by Fu and Booth[2]. Such an exploration could provide a foundation for research into unsupervised clustering analysis.

## REFERENCES

1. K.S. Fu, *Syntactic Pattern Recognition and Applications* (Prentice Hall, 1982).
2. K.S. Fu and T.L. Booth, "Grammatical inference. Introduction and survey — Parts I and II", *IEEE Trans. Systems, Man and Cybernetics* 5 (1975) 95-111, 409-423.
3. R.A. Kirsch, "Computer interpretation of English text and picture patterns", *IEEE Trans. Electron. Comput.* 13 (1964) 363-376.
4. A. Rosenfeld, *Picture Languages* (Academic Press, New York 1979).
5. P.S.P. Wang, "An application of array grammars to clustering analysis for syntactic pattern", *Pattern Recognition* 17 (1984) 441-451.
6. C.R. Cook and P.S.P. Wang, "A chomsky hierarchy of isotonic array grammars and languages", *Computer Graphics and Image Process.* 8 (1978) 144-152.
7. J.E. Hopcroft and J.D. Ullman, *Introduction to Automata Theory, Languages and Computation* (Addison Wesley, Reading, MA, 1979).
8. P.S.P. Wang, ed., *Intelligent Systems, Imaging Technologies and Software Engineering* (Sungkang Computer Book Co., 1984).
9. P.S.P. Wang, "Hierarchical structures and complexities of parallel isometric array patterns", *IEEE Trans. Pattern Analysis and Machine Intelligence* 5 (1983) 92-99.
10. P.S.P. Wang and Grosky, "The relation between uniformly structured tessellation automata and parallel array grammars", *Proc. Int. Symp. on Unif. Struc. Auto. and Lang.* Tokyo, Japan (1975) pp. 97-102.
11. P.S.P. Wang and H.J. Lin, "A pumping lemma for two-dimensional array languages", *Proc. 8th ICPR*, 27-31 Oct, Paris, France (1986) Vol. 1, pp. 126-128.
12. P.S.P. Wang and X.W. Dai, "A grammatical inference algorithm for digitized array patterns", *Proc. 8th ICPR*, 27-31 Oct. Paris, France (1986) Vol. 1, pp. 129-131.
13. A. Mercer and A. Rosenfeld, "An array grammar programming system", *Commun. ACM* 16 (1973) 299-395.
14. T.Y. Zhang and C.Y. Suen, "A fast parallel algorithm for thinning digital patterns", *Commun. ACM* 27 (1984) 236-239.
15. K.S. Fu, ed., *Applications of Pattern Recognition* (CRC Press, 1982).
16. K. Morita, Y. Yamamoto and K. Sugata, "The complexity of some decision problems about two-dimensional array grammars", *Information Sciences* 30 (1983) 241-262.

17. A. Nakamura, "Parallel $\Sigma$-erasing array acceptors", *Computer Graphics and Image Processing* **14** (1980) 80-86.

18. A.R. Smith, III," Two-dimensional formal languages and pattern recognition by cellular automata", *Proc. 12th IEEE Symp. on Switching and Automata Theory*, (1971) pp. 144-150.

19. P.S.P. Wang, "Parallel context-free array grammar normal forms", *Computer Graphics and Image Processing* **15** (1981) 296-300.

20. T. Pavlidis, *Structural Pattern Recognition* (Springer-Verlag, New York, 1977).

21. A.C. Shaw, "A formal picture description scheme as a basis for picture processing systems", *Information and Control* **14** (1969) 9-52.

# Hybrid  Approaches

# 11

---

# HYBRID PATTERN RECOGNITION METHODS

H. BUNKE

*Universität Bern*
*Institut für Informatik und angewandte Mathematik*
*Länggass-Strasse 51, CH-3012 Bern*
*Switzerland*

The pattern recognition methods developed until now can be categorized into statistical, structural and artificial intelligence based approaches. Each of the methods has its strength and its limitations. In order to overcome these limitations, different methods are combined sometimes. This results in a hybrid approach. In this chapter, the relations, borderlines and the possibilities of combining statistical, structural and artificial intelligence based approaches are discussed.

## 1. INTRODUCTION

During the past three decades, there has been a considerable growth of interest in problems of pattern recognition leading to a variety of mathematical methods. Traditionally, these methods can be grouped into two major categories: (1) decision-theoretic or statistical, and (2) structural. Additionally, artificial intelligence based approaches to pattern recognition have become very important during the last years. Each of the different methods has its strength and its limitations. In order to overcome these limitations, statistical, structural and artificial intelligence based methods are mixed sometimes. This results in a *hybrid method*.

The present book is on syntactic and structural pattern recognition. In the present and the following chapter, the relations, boundaries and intersections of syntactic and structural with statistical and artificial intelligence based pattern recognition are discussed. The organization of this chapter follows the diagram shown in Fig. 1. Among the traditional approaches to pattern recognition, we give a brief review of statistical, or decision-theoretic and structural methods in Sec. 2, where the field of structural methods is further subdivided into syntactic methods, structural prototype matching and relaxation. Although the latter category of methods is not addressed in the rest of this book, it is felt that it fits very well into the framework of structural methods. In Sec. 3, hybrid pattern recognition methods based on statistical and structural approaches are discussed. Three important approaches to knowledge representation, namely, formal logic, production systems and semantic nets, including their relationships, are reviewed in Sec. 4. Hybrid methods combining artificial intelligence based knowledge representation with structural and statistical pattern recognition are the topic of Sec. 5. Further questions concerning search, control and system architecture are addressed in Sec. 6.

## 2. A BRIEF REVIEW OF STATISTICAL AND STRUCTURAL METHODS

*Statistical* or *decision-theoretic methods* are applied primarily for the purpose of pattern classification. The concept of pattern classification may be expressed in terms of partitioning the pattern feature space. After digitization, a pattern is transformed into a feature vector $\underline{x} = (x_1, \ldots, x_n)$ by taking $n$ characteristic measurements, or features, $x_i$. So each pattern can be considered as a point in the $n$-dimensional space of real numbers, i.e. the feature space. The problem of classification is to assign each possible

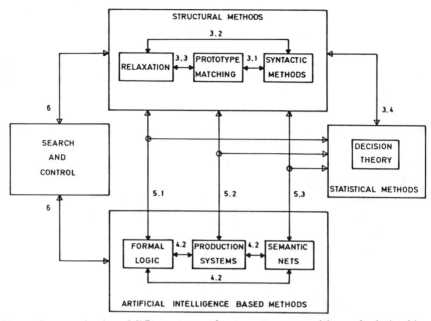

Fig. 1. A categorization of different approaches to pattern recognition and relationships among them. Numbers at arrows refer to sections of this chapter where the corresponding relationships are discussed.

vector $\underline{x}$ to a proper pattern class $\omega_i$ out of $M$ classes $\omega_1, \dots , \omega_M$. This can be interpreted as a partition of the feature space into mutually exclusive regions where each region corresponds to a particular pattern class.

In statistical classification, one typically substitutes an unknown input pattern, represented by its vector $\underline{x}$, into a number of decision functions $d_j(\underline{x})$ and determines the maximum, or minimum, of the values returned by these decision functions. The function yielding the maximum, or minimum, value uniquely corresponds to the class $\omega_i$ for which the decision $\underline{x} \in \omega_i$ is made. Depending on the way the classes and their boundaries are represented, we distinguish between parametric and nonparametric statistical classification. In the first case, the parametric probability distributions of the patterns of each class $\omega_i$ and the *a priori* probability of the different classes are required, in order to design the decision functions $d_j(\underline{x})$. In nonparametric statistical classification, no such distribution is required. The most important instances of parametric and nonparametric statistical classification are Bayes-classification and nearest neighbor, or NN, classification. For more details on statistical classification, the reader is referred to Refs. 1-3.

Decision-theoretic methods have a long tradition in pattern recognition and are based on a well founded mathematical theory. They have been proven useful in numerous applications. Particularly, they are well suitable for coping with noisy and distorted patterns. The algorithms are usually computationally inexpensive as compared to structural or artificial intelligence based methods. However, this statistical approach also has several disadvantages and limitations. Although a great deal of effort has been undertaken in deriving optimal algorithms with respect to classifying the extracted features, the features themselves are often chosen arbitrarily. Statistical methods provide only a class description of a pattern. They do not describe a pattern so as to allow its generation given its class, nor do they describe aspects of a pattern which make it ineligible for assignment to another class. Moreover, the various relations which may exist between the chosen features are completely neglected in the statistical approach.

The fundamental idea in *structural pattern recognition* is the explicit utilization of structural information for pattern representation. Structural information is used for modelling two important aspects, namely, the hierarchical composition of a complex pattern from simpler subpatterns and the various relations which may exist between different subpatterns and/or characteristic features.

One of the main subcategories of the structural approach is *syntactic pattern recognition*, where formal grammars are used for pattern class representation. The terminals of the grammar correspond to primitive subpatterns which can be directly extracted from an input pattern by means of suitable preprocessing and segmentation methods. The set of grammar nonterminals corresponds to subpatterns of greater complexity which are successively built up from primitive elements. The process of building up complex (sub)patterns from simpler constituents is modelled by the grammar productions. Finally, the recognition process is based on a parser which analyzes an unknown input pattern according to the given grammar. Various types of grammars for a wide variety of applications have been proposed within this framework. All further details as well as applications may be found in other chapters of this book, particularly in Chapters 1 to 4, 13 and 15 to 18.

Syntactic methods are advantageous for many tasks since they allow, as recognition results, not only pattern classification but also the inference of a structural description of an unknown input pattern. Similar to the statistical approach, syntactic methods are based on a well founded mathematical theory, namely the theory of formal languages and automata[4]. This theory provides many useful results about power, limitations and computational complexity of recognition procedures. On the other hand, there are problems with the syntactic approach when patterns which are corrupted by noise and distortions are involved. The "pure" concepts from the theory of formal languages and abstract automata are not powerful enough to handle the majority of "real world" applications where distorted patterns with a greater degree of complexity occur. So an augmentation of the pure concepts by additional means is required. The resulting approaches, however, do not fall into the categories of formal language theory any longer and lack therefore a strong theoretical basis. Another problem with the syntactic approach is grammatical inference. Many procedures have been proposed (see Chapter 9) but their usefulness for practical applications has still to be demonstrated.

*Structural prototypes* can be considered as a viable alternative to formal grammars for pattern class representation. The idea is to store, in an explicit way, a finite number of pattern prototypes. In contrast with statistical NN classification, patterns are not stored as $n$-dimensional feature vectors. Instead, structural representations based on strings, trees or graphs are preferred. For the recognition of an unknown input pattern $x$ it is necessary to match $x$ with the prototypes in order to detect that prototype pattern which is most similar to $x$. Inevitably, inexact or error-correcting matching procedures are required for this purpose. A number of algorithms have been proposed in the literature. An introduction to, and overview of, the subject of prototype matching is given in Chapters 5 and 6 of this book. Applications of prototype matching are reported in Chapters 7 and 14. For an introductory discussion see also Chapter 1.

The use of structural prototypes together with a distance measure is advantageous since this method can provide structural information in a very explicit way. Particularly the detection of the similarities and dissimilarities between a reference pattern and an input pattern is one of the key concepts in structural matching. A great advantage over syntactic methods is the fact that there is no need for grammatical inference. So in cases where too few sample patterns are available for the inference of an abstract class description in terms of a grammar, structural prototype matching is the method to be preferred. On the other hand, structural prototype matching lacks a well founded theory at the moment. Particularly, the representational data structures are usually chosen in an *ad hoc* manner, although these data structures have a fundamental influence on the matching procedure with respect to computational complexity. While string and tree matching is of polynomial time complexity (see Chapters 5 and 6), subgraph and error-tolerant subgraph isomorphism detection is known to be NP-complete[5]. This makes the use of good heuristics inevitable if large graphs are involved (see also Chapter 7, Sec. 3).

*Relaxation* is another class of structural methods. Since this topic is not addressed in the rest of this book, we give a more detailed introduction here. Relaxation aims at deriving a unique interpretation of all primitive parts of a pattern, which is globally consistent under a given set of constraints. The method is iterative and starts with the maximum set of possible interpretations for each part. Based on a set of constraints, defining whether an interpretation $I$ for a part $O$ is compatible with another interpretation $I'$ for another part $O'$ standing in a relation $R$ with $O$, all those interpretations which are inconsistent under the given constraints are successively removed. More formally, this procedure is given by

**while** an interpretation has been removed in the last iteration **do**
    **for** all parts $O$ **do**
    **for** all interpretations $I$ of $O$ **do**
    **for** all parts $O'$ standing in a relation $R$ to $O$ **do**
    remove $I$ from the set of possible interpretations of $O$ if no $I'$ exists
    in the set of possible interpretations of $O'$ which is compatible
    according to the given constraints.

It can easily be shown that this algorithm is guaranteed to terminate. However, it depends on proper initial interpretations and on a proper set of constraints as to whether the algorithm yields a unique and correct solution.

The above algorithm is known as *discrete* relaxation. There is another family of algorithms known from the literature which are called continuous, or *probabilistic*, relaxation. In probabilistic relaxation, a vector $(p(I_1), \ldots, p(I_n))$ is assigned to each pattern part $O$ where $p(I_j)$ is the probability that $I_j$ is the correct interpretation for the part $O$. The concept of compatibility is generalized in such a way that the compatibility of two interpretations of different objects standing in a relation $R$ can take on continuous values from a predefined interval rather than taking on only binary values **yes** and **no**. The iteration procedure given above is replaced by probability updating rules which successively change the probability $p(I_j)$ at each object depending on the probabilities $p(I_k)$ at neighboring parts and the compatibilities between $I_j$ and $I_k$. While discrete relaxation can be considered as a pure structural method, continuous relaxation also possesses a numerical/statistical flavor. The classical papers on discrete and continuous relaxation are Refs. 6 and 7 respectively. A recent overview can be found in Ref. 8.

Relaxation is suitable for reducing local ambiguities. It has been successfully applied to many pattern recognition problems. The method is appealing particularly for those applications where the available *a priori* knowledge is in the form of local constraints. On the other hand, there are some problems with relaxation. From a theoretical point of view, convergence is critical although interesting results have been reported recently[9-12]. From an application oriented point of view, relaxation is limited since only local interpretations of pattern constituents are derived and no interpretation of a pattern as a whole can be achieved.

## 3. HYBRID METHODS BASED ON STATISTICAL AND STRUCTURAL APPROACHES

It can be clearly seen from the review in the last section that each family of methods has its strengths and its deficiencies. Some of the considered approaches are just complementary to each other. So it can be expected that the combination of two or more techniques results in an approach with improved flexibility, power and performance. In the following sections, particular ways of such a combination will be discussed.

### 3.1. Syntactic Methods — Structural Prototypes

Pattern recognition by means of prototype matching has several aspects in common with syntactic methods. First, both methods emphasize structural properties of patterns, i.e. the composition of patterns from subpatterns including relations between subpatterns. Secondly, both approaches rely on the same data structures, namely, strings, trees and graphs. Finally, in both cases, capabilities for error-correction are required in order to cope with noisy and distorted data.

Obviously, each finite set of prototype patterns $x_1, \dots, x_n$ can be described by a grammar. Consider $M$ pattern classes $\omega_1, \dots, \omega_M$ with prototypes $p_{i1}, \dots, p_{in_i}$ for each $\omega_i$. In its simplest form, the grammar consists of productions

$$S \longrightarrow S_1, \quad S \longrightarrow S_2, \dots, S \longrightarrow S_M$$

and

$$S_i \longrightarrow p_{i1}, \quad S_i \longrightarrow p_{i2}, \dots, S_i \longrightarrow p_{in_i}, \quad i = 1, \dots, M \, .$$

Based on this grammar, pattern recognition by means of prototype matching can be "simulated" by syntactic pattern recognition using an error-correcting parser. Conversely, given a grammar $G$ with a finite language $L(G) = \{x_1, \dots, x_n\}$, we can directly use each $x_i$ as a prototype and drop all grammar productions. Replacing the (error-correcting) parser used together with the grammar $G$ by a prototype matcher results in a recognition method which is a prototype matching procedure equivalent to the original syntactic approach.

Despite this equivalence for finite sample sets one method can be superior to the other for a specific application. Generally, if the number of prototype patterns is small it is usually not possible to derive a grammar, or there is no need for a "condensed" class representation by means of a grammar. Instead, a "direct" representation by means of prototypes is preferable. On the other hand, if a large number of sample patterns is involved, pattern recognition and pattern class representation is perhaps more efficient if a grammar is used. One has to notice, however, that pattern class representation by means of a grammar makes sense only if there are common substructures among all patterns. Otherwise, the grammar behaves like the example given above, generating the individual patterns in one step each. For a practical application, the *existence* of common substructures among different patterns is not sufficient. Instead, such substructures must be *explicitly known* to the system designer. If this knowledge is not available, grammatical inference will not succeed and a prototype matching approach has to be adopted. A graphical illustration, as a summary of the discussion whether to follow a syntactical or prototype matching approach, is given in Fig. 2.

Formal grammars are more powerful than structural prototypes in the sense that they can generate an infinite number of elements. Furthermore, the derivation tree mirrors, as a result of parsing, the aggregation of subpatterns into more complex patterns along a potentially unbounded number of hierarchical levels. This is in contrast with structural prototypes, where the hierarchical composition of a pattern is limited to only two levels. An illustration is given in Fig. 3. A simple arrow pattern and a chain code scheme is shown in Fig. 3a. The chain-coded pattern is given in Fig. 3b.

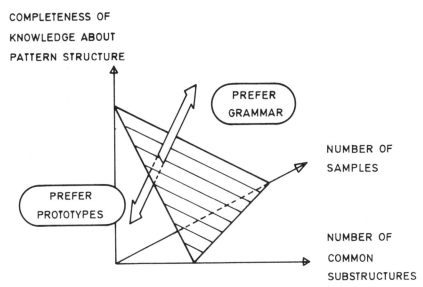

Fig. 2. Practical aspects favoring either a syntactic or a prototype matching approach.

It can be interpreted as a two-level hierarchical representation consisting of one level with pattern primitives and another where the pattern is considered as a whole. This restriction to two hierarchical levels is inherent in all prototype representations with the exception of representations with priorities, like PDL (see Chapter 2), or hierarchical graphs (see Sec. 5.3). In contrast with Fig. 3b, the derivation tree shown in Fig. 3c mirrors a hierarchical decomposition of the pattern into four levels. Such a multilevel representation can easily be achieved by grammatical parsing.

A hybrid approach combining structural prototypes and formal grammars has been proposed in Ref. 13. For the purpose of classification, an unknown pattern which is represented by means of a graph, is compared with a number of prototype graphs. The distance between a graph $g$ and a prototype $p$ is defined as the number of derivation steps of a grammar required in order to transform $p$ into $g$. Thus inexact graph matching is accomplished by means of a transformation which is based on a grammar. A similar idea for string matching has been proposed in Ref. 14. However, no practical experience demonstrating the utility of these hybrid approaches has been reported so far.

There is another hybrid approach based on graph grammars which combines techniques from syntactic and structural pattern recognition. In

(a)

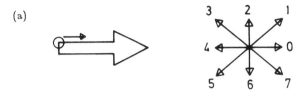

(b)

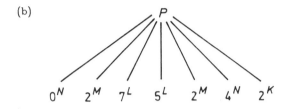

(c)

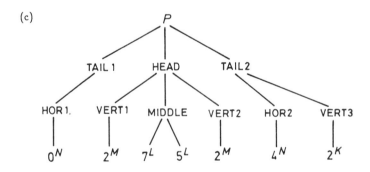

Fig. 3.  (a) A simple pattern and a chain code scheme, (b) chain coded pattern as prototype, (c) chain coded pattern as derivation tree.

Ref. 15, graph grammars for the recognition of schematic diagrams, including heavily distorted drawings, have been proposed. In contrast with the "classical" syntactic approaches where the recognition of an unknown pattern is based on parsing, the grammar is used as a tool that directly transforms an input pattern into the desired output description. The basic operation cycle of a graph grammar as proposed in Ref. 15 consists of two steps, namely subgraph-isomorphism detection, and subgraph replacement. Therefore, this graph grammar approach can be considered as a typical example of a hybrid technique integrating graph matching with graph rewriting.

Another approach combining graph rewriting with graph matching has been proposed in Ref. 16. An error-correcting precedence graph parser is introduced that can be used to compute the minimum error distance between two graphs. As a remarkable property, this procedure has a time complexity of only $O(n^3)$ where $n$ gives the number of nodes in the input graph. However, the proposed approach is applicable only to a restricted class of graphs. No practical application of this approach has been reported until now.

## 3.2. Syntactic Methods — Relaxation

Relaxation follows the principle of least commitment. Initially the maximum number of labels, or interpretations, for each object is considered. This idea can be adopted in syntactic pattern recognition in such a way that a vector $(x_1, \ldots, x_m)$ of possible symbols and not a fixed symbol $x_i$, is considered at each position in an input string. Usually, a measure of confidence, or a probability, is assigned to each possible symbol at each position. Assuming an input string of length $n$ with $m$ alternative symbols at each position, representing an unknown pattern, we have a pattern representation

$$\begin{bmatrix} p_1(x_1) \\ p_1(x_2) \\ \vdots \\ p_1(x_m) \end{bmatrix} \begin{bmatrix} p_2(x_1) \\ p_2(x_2) \\ \vdots \\ p_2(x_m) \end{bmatrix} \cdots \begin{bmatrix} p_n(x_1) \\ p_n(x_2) \\ \vdots \\ p_n(x_m) \end{bmatrix} .$$

Notice that this representation is very meaningful if the extraction of pattern primitives is unreliable due to noise and distortions. The "brute force" approach to syntactic recognition is the application of a parser to all possible $m^n$ strings which can be formed from the above representation and the determination of that sequence of $n$ symbols which is compatible with the given grammar and has maximum probability among all compatible strings.

If $n$ and $m$ are large, this becomes prohibitive. In order to reduce the effort required for parsing, discrete relaxation can be applied beforehand, eliminating successively the symbols in the input string which are incompatible with the given grammar. Using alternatively a probabilistic relaxation scheme, those strings among all possible $m^n$ strings which are compatible with the given grammar will be enhanced while all other strings will be suppressed. Notice that probabilistic relaxation can be directly applied to the above pattern representation.

This combination of probabilistic relaxation and syntactic pattern recognition was called "syntax-directed probabilistic relaxation" in a recent article[17]. The authors proposed the following hybrid method. Given $n$ string positions with $m$ possible symbols at each position, where $p_i(x_j)$ denotes the probability that symbol $x_j$ is correct at position $i(j = 1, \ldots, m;$ $i = 1, \ldots, n)$, probabilistic relaxation is applied first in order to enhance the probability of those symbols which are consistent with the given grammar. After some iterations, all symbols $x_j$ at position $i$ with a low probability $p_i(x_j)$ are eliminated. From the remaining symbols all possible strings are formed and fed into an error-correcting parser. Using the results of this parser and the overall probability of an input string (before relaxation), a final decision, i.e. the most likely parse of the input pattern, is derived.

Given an input of length $n$ with $m$ alternative symbols at each position, there is another possibility of determining the input string which is compatible with the given grammar and has the maximum probability. It is the application of a parser which scans the input from left to right, inspecting each alternative symbol at each position, and keeping track of the best alternatives. Such a parser closely corresponds to an error-correcting parser as described in Chapter 3. The only difference is that an error-correcting parser uses substitution costs for ranking different alternatives, while the parser considered here is based on the probabilities $p_i(x_j)$ instead. A particular method for syntax analysis of this kind for finite state grammars has been described in Ref. 18. Since only finite state grammars are considered, parsing can be solved by means of dynamic programming. The resulting method is very efficient with respect to time and space, and implementation effort as well. The time and space complexity is $O(n)$ each, where $n$ is the length of the input. A generalization to context-free grammars is presented in Chapter 2, Sec. 5.2 of this book.

The application of grammatical constraints for reduction of ambiguities is limited to terminal symbols in Refs. 17 and 18. Another approach taking into regard also constraints between higher-level nonterminals is hierarchical relaxation[19]. It is basically a bottom-up parsing procedure where, during the whole recognition process, reduction of symbols according to the rules of the given grammar and exploitation of contextual constraints for elimination of inconsistent symbols are intertwined.

## 3.3. Relaxation — Structural Prototypes

Relaxation is based on constraint exploitation for the purpose of reducing local ambiguities. In their most general form, constraints are given by expressions $R(x_1, \ldots, x_n)$, which indicate the likelihood that $x_1, \ldots, x_n$ is a correct interpretation of objects $O_1, \ldots, O_n$, if there is a relation $R$ between $O_1, \ldots, O_n$. From this point of view, a structural prototype, e.g. a graph, can be considered as an aggregation of several unary and binary constraints. Thus finding an interpretation of a set of objects, or object parts, using a relaxation procedure based on constraints can be considered as a particular kind of matching.

This idea is illustrated in greater detail by means of the example in Fig. 4. Let us consider the task of distributing labels 1, 2 and 3 to the nodes $A, B, C$ and $D$ in the graph of Fig. 4a in such a way that the constraints in Fig. 4b are satisfied. It is required, for example, that there exist a neighbor labeled with 2 and a neighbor labeled with 3 for any node with label 1. Starting with the maximum set of labels, i.e. 1, 2 and 3, at each node and applying the discrete relaxation procedure described in Sec. 2, we successively eliminate those interpretations which are inconsistent with respect to the given constraints. The sequence of iteration steps is shown in Fig. 4c. After two steps, the procedure converges. The final interpretation is shown in Fig. 4d. Notice that this result can also be obtained by aggregating the constraints given in Fig. 4b into the graph shown in Fig. 4e and determining the possible subgraph isomorphisms.

Having shown for the particular example in Fig. 4 that constraint satisfaction can alternatively be solved by graph matching, it can be shown that the other direction is also possible. Relaxation can be used as a special technique for finding a match between a model and an unknown object. This idea has been applied in a system for aerial image understanding[20]. The nodes in the model and the object graph correspond to lines and regions in an image. Node attributes represent features like color, texture, size, etc. Spatial relations between lines and regions, like adjacency, nearby, above, etc., are represented by graph edges. Initially, only a fixed number of best matching image nodes are assigned to each model node. For updating of probabilities, the relations between pairs of model nodes are systematically compared with those of corresponding image nodes. Good experimental results have been reported by the authors. Similar approaches to matching

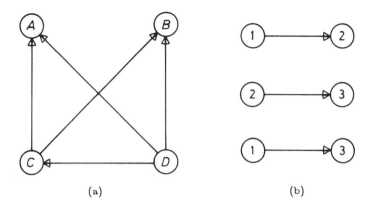

(a)                                              (b)

| Objects | Initial Interpretation | Iteration 1 | Iteration 2 |
|:-------:|:----------------------:|:-----------:|:-----------:|
| A       | 1,2,3                  | 3           | 3           |
| B       | 1,2,3                  | 3           | 3           |
| C       | 1,2,3                  | 1,2,3       | 2           |
| D       | 1,2,3                  | 1           | 1           |

(c)

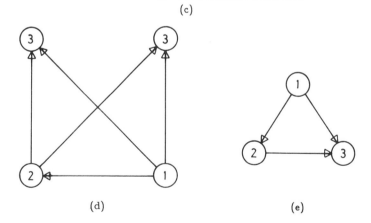

(d)                                              (e)

Fig. 4. An example of the relationships between graph matching and relaxation (see text).

relational structures by means of relaxation have been proposed in Refs. 21 and 22.

In conclusion, structural matching can be considered as a particular constraint satisfaction paradigm, while on the other hand constraint satisfaction, i.e. relaxation, can be used as a special technique for accomplishing structural matching.

### 3.4. Structural Methods — Statistical Methods

There are many interesting relationships between structural prototype matching and decision-theoretic methods. Particularly, determining the prototype most similar to the input pattern is closely related with statistical NN classification as mentioned in Sec. 2. One of the major problems with NN classification in statistical pattern recognition is the efficient computation of the nearest neighbor if the set of sample patterns is large. Several algorithms have been proposed. They are based on the idea of computing the nearest neighbor without exhaustively searching through the whole sample set. Two of these algorithms are also mentioned in Chapter 5[23,24]. If the similarity measure used in structural pattern recognition is a metric, then the ideas developed for speeding up nearest neighbor calculation in the statistical case can be adopted for the computation of distances between strings, trees or graphs. An example is given in Ref. 25. Similarly, techniques like clustering or binary search can be applied for the efficient organization of structural models[26,27].

Another very interesting relationship between NN classification and matching of unknown patterns against structural prototypes is established in Ref. 28. The authors consider a set of structural prototypes from different classes together with a pseudometric (i.e. a "distance" function not necessarily fulfilling the triangle inequality) and show how the prototypes can be mapped into an $n$-dimensional numerical vector representation in such a way that the distance between the prototypes is preserved. In a further step this representation is mapped into another vector representation of low dimensionality (dimensionality one in the example given in Ref. 28). It is claimed that it should be possible, by analysis of this low dimensional training set representation, to select a few characteristic sample patterns for each class, for example the element closest to the mean, or the elements corresponding to the piecewise linear boundaries. Therefore, by mapping structural prototypes into a vector representation, a reduction of the sample set size can be achieved. This is similar in its spirit to sample set condensation or sample set editing for numerical NN classification as described in Ref. 3.

The random graph method described in Chapter 8 of this book is another typical example of a hybrid method combining techniques from statistical decision theory with prototype matching. The work reported in Ref. 29 is based on an idea similar to random graphs.

There are many other links between statistical methods and prototype matching, which are discussed in greater detail in the following chapter. Chapter 12 also covers all existing relationships between syntactic, i.e. grammar based, and statistical methods. An earlier paper discussing similar questions is Ref. 30.

In a number of papers, primarily addressed to the field of pictorial pattern recognition, the combination of statistical classification and relaxation has been proposed. The idea common to all these approaches is to make a classification of each pixel using a statistical method and to subsequently refine this initial classification by means of relaxation. The initial classification can be based on a Bayes-classifier[31], on a particular distance function[32], on thresholding[33], or on other histogram based features[34]. Notice that no contextual information is exploited in this first classification stage, i.e. the classification of a pixel is made without reference to the class of the neighboring pixels. Notice also that the statistical classification may yield ties or near ties between different classes. Relaxation following the initial classification is a suitable tool for making use of contextual knowledge and for breaking ties. In order to facilitate relaxation, it is required that the statistical classifier yields not only a classname $\omega_j$ for each pixel $i$ but a vector $[p_i(\omega_1), \ldots, p_i(\omega_M)]$ where $p_i(\omega_j)$ is the probability that $\omega_j$ is the correct class of pixel $i$. The principal idea for the exploitation of contextual constraints is to define compatibility coefficients in such a way that identical labels at neighboring pixels reinforce each other while different labels suppress each other. (This principle may be further refined if particular knowledge about the shape of the objects under consideration is available). An extension to also using temporal context in image sequence has been reported in Ref. 32.

An interesting relationship between probabilistic relaxation and Bayes-classification is derived in Ref. 35. It is shown that under some general conditional independence assumptions, probabilistic relaxation can be interpreted as a process that computes conditional probabilities. More specifically, each iteration computes the conditional probability of each class for each object, on the basis of a context which is the context of the previous iteration enlarged by one neighborhood width. Initially, only measurements made on an object itself are used as context. Thus relaxation iterations must only continue until either the conditional independence assumptions no longer hold or until the entire context is taken into account. Assigning finally the class with the highest probability to an object can thus be considered as a special Bayes decision rule.

## 4. KNOWLEDGE REPRESENTATION IN ARTIFICIAL INTELLIGENCE

Artificial intelligence based methods in pattern recognition are characterized by considering pattern classes as abstract concepts and individual patterns as instances thereof. Pattern classes are represented by explicitly storing knowledge describing them. Applying this knowledge to the measurements made on an unknown pattern, recognition is accomplished by drawing domain specific inferences or logical conclusions. Therefore artificial intelligence based pattern recognition emphasizes the issues of knowledge representation and control of problem solving. A very important category of tasks where these ideas have been applied is diagnostic classification[36–38].

In Sec. 4.1 we will briefly review the most important techniques for knowledge representation. In Sec. 4.2 we discuss how they are related with each other. The relationship with pattern recognition methods will be studied in Sec. 5.

### 4.1. A Brief Review of Basic Knowledge Representation Methods

*Formal logic* is a classical artificial intelligence approach to knowledge representation and inference. There are several logic calculi known in artificial intelligence. Presently, *first-order predicate calculus* plays the most prominent role. In the following we will restrict our consideration to this type. For other logics see Ref. 39, for example.

The use of predicate calculus for knowledge representation is based on the idea of expressing knowledge about the actual problem domain by means of well-formed formulas which are constructed according to a particular syntax. The basic constituents for building a well-formed formula are predicates, functions, variables and constants, together with (universal- and existential-) quantifiers and logical connectives (and, or, not, implication, equivalence, etc.). Constants and predicates are used for the representation of objects and relations in the problem domain, respectively. So one may write, for example,

$$\text{AVERAGE-BRIGHTNESS(REGION1, 128)}$$

in order to represent the fact that the average brightness of REGION1 is 128. In this example, AVERAGE-BRIGHTNESS is a two-argument predicate, while REGION1 and 128 are constants. Similarly, the well-formed formula

$$\forall x, y \ (\text{LEFT-OF}(x, y) \longrightarrow \text{RIGHT-OF} \ (y, x))$$

can be interpreted as a representation of the conclusion that for any two regions $x$ and $y$, $y$ is to the right of $x$ if $x$ is to the left of $y$.

In predicate calculus, logical conclusions can be inferred from well-formed formulas by means of inference rules. There are several well-known inference rules in formal logic, like modus ponens, modus tollens, etc. The most important rule with respect to automatic inference is resolution[40]. Given a set of well-formed formulas, the axioms, and another well-formed formula, the theorem, the resolution rule can successively be applied in order to find out if the theorem logically follows from the axioms. This inference procedure has the properties of completeness and consistency. Completeness means that any theorem which logically follows from the axioms can be verified, while consistency means that the verification works only for theorems following from the axioms. For a more detailed introduction to formal logic and first-order predicate calculus see Refs. 41-43.

Several logic programming languages have been proposed recently. Among them, Prolog has gained most popularity. For an introduction see Ref. 44. A Prolog program consists of a set of axioms, according to a particular syntax, and a set of theorems to be proven in close correspondence with the principles of first-order predicate calculus sketched above. Besides, there exist several built-in features, like datastructures, arithmetic operators, input/output functions, etc. for making programming more convenient. Theoretically speaking, Prolog covers only a part of first-order predicate calculus. However, from an application oriented point of view, there are no severe restrictions as compared to full first-order predicate calculus. Applications of Prolog to pattern recognition problems are described in Refs. 45 and 46.

Predicate calculus and Prolog can be understood as high-level knowledge representation languages. There is an underlying theory which has a long tradition and seems to be well-developed. Logic programming supports, to a high degree, formal program verification. Typically, a logic program puts emphasis on *what* the problem is rather than on *how* a solution is algorithmically obtained. This can significantly speed up the process of building a system prototype.

However, there is also a number of shortcomings and limitations in predicate calculus and logic programming. First, from a theoretical point of view, first-order predicate calculus is only partially decidable. This means that a theorem proving procedure cannot be guaranteed to terminate if it is confronted with a non-theorem, i.e. a formula which does not follow from the given axioms. Another problem in first-order predicate calculus comes from the property of monotony. Any given axiom as well as any derived conclusion can never be retracted at a later point of time. This turns out to be a major obstacle for many reasoning tasks. An example in pattern recognition is the analysis of image sequences, where a situation depicted in an image may change over the course of time. As a remedy for the monotony problem, situational variables have been proposed. However, their use implies the so-called frame problem. For a deeper discussion of this subject, the reader is referred to Ref. 47. As an alternative solution to the problem arising from monotony, several non-monotonic logic calculi have been proposed. For an introduction see Ref. 48.

From a practical point of view, there are also some shortcomings and limitations in predicate calculus and logic programming. The execution of a Prolog program is based on an exhaustive depth-first search with backtracking resulting in exponential time complexity. This is not elegant and leads to slow execution. There are several efforts underway in order to improve execution efficiency, e.g. by building special hardware architectures for parallel execution[49].

*Production systems* are another well-known approach to knowledge representation in artificial intelligence. Originally, production systems have been proposed in the context of computability theory[50]. In the meantime, this formalism has been modified and extended in a variety of ways in order to meet the requirements arising from fields like cognitive psychology, computational linguistics, expert systems and pattern recognition.

A production system consists of three components, namely, a set of facts and rules, an interpreter and a database. A rule has the form

if PREMISE then CONCLUSION .

The PREMISE is also called the (pre)condition and the CONCLUSION is called the postcondition or action of a rule. There is a particular syntax for PREMISE and CONCLUSION which varies from system to system. The rules and facts represent long term knowledge about a problem domain, which is independent from particular input data. By contrast, the database plays the role of a short-term memory where specific conclusions, derived from actual input data by means of facts and rules, are stored.

There are two major approaches to rule application by the interpreter, namely, forward-chaining (which is also called data driven, or bottom-up, inference) and backward-chaining (also called goal driven, or top-down, inference). In a forward-chaining system the interpreter determines all rules which are applicable to the current database. Applicability means that the PREMISE of a rule is fulfilled. Next, one rule is selected and applied. This means execution of the CONCLUSION which causes, for example, the addition of a number of assertions to the current database. Based on the new contents of the database, the set of applicable rules is determined again and one rule from this set is selected and applied, and so on. This process continues until a termination condition becomes true. In a backward-chaining system, a goal is established first. Next, a rule which matches the goal in its CONCLUSION is determined. The PREMISE of this rule becomes a new goal for the next execution cycle while the CONCLUSION is removed from the list of actual goals. The procedure terminates if the list of actual goals is empty, i.e. if the original goal has been verified, or if another termination condition is fulfilled. For an introduction to, and overview of, the field of production systems see Refs. 51 and 52. In a number of papers, extensions to production systems have been proposed; examples are control sets[53], Petri-nets[54] and metarules[55].

Today, there exist a great number of production system implementations known as expert system shells. Some of them are commercially available for several computers. As a matter of fact, production system is the formalism for knowledge representation which has mostly been used in current expert systems. An expert system shell can be considered as an expert system with an empty knowledge base, i.e. a production system with an empty set of facts and rules. This means that the user may fill the knowledge base with facts and rules from his current problem domain, while the interpreter remains unchanged from one application to the other. Two examples of expert system shells are the forward-chaining system OPS5 (Ref. 56) and the backward-chaining system M.1 (Ref. 57). M.1 has the property of monotony (see above) while OPS5 is a non-monotone system. Besides pure forward- or backward-chaining systems, there exist also systems with a mixed control strategy. This provides increased flexibility. For an overview of commercially available production systems see Ref. 57.

There is a huge number of applications of production systems in pattern recognition. Particular fields of applications include image segmentation[58], image interpretation and understanding[59-64] and speech recognition[65,66].

Production systems have several advantages. They provide a great degree of flexibility and modularity since the knowledge is distributed over individual rules which are independent from each other. Thus one can incrementally build up and verify a system. When adding, deleting, or modifying rules, only those rules which are directly affected must be considered. Usually, there is only a minimum degree of side effects to be taken into account. The interpreter and the database management routines can be left unchanged when going from one application to the other. Furthermore, it is claimed that the if-then formalism is a very natural style of knowledge representation, suitable for a large class of applications. The strict if-then form of rules is advantageous since it supports automatic checking of rules for completeness and consistency.

Shortcomings and limitations of production systems include the lack of expressive power and sufficient control structures. For example, it is not possible to directly program the application of a number of rules in sequence. The only control structure directly available is if-then. Another shortcoming is a significant degree of inefficiency. Determining the set of applicable rules is perhaps computationally more costly than the application of the rule which is selected. So there is an overhead in the interpreter. This problem exists in both forward- and backward-chaining systems. However, there are approaches to improving efficiency, for example, the RETE matching algorithm in OPS5 (Ref. 56).

*Semantic nets* and *frames* are another very important approach to knowledge representation developed in artificial intelligence. They are particularly suitable for modelling collections of objects, including relationships between them. From a global point of view, a semantic net is a structure which is similar to a graph. It consists of a number of nodes and a number of edges. The nodes are called concepts or frames. They are used for the representation of objects or object classes from a problem domain. The edges represent various relations which may exist between the entities modelled by the concepts. In contrast with a graph where the nodes are "atomic" units, the concepts in a semantic net are structured, i.e. they consist of subunits, sometimes called slots. Slots are used for defining the details of an object, or an object class, represented by a concept. Thus slots typically contain object attributes or pointers to other concepts. These pointers correspond to the relations which exist between different concepts. Concepts in a semantic net are generic in their nature. That is, a concept usually represents a number of individual objects. In order to distinguish them from generic concepts, nodes in a semantic net representing individual elements are often called instances.

In a semantic net or a collection of frames we usually find both user defined and built-in relations. A typical example of the latter category is the "is-a" relation. By means of this relation, concepts representing subclasses are linked to their superclasses. For example, a convertible "is-a" car, a car "is-a" vehicle, etc. This "is-a" relation plays an important role with respect to property inheritance. This means that a subclass inherits all the properties, i.e. slots, which are specified in its superclass. This inheritance mechanism facilitates a natural and compact style of knowledge representation.

While in predicate calculus and production systems we find fixed inference strategies based on the resolution rule on forward- or on backward-chaining, there are no such fixed inference procedures in semantic nets and frames. Instead, inference and reasoning are dependent on the particular application and are to be provided by the user. However, there do exist some basic operations in most application independent semantic net implementations. Examples of such basic operations are the creation and deletion of concepts and instances, the reading and writing of slots, etc. For an introduction to, and overview of, semantic nets and frames see Refs. 51 and 67.

Analogously to rule based expert system shells, there exist a number of application independent implementations of semantic nets and frames. Examples are FRL[68], KRL[69], and KL-ONE[70]. Applications of semantic nets in pattern recognition include image understanding and computer vision[71-74], natural language understanding[75], speech recognition[76,77], and ECG understanding[78].

In a sense, semantic nets have more expressive power than predicate calculus formulae or production rules. They are suitable for the representation of complex objects, particularly for describing how an object is built up from simpler parts and how it is related with other objects. A frame may have procedures attached to its slots. This provides a great degree of flexibility to the user. On the other hand, this increased power may lead to a decrease in perspicuity. Since the inference strategy in a semantic net is user dependent, i.e. may vary from application to application, the "meaning" of a collection of frames, or a semantic net, becomes clear only in conjunction with a particular inference procedure. In other words, the semantics of a semantic net are usually not as clear as the semantics of a set of predicates calculus clauses or production rules. One has to keep in mind, however, that the use of a semantic net does not exclude the use of production rules and predicate calculus formulae within the same application. Instead, it is just the combination of different knowledge representation methods which can contribute to a great improvement with respect to expressive power, programming comfort, and perspicuity. More details concerning the combination of different methods will be discussed in the following section.

## 4.2. Relationships Between the Basic Approaches

There are various relationships between predicate calculus, production systems and semantic nets, and these methods can be integrated into a hybrid approach in a variety of ways. First, one observes a close correspondence between predicate calculus and production systems. On the one hand, the if-then structure of a rule in a production system can be interpreted as an implication in the logical sense. This means that production system rules can be understood as particular formulas from predicate calculus. On the other hand, it can be shown that any set of first order predicate calculus formulas can be equivalently transformed into a set of if-then implications[42,47]. The close correspondence between predicate calculus and production systems also becomes obvious from the fact that Prolog is very suitable for the implementation of production systems[79]. An example of a commercially available expert system shell implemented in Prolog is M.1 (Ref. 57).

Differences between predicate calculus and production systems may arise from the particular form of the PREMISE and CONCLUSION in a rule. While in predicate calculus the only possible action triggered by the CONCLUSION is the addition of a clause to the database, some production systems allow more complex operations. An example is OPS5, where not only the addition to but also the retraction from the database is possible[56]. This results in a non-monotone behavior.

There is also a close correspondence between predicate calculus and semantic nets. In Ref. 80 it is shown how the information contained in a semantic net can equivalently be represented by means of first order predicate calculus formulas. Moreover, it becomes obvious that certain inference operations defined on semantic nets can be expressed in terms of the resolution rule. Similar results are also described in Ref. 42. This can be interpreted in two different ways. First, one can conclude that predicate calculus can be used as a tool for the implementation of semantic nets. Secondly, predicate calculus can be considered as a formal basis for defining the semantics of semantic nets. While in Ref. 80 only fundamentals of semantic networks are modelled by means of predicate calculus, it is shown in Ref. 81 how more complicated features like property inheritance, default values, etc. can be implemented in Prolog. Another interesting link between predicate calculus and semantic nets is established in Ref. 82. The authors define a particular class of semantic nets. These nets can be considered as a particular datastructure for the representation of predicate calculus formulae. A potential advantage is that this datastructure can be used for guiding a theorem prover.

From the foregoing discussion it is clear that both production systems and semantic nets can be interpreted in terms of predicate calculus. Thus formal logic can be considered as a link between these two representation formalisms. From a practical point of view, production systems and semantic nets can be combined into a useful and powerful knowledge representation formalism. First, one can consider the concepts and relations of a semantic net as an aid to partitioning a large set of rules into smaller units. Such a partition usually results in a more efficient control structure with respect to rule application[83]. On the other hand, rules can be integrated into a semantic net by attaching them to the slots of a frame. In this way, rules can play the role of procedural components in a semantic net used for the calculation of attribute values. An example is Ref. 74.

Recently, there have been many efforts devoted to the development of hybrid expert system shells and knowledge representation languages. The idea is to provide a representation mechanism, together with suitable inference procedures, which allows the integration of a variety of pieces of knowledge, each represented by means of a different formalism, into one consistent framework. For example, hybrid expert system shells offer the possibility of integrating rules and frames as sketched above. Particularly, it is possible to reference the slots of a frame within the PREMISE or CONCLUSION of a rule. Similarly, one may use elements of a logic programming language like Prolog within a rule or frame. Examples of hybrid expert system shells are ART, KEE and BABYLON[57,84].

## 5. HYBRID APPROACHES BASED ON METHODS AND TOOLS FROM ARTIFICIAL INTELLIGENCE

In this section we study relations between artificial intelligence based knowledge representation, on the one hand, and structural and statistical pattern recognition, on the other hand. It is also discussed how different techniques can be combined for a hybrid approach.

### 5.1. Formal Logic — Structural and Statistical Pattern Recognition

It is well-known that the implementation of a top-down parser for context free languages in Prolog is very straightforward[44,79,81]. There is a one-to-one relation between the rules of a grammar and the corresponding Prolog clauses. In other words, given a grammar, the corresponding parser can be automatically constructed. For example, consider two productions of the well-known chromosome grammar[85]

$$\text{SUBMEDIAN} ::= \text{ARMPAIR, ARMPAIR}$$
$$\text{TELOCENTRIC} ::= \text{BOTTOM, ARMPAIR .}$$

The corresponding clauses of a top-down parser in Prolog are

$$\text{submedian}(S0, S) : -$$
$$\text{armpair}(S0, S1) ,$$
$$\text{armpair}(S1, S) .$$
$$\text{telocentric}(S0, S) : -$$
$$\text{bottom}(S0, S1) ,$$
$$\text{armpair}(S1, S) .$$

This solution corresponds to a backtracking parser with exponential time complexity. In a recent thesis, it is shown that other types of parsers also, i.e. an LL($k$)-parser and a CYK-parser with linear and cubic time complexity, respectively, can be easily implemented in Prolog[86].

In Ref. 86 a study is described where the goal was to find out if logic programming is powerful enough for the implementation of pattern recognition algorithms which have been traditionally implemented in procedural oriented programming languages like PASCAL, FORTRAN, or C. Among other algorithms, matching of string and graph prototypes and discrete relaxation were considered. As a result, it was shown that all these algorithms can be implemented in Prolog in a very straightforward and elegant way. The only problem may be execution speed for large applications. Regardless of such pragmatic aspects, it can be concluded that predicate calculus has enough expressive power to represent, in a clear and elegant way, formal language parsing, prototype matching and relaxation. A condensed version of Ref. 86 is given in Refs. 87 and 88.

Another close relationship between predicate calculus and formal grammars can be concluded from the STRIPS-system[42]. There are predicate calculus rules for manipulating other predicate calculus formulas. Each rule consists of three lists of predicates, namely, precondition-, delete- and add-list. A rule is applicable if its preconditions can be matched with the actual database. Rule application consists of removing the elements in the delete-list from, and adding the elements in the add-list to the database. If precondition- and delete-list are identical—as it is often the case—the application of a STRIPS-rule is equivalent to the application of a rule of a scattered-context grammar[89].

STRIPS rules may contain variables which can be matched to other variables or constants. This mechanism is not directly available in a grammar. However, it can be simulated when the grammar is augmented by attributes. Consider, for example, the STRIPS-rule

$$\text{ONTABLE}(x), \text{CLEAR}(x), \text{HANDEMPTY} \longrightarrow \text{HOLDING}\ (x)$$

where ONTABLE, CLEAR, HANDEMPTY and HOLDING are predicates. The corresponding grammar rule is

$$\langle \text{ONTABLE} \rangle, \langle \text{CLEAR} \rangle, \langle \text{HANDEMPTY} \rangle \longrightarrow \langle\ \text{HOLDING} \rangle\ ,$$

where we define attributes $x(\text{ONTABLE})$, $x(\text{CLEAR})$, $x(\text{HOLDING})$. The attribute transfer function is defined by

$$x(\text{HOLDING}) := \begin{cases} x(\text{ONTABLE}), & \text{if } x(\text{ONTABLE}) = x(\text{CLEAR}) \\ \text{undefined, otherwise} \ . \end{cases}$$

If rule application is restricted to those cases where the attribute transfer function is defined, then the above grammar rule will behave exactly like a STRIPS-rule. Originally, the work on STRIPS was motivated by robot action planning. But the formalism may be used also in pattern recognition, for planning or for inferring conclusions about patterns. It can be considered as a bridge between predicate calculus and formal grammars.

Predicate calculus is based on the binary truth values true and false. A generalization to a continuous interval of truth values, usually $[0,1]$, is provided in fuzzy logic and the theory of fuzzy sets[90,91]. Thus fuzzy logic can be considered as a strong link between predicate calculus and statistical decision theory. The basic idea in fuzzy logic is to assign a truth value from the interval $[0,1]$ to any logic formula. Combining two formulas $p_1$ and $p_2$ with truth values $t_1$ and $t_2$, respectively, into a new formula $p$ requires combining $t_1$ and $t_2$ into the truth value $t$ of $p$. Examples for such a combination are

$$p = p_1 \wedge p_2 , \quad t = \min(t_1, t_2) ,$$
$$p = p_1 \vee p_2 , \quad t = \max(t_1, t_2) ,$$
$$p = \sim p_1 , \quad\quad t = 1 - t_1 .$$

There is a huge number of applications of fuzzy set theory in pattern recognition. Examples can be found in Ref. 92.

## 5.2. Production Systems — Structural and Statistical Pattern Recognition

In Sec. 4.2 it was shown that production systems and predicate calculus are closely related with each other while in Sec. 5.1 the relations between predicate calculus and formal grammars were discussed. Putting the arguments together, the conclusion is that production systems and formal grammars have much in common.

This may become even more obvious by means of the following consideration. Imagine a special type of production system where the database is a linear string of facts. Each time a rule is applied, its if-part is removed from the database while its then-part is inserted in place of the if-part. Assume furthermore that the facts are divided into terminal and nonterminal facts. Initially, there is only one nonterminal fact in the database. The termination condition is that there are only terminal facts in the database. Control is by forward-chaining. Obviously, such a production system can simulate any formal grammar. Conversely, since type-0 grammars have the same computational power as Turing machines, any production system can certainly be simulated by a formal grammar. So the conclusion is that formal grammars and production systems are equivalent.

From a theoretical point of view, this equivalence is not surprising. However, from a practical point of view it is interesting to notice that many production systems and rule based expert system shells can be used like programming languages. Examples are given in Ref. 56. As another example, it is shown in Refs. 86-88 that not only Prolog but also the backward-chaining rule based expert system shell M.1 can be used for implementing various parsers, prototype matching algorithms and relaxation. For example, the M.1 rules corresponding to the grammar rules given in Sec. 5.1 are

$$\begin{aligned}
&\text{if} && \text{armpair}(S0) = [S1] \\
&\text{and} && \text{armpair}(S1) = [S] \\
&\text{then} && \text{submedian}(S0) = [S]\ , \\
&\text{if} && \text{bottom}(S0) = [S1] \\
&\text{and} && \text{armpair}(S1) = [S] \\
&\text{then} && \text{submedian}(S0) = [S]\ .
\end{aligned}$$

There is a one-to-one correspondence not only between the grammar and the production rules, but also between the production rules and the Prolog clauses given in Sec. 5.1. A similar correspondence has been observed also for the M.1 implementations of string and graph prototype matching, and relaxation.

Another link between production systems and syntactic pattern recognition has been established in Ref. 93. The authors have shown how production systems can be modelled by finite state stochastic programmed grammars. Each rule $p_i$ of a production system is individually represented by a grammar $G_i$. Next, all grammars $G_i$ are combined into one grammar $G$. Thus inference in the production system can be modelled by rewriting steps in the grammar $G$. The authors claim that their approach is able to represent most reasoning and control methods used in expert systems today, and may help to bring about a better understanding of the theory of expert systems.

Another formalism incorporating elements from production systems, predicate calculus and formal grammars is the relational production system model according to Ref. 94. This system is similar to STRIPS (see Sec. 5.1) with a particular emphasis on mathematical simplicity which allows proof of some useful results concerning the composition of rules, for example.

Many rule based expert systems are applied in diagnostic classification[38] — a task that has traditionally been solved by means of statistical classification techniques. A closer look reveals that diagnostic classification using if-then rules can be interpreted as hierarchical classification, i.e. as a decision tree procedure where sequential measurements are made in order to successively rule out certain classes until only one class remains, or the input pattern is rejected.

As an example, consider the following zoo-rules from Ref. 47

1) if     the animal has hair

   then    it is a mammal

2) if     the animal gives milk

   then    it is a mammal

3) if     the animal is a mammal

   and    it eats meat

   then    it is a carnivore

4) if     the animal is a mammal

   and    it has pointed teeth

   and    it has claws

   then    it is a carnivore

5) if     the animal is a carnivore

   and    it has dark spots

   then    it is a cheetah

6) if     the animal is a carnivore

   and    it has black stripes

   then    it is a tiger .

These rules can be equivalently represented by the AND/OR-graph in Fig. 5a (see also Sec. 6). Besides, they can also be represented by the decision tree shown in Fig. 5b. For more details about hierarchical classification see Ref. 95. Further examples are seen in Refs. 96 and 97.

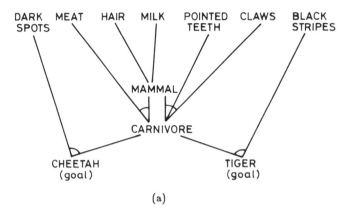

(a)

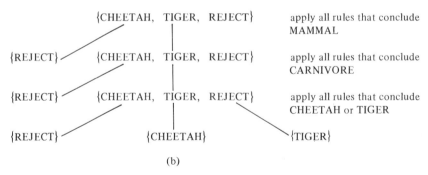

(b)

Fig. 5. An example of the relationships between production systems and hierarchical classifiers (see text).

Most rule based expert system shells include means for coping with uncertainty, i.e. uncertain data and knowledge. Examples are certainty factors[36], concepts from Dempster/Shafer's theory[98], or Bayesian uncertainties[83]. This can be considered as another link with statistical classification methods. For more details see Refs. 99 and 100.

## 5.3. Semantic Nets — Structural and Statistical Pattern Recognition

A structural prototype, particularly a relational structure or a graph, can be considered as a simple semantic net. The nodes in the prototype graph are interpreted as concepts, with node attributes and labels corresponding to particular slots. A prototype graph is a generic object, representing knowledge about not only a single pattern but a whole pattern class. An individual pattern is an instance of such a generic concept. This is in exact correspondence with the role of concepts and instances in semantic nets. In a structural prototype there are problem dependent relations between nodes. They correspond exactly with problem dependent relations between the concepts in a semantic net. However, semantic nets are more general and powerful in the sense that there is no "is-a" relation with property inheritance in a graph or a relational structure.

It was mentioned in Sec. 4.1 that reasoning and inference in a semantic net is usually problem dependent. Thus there is a great number of different reasoning procedures which are principally useful for semantic nets. This is in contrast with reasoning and inference based on prototypes where matching is the only feasible type of inference. Of course, depending on the particular data structures used for prototype representation, and depending on the particular error-correcting operations and the costs of elementary matching steps, there is also a great number of matching procedures for structural prototypes. However, the variety of inference procedures for semantic nets is much greater, including matching as a special case.

The links between semantic nets and structural prototypes become even more obvious if we consider hierarchical graphs. They are a generalization of graphs and relational structures as discussed above. The idea of hierarchical graphs is to model the aggregation of simpler constitutents into more complex patterns on several levels using a particular "part"-relation. Usually, more sophisticated inference procedures than just error-correcting matching are required, taking into account the particular meaning of the "part"-relation. Along this relation, other relations are inherited in a way which is somewhat similar to property inheritance in semantic nets. An example is shown in Fig. 6. Figure 6a shows the generic model of a prototype scene. An instance is depicted in Fig. 6b. The dashed arrows in Fig. 6a represent the part relation while the other arrows stand for spatial relations. From Fig. 6a one can infer, for example, that one of the boxes is on the board although no explicit subgraph indicating this relation, i.e. a subgraph as shown in Fig. 6c, is contained in Fig. 6a. Therefore, an inference mechanism for hierarchical graphs must certainly contain the means for inheriting spatial relations along the "part"-relation, besides "pure" error-correcting graph matching capabilities.

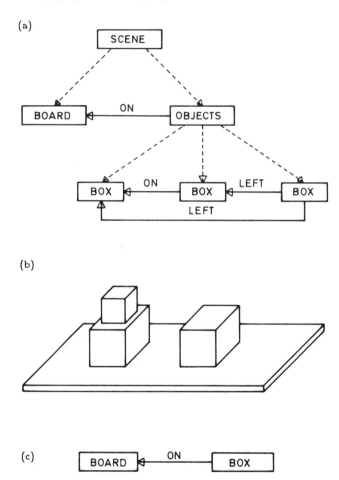

Fig. 6. An example of a hierarchical graph (see text).

Finally, there are also links between semantic nets and formal grammars. A grammar can be easily represented by a semantic net. Consider, for example, the grammar

$$S \longrightarrow aSb$$
$$S \longrightarrow ab$$

generating strings $a^n b^n$, $n \geq 1$. This grammar can be represented by concepts like

> concept $S$
> > type: nonterminal
> > 1. alternative : $(a, S, b)$
> > 2. alternative : $(a, b)$
>
> concept $a$
> > type: terminal
>
> concept $b$
> > type: terminal .

Given such a semantic net, the task of a parser is equivalent to determining whether an input string is an instance of the start symbol concept. Given the string $aabb$, for example, the parser, i.e. inference procedure, will find instances of concept $a$ at positions 1 and 2, instances of concept $b$ at positions 3 and 4, and instances of concept $S$ from positions 2 to 3 and from 1 to 4. Since the second instance of $S$ covers the whole input string, this input string is an element of the language. From the above example, one can conclude that formal grammars can be simulated (or implemented) by semantic nets. On the other hand, since type-0 grammars have the same computational power as Turing machines, one can certainly also model any semantic net and any inference procedure in a semantic net by a grammar.

## 6. CONTROL, SEARCH AND SYSTEM ORGANIZATION

The emphasis in Secs. 4 and 5 was on knowledge representation. Control, search and system organization are other issues from artificial intelligence which are very important in pattern recognition. They are discussed below.

If we define the term "hybrid system" in a broad sense then almost any pattern recognition system falls into this category — integrating techniques from preprocessing, segmentation, feature extraction, feature representation, classification, interpretation, etc. From a general point of view, the task of a pattern recognition system is the transformation of raw sensory input data into a pattern description, for example, a class name or a more complex representation. Such a transformation is achieved by a sequence of processing steps with a number of intermediate results involving different procedures and techniques. Only in special cases do the sequence of processing steps remain fixed for any input data and can be uniquely determined in the system design stage. In the general case, however, particularly in systems involving structural or artificial intelligence based techniques, the optimal sequence of processing steps is dependent on the particular input data and can be determined only at runtime. So a control module for the optimal selection of processing steps is required. Another important question is the overall architecture of such a hybrid system. These topics will be discussed in the rest of this section.

The *blackboard model* seems to be particularly useful as an architecture for hybrid pattern recognition systems. A blackboard model consists of a number of independent knowledge sources with a common short-term memory. The knowledge sources are completely independent from each other and they may be built according to completely different criteria, based on various techniques for knowledge representation and inference. The only possibility of communication among the knowledge sources is via the blackboard where intermediate results and messages are stored. There are several variations possible within the framework of a blackboard system. For example, there can be an overall control process which activates the different knowledge sources according to a particular agenda. Alternatively, each knowledge source can behave like a demon activating itself as soon as there are particular entries in the blackboard. Notice that modularity is a great advantage of blackboard systems. The individual knowledge sources can be modified, replaced, or removed, and new knowledge sources can be added without directly influencing the other knowledge sources. The blackboard model was originally developed in the context of speech understanding[101]. Besides this area, other applications have been reported[60,102].

Search techniques provide a solution to the problem of optimal selection of processing steps depending on the input data and intermediate results. Notice that this problem can occur both in a coarse and a fine grained fashion. In the first case, the problem is, for example, the activation of a knowledge source in a blackboard system by the global scheduler. An example of the second case is the situation where there are different alternative choices for proceeding within a knowledge source. Such a situation can arise from ambiguities in the input data or the intermediate results.

Any search problem can more or less be transformed into a standard form, i.e. search for an optimal path in a graph from a start node to a goal node. The crucial point is to design a search procedure in such a way that combinatorial explosion, i.e. the examination of every possible existing path, is avoided.

There is a great variety of search procedures known from the literature. Two standard procedures are depth-first and breadth-first search. Both procedures are not difficult to implement. However, they are restricted to small problems since they explore too many redundant paths in the search graph in general. An improvement can be achieved by a best-first search using a heuristic evaluation function. This can result in a reduction of the number of explored alternative paths, leading to a speed-up of the search. Other search procedures are beam search, branch-and-bound search, bidirectional search and dynamic programming. For an introduction and overview see Refs. 42 and 103. Examples of search in pattern recognition are the ARGOS image understanding system[104], speech recognition systems[105,106] and medical image sequence understanding[74]. For a general discussion of search in pattern recognition, including further references, see Ref. 107.

Search plays a fundamental role in inference procedures which are based on the knowledge representation concepts discussed in Sec. 4.1. Any predicate calculus theorem prover needs an underlying search procedure controlling the order in which clauses are examined for application of the resolution rule. As a particular example, most Prolog interpreters are based on a depth-first search. Similarly, forward- and backward-chaining in rule based systems need an underlying search procedure. If the rules are restricted in such a way that the then-part consists of only one clause, then a production system can be equivalently represented by an AND/OR-tree very easily[42]. In this case satisfying a goal is equivalent to finding a solution of an AND/OR-tree. For this task, search procedures which are variants of general graph search techniques are known. No general comments about the relationship between inference in semantic nets and search can be made since there is too great a number of different inference procedures. It is sure, nevertheless, that search will be inevitable if inference has to cope with ambiguities.

Search also plays a fundamental role in structural pattern recognition. It was shown in Ref. 108 that context-free grammars can be equivalently represented by AND/OR-graphs. Thus parsing is equivalent to finding a solution graph. This problem can be attacked, as it was already pointed out above, by means of search. Particular parsing algorithms, like EAR-LEY's algorithm or CYK-parsing (see Chapter 3) can be considered as dynamic programming procedures. Another more sophisticated parser and its relations with search is described in Ref. 109. All algorithms for prototype matching lie, as a matter of fact, completely inside the domain of search. First, all procedures currently used for string matching are based on dynamic programming. Also tree matching belongs to this category. Since (error-correcting) subgraph isomorphism detection is known to be NP-complete[5] and since there are only exponential algorithms known for this class of problems today, heuristic search is often used for graph matching. By means of suitable heuristics, computational efforts can be reduced in the average case[110,111]. There are also relationships between relaxation and dynamic programming. A deeper discussion of this topic can be found in Ref. 112.

## 7. SUMMARY AND CONCLUSIONS

In this chapter we have reviewed basic methods in structural and statistical pattern recognition, and artificial intelligence. We have studied relationships between various techniques, and have discussed possibilities of combining different techniques for a hybrid approach. Some of the considered basic methods are more or less complementary to each other, so it can be expected that a hybrid approach increases flexibility and power while retaining the advantages of the "pure" methods involved.

The idea of using a hybrid approach is not new in pattern recognition[30] and many hybrid systems have been reported in the literature. Nevertheless, the author feels that we are far away from a complete understanding of the strength, and the drawbacks and limitations of the different methods used today. Similarly, there is no complete understanding of the various relationships which may exist between the different approaches. On the other hand, the rapid growth of interest in pattern recognition and artificial intelligence, and particularly the tendency to develop more complex and sophisticated systems, will certainly enhance the importance of studying hybrid approaches. It can be expected that there will be a stimulation of further research in this area by many current research issues like knowledge based reasoning systems, knowledge based robotics assembly, or autonomous vehicles with multiple sensor integration.

## REFERENCES

1. R.O. Duda and P.E. Hart, *Pattern Classification and Scene Analysis* (John Wiley & Sons, 1973).

2. J.T. Tou and R.C. Gonzalez, *Pattern Recognition Principles* (Addison-Wesley, Reading, MA, 1974).

3. P. Devijver and J. Kittler, *Pattern Recognition: A Statistical Approach* (Prentice Hall Int., 1982).

4. J.E. Hopcroft and J.D. Ullman, *Introduction to Automata Theory, Languages and Computation* (Addison Wesley, Reading, MA, 1979).

5. M.R. Garey and D.S. Johnson, *Computers and Intractability: A Guide to the Theory of NP-Completeness* (H. Freeman, San Francisco, 1979).

6. D. Waltz, "Understanding line drawings of scenes with shadows", in *The psychology of computer vision*, (McGraw Hill, 1975) pp. 19-91.

7. A. Rosenfeld, R.A. Hummel and S.W. Zucker "Scene labelling by relaxation operations", *IEEE Trans. SMC* 6 (1976) 420-443.

8. J. Kittler and J. Illingworth, "A review of relaxation labelling algorithms", *Image and Vision Computing* 3 (1985) 206-216.

9. O. Faugeras and M. Berthod, "Improving consistency and reducing ambiguities in stochastic labeling: An optimization approach", *IEEE Trans. PAMI* 3 (1981) 412-424.

10. R.M. Haralick, "An interpretation for probabilistic relaxation", *Comp. Vision, Graphics, and Image Processing* 22 (1983).

11. R. Hummel and S. Zucker, "On the foundations of relaxation labelling processes", *IEEE Trans. PAMI* 5 (1983) 267-287.

12. T.C. Henderson, "A note on discrete relaxation", *Comp. Vision, Graphics and Image Processing* 28 (1984) 384-388.

13. D. Gernert, "Distance or similarity measures which respect the internal structure of the objects", *Methods of Operations Research* 43 (1981) 329-335.

14. J.W. Tai and K.S. Fu, "Semantic syntax-directed translation for pictorial pattern recognition", *Proc. 6th ICPR*, Munich, 1982, pp. 169-171.

15. H. Bunke, "Attributed programmed graph grammars and their application to schematic diagram interpretation", *IEEE Trans. PAMI* 4 (1982) 574-582.

16. M. Kaul, "'Computing the minimum error distance of graphs in $O(n^3)$ time with precedence graph grammars", in *Syntactic and Structural Pattern Recognition*, eds. G. Ferrate, T. Pavlidis, A. Sanfeliu and H. Bunke (Springer-Verlag, 1988) pp. 69-83.

17. H.S. Don and K.S. Fu, "A syntactic method for image segmentation and object recognition", *Pattern Recognition* 18 (1985) 73-87.

18. H. Bunke, K. Grebner and G. Sagerer, "Syntactic analysis of noisy input strings with an application to the analysis of heart-volume curves", *Proc. 7th ICPR*, Montreal, 1984, pp. 1145-1147.

19. L.S. Davis and T.C. Henderson, "Hierarchical constraint processes for shape analysis", *IEEE Trans. PAMI* 3 (1981) 265-277.

20. O.D. Faugeras and K.E. Price, "Semantic description of aerial images using stochastic labeling", *IEEE Trans. PAMI* 3 (1981) 633-642.

21. L. Kitchen, "Relaxation applied to matching quantitative relational structures", *IEEE Trans. SMC* 10 (1980) 96-101.

22. J.K. Cheng and T.S. Huang, "Image recognition by matching relational structures", *IEEE Proc. PRIP*, Dallas, 1981, pp. 542-547.

23. J.H. Friedman *et al.*, "An algorithm for finding nearest neighbors", *IEEE Trans. Computers* **24** (1975) 1000-1006.

24. K. Fukunaga and P.M. Narendra, "A branch and bound algorithm for computing k-nearest neighbors", *IEEE Trans. Computers* **24** (1975) 750-753.

25. D.C. Feustel and G. Shapiro, "The nearest neighbor problem in an abstract metric space", *Pattern Recognition Lett.* **1** (1982) 125-128.

26. L.G. Shapiro and R.M. Haralick, "Organization of relational models for scene analysis", *IEEE Trans. PAMI* **4** (1982).

27. L.G. Shapiro, "The use of numerical relational distance and symbolic differences for organizing models and for matching", in *Techniques for 3-D Machine Perception*, ed. A. Rosenfeld (Elsevier Science Publisher B.V., 1986) pp. 255-270.

28. L. Goldfarb and T.Y.T. Chan, "On a new unified approach to pattern recognition, *Proc. 7th ICPR*, Montreal, 1984, pp. 705-708.

29. F.C.A. Groen, A.C. Sanderson and J.F. Schlag, "Symbol recognition in electrical diagrams using probabilistic graph matching", *Pattern Recognition Lett.* **3** (1985) 343-350.

30. K.S. Fu, "Hybrid approaches to pattern recognition", in *Pattern Recognition, Theory and Applications*, eds. J. Kittler, K.S. Fu and L.F. Pau (D. Reidel Publ., 1981) pp. 139-155.

31. R.F. Kubichek and E.A. Quincy, "Identification of seismic stratigraphic traps using statistical pattern recognition", *Pattern Recognition* **18** (1985) 440-458.

32. L.S. Davis, C.Y. Wang and H.C. Xie, "An experiment in multispectral, multitemporal crop classification using relaxation techniques", *Comp. Vision, Graphics, and Image Processing* **23** (1983) 227-235.

33. B. Bhanu and O.D. Faugeras, "Segmentation of images having unimodal distributions", *IEEE Trans. PAMI* **4** (1982) 408-419.

34. P.A. Nagin, A.R. Hanson and E.M. Riseman, "Studies in global and local histogram guided relaxation algorithms", *IEEE Trans. PAMI* **4** (1982) 263-277.

35. R.M. Haralick, "Decision making in context", *IEEE Trans. PAMI* **5** (1983) 417-428.

36. E.A. Shortliffe, "Computer-based medical consultations: MYCIN", (American Elsevier, New York, 1976).

37. A. Barr and E.A. Feigenbaum, eds. *The Handbook of Artificial Intelligence*, Vol. 2 (Pitman Books, London, 1982).

38. B. Chandrasekaran, "From numbers to symbols to knowledge structures: Pattern recognition and artificial intelligence perspectives on the classification task", in *Pattern Recognition in Practice II*, eds. E.S. Gelsema and L.N. Kamal (Elsevier Science Publ. B.V., 1986) pp. 547-559.

39. R. Turner, *Logics for Artificial Intelligence* (Ellis Horwood Ltd., Chichester, 1984).

40. J.A. Robinson, "A machine-oriented logic based on the resolution principle", *J. ACM* **12** (1965) 23-41.

41. C. Chang and R.C. Lee, *Symbolic Logic and Mechanical Theorem Proving* (Academic Press, New York, 1973).

42. N.J. Nilsson, *Principles of Artificial Intelligence* (Springer-Verlag, 1982).

43. L. Wos, R. Overbeek, E. Lusk and J. Boyle *Automated Reasoning Introduction and Applications* (Prentice Hall, Englewood Cliffs, NJ, 1984).

44. W.F. Clocksin and C.S. Mellish, *Programming in Prolog* (Springer-Verlag, 1984).

45. D.H. Mott ed., "Prolog-based image processing using Viking XA", in *Proc. 2nd Int. Conf. on Machine Intell.*, London, 1985, ed. A. Pugh, pp. 37-52.

46. D. Niyogi and S.N. Srihari, "A rule-based system for document understanding", *Proc. AAAI-86*, Philadelphia, 1986, pp. 786-793.

47. P.H. Winston, *Artificial Intelligence (2nd ed.)*, (Addison-Wesley, Reading, MA, 1984).

48. D.G. Bobrow, ed., "Special issue on non-monotonic logic", *Artificial Intelligence* **13** (1980).

49. K. Hwang, J. Ghosh and R. Chowkwanyun, "Computer architectures for artificial intelligence processing", *Computer* **20** (1987) 19-27.

50. E. Post, "Formal reductions of the general combinatorial problem", *American Journal of Mathematics* **65** (1943) 197-268.

51. A. Barr and E.A. Feigenbaum, eds. *The Handbook of Artificial Intelligence, Vol. 1* (Pitman Books, London, 1981).

52. B.G. Buchanan and E. Shortliffe, *Rule-based Expert Systems* (Addison-Wesley, Reading, MA, 1985).

53. M. Georgeff, "Procedural control in production systems", *Artificial Intelligence* **18** (1982) 175-201.

54. M.O. Zisman, "Use of production systems for modelling asynchronous concurrent processes", in *Pattern Directed Inference Systems*, eds. D.A. Waterman and F. Hayes-Roth (Academic Press, New York, 1978).

55. R. Davis, "Meta-rules: reasoning about control", *Artificial Intelligence*, **15** (1980) 179-222.

56. L. Brownston, R. Farrell, E. Kant and N. Martin, *Programming Expert-Systems in OPS5* (Addison Wesley, Reading, MA, 1986).

57. P. Harmon and D. King, *Expert-Systems — Artificial Intelligence in Business* (John Wiley, New York, 1985).

58. A.M. Nazif and M.D. Levine, "Low level image segmentation: an expert system", *IEEE Trans. PAMI* **6** (1984) 555-557.

59. Y. Ohta, A Region Oriented Image-analysis System by Computer, Ph.D. dissertation, Dept. of Information Sciences, Kyoto Univ., Japan, 1980.

60. M. Nagao and T. Matsuyama, *A Structural Analysis of Complex Aerial Photographs* (Plenum Press, New York, 1980).

61. D.M. McKeown, W.A. Harvey and J. McDermott, "Rule-based interpretation of aerial imagery", *IEEE Trans. PAMI* **7** (1985) 570-585.

62. L. Massone, "SYRIO: a knowledge based approach to 2-D robotic vision", in *GWAI-83, 7th German Workshop on Artificial Intelligence, Informatik Fachberichte 76*, ed. B. Neumann (Springer-Verlag, 1983) pp. 60-68

63. J.H. Kim, D.W. Payton and K.E. Olin, "An expert system for object recognition in natural scenes", *Proc. 1st Conf. on Artificial Intelligence Applications*, 1984 pp. 170-175.

64. G.S. Duane, S.F. Venable, D.J. Richter and A.M. Wiedemann, "A production system for scene analysis and semantically guided segmentation", *SPIE Vol. 548, Applications of Artificial Intelligence II*, 1985, pp. 35-45.

65. D.L. McCracken, *A Production System Version of the HEARSAY II Speech Understanding System*, (Univ. Research Press, 1981).

66. R. De Mori, L. Lam and D. Probst, "Rule-based detection of speech features for automatic speech recognition", in *Fundamentals in Computer Understanding: Speech and Vision*, ed. J.-P. Haton (Cambridge Univ. Press, 1987) pp. 155-179.

67. N.V. Findler, ed., *Associate Networks* (Academic Press, New York, 1979).

68. R.B. Roberts and I.P. Goldstein, The FRL Primer, Memo No. 408, AI Lab., MIT, Cambridge, MA, 1977.

346    *Syntactic and Structural Pattern Recognition — Theory and Applications*

69. D.G. Bobrow and T. Winograd, "An overview of KRL, a knowledge representation language", *Cognitive Science* **1** (1977) 3-46.
70. R.J. Brachman and J.G. Schmolze, "An overview of the KL-ONE knowledge representation system", *Cognitive Science* **9** (1985) 171-216.
71. A.R. Hanson and E.M. Riseman, "Visions: a computer system for interpreting scenes", in *Computer Vision Systems*, eds. A.R. Hanson and E.M. Riseman (Academic Press, New York, 1978) pp. 303-333.
72. D.H. Ballard, C.M. Brown and J.A. Feldman, "An approach to knowledge directed image analysis", in Computer Vision Systems, eds. A.R. Hanson and E.M. Riseman (Academic Press, New York, 1978) pp. 664-670.
73. J.K. Tsotsos, J. Mylopoulos, H.D. Covvey and S.W. Zucker, "A framework for visual motion understanding", *IEEE Trans. PAMI* **2** (1980) 563-573.
74. H. Niemann, H. Bunke, I. Hofmann, G. Sagerer, F. Wolf and H. Feistel, "A knowledge based system for analysis of gated blood pool studies", *IEEE Trans. PAMI* **7** (1985) 246-259.
75. R.C. Shank, *Conceptual Information Processing* (North-Holland, 1975).
76. P.D. Green and A.R. Wood, "Knowledge based speech understanding: towards a representational approach", *Proc. ECAI-84*, 1984, pp. 337-340.
77. J.-P. Haton and J.P. Damestoy, "A frame language for the control of phonetic decoding in continuous speech recognition", *Proc. ICASSP*, Tampa, FL, 1985.
78. H.S. Lee and N.V. Thakor, "Frame-based understanding of ECG signals", *Proc. 1st Conf. on Intell. Applications*, 1984, pp. 624-629.
79. I. Bratko, *Prolog Programming for Artificial Intelligence* (Addison Wesley, Reading, MA, 1986).
80. P.H. Hayes, "The logic of frames", in *Frame Conceptions and Text Understanding*, ed. D. Metzing (de Gruyter, Berlin, 1979).
81. J. Malpas, *Prolog: A Relational Language and Its Applications* (Prentice Hall Int., London, 1987).
82. A. Deliyanni and R.A. Kowalski, "Logic and semantic networks", *CACM* **22** (1979) 184-192.
83. R.O. Duda, J. Gaschnig and P. Hart, "Model design in the prospector consultant system for mineral exploration", in *Expert Systems in the Micro-electronic Age*, ed. D. Michie (Edinburgh Univ. Press, 1979) pp. 153-167.
84. F. Di Primio and G. Brewka, "Babylon, kernel system of an integrated environment for expert system development and operation", *Proc. 5th Int. Workshop on Expert Systems and Their Applications*, Avignon, 1985, pp. 573-583.
85. K.S. Fu, *Syntactic Pattern Recognition and Applications* (Prentice Hall, 1982).
86. J. Dvorak, Artificial Intelligence Programming with Rule Based Systems, M.S. Thesis, Dept. of Computer Science, University of Bern, Switzerland, 1986 (in German).
87. J. Dvorak and H. Bunke, "Expert system shells and logic programming for the implementation of image analysis algorithms", *Proc. 5th Scandinavian Conf. on Image Analysis*, Stockholm, 1987, pp. 93-100.
88. H. Bunke and J. Dvorak, "Rule based expert system shells — new software tools for pattern recognition?" *Int. J. Pattern Recognition and Artificial Intelligence* **3** (1989) 85-102.
89. S. Greibach and J. Hopcroft, "Scattered contex grammars", *Journal of Comp. and System Sciences* **3** (1969) 233-247.
90. L.A. Zadeh, "Fuzzy sets", *Inf. Control* **8** (1965) 338-353.

91. H.J. Zimmermann, *Fuzzy Set Theory — and Its Applications* (Kluwer-Nijhoff Publishing, 1985).
92. A. Kandel, *Fuzzy Techniques in Pattern Recognition* (John Wiley, New York, 1982).
93. C. Tsatsoulis and K.S. Fu, "Modelling rule-based systems by stochastic programmed production systems", *Inf. Sci.* **36** (1985) 207-230.
94. S.A. Vere, "Relational production systems", *Artificial Intelligence* **8** (1977) 47-68.
95. B.M.E. Moret, "Decision trees and diagrams, *Comp. Surveys* **14** (1982) 593-623.
96. J.K. Mui and K.S. Fu, "Automated classification of nucleated blood-cells using a binary tree classifier", *IEEE Trans. PAMI* **2** (1980) 429-443.
97. G.R. Dattatreya and V.V.S. Sarma, "Bayesian and decision tree approaches for pattern recognition including feature measurement costs", *IEEE Trans. PAMI* **3** (1981) 293-298.
98. M. Ishizuka, K.S. Fu and T.P. Yao, "SPERIL: an expert system for damage assessment of existing structures", *Proc. 6th ICPR, Munich*, 1982, pp. 932-937.
99. L.N. Kanal and J.F. Lemmer, eds., *Uncertainty in Artificial Intelligence* (North-Holland, 1986).
100. M.M. Gupta, A. Kandel, W. Bandler and J.B. Kiszka, *Approximate Reasoning in Expert Systems* (North-Holland, 1985).
101. L.D. Erman, F. Hayes-Roth, V.R. Lesser and R. Reddy, "The HEARSAY-II speech-understanding system", *Comp. surveys* **12** (1980) 213-253.
102. M.D. Levine and S.I. Shaheen, "A modular computer vision system for picture segmentation and interpretation", *IEEE Trans. PAMI* **3** (1981) 540-556.
103. J. Pearl, *Heuristics: Intelligent Search Strategies for Computer Problem Solving* (Addison Wesley, Reading, MA, 1984).
104. S.M. Rubin, "Natural scene recognition using locus search", *Comp. Graphics and Image Processing* **13** (1980) 298-333.
105. B.T. Lowerre, The HARPY Speech Recognition System, Tech. Report, Carnegie Mellon University, Dept. of Computer Science, Pittsburgh, Pennsylvania, 1976.
106. S.E. Levinson, L.R. Rabiner and M.M. Sondhi, "An introduction to the application of the theory of probabilistic functions of a Markov process to automatic speech recognition", *Bell System Tech. Journal* **62** (1983) 1035-1074.
107. L.N. Kanal, "Problem-solving models and search strategies for pattern recognition", *IEEE Trans. PAMI* **1** (1979) 193-201.
108. P.A.N. Hall, "Equivalence between AND/OR graphs and context-free grammars", *CACM* **16** (1973) 444-445.
109. G. Stockman and L. Kanal, "Problem-reduction representation for the linguistic analysis of waveforms", *IEEE Trans. PAMI* **5** (1983) 287-298.
110. L.G. Shapiro and R.M. Haralick, "Structural descriptions and inexact matching", *IEEE Trans. PAMI* **3** (1981) 501-519.
111. H. Bunke and G. Allermann, "Inexact graph matching for structural pattern recognition", *Pattern Recognition Lett.* **1** (1983) 245-253.
112. D.H. Ballard and C.M. Brown, *Computer Vision* (Prentice Hall, Englewood Cliffs, NJ, 1982).

# 12

# COMBINING STATISTICAL AND STRUCTURAL METHODS

WEN-HSIANG TSAI

*Department of Computer and Information Science*
*National Chiao Tung University*
*Hsinchu, Taiwan 30050*
*Republic of China*

A review on existing approaches to combining statistical and structural pattern recognition methods is given. The review is based on a unified viewpoint about how attributes and statistical information are introduced into the structures and the relations of primitives and subpatterns. Emphasis is placed on the contribution of existing approaches to the development of a general combined pattern recognition theory.

## 1. INTRODUCTION

There are two major approaches to pattern recognition, namely, the statistical (or the decision-theoretic) method and the structural (or the syntactic) method[1]. Simply speaking, in the statistical method a set of characteristic measurements, usually called *features*, are extracted from the patterns, and the recognition of a pattern can be regarded as a process of feature space partitioning[2]. In the structural method, pattern structures are expressed as compositions of structural units, called *primitives*, and a pattern is recognized by *matching* its structural representation with that of a reference pattern or by *parsing* the representation according to a set of syntax rules[3].

An advantage of using the statistical method is the ease of handling pattern deformations caused by noise or distortion. This advantage comes from the use of numerical feature data and probability distribution functions. Another advantage is the applicability of well-established statistical or decision theory. However, the statistical method is basically classification-oriented; it provides no pattern description. Certain pattern structures are also difficult to describe with numerical features, causing ineffectiveness in feature extraction.

The above-mentioned shortcomings of the statistical method are not found in the structural method. However, in the conventional structural method which originates from the formal language theory, discrete symbols are used to represent pattern primitives, resulting in inconvenience in handling numerical types of pattern characteristics. Also, the lack of statistical consideration makes the method incapable of handling pattern noise or distortion. Finally, the pattern representations and the syntax rules for describing complicated pattern structures are often found to be so complex that time-consuming pattern matching or parsing is required.

From the above discussion, it is seen that the statistical and the structural methods are complementary. Furthermore, neither the statistical nor the structural method can solve certain application problems. Therefore, it has been advocated for a long time that the two methods should be combined[4−6]. It is desirable to develop a *combined approach* which keeps the advantages of both methods, removes their respective shortcomings, and offers a general theory for most pattern recognition applications.

In the past decade, improvement on the conventional structural method has been studied extensively. Most proposed approaches try to include error-handling capabilities into the structural method. These approaches, though unable to offer a general combined theory, provide a basis for doing so, as can be seen from recent progress in this aspect[6-14].

In this chapter, possible ways of introducing statistical pattern recognition techniques into the structural method are first identified. This leads to a unified viewpoint for reviewing various existing approaches which contribute to the desirable combined pattern recognition theory. Emphasis is put on the development of the theoretical structure. Applications[3,15], which are solved by the use of separate statistical and structural analysis techniques instead of by a single combined approach are not discussed. Finally, a summary is included.

## 2. HOW TO INTRODUCE STATISTICAL PATTERN RECOGNITION TECHNIQUES INTO THE STRUCTURAL METHOD

### 2.1. Basic Concepts

Structurally, a pattern may be decomposed into a set of *subpatterns*, and a subpattern may be decomposed further into other subpatterns or primitives. There may also exist certain relationships among primitives and subpatterns. Depending on the types of such relationships, at least three types of data structures have been used for pattern representation, namely, string, tree and graph.

The string is suitable for representing a pattern structure whose primitives are concatenated in a sequential order. An example is a shape boundary with boundary curve segments as the primitives. The tree or the graph is suitable for representing a pattern structure whose primitives are connected in a 2-D or a 3-D fashion.

Two major techniques in structural pattern recognition are matching and parsing. The former is applicable to cases where each single pattern may be considered as a pattern class. For example, if we represent each pattern by a string of primitives, then we can recognize a pattern by matching its string representation with those of the reference patterns. Parsing or syntax analysis is suitable for cases where each pattern class consists of a set of structurally similar patterns which can be described by a pattern grammar. Parsing an input pattern representation means to determine if the representation is syntactically acceptable by the grammar, or equivalently, to decide if the pattern belongs structurally to the pattern class.

In this chapter, we will focus on matching and parsing patterns represented by strings, emphasizing how to include statistical pattern recognition techniques into the conventional string analysis methods. No discussion on the matching or parsing of tree and graph representations will be included.

Conventionally, each pattern primitive is denoted by a symbol, and a pattern with $n$ concatenated primitives is denoted by a string of symbols $x = a_1 a_2 \ldots a_n$. Recognition of the pattern can thus be transformed into matching $x$ with the string of symbols $y = b_1 b_2 \ldots b_m$ of each reference pattern, or into parsing $x$ according to the grammar $G$ describing the structure of each pattern class. A grammar $G$ is a 4-tuple $G = (V_N, V_T, S, P)$ where $V_N$ is a set of *nonterminal* symbols, $V_T$ is a set of *terminal* symbols, $S \in V_N$ is the start symbol and $P$ is a set of production rules of the form $\alpha \to \beta, \alpha, \beta \in (V_N \cup V_T)^*$. Each terminal symbol may be considered to represent a primitive, and each nonterminal symbol a subpattern. The start symbol $S$ may be considered to represent the whole pattern.

The previously mentioned weak points of the conventional structural method stem partially from the *discreteness* implicitly carried by the symbols (terminals or nonterminals) and the production rules. Such discreteness implies that only discrete primitives, subpatterns, and thus pattern structures, can be analyzed. Continuous types of numerical features extracted from the primitives or the subpatterns, if they are to be analyzed by the conventional string analysis method, must be discretized first and then transformed into symbols for use in matching or parsing. This increases rounding or truncation errors and reduces recognition accuracy. On the other hand, only *exact* matching or parsing is allowed in the conventional string analysis method. Thus structural variations which come from pattern noise or distortion and result in the changes of string symbols cannot be handled easily.

### 2.2. Possible Ways to Introduce Statistical Techniques into the String Analysis Method

If a pattern is considered to consist structurally of primitives, subpatterns and their relations, we can remove the two weak points, discreteness and exactness, of the conventional string analysis method by introducing *numerical features* (called *attributes* in the structural method) and *statistical information* into the symbolic representations for the primitives, subpatterns and relations of each pattern. This provides a new and unified viewpoint, as mentioned before, for reviewing the various approaches proposed for improving the conventional structural method and for combining the statistical and the structural methods. More specific descriptions of the possible ways to include attributes and statistics into pattern structures are discussed in the following.

### 2.2.1. Including statistical information in primitive structures

Inclusion of statistical information (or simply, statistics) in primitive structures facilitates the analysis of discrete primitive structure variations caused by noise or distortion. Symbolically, this is equivalent to allowing a symbol in a string to transform into another symbol according to a set of possible operations, such as insertions, deletions, substitutions, transpositions, etc. These operations are usually called *error transformations*, and the analysis techniques are called *error-correcting matching* or *parsing*[3]. Depending on the statistics introduced into the error transformations, various types of error-correcting string analysis techniques can be identified, such as nonweighted, weighted, or probabilistic error correction, etc. Error-correcting analysis removes partially the weakness of exactness from the conventional structural method and improves the error-handling capability of the method. Detailed discussions on error-correcting parsing and matching can be found in Chapters 3 and 5, respectively.

### 2.2.2. Including statistics in subpattern structures

Each production rule $\alpha \rightarrow \beta$ includes at least one nonterminal in its left-hand side $\alpha$. For context-free grammars, $\alpha$ is exactly a nonterminal $A$. Therefore, one way to introduce statistics into subpattern structures is to use the so-called stochastic production rules[3] because each nonterminal symbol $A$ represents a subpattern semantically. A stochastic production rule for a context-free grammar is of the form $A \overset{p}{\rightarrow} \beta$ where $p$ is a probability value associated with the rule and may be considered in certain cases to specify the occurrence probability of the subpattern represented by $A$. Use of multiple stochastic production rules all with an identical nonterminal $A$ on the left-hand side of the rules is equivalent to allowing probabilistic structure variations of the subpattern represented by $A$. When the string representation of a given pattern is parsed and accepted by a stochastic context-free grammar, a *pattern occurrence probability* value can also be generated, which is just the product of the probability values of all the production rules used in the parsing process[3]. Such *stochastic parsing* provides a partial solution to the discreteness problem inherent in the use of conventional nonstochastic production rules. Detailed discussions on stochastic grammars can also be found in Chapter 2.

### 2.2.3. Including attributes and statistics in primitive representations

Conventionally, only symbols are used for primitive representation. A generalization is to use a 2-tuple $(a, V)$ to represent a primitive, where in addition to the conventional symbol $a$ used to represent the primitive structure, a vector $V$ is included to denote the set of numerical attributes which may be extracted to specify other characteristics of the primitive. This increases flexibility in primitive representation and extraction; any non-structural primitive features may be included in $V$, resulting in easier treatment of noise or distortion. The main concern here is how to modify the conventional string matching and parsing methods to process the additional attribute vectors. Furthermore, statistical pattern recognition techniques may also be applied to the attribute vectors for pattern classification. Several investigations of this primitive generalization for structural pattern recognition have been reported[7-13,16-18].

### 2.2.4. Including attributes and statistics in subpattern representations

A subpattern may also possess certain attributes which are useful for pattern discrimination. They can usually be expressed or computed in terms of the attributes of the composite primitives of the subpattern. One way to make possible the computation of subpattern attributes *during the parsing process* is to use the attributed grammar[7-13]; see also Chapter 2 of this book. In an attributed grammar, each production rule includes a *semantic rule* in addition to the conventional *syntactic production rule* used in nonattributed grammars. For example, in an attributed context-free grammar, a production rule is of the form

$$A \rightarrow \beta, \quad V(A) \leftarrow f(V(\beta), V')$$

where $V(A)$ is the attribute vector of nonterminal $A$, which is computed by the function (or algorithm) $f$ using the attributes of $\beta$ and any other available information $V'$ as the input. The use of semantic rules makes it possible to compute subpattern and pattern attributes for statistical pattern recognition in addition to syntactic parsing.

### 2.2.5. Including attributes and statistics in primitive and subpattern relations

The concatenation relation is implicitly assumed in most string representations. But generalization can be found in certain investigations[10-12,16].

The use of subpattern relations has also been reported[11,12]. A representational generalization here is to use a 2-tuple $(b, U)$ to represent a primitive or a subpattern relation, where $b$ denotes the structure of the relation and $U$ denotes the attribute vector associated with the relation.

## 2.3. String Representation Schemes

In the conventional *symbolic string* representation $x = a_1 a_2 \ldots a_n$ for a pattern consisting of $n$ primitives $p_1, p_2, \ldots, p_n$, neither primitive attributes nor inter-primitive relations are included. When attributes are included in the primitive representations, the resulting pattern representation is called an *attributed string* and is denoted by the form $x = (a_1, V_1)(a_2, V_2) \ldots (a_n, V_n)$ where $V_i$ is the attribute vector of primitive $p_i$. In the use of symbolic strings and attributed strings, concatenation is implicitly assumed to be the only type of primitive relation. A more general type of string representation is an *attributed string with attributed relations*, denoted by

$$x = (a_1, V_1)(r_1, W_1)(a_2, V_2)(r_2, W_2)(a_3, V_3) \ldots (r_{n-1}, W_{n-1})(a_n, V_n) \, ,$$

where $(r_j, W_j)$ specifies the relation between primitives $p_j$ and $p_{j+1}$ with $r_j$ representing the discrete structure of the relation and $W_j$ specifying the vector of the attributes extracted from the relation. Attributed strings with various types of primitive and relation structures and attributes will be discussed later when various approaches are reviewed.

## 3. A SURVEY OF EXISTING STRUCTURAL METHODS WHICH INCLUDE STATISTICAL PATTERN RECOGNITION TECHNIQUES

In this section, existing structural methods which use statistical pattern recognition techniques are reviewed briefly from the unified viewpoint as discussed in Sec. 2. Special attention is paid to their possible contribution to the desirable general combined pattern recognition theory.

## 3.1. Error-Correcting Symbolic String Matching

Polynomial-time dynamic programming algorithms were proposed in Refs. 19 and 20 to solve the string-to-string error correction problem encountered mainly in language compiling or translation. Three types of error-correcting transformation, namely, substitution (also called change), deletion and insertion, are defined. The distance between two symbolic strings $x$ and $y$ (also called the *Levenshtein distance*) is defined as the smallest number of transformations required to derive $y$ from $x$ (or $x$ from $y$). No weights are assigned to the error transformations, which means that the three types of errors are implicitly assumed to have an equal probability of occurring.

Lu and Fu[21] extended the Levenshtein distance to two weighted versions called *weighted Levenshtein distance* and *weighted distance* for use in string-to-string clustering. The weighted Levenshtein distance between symbolic strings $x$ and $y$ is defined, after assigning non-negative weights to different types of transformations, as the minimum of the total weights of all the transformation sequences taking $x$ to $y$. The weighted distance is defined similarly except that the weights are assigned to reflect the difference of the same type of error made on different symbols. More details are given in Chapter 5 of this book.

Weighted error-correcting symbolic string matching can also be extended to probabilistic matching by generalizing weighted error transformations to probabilistic ones. But so far probabilistic error transformations have been defined for use in error-correcting string parsing[22]. Note that the use of nonweighted, weighted and probabilistic error transformations is just a form of introducing statistic information into the primitive structures (represented by terminal symbols).

## 3.2. Error-Correcting Symbolic String Parsing

All the Levenshtein, weighted Levenshtein and weighted distances defined previously can be used as string-to-string similarity measures in error-correcting symbolic string parsing. The main concern here is how to construct a proper parsing algorithm from a grammar $G$ by which an input erroneous string $x$ can be corrected optimally during parsing in the sense of computing a minimum distance $d(x, G)$ from $x$ to $G$ which actually is the distance from $x$ to an error-free string $y$ accepted by $G$.

Aho and Peterson[23] used the Levenshtein distance in minimum-distance error-correcting parsing of context-free languages. Fung and Fu[24] extended the approach to cover probabilistic error transformations but only substitution errors were considered. A maximum-likelihood error-correcting parsing algorithm constructed from the Cocke-Younger-Kasami parser for context-free languages was proposed. Thomason and Gonzalez[25] described a further extension to include insertion and deletion errors. Error-correcting parsing for context-free programmed and context-sensitive languages has also been proposed[3,26].

## 3.3. Symbolic String Parsing Using Stochastic Grammars

Stochastic grammars have been suggested to model the uncertainty and the randomness of the strings accepted by grammars[3,27-30]. By assigning appropriate probability values to the production rules of a given grammar $G$, each string accepted by $G$ can be associated with a string probability $p(x)$ which can be used to specify the pattern occurrence probability of $x$ within the pattern class represented by $G$.

Let the language accepted by grammar $G$ be denoted as $L(G)$, and let each stochastic production rule be denoted as $\alpha_i \xrightarrow{p_{ij}} \beta_j$, then the following conditions should be satisfied in a stochastic grammar:

$$(1) \sum_{x \in L(G)} p(x) = 1 \; ; \quad (2) \; 0 \leq p_{ij} \leq 1 \; ; \quad (3) \sum_{j=1}^{n_i} p_{ij} = 1$$

where $n_i$ is the total number of production rules with $\alpha_i$ appearing in the left-hand sides of the rules. Weighted grammars[31] and discriminant grammars[32] are special cases of stochastic grammars with the probability values replaced by weights and numbers, respectively. In the remainder of this chapter, to simplify theoretic description, we assume that all grammars mentioned are unambiguous.

For the case where a string may be accepted by multiple grammars, if $P(x|G_i)$ specifies the pattern occurrence probability that $x$ comes from $L(G_i)$, and if $P(G_i)$ denotes the *a priori* probability for the pattern class represented by $G$, then classification of $x$ (i.e. assignment of $x$ to a language $L(G_i)$) can be performed in a way similar to the Bayes' decision rule in statistical pattern recognition:

$$\text{assign } x \text{ to } L(G_k) \text{ if } p(x|G_k)P(G_k) = \max_i p(x|G_i)P(G_i) \; .$$

Note that $p(x|G_i) = 0$ if $x$ does not belong to $L(G_i)$.

Therefore, the stochastic grammar as discussed above may be considered as a tool for combining structural and statistical methods in dealing with discrete pattern structures. More specifically, while the use of the production rules facilitates the syntax analysis of pattern structures, the computation of pattern occurrence probability values makes statistical classification possible. Inference of production rule probability values ($p_{ij}$ above) has also been proposed[30,33,34]. Note that the use of stochastic production rules allows implicitly the inclusion of subpattern variations, as mentioned in Sec. 2.2.2. Note too that stochastic production rules can also be used to cover primitive structure variations due to substitutions. Inference of stochastic grammars is discussed in Chapter 9.

## 3.4. Stochastic Error-Correcting Symbolic String Parsing

Lu and Fu[22] combined the use of error-correcting parsing and stochastic grammars to recognize noisy patterns. The recognition scheme is based on a stochastic pattern deformational model. It may be regarded that the stochastic grammar for each pattern class accepts a set of error-free strings, and error-correcting parsing is used to handle primitive deformations. A similar approach is found in Ref. 35. Let $x$ be an input noisy string which is supposed to be a deformed version of an error-free string $y$ accepted by pattern grammar $G$, a parsing algorithm was proposed to search for $y$ in $L(G)$, and to compute the pattern occurrence probability $p(y|G)$ for $y$ to be in $L(G)$ as well as the deformation probability $q(x|y)$ of $x$ from $y$. Let $p(x|G) = q(x|y)p(y|G)$ be called the *pattern deformation probability of $x$ in $L(G)$*. When more than one grammar is used to assign an input noisy pattern $x$ to a pattern class, the Bayes' decision rule described in Sec. 3.3 can again be used.

The above syntax analysis and error-correcting parsers will be called *stochastic error-correcting parsing*. Use of such a syntax analysis scheme is another step toward the goal of developing a combined pattern recognition theory, because both subpattern and primitive variations can be covered.

On the other hand, stochastic error correction can also be accomplished by language translation. Thomason[36] proposed a stochastic syntax-directed translation scheme for transforming an input erroneous string into its error-free form. Types of errors considered include substitution, insertion and deletion. Context-free grammars are used in the translation. An advantage is that desirable error-free strings can be recovered as the output. A similar approach is found in Ref. 47. More discussions on stochastic syntax-directed translation can be found in Chapter 1.

## 3.5. Error-Correcting Attributed String Matching

Tsai and Yu[18] presented a method for error-correcting matching of attributed strings with concatenation relations implicitly assumed. The primitive representation consists of a single type of primitive structure, the line segment, and two primitive attributes, the length and the direction of the line segment. In addition to the conventional error-correcting operations (substitutions, deletions and insertions), a new type of operation, called merge, was proposed to solve certain primitive-splitting problems caused by noise or distortion. The merge operation was shown to be a generalization of the conventional substitution operation. Since only a single structure type (line segment) is used, the weights of error transformations were defined in terms of the primitive attributes (line-segment lengths and directions). String-to-string distances can be computed from a modified version of the Wagner and Fischer algorithm[19].

Fu[10] discussed a more general weighted distance measure for attributed strings with multiple primitive structures. The distance is defined as $d(x, y) = a * d_L(x, y) + b * d_A(x', y')$ where $a$ and $b$ are two weighting coefficients, $d_L(x, y)$ is the Levenshtein distance between $x$ and $y$, and $d_A(x', y')$ is an attribute distance between $x$ and $y$ after the error transformations from $x$ to $y$ are performed (i.e. after the symbolic differences between $x$ and $y$ are removed), with $x'$ and $y'$ being the transformed versions of $x$ and $y$, respectively. A possible version for $d_A$ could be defined as a weighted distance of the attribute vectors of $x'$ and $y'$:

$$d_A(x', y') = \sum_{i=1}^{n} w_i d(V_i', U_i')$$

where $x' = (a_1', V_1')(a_2', V_2') \ldots (a_n', V_n')$, $y' = (b_1', U_1')(b_2', U_2') \ldots (b_n', U_n')$. The applicability of this distance measure to practical problems still has to be examined.

### 3.6. Stochastic Error-Correcting Attributed String Parsing

Tsai and Fu[17] proposed a pattern deformational model based on which stochastic error-correcting parsing of attributed strings (and trees) is made possible. The approach is a generalization of the stochastic error-correcting symbolic string parsing discussed in Sec. 3.4 in the aspect of including primitive attributes, although syntactically only substitution errors were considered (the resulting pattern deformation is called *structure-preserved deformation*).

Given two attributed strings $x = (a_1, V_1)(a_2, V_2) \ldots (a_n, V_n)$ and $y = (b_1, U_1)(b_2, U_2) \ldots (b_n, U_n)$ under the structure preserving condition that each $(a_i, V_i)$ is an independent observed version of $(b_i, U_i)$, the pattern deformation probability $q(x|y)$ of $x$ from $y$ was derived to be

$$q(x|y) = \sum_{i=1}^{n} p(U_i|a_i, b_i) p(a_i|b_i)$$

where $p(a_i|b_i)$ is the probability for $b_i$ to deform structurally into $a_i$, and $p(U_i|a_i,b_i)$ is the probability for $U_i$ to be observed under the condition that $U_i$ is an attribute vector of $a_i$ coming from $b_i$. String $y$ above may be regarded as an error-free string accepted by a stochastic grammar $G$ with pattern occurrence probability $p(y|G)$. Then the pattern deformation probability of $x$ from $y$ in the pattern class specified by $G$ is $p(x|G) = q(x|y)p(y|G)$. And the Bayes' decision rule described in Sec. 3.3 can again be used for pattern recognition in multiclass cases.

The above approach is not general enough to cover deletion and substitution errors. The generalization seems possible if the stochastic model by Lu and Fu[22] can be included into the above deformational model. Note that primitive attributes are involved here, and that the relevant statistical information is included in the term $p(U_i|a_i,b_i)$ above.

### 3.7. Attributed String Parsing Using Attributed Grammars

The attributed grammar has been suggested as a good tool for combining the structural and statistical methods for pattern recognition[8,10,13,16], although it has also been used for pattern recognition applications with less emphasis on theoretic combination of the two conventional methods[7,11,12,16].

Tang and Huang[7] used the attributed grammar for *image creation* which is a process of utilizing the attributed grammar to extract relevant primitives out of an input picture and to combine them into meaningful target patterns. An application example of line segment extraction was included. A similar concept, called primitive-extraction-embedded (PEE) parsing, is applied by You and Fu[11,12] to shape recognition. In both approaches, the semantic rules are employed mainly as an aid to primitive extraction. Computed subpattern attributes are not used for statistical classification but for nonterminal derivation in the parsing. Tai and Fu[16] used attributed grammars for semantic syntax-directed translation but only translation from error-free patterns to noisy patterns was demonstrated, which essentially is equivalent to the image creation concept. The translation scheme is not suitable for recognizing noisy patterns (i.e. for correcting noisy patterns into error-free ones). Fu[10,13] mentioned the possibility of formulating a statistical classification problem in terms of an attributed grammar. The use of semantic rules was also shown useful in reducing the complexity of syntax rules (and so in changing the grammar into a simpler type), although similar observation has been reported elsewhere[8,16,17].

Tsai and Fu[8] provided a detailed theoretic analysis on the combined approach using attributed grammars. The grammars are supposed to be stochastic and context-free. The semantic rules are used for *synthesizing* subpattern as well as pattern attributes from low-level primitive attributes, forming a so-called *total attribute vector*. Let $x$ be an input attributed string $x = (a_1, V_1)(a_2, V_2) \ldots (a_n, V_n)$, and let $y$ denote the symbolic string $a_1 a_2 \ldots a_n$ which represents the structural part of the pattern represented by $x$. After $y$ is parsed and accepted by the syntax rules of a stochastic context-free attributed grammar $G$, a pattern occurrence probability $p(y|G)$ for $y$ is computed which is just the product of the probability values associated with all the production rules used in the parsing of $y$. Meanwhile, a total attribute vector $X$ is also synthesized, using the semantic rules of $G$. A probability value $p(X|y, G)$ may be introduced to specify the occurrence probability of $X$ under the structure $y$ within the pattern class specified by $G$. Then the pattern deformation probability of $x$ in the class of $G$ is $p(x|G) = p(X|y, G)p(y|G)$. Once again the Bayes' decision rule in Sec. 3.3 can be used for multiclass statistical classification.

It is not difficult to figure out that if no substitution error is allowed in the pattern deformational model proposed by Tsai and Fu[17], then the resulting stochastic attributed string parsing method (described in Sec. 3.6) is just a special case of the attributed grammar approach[8] described above. However, on the contrary, it seems that a more general combined pattern recognition theory can be based on a combination of the stochastic model proposed by Lu and Fu[22] described in Sec. 3.4 and the attribute grammar theory by Tsai and Fu[8] described above.

## 3.8. Analysis of Attributed Strings with Relations

The string representations mentioned in most studies are assumed implicitly to include structural concatenation relations among the primitives. Concatenation relations with angle attributes were used in Refs. 11 and 12, but they are treated as primitives in the PEE parsing process. More general attributed concatenation relations were defined in Refs. 10 and 16 as an extension of Ref. 37. Tai and Fu[16] included relation descriptions in the semantic parts of an attributed grammar to reduce grammatical complexity. They also defined a distance measure for attributed strings with attributed relations from a translational point of view. General matching and parsing algorithms for attributed strings with attributed relations have yet to be developed.

## 4. CONCLUSIONS

A summary of previous discussions is included in Table 1. Existing approaches which contribute to the desired combined theory are classified into nine types, six of parsing and three of matching. For each type, the techniques of including attributes and statistical information in primitive, subpattern and relation representations are identified. Also included are examples of typical studies of each type.

Recent developments in syntactic pattern recognition[38−46] reveal the widespread use of attributed trees and graphs, and attributed tree and graph grammars which are extensions of 1-D attributed strings and string grammars. For string parsing, the previous unified review of existing approaches indicates that the stochastic error-correcting attributed string grammar is the most general tool for developing a combined theory. Tai and Fu[16] show that the attributed finite-state grammar may be used as the normal form for attributed string parsing because the inclusion of attributes eliminates the need for more complicated grammars. However, a general probabilistic model for attributed string parsing using the stochastic error-correcting attributed string grammar is still lacking. The difficulty seems to lie partially in the modeling of probabilistic error transformations for insertions and deletions involving both primitive structures and attributes. Assuming that this desired model was already established, the following is a possible description of the combined pattern recognition procedure using a stochastic error-correcting attributed string grammar $G$.

Given an input noisy attributed string $x$ which includes $y$ as the symbolic string, use the grammar to parse $x$. The syntax analysis process is stochastic and error-correcting. Let $z$ be the error-free version of $y$ accepted by $G$. Then the pattern deformation probability of $x$ in the class represented by $G$ is $p(x|G) = p(X|z,G)q(y|z,G)p(z|G)$, where $p(z|G)$ is computed in terms of production rule probability values, $q(y|z,G)$ is computed in terms of error transformation probability values, and $p(X|z,G)$ is the attribute occurrence probability value. And the Bayes' decision rule for statistical classification is:

$$\text{assign } x \text{ to } G_k \text{ if } p(x|G_k)P(G_k) = \max_i p(x|G_i)P(G_i) \ .$$

Table 1. Techniques used in existing approaches for combining the statistical and the structural pattern recognition methods (only typical papers dealing with pattern recognition problems are included; the list is not exhaustive).

| | | Types of existing approaches | Including statistics in primitive structures | Including statistics in primitive attributes | Including statistics in sub-pattern structures | Including statistics in sub-pattern attributes | Including statistics in relation structures and attributes | Examples of related studies (for string languages only) |
|---|---|---|---|---|---|---|---|---|
| parsing | | Error-correcting symbolic string parsing | X | | | | | Fung and Fu[24], Thomason and Gonzalez[25], Tanaka and Fu[26]. |
| | | Symbolic string parsing using stochastic grammars | | | X | | | Fu and Huang[27], Booth and Thompson[28], Lee and Fu[29], Fu[30] |
| | | Stochastic error-correcting symbolic string parsing | X | | X | | | Thompson[35], Lu and Fu[22], Thomason[36], Fan and Fu[47] |
| | | Stochastic error-correcting attributed string parsing | X | X | X | | | Tsai and Fu[17] |
| | | Attributed string parsing using stochastic attributed grammars | | X | X | X | | Tang and Huang[7], Tsai and Fu[8], Fu[10], You and Fu[11,12], Tai and Fu[16] |
| | | Error-correcting attributed string parsing using stochastic attributed grammars | X | X | X | X | | None |
| matching | | Error-correcting symbolic string matching | X | | | | | Lu and Fu[21] |
| | | Error-correcting attributed string matching | | X | | | | Fu[10], Tsai and Yu[18] |
| | | Analysis of attributed strings with relations | X | X | | | X | You and Fu[11,12], Fu[10], Tai and Fu[16] |

## REFERENCES

1. T.Y. Young and K.S. Fu, eds., *Handbook of Pattern Recognition and Image Processing*, (Academic Press, New York, 1986).

2. P.A. Devijver and J. Kittler, *Pattern Recognition: A Statistical Approach* (Prentice-Hall, Englewood Cliffs, NJ, 1982).

3. K.S. Fu, *Syntactic Pattern Recognition and Applications* (Prentice-Hall, Englewood Cliffs, NJ, 1982).

4. L. Kanal and B. Chandrasekaran, "On linguistic, statistical and mixed models for pattern recognition", *Int. Conf. Frontiers of Pattern Recognition*, 1972, pp. 161-185.

5. U. Grenander, "A unified approach to pattern analysis", in *Advances in Computers*, *Vol. 10* (Academic Press, New York, 1970).

6. W.H. Tsai and K.S. Fu, "Recognition of patterns with syntactic and semantic deformations", Tech. Report, TR-EE 79-48, School of Electr. Eng., Purdue Univ., West Lafayette, IN, Dec. 1979.

7. G.Y. Tang and T.S. Huang, "A syntactic-semantic approach to image understanding and creation", *IEEE Trans. PAMI* **1** (1979) 135-144.

8. W.H. Tsai and K.S. Fu, "Attributed grammar — a tool for combining syntactic and statistical approaches to pattern recognition", *IEEE Trans. SMC*, **10** (1980) 873-855; also in *Context-Directed Pattern Recognition and Machine Intelligence Techniques for Information Processing*, eds. Y.H. Pao and G.W. Ernst (IEEE Comput. Soc. Press, Silver Spring, MD, 1982), pp. 79-91.

9. W.H. Tsai and K.S. Fu, "A syntactic-statistical approach to recognition of industrial parts", *Proc. 5th ICPR*, Miami Beach, Florida, Dec. 1980, pp. 251-259.

10. K.S. Fu, "A step towards unification of syntactic and statistical pattern recognition", *IEEE Trans. PAMI* **5** (1983) 200-205.

11. K.C. You and K.S. Fu, "A syntactic approach to shape recognition using attributed grammar", *IEEE Trans. SMC* **9** (1979) 334-345.

12. K.C. You and K.S. Fu, "Distorted shape recognition using attributed grammars and error-correcting techniques", *CGIP* **12** (1980) 1-16.

13. K.S. Fu, "Attributed grammars for pattern recognition - A general (syntactic-semantic) approach", *Proc. 1982 PRIP Conf.*, Las Vegas, Nevada, June 1982, pp. 18-27.

14. K.S. Fu, "A syntactic-semantic approach to pictorial pattern analysis", in *Pictorial Data Analysis*, ed. R.M. Haralick, (Springer-Verlag, Berlin, 1983) pp. 335-349.

15. B. Duerr, W. Haettich, H. Tropf and G. Winkler, "A combination of statistical and syntactic pattern recognition applied to classification of unconstrained handwritten numerals", *Pattern Recognition* **12** (1980) 189-199.

16. J.W. Tai and K.S. Fu, "Semantic syntax-directed translation for pictorial pattern recognition", *Proc. 6th ICPR*, Munich, Germany, Oct. 1982, pp. 169-171; also Technical Report TR-EE-81-38, School of Electr. Eng., Purdue University, West Lafayette, IN, Oct. 1981.

17. W.H. Tsai and K.S. Fu, "A pattern of deformational model and Bayes error-correcting recognition system", *IEEE Trans. SMC* **9** (1979) 745-756.

18. W.H. Tsai and S.S. Yu, "Attributed string matching with merging for shape recognition", *IEEE Trans. PAMI* **7** (1985) 453-462.

19. R.A. Wagner and M.J. Fischer, "The string-to-string correction problem", *J. ACM* **21** (1974) 168-173.

20. R. Lowrance and R.A. Wagner, "An extension of the string-to-string correction problem", *J. ACM* **22** (1975) 177-183.

21. S.Y. Lu and K.S. Fu, "A sentence to sentence clustering procedure for pattern analysis", *IEEE Trans. SMC* **8** (1978) 381-389.

22. S.Y. Lu and K.S. Fu, "Stochastic error-correcting syntax analysis for recognition of noisy patterns", *IEEE Trans. Comput.* **26** (1977) 1268-1276.

23. A.V. Aho and T.G. Peterson, "A minimum-distance error-correcting parser for context-free languages", *SIAM J. Computing* **4** (1972) 305-312.

24. L.W. Fung and K.S. Fu, "Stochastic syntactic decoding for pattern classification", *IEEE Trans. Comput.* **24** (1975) 662-669.

25. M.G. Thomason and R.C. Gonzalez, "Syntactic recognition of imperfectly specified patterns", *IEEE Trans. Comput.* **24** (1975) 93-95.

26. E. Tanaka and K.S. Fu, "Error-correcting parsers for formal languages", *IEEE Trans. Comput.* **27** (1978) 605-616.

27. K.S. Fu and T. Huang, "Stochastic grammars and languages", *Int. J. Comput. Inform. Sci.* **1** (1972) 135-170.

28. T.L. Booth and R.A. Thompson, "Applying probability measures to abstract languages", *IEEE Trans. Comput.* **22** (1973) 442-450.

29. H.C. Lee and K.S. Fu, "A stochastic syntax analysis procedure and its application to pattern classification", *IEEE Trans. Comput.* **21** (1972) 660-666.

30. K.S. Fu "Stochastic language for picture analysis", *CGIP* **2** (1973) 433-453.

31. A. Saloma, "Probabilistic and weighted grammars", *Info. Control* **15** (1969) 529-544.

32. C. Page and A. Filipski, "Discriminant grammars: an alternative to parsing for pattern classification", *Proc. IEEE Workshop on Picture Data Description and Management*, Chicago, Illinois, Apr. 1977, pp. 10-15.

33. H.C. Lee and K.S. Fu, "A syntactic pattern recognition with learning capability", *4th Int. Symp. Comput. Inf. Sci.*, Miami Beach, Florida, Dec. 1973; also in *Information System COINS IV*, ed. J.T. Tou (Academic Press, New York, 1974) pp. 425-449

34. R.A. Thompson, "Determination of probabilistic grammars for functionally specified probability-measure languages", *IEEE Trans. Comput.* **23** (1974) 603-614.

35. R.A. Thompson, "Language correction using probabilistic grammars", *IEEE Trans. Comput.* **25** (1976) 275-286.

36. M.G. Thomason, "Stochastic syntax-directed translation schemata for correction of errors in context-free languages", *IEEE Trans. Comput.* **24** (1975) 1211-1216.

37. A.C. Shaw, "A formal picture description scheme as a basis for picture processing system", *Info. Control* **14** (1969) 9-52.

38. H. Bunke and A. Sanfeliu, "Introduction", *Special Issue on Syntactic Pattern Recognition, Pattern Recognition* **19** (1986) 249-254.

39. H. Bunke, "Attributed programmed graph grammars and their applications to schematic diagram interpretation", *IEEE Trans. PAMI* **4** (1982) 574-582.

40. Q.Y. Shi and K.S. Fu, "Parsing and translation of (attributed) expansive graph languages for scene analysis", *IEEE Trans. PAMI* **5** (1983) 472-484.

41. W.H. Tsai and K.S. Fu, "Error-correcting isomorphism of attributed relational graphs for pattern analysis", *IEEE Trans. SMC* **9** (1979) 745-756.

42. W.H. Tsai and K.S. Fu, "Subgraph error-correcting isomorphisms for syntactic pattern recognition", *IEEE Trans. SMC* **13** (1983) 48-62.

43. A. Sanfeliu and K.S. Fu, "A distance measure between attributed relational graphs for pattern recognition", *IEEE Trans. SMC* **13** (1983) 353-362.

44. Q.Y. Shi and K.S. Fu, "Efficient error-correcting parsing for (attributed and stochastic) tree grammars", *Inform. Sci.* **26** (1982) 159-188.

45. J.W. Tai, "Attributed parallel tree grammars and tree automata for syntactic pattern recognition", *Proc. 5th ICPR*, Miami Beach, Florida, Dec. 1980, pp. 1001-1003.

46. W.H. Tsai and K.S. Fu, "Image segmentation and recognition by texture discrimination: a syntactic approach", *Proc. 4th IJCPR*, Kyoto, Japan, Nov. 1978, pp. 560-564.

47. T.I. Fan and K.S. Fu, "A syntactic approach to time-varying image analysis", *CGIP* **11** (1979) 138-149.

# PART II: APPLICATIONS

# 13

# INDUSTRIAL APPLICATIONS

HENRY S. BAIRD
*AT&T Bell Laboratories*
*600 Mountain Ave*
*Murray Hill, NJ 07974*
*USA*

The extent to which research on syntactic and structural pattern recognition has been reduced to practice is described. Useful applications and exploitation in commercial products are surveyed, and experiences of applications engineers are related. Promising new application areas, as well as persistent obstacles, are pointed out.

## 1. INTRODUCTION

Industrial applications of syntactic and structural pattern recognition (SSPR) ideas are surveyed in this chapter. The question is posed: to what extent, and through what difficulties, have these theories been reduced to practice? Experiences of application engineers are related, and some obstacles to the spread of SSPR techniques are identified, along with some promising new application fields.

"Industrial" will be interpreted broadly here to include any application, not only in factories (inspection and robotics), but in offices (optical character recognition) and in exotic niches such as remote sensing and biomedicine. Since other chapters in this volume cover Chinese character recognition and line drawing analysis, they will be omitted here. Also, to limit the scope of discussion, we will focus on imagery and exclude waveform analysis, which arises in the interpretation of speech, EEGs and ECGs (see Chapter 18 in this volume).

"Applications" will be interpreted rather strictly. To be included, an SSPR technique must have moved beyond the stage of a laboratory testbed or feasibility demonstration, and have (1) *performed useful work* or (2) *been incorporated into a commercially available product.* These criteria are admittedly somewhat inconsistent, since a product feature may never have been effectively applied, or, as has happened, the manufacturer may have rapidly gone out of business. And they may be unfair, since a well-engineered proof-of-concept system sometimes lacks only a business decision to move into successful application. However, they have at least the merit of reflecting the judgment of someone other than the developer, whether a consumer, factory manager, or venture capitalist.

"Syntactic" and "structural" are of course defined rigorously in other chapters of this volume. For the purposes of this chapter, a rather broad definition applies, including virtually all varieties of combinatorial matching. Syntactic techniques use phrase-structure grammars and their variants to represent families of similar shapes, and matching occurs through parsing. I will admit as "structural" any method that decomposes or analyzes a scene (or isolated shape) into a set of elementary shape features, and then matches sets of features. A great variety of feature-extraction techniques are in use, most commonly, matched filtering (e.g. edge-finding), contour-fitting, area-thinning, Hough transforms, and morphological (cellular automata) operations. Much of the literature has been inspired by the case where the set of features is enriched with relations, but it is also often possible to exploit geometrical invariants (e.g. rigidity) and diversity of feature type (e.g. convex *vs.* concave arcs) effectively to prune a search of consistent interpretations. In some fields SSPR has arrived on the scene following years of successful use of statistical (or decision-theoretic) PR methods, and everywhere I stress the distinction between SSPR and statistical methods.

Machine vision applications generally, and SSPR applications particularly, have surfaced in three major ways. The most ambitious systems have typically been first developed at major industrial laboratories and applied exclusively in-house. Some have migrated from academic or contract-research laboratories into relatively sophisticated companies, again for use in-house. This pattern has been more common in Japan and Europe than in the USA. Finally, some are featured in commercially available equipment.

## 2. CAVEAT

This survey may not be exhaustive. It is likely that many proprietary details remain unpublished. Certainly, reticence is the rule on algorithms for matching, while greater candor is common concerning the set of elementary shape features employed. In some corporations it is axiomatic that what has been released has not be applied and *vice versa*.

It is not only sensitive matters such as throughput and error rates that have been concealed. It sometimes happens that the responsible engineers, suspecting a design decision of theirs to be *ad hoc*, suppress it out of embarrassment, even though it is required to make the system work. This is unfortunate, since "troublesome details" can suggest important flaws in approaches taken for granted in the literature.

In fields crowded with competing products, I have chosen not to compile a trade directory, and instead have selected one or two representative systems for detailed description.

I am grateful to the many machine vision engineers whose candid conversations contributed to this survey. I have included references to the literature wherever possible, but in some cases I have been reduced to the unusual practice of referencing private communications; in these cases, the person expressed a willingness to reply to similar enquiries from any reader of this chapter.

## 3. CHARACTER RECOGNITION

The optical character recognition (OCR) industry is over thirty years old[1] and is technologically mature in many respects. The range of applications include postal address sorting, special forms data entry, handheld wand readers, aids for the blind and page readers. Much of the earliest, as well as the most recent, research on pattern recognition generally, and SSPR methods in particular, has focused on this area. Techniques for machine- and hand-printed characters overlap in many respects, although unconstrained handwriting is significantly harder.

The statistical correlation technique of template- (or mask-) matching has, in various guises, dominated commercial OCR for most of its history. Until recently, the conventional wisdom has been that template matching is robust but rigid: that is, it tolerates poor segmentation due to noise and variable print quality, but is sensitive to type-style (font) and -size variations. A symptom of this rigidity has appeared in the restriction of moderately-priced machines (under US\$50,000) to a small number of fonts at fixed sizes[a]. The opposite has been thought true of SSPR techniques: they generalize well across fonts, but resist being pushed to the near-perfect accuracy required. Nevertheless, structural shape analysis and matching have played a role in many machines. An early example among moderately-priced machines[2] extracted boundary features (e.g. convex arcs) and area-based features (e.g. strokes), matching them (in some way) to structural descriptions.

Today the field appears to be in an unusual state of flux, and the conventional wisdom is called in question. A pioneering constrained-handprint machine[3] achieves excellent accuracy by analyzing convex hulls and matching them structurally[4]. On the other hand, a moderately-priced page reader[5] accepting a wide range of fonts and sizes relies on a decision-theoretic approach: a sequential polynomial classifier operating on pixel values, after affine normalization for size, slant and aspect-ratio[6].

The last two years have seen a flurry of announcements of moderately-priced omnifont machines[5,7,8] targeting a new population of casual OCR users familiar with personal computers and networked desk-top terminals. Casual use requires both omnifont and variable-page-format capability,

---

[a]Machines accepting more than 30 fonts have been available since 1966, but at such high cost that they have been relegated to batch-processing service bureaus. Not coincidentally, the OCR-A font standard was adopted in the same year.

both of which are promising application areas for SSPR techniques. Applications engineers for the most part are familiar with the pattern recognition literature and often attempt to integrate a wide variety of general- and special-purpose classification strategies. "I have never seen a general AI heuristic"[9] is a characteristic remark.

In the recognition of handprinted characters and symbols, structural shape analysis and matching has been an important theme almost from the start[10]. When handprint is constrained (e.g. symbols written singly within boxes), high recognition rates have been achieved in large-scale applications (e.g. Japanese postal code readers[3]). It is interesting that hand-tuning of the algorithms continues to be required after installation, to adapt to regional writing styles and cultural drift[11].

Unconstrained handwriting becomes somewhat more tractable when pen motions are available for analysis. The early work of Applicon in on-line handprinted symbol recognition[12] has been followed by several commercially-available systems, notably Penpad 320[13] which performs static structural shape analysis[14] as well as pen motion analysis[15].

## 4. ROBOTIC VISION

The characteristic goals of robot vision are location and recognition. Whether in two or three dimensions, the object's position and sometimes orientation must be determined, while scale is commonly fixed. The set of possible objects, although large in some cases, is known in advance. The emphasis is therefore on segmentation, feature extraction and model-based matching. (See also Chapter 14 in this volume.)

The first vision software applied with industrial robots[16] relied on perfect segmentation (isolated, connected regions in binary images resulting from thresholding) and used a few numerical shape properties (such as moments) in a statistical training and classification framework. This prototype rapidly became a virtual standard, and the majority of robot vision systems incorporate some version of this approach.

Increasingly, however, models of shape are structural rather than statistical, and grey images are successfully analyzed, generally in one of two ways:

(1) individual local features are found, each using a different strategy (e.g. a variety of convolutions) followed by matching; or

(2) segmentation of the entire image is performed using a single strategy

(e.g. edge-finding), after which local features are identified (e.g. ridge-following) and matched.

An example of the first type is the GMF Robotics V-210 vision system[17]. This system is designed for model-based location and recognition. Models may be derived from CAD/CAM descriptions or from examples presented to the camera. A model is a set of named edges, vertices, circles and arcs, some of which are manually selected for use in recognition. During training, the model is manually superimposed on an image of the part, and an automatic procedure then chooses a feature-extraction technique for each selected feature. This involves automatically selecting from a set of convolutions (and other transforms) and tuning it to the particular feature. Only small variations in object orientation and scale are permitted. Matching is successful if a sufficiently large number of features are matched, consistent with the rigid model. After matching, the implied location of *all* model features is available (by name) to the application program, which can then perform inspection or robot control tasks specialized to that part. This system has been heavily used (on more than 100,000 images) in a variety of factory installations.

An example of the second type is the Adept vision system[18] which can recognize objects touching or occluded by other parts. Line, arc, corner and hole features are extracted first over whole image (in some way), and the resulting set of features is matched to structured models using exhaustive search pruned by nearness-constraints derived from the model (an adaptation of that by Bolles and Cain[19]).

At General Motors, home of some of the most ambitious early robotic vision applications[20,21], there have been no applications of syntactic methods, but a few arguably structural approaches, especially involving the use of morphological shape operators[22].

## 5. INSPECTION

The characteristic goals of visual inspection are error detection and mensuration. In contrast to robot vision, objects are often isolated and fixtured or travel past the imager on a fixed path at a fixed orientation. Thus scale and orientation (and often location) are known precisely. Recognition is seldom required.

An early successful syntactic application[23], using a regular shape grammar, has been in use for the last ten years[24]. The application required a high sustained piece-rate (15/sec), and thus an important attraction of syntactic methods was the promise of high parsing speed. Part presentation, illumination, and image acquisition proved to be challenging engineering problems. The resulting binary image was filtered to remove isolated gaps and dirt, using special purpose hardware. The shape of interest was the median-line of an industrial part; this line was approximated by a polygon using a modified Tomek[25] algorithm, implemented in microcode for speed. The polygonal line was tokenized and the resulting string parsed using a regular grammar with 1360 productions. This grammar was inferred laboriously by hand, and interactive production-editing tools were needed to make the chore palatable. No "standard" parsing tools of any kind were used. The shape to be inspected consisted for the most part of many repetitions of short, similar patterns and the developers credit much of the success of the approach to this fact. The large size of the grammar resulted from difficulties in representing transitions between regular and irregular regions, for example at the start and end of the part.

The last five years has seen a proliferation of image processing workstation products. Some were originally intended for robotics, but were rapidly redirected to fixtured inspection applications. Many companies, hoping to sell generic "vision tool-kits" which a user would configure to his own needs, have nevertheless remain entangled in custom system development. The tools supplied in these workstations reveal a growing interest in shape analysis and decomposition. A typical vision workstation[26] offers about 150 image-processing primitives, of which ten are "non-local" in nature: connectivity, boundary-tracing, convex hull, dilation/erosion and medial-axis transform. There are two operators that perform matching, one on numerical vectors and another on "ridge graphs".

With such a system, an engineer wishing to implement an SSPR algorithm would find few relevant tools at hand, and would be forced to write the bulk of the implementation from scratch.

## 6. VLSI MASK INSPECTION

A particularly demanding inspection problem arises for VLSI marks and wafers, where microlithographed patterns may have features comparable in size to the wavelength of light used to inspect them. The dominant technique has been, in essence, pixel-by-pixel template matching, made possible through careful control of mechanical and optical registration. Two types of comparison are possible: either (a) to another reference mask that is guaranteed to be correct, or (b) to a geometrical CAD database. Defects reported by the automatic inspection machines are then re-examined by eye since some are spurious and others can be repaired.

Recently there have been ambitious attempts to push inspection tolerances below 1µm, where optical interference effects defeat template matching. One product[27] used special purpose parallel hardware running at an effective rate of 1M pixels/second to find edges with subpixel accuracy using matched filtering. The resulting edge fragments were linked into polygons and the polygons compared to the CAD database. The relevance of this to SSPR techniques is that the presence of the CAD model was also *required* to complete the linking process reliably. Thus feature-extraction and model-matching were both model-driven, resulting in a unique and extreme form of structural matching.

As device geometries shrink, the fraction of reported defects that are false alarms rise. This suggests that reclassification of VLSI mask and wafer defects is a promising area for future SSPR applications.

## 7. MISCELLANEOUS

There were several fields where image processing applications are important, but where careful inquiries were unable to discover any applications of SSPR methods

One of these is remote sensing (typically of satellite imagery). Here the dominant technique in practice is statistical classification of pixels[28]. There is also limited use of segmentation by growing regions with uniform statistics.

Biomedical applications of SSPR techniques are similarly rare. Most current applications stress image restoration and enhancement (e.g. Ref. 29). However, from an unexpected direction there has come evidence that even elementary "structural" analysis of images can be surprisingly revealing[30]: interesting parts of variously-stained cancer cell specimens (e.g. centers of nuclei) were located manually, and the Delauney[31] triangulation of these points computed. Numerical properties of the triangulation were correlated with known patient survival rates. Two of these properties, minimum distance between first neighboring cells and cyclomatic number, have been shown in prospective trials "to be of prognostic significance" in cases that are difficult for experts to diagnose by eye.

## 8. CONCLUSION

Outside of the relatively mature field of OCR, very few applications of SSPR have surfaced. Of course, the field is still young: it is only thirteen years since Fu's milestone book[32], and ten years since Pavlidis'[33].

Until about 1980 one could also point to the absence of factory-hardened vision systems with adequate software development tools and computing power. Today, however, a variety of machine vision systems and image processing workstations are for sale, and while speed is sometimes a problem, the principal obstacle to SSPR use appears to be a lack of sound engineering methodology — fundamentally, the absence of proven general methods — and the resulting high cost of custom development and maintenance.

The experiences of applications engineers volunteered during the survey, suggest a few remarks.

Repeatedly, engineers stressed the primacy of speed. OCR machines typically must process better than 50 characters/second. Return-on-investment guidelines for factory equipment often favor high-throughout applications. Even robotic applications are rarely allowed more than a few seconds per image. Naturally, increasing processing speed will gradually relieve this problem.

The characteristic concerns of SSPR are model-formation and model-guided matching. However, in many vision applications, these are relatively late stages in a sequence of computations whose earlier stages are themselves hard. A large fraction of development time is commonly devoted to arriving at a clear and stable characterization of the problem. Once this is done, choice of illumination and design of the image acquisition strategy can require a large interdisciplinary effort. In this we may include image restoration (or filtering) and segmentation. There is a felt need for an engineering methodology for stable image acquisition.

In the majority of inspection applications, once a stable image is acquired, all that remains are straightforward details of installation, maintenance, ease-of-use, data logging, training, etc. Under these circumstances, technical managers are understandably reluctant to commit, in addition, to a matching method which has not been convincingly tested, or which does not have an immediate intuitive appeal.

However, there are other reasons why SSPR techniques may continue to lag behind approaches based on relatively simple image operators that are easily implemented in parallel/pipelined hardware. In many commercially available vision systems, the applications programming language is interpreted and thus runs as much as a factor of ten slower than the underlying CPU. By contrast, built-in image-processing operators are optimized for speed, often assisted by special hardware. Their speed is often highlighted in advertisements, presumably for lack of other generally-recognized virtues to point to. In this environment, the penalty for adding a thick layer of application code is severe, and the reward for making do with the available operators is great. This may partly explain the growing popularity of the relatively poorly-characterized "morphological" operators. It is clear that the complexity of most SSPR algorithms counts heavily against them.

For robotic vision especially, ease-of-training appears to be crucial for acceptance among factory engineers. Here, SSPR research has not been strikingly helpful. The motivation for much SSPR work has been the belief that many scenes possess an intrinsic structure which can be automatically inferred, concisely represented, and rapidly matched. Persistent practical (and theoretical) difficulties in the automatic inference of grammars (even subregular ones), and the large size of those inferred by any means, suggest that this assumption often does not hold, at least for syntactic models of structure. One engineer suggested that image structure is often "more like natural than artificial languages." The literature on structural techniques acknowledges the problem indirectly: it generally assumes the existence of an ideal CAD model, and of image features similar to the geometric primitives of the model. In practice, it is often difficult to extract well-formed features without reference to an implicit model of feature-formation.

One obstacle that time can remove is incorrect perceptions. Some applications engineers believe that parsing algorithms are inevitably slow. Of course, on the contrary, speed is one of their greatest strengths. Parsers for regular languages in particular, run at impressively high speeds. Not only are there provably asymptotically low-order polynomial algorithms for parsing several useful classes of languages, but automated tools exist to construct parsers for regular and LR(1) languages.

But some of the obstacles to the spread of SSPR research will not melt away of themselves. Most vision engineers I know would experience a flash of recognition on encountering the following quotes from computer vision theoreticians. "Practicing engineers have difficulty in selecting a method that will solve their problems because publications rarely provide any information about the domain of applicability of the technique."[34] "Very few experiments are reported on enough image data so that the certainty of the results can be stated."[35] "Production quality software requires many times the effort that researchers are able to devote to such work."[36]

In addition, one can point to a trend towards specialization and fragmentation in the literature. Vision engineers often find little guidance when they attempt to build an integrated system out of published techniques. The time may be ripe for increased research into the architecture of small, complete, high-performance vision systems. One issue urgently needing attention is the coherent management of error in complex vision systems.

In spite of these obstacles, SSPR methods appear to be taking hold gradually, first in the mature field of OCR, home of many experienced software engineers, and next in the new field of robot vision, where the transfer of ideas from academic laboratories has taken place efficiently by the movement of several generations of talented graduate students directly into industry.

I urge readers who know of applications that I have omitted, to write me about them. I hope to have assembled a fair and accurate portrait of the state of the applied art of SSPR methods. If it is a good likeness, it owes much to the confidences of many co-workers.

## REFERENCES

1. H.F. Schantz, *The History of OCR, Optical Character Recognition* (Recognition Technologies Users Association, 1982).
2. A. Medici, Kurzweil Computer Products, Inc., Cambridge, MA (24 Feb. 1987). Personal communication.
3. PRODATA TO-300 (TOTEC, USA, Northridge, CA, 1986).
4. S. Mori, K. Yamamoto and M. Yasuda, "Research on machine recognition of hand-printed characters", *IEEE Trans. Pattern Analysis and Machine Intelligence* **6** (1984) 386-405.
5. *"Polyfont" Form Reader Model PPFL-6150* (AEG Aktiengesellschaft, Ulm, FR Germany, 1986).
6. J. Schurmann, *Polynomklassifikatoren fur die Zeichenerkennung* (in German), (Univ. Oldenbourg, Munchen, Wien, 1977).
7. *The Compound Document Processor* (The Palantir Corporation, Santa Clara, CA 1986).
8. *OCR – + Page Reader* (Datacopy Corporation, Mountain View, CA, 1986).
9. M. Korns, Datacopy Corporation, Mountain View, CA (4 Mar. 1987). Personal communication.
10. C.Y. Suen, M. Berthod and S. Mori, "Automatic recognition of handprinted characters — The state of the art", *Proc. IEEE* **68** (1980) pp. 469-487.
11. S. Mori, Nippon-Schlumberger, Schinjiku-Daiichiseimei, Tokyo, Japan (Oct. 1986). Personal communication.
12. *Computerized Graphics Processing System: System User's Manual* (Applicon, Inc., Boston, MA, 1973).

13. *Penpad 320 Technical Data* (Pencept, Inc., Waltham, MA, 1983).
14. R. Shillman, "Character Recognition Based on Phenomenological Attributes: Theory and Methods", Ph.D. Thesis, MIT Dept. of Electrical Engineering (1974).
15. J. Ward and T. Kuklinski, *A Model for Variability Effects in Hand-printing, etc.* (Pencept, Inc., 39 Green St, Waltham, MA, 1987).
16. G. Agin and G. Gleason, "A modular vision system for sensor controlled manipulation and inspection", A.I. Center Technical Note no. 178, SRI International, Menlo Park, CA (1979).
17. K. Krause and B. Coldren, Machine Perception Dept., Research & Development, GMF Robotics, Troy, MI (25 Feb. 1987). Personal communication.
18. S. Burt, Adept Technologies, San Jose, CA (5 Mar. 1987). Personal communication.
19. R.C. Bolles and R.A. Cain, "Recognizing and locating partially visible objects: the local-feature-focus method", *Int. J. Robotics Research* **1** (1982) 57-82.
20. W.A. Perkins, "A model-based vision system for industrial parts", *IEEE Trans. Computers* **27** (1979) 126-143.
21. S.W. Holland, L. Rossol and M.R. Ward, "Consight-I: A vision-controlled robot system for transferring parts from belt conveyors", *GMR Symp.: Computer Vision and Sensor-Based Robots*, GM Research Laboratories, Warren, MI (Sept. 1978).
22. R. Tilove, Computer Science Research Dept., GM Research Labs, Dearborn, MI (26 Feb. 1987). Personal communication.
23. J.L. Mundy and R.E. Joynson, "Automatic visual inspection using syntactic analysis", *Proc. IEEE Computer Society Conf. on Pattern Recognition and Image Processing*, Troy, New York, 6-8 June 1977, pp. 144-147.
24. J.L. Mundy, (5 Mar. 1987). Personal communication.
25. I. Tomek, "Two algorithms for piecewise linear continuous approximation of functions of one variable", *IEEE Trans. Computers* **23** (1974) 445-448.
26. *3M Model PV Vision Workstation* (Vision Systems/3M, McLean, VA, 1986).
27. *The Wafer Vision System* (Contrex, Inc., Billerica, MA, 1986).
28. P. Swain, Dept. of Electrical Engineering, Purdue University, West Lafayette, IN (24 Feb. 1987). Personal communication.
29. D.J. Ip and H.H-S. Potter, "Biomedical image processing using the CLIP system", *Image and Vision Computing* **4** (1986) 2-10.
30. K. Kayser, H. Stute, W. Ebert and M. Fitzer, "Application of structural pattern recognition in histo-pathology", in *Proc. NATO Advanced Workshop on Syntactic & Structural Pattern Recognition*, Sitges (Barcelona), Spain, 23-25 Oct. 1986.
31. B. Delauney, "Sur la sphère vide", *Bull. Acad. Sci. USSR* **VII** (1934) 793-800, Classe Sci. Ma. Nat.
32. K-S. Fu, *Syntactic Methods in Pattern Recognition* (Academic Press, New York, 1974).
33. T. Pavlidis, *Structural Pattern Recognition* (Springer-Verlag, New York, 1977).
34. T. Pavlidis, "A critical survey of image analysis methods", *Proc. 8th Int. Conf. on Pattern Recognition*, Paris, France, 27-31 Oct. 1986, pp. 502-511.
35. R.M. Haralick, "Computer vision theory: The lack thereof", *Proc. 3rd Workshop on Computer Vision: Representation and Control*, Bellaire, Michigan, 13-16 Oct., 1985, pp. 113-121.
36. K. Price, "I've seen your demo; so what?", *Proc. 3rd Workshop on Computer Vision: Representation and Control*, Bellaire, Michigan, 13-16 Oct., 1985, pp. 122-124.

# 14

## THREE-DIMENSIONAL OBJECT RECOGNITION BY ATTRIBUTED GRAPHS

E.K. WONG

*Department of Electrical Engineering and Computer Science*
*Polytechnic University*
*333 Jay Street*
*Brooklyn, NY 11201, USA*

The problem of 3-D object recognition is posed as a subgraph searching problem. 3-D objects are modeled as attributed graphs where the nodes correspond to object vertices and the branches correspond to object edges. The set of attributes assigned to a node in a model graph includes the set of allowable-junction-types and the set of allowable-junction-type combination of its neighboring nodes. The 2-D projections of an object are modeled as subgraph isomorphisms of its model graph. Recognition is by searching if a 2-D projection graph, constructed from a 2-D projection of an object, is a subgraph isomorphism of the model graph. Experiments are conducted to evaluate the performance. Finally, the inclusion of 3-D coordinate values for vertices, edge length for straight edges and parametric cubic representation for the curved edges as additional attributes is discussed. The inclusion of these additional attributes results in a more complete representation for a large class of 3-D curved objects.

## 1. INTRODUCTION

Computer vision is an area in artificial intelligence that deals with equipping machines with the ability to see. One of the important goals of computer vision is to provide information about the configuration of 3-D objects in an environment such that appropriate actions can be performed on the objects. An example is in the area of sensor-based robot control, which involves integrating the information gathered from sensors and the internal representation of the world model to plan various robot motions, including grasping and moving the objects for many assembly operations. The necessary tasks that must be performed by the vision system include recognizing the objects in the workspace, and estimating the objects' positions and orientations. Recognition is often the first step taken before estimation of positions and orientations of the objects.

The acquisition of an image may be entirely passive, taking as input a digitized image from a sensor such as a TV camera, or it may be an active process, which involves controlling and regulating the sensor and the light source to obtain some characteristic measurements from a robot workspace. An example of an active imaging process is to use a series of parallel planes of light that fall on the scene in stripes. Shape and range information of the objects in the scene can be obtained with this method. In Ref. 1, the light striping method was used for gathering of range data.

In all recognition schemes, the computer stores canonical models of the 3-D objects to be recognized. The process of recognition is to match the input 2-D image against the stored models for the best fit. The canonical models stored by the computer can be categorized as 2-D or 3-D in nature. 2-D models are characterized by a set of silhouettes, a set of characteristic views[2], a set of symbolic sentences[3] and multiple-views representation[4]. 3-D geometric models are characterized by (1) volumetric representations based on spatial occupancy, cell decomposition or constructive solid geometry; (2) surface representations utilizing bicubic patches, quadric-surface patches and others; and (3) generalized cylinder representations[5]. However, not all of the modeling schemes are suitable for recognition. The intrinsic difficulty lies in the fact that a 3-D model takes on an infinite number of possible 2-D projections.

To resolve the infeasible task of matching an input 2-D projection against an infinite number of 2-D projections of a 3-D model, various other approaches have been attempted. One approach is characterized by the classical work of Roberts[6]. In Roberts' work, a line drawing of the 2-D image is first extracted. A list of two-dimensional features is associated with each model. For example, in the line drawing of a cube in Fig. 1, the interior polygons $A, B$ and $C$ correspond to unoccluded faces of the object. The point $P$, surrounded by three unoccluded regions, constitutes a feature to be searched for in the input image. Once the feature point is found, other corresponding points are established between the input image and the model. A transform between the model and the object is found from these points and the final match is verified by projecting the model onto the 2-D plane with the transform found. Features other than those in the above example could be used. Other features include a line surrounded by unoccluded polygons (such as the line between polygons $B$ and $C$ for the cube example); a single unoccluded polygon, and others. This feature matching method is effective only if the two dimensional features associated with a model is visible. Also, in the case of a complex object, it is sometimes difficult to isolate a feature in a 2-D projection which corresponds to a single unique part of the object (i.e. many different parts of an object may result in the same 2-D feature), therefore complicating the correspondence search between the 2-D projection and the 3-D model. In the case of many models to be matched, different models may result in the same 2-D features. This approach is therefore not general for the above reasons.

Fig. 1. Line drawing of a picture of a cube.

Another representative approach is that of Chakravarty and Freeman[2] in which the space of all possible perspective projections of an object is factored into a set of characteristic views, where each such view defines a characteristic view domain within which all projections are topologically identical and related by a linear transformation. The characteristic views of an object can then be hierarchically structured for efficient classification. This approach suffers in storage space requirement when the number of models to be matched is large, as there may be a large set of characteristic views even for a simple object[2]. In fact, objects are restricted to stable positions[2] to limit the size of the projection set. Stable positions are the positions in which the object would come to rest if thrown on a flat, horizontal surface. This assumption is invalid in an uncontrolled environment where the supporting surface is not flat, or when there are other irregular objects between the object of interest and the supporting plane.

Other approaches to 3-D object recognition can be found in Refs. 7-9. In Ref. 7, a model-based image understanding system called ACRONYM is described. This system demonstrated mechanisms for interpretation of images with generic object classes and generic viewing conditions, in a way that is generalizable. In Ref. 8, the three dimensional relationships of observables are used to locate a mechanical part accurately, assuming the position of the part is known in advance to within a few inches, and its orientation to within about fifteen degrees. The observables are characterized by local operators such as edge detectors and blob characterizers. In Ref. 9, volumetric primitives and their relations are extracted from 2-D images for 3-D object representation and recognition. One disadvantage with volumetric representation is that the decomposition of an object into primitives is often not unique, and hence, the object description derived from an image may not be the same as the object's model in the computer.

In the next section, we present and describe an alternative method of modeling 3-D objects by attributed graphs and pose the matching problem as a subgraph searching problem. This method is based on taking a single view of the scene with a TV camera, without using active imaging procedure. Section 3 discusses searching in the case of imperfect line drawings. Section 4 discusses camera transform estimation and hypothesis verification. Section 5 gives experimental results. Section 6 discusses the inclusion of 3-D coordinates for object vertices, edge length for straight edges and parametric cubic curves representation for curved edges as additional attributes for the nodes and branches of a graph. Finally, Sec. 7 gives concluding remarks.

## 2. GRAPH-THEORETIC MATCHING OF 3-D MODELS

Many techniques have been developed for graph analysis with applications in image analysis and computer vision. Among these are those described in Refs. 10-15. Also, in Ref. 16, a relaxation labeling technique that seeks to maximize a certain function in the graph representation of a scene is described.

For the purpose of this paper, an attributed-graph (AG) can be defined as a 2-tuple over $V = V_N \cup V_B$:

$$G = (N, B) \tag{1}$$

where $N$ is the finite set of nodes of graph $G$ defined as

$$N = \{n_i | 1 \leq i \leq k\} \tag{2}$$

where each node $n_i$ is a distinct node in $N$. $B$ is the finite set of branches of graph $G$ defined as

$$B = \{b_{ij} | b_{ij} = (n_i, n_j), \ 1 \leq i, j \leq k\} \tag{3}$$

where each branch $b_{ij}$ is a distinct branch in $B$ connecting nodes $i$ and $j$. $V_N$ is the finite set of node attributes and $V_B$ is the finite set of branch attributes. A node in $N$ may have an attribute $a$ from $V_N$ assigned to it. Similarly, a branch in $B$ may have an attribute $e$ from $V_B$ assigned to it.

In our approach, an input image is first preprocessed to extract its 2-D line drawing. The line drawing is then represented by an attributed graph in the recognition procedure. Methodology for extracting line drawing from a 2-D image can be found in Ref. 17.

### 2.1. 3-D Model Graph

The domain of 3-D objects we are dealing with are planar-faced or curved-surface solid *bodies*, having *vertices* formed by the intersection of at most three *surfaces*, and *edges* formed by the intersection of two surfaces. We define a *virtual edge* to be a locus of points of tangency on a surface with the lines of projection (as shown in Fig. 2). Throughout this chapter, we differentiate those edges formed by the intersection of two surfaces from the virtual edges by calling the former *physical edges*. Quantitatively, the two types of edges can be differentiated on the basis of surface normal orientation. A physical edge is a locus of points at which there are discontinuities in surface normal orientations. A virtual edge does not show discontinuities in surface normal orientations. A virtual edge (limb) may not pass through a vertex[18]. In a 2-D projection of a *scene*, called an *image*, *bodies* are projected as *objects*, physical edges and virtual edges as *lines*, and vertices as *junctions*. We define a *virtual junction* to be a junction at which at least one of the lines forming the junction is a projection of a virtual edge. A *face* is a portion of a surface bounded by physical edges or closed on itself.

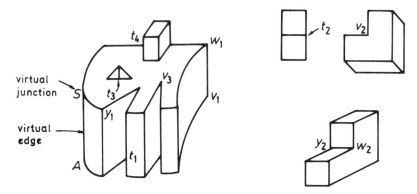

Fig. 2. Labeling with generalized junction types.

A *region* is a connected visible part of the projection of a face; a face may correspond to zero, one, or more regions[19].

We adopt the generalized line and junction labeling scheme developed by Chakravarty[19] for planar-faced and curved-surface solid bodies as our basis in labeling junctions in a 2-D line drawing. The labeling scheme may be considered as an extension to the Hoffman-Clowes[20,21] scheme for polyhedral bodies. Six classes of generalized junction types were identified by Shapira[18], as shown in Fig. 3. Note that class $A$ and class $S$ are virtual junctions classes. Class $W$, class $Y$, class $T$ and class $V$ junctions can be subcategorized based on the number of regions associated with the junction. We thus define 13 generalized junction types as shown in Fig. 4. Figure 2 depicts a line drawing labeled with these junction types. We model a 3-D object as an undirected graph where a *node* of the graph corresponds to a vertex in the 3-D object and a branch connecting two nodes corresponds to an edge between two vertices in the 3-D object. The edge may be a straight physical edge or a curved physical edge. The model graph thus constructed therefore captures the topology of how vertices are connected by edges in the 3-D object. An example is shown in Fig. 5a and b. Note that each vertex in the 3-D object corresponds to a unique node in the graph and each edge corresponds to a unique branch in the graph. We thus have the following two lemmas:

**Lemma 1.** The total number of nodes in a model graph represents the total number of vertices in the 3-D object it represents.

**Lemma 2.** The total number of branches in a model graph represents the

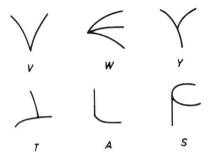

Fig. 3. Generalized junction classes.

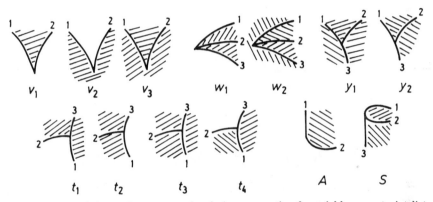

Fig. 4. Generalized junction types and ordering convention for neighbor-constraint-list.

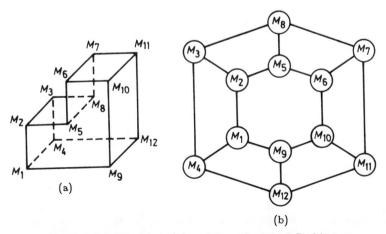

Fig. 5. (a) A 3-D object, (b) model graph of the 3-D object.

| Nodes: | $M_3, M_6$ | $M_2, M_7$ | $M_1, M_4, M_9, M_{10}, M_{11}, M_{12}$ | $M_5, M_8$ |
|---|---|---|---|---|
| Allowable Junction Set | $\{v_1, t_2, w_1, y_1\}$ | $\{v_1, t_2, w_1, y_1\}$ | $\{v_1, t_2, w_1, y_1\}$ | $\{v_3, v_2, t_2, w_2, y_2\}$ |
| Neighbor-constraint-set: | Junction type $v_1$:<br>$(v_1, v_2, \varphi)$<br>$(w_1, v_2, \varphi)$<br>$(t_2, v_2, \varphi)$<br>$(\varphi, v_1, \varphi)$<br>$(\varphi, t_2, \varphi)$<br>$(\varphi, w_1, \varphi)$<br>$(v_1, v_1, \varphi)$<br>$(t_2, v_1, \varphi)$<br>$(v_1, t_2, \varphi)$<br>$(w_1, w_1, \varphi)$<br><br>Junction type $t_2$:<br>$(v_1, v_3, v_1)$<br>$(v_1, t_2, v_3)$<br>$(t_2, t_2, v_1)$<br><br>Junction type $w_1$:<br>$(v_1, v_3, v_1)$<br>$(y_2, y_1, v_1)$<br>$(v_1, y_1, v_3)$<br><br>Junction type $y_1$:<br>$\{(w_2, w_1, w_1)\}$ | Junction type $v_1$:<br>$(v_2, v_1, \varphi)$<br>$(v_2, w_1, \varphi)$<br>$(v_2, t_2, \varphi)$<br>$(v_1, \varphi, \varphi)$<br>$(t_2, \varphi, \varphi)$<br>$(w_1, \varphi, \varphi)$<br>$(v_1, v_1, \varphi)$<br>$(v_1, t_2, \varphi)$<br>$(t_2, v_1, \varphi)$<br>$(w_1, w_1, \varphi)$<br><br>Junction type $t_2$:<br>$(v_1, v_3, v_1)$<br>$(v_3, t_2, v_1)$<br>$(v_1, t_2, t_2)$<br><br>Junction type $w_1$:<br>$(v_1, v_3, v_1)$<br>$(v_1, y_1, y_2)$<br>$(v_3, y_1, v_1)$<br><br>Junction type $y_1$:<br>$\{(w_2, w_1, w_1)\}$ | Junction type $v_1$:<br>$(v_1, v_1, \varphi)$<br>$(t_2, v_1, \varphi)$<br>$(w_1, w_1, \varphi)$<br>$(v_1, t_2, \varphi)$<br><br>Junction type $t_2$:<br>$\{(v_1, t_2, v_1)\}$<br><br>Junction type $w_1$:<br>$\{(v_1, y_1, v_1)\}$<br><br>Junction type $y_1$:<br>$\{(w_1, w_1, w_1)\}$ | Junction type $t_2$:<br>$\{(t_2, t_2, t_2)\}$<br><br>Junction type $w_2$:<br>$\{(y_1, y_2, y_1)\}$<br><br>Junction type $y_2$:<br>$\{(w_1, w_2, w_1)\}$<br><br>Junction type $v_2$:<br>$\{(v_1, v_1, \varphi)\}$<br><br>Junction type $v_3$:<br>$(t_2, t_2, \varphi)$<br>$(w_1, w_1, \varphi)$ |

**Fig. 5 Cont'd.** (c) Allowable-junction-sets and neighbor-constraint-sets of the 3-D object.

total number of edges in the 3-D object it represents. An edge may be a straight or curved physical edge.

Since we are dealing with objects whose vertices are formed by the intersection of three surfaces, and edges formed by the intersection of two surfaces, the number of edges meeting at a vertex must be exactly three. Therefore, the following lemma holds:

**Lemma 3.** The number of branches emerging from a model graph node is exactly three.

Assume that the nodes in a model graph are initially not connected to each other by branches and that each has three open branches attached to it. Therefore an odd number of nodes gives rise to an odd number of total branches and an even number of nodes gives rise to an even number of total branches. Now, to form a model graph, two open branches from two different nodes must be connected to form a single branch connecting two nodes. Therefore, the total number of branches must initially be even for no open branch to be left after the connecting processes. Consequently, the total number of nodes must initially be even and we have the following two lemmas:

**Lemma 4.** The total number of nodes in a model graph is even.

**Lemma 5.** The total number of branches in a model graph is $\frac{3m}{2}$ where $m$ is the total number of nodes in the model graph.

For curved objects with convex surfaces, virtual junctions and lines resulting from virtual edges may occur in their 2-D projections. Since they do not correspond to actual physical junctions and physical edges, we do not create nodes or branches in the model graph for them. Figure 6a shows a curved object and Fig. 6b shows its model graph.

### 2.2. Junction Types Constraint Propagation

In this section constraints for the types of possible junction projections allowable between *neighboring vertices* of a 3-D object are expressed as the constraints between *neighboring nodes* of the model graph.

In the analysis that follows, let us assume that the viewpoint will be in such a position that no accidental alignment of a vertex and an edge will occur (see Fig. 7). That is, when projected on a 2-D plane, all lines meeting at a junction are actually projections of physical or virtual edges meeting

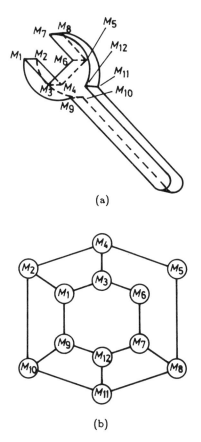

(a)

(b)

Fig. 6. A convex-curved-object "wrench" and its model graph (allowable-junction-types and neighbor-constraints-sets not shown).

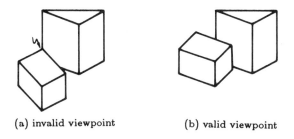

(a) invalid viewpoint          (b) valid viewpoint

Fig. 7. Accidental alignment of vertex and edge.

in 3-D space. In practice, we can take stereo images of a scene and choose one of the images with no accidental alignment, since accidental alignment at a given vertex will not occur at both positions of the stereo cameras. We define the *neighboring vertices* of a given vertex to be all vertices which are connected by an edge to the given vertex in a 3-D object. We define the *neighboring junctions* of a given junction to be all the junctions which are connected to the given junction by a line in a 2-D line drawing. We define the *neighboring nodes* of a given node to be all the nodes which are connected by a branch to the given node in a model graph. We define the *allowable-junction-set* for a vertex to be the set of all possible junction types which can occur in the 2-D projections of the vertex. Each member in the set is called an *allowable-junction-type*. As an example, the set of all possible junction types for vertex $M_1$ in the object of Fig. 5a is the set $\{v_1, w_1, y_1, t_2\}$ as shown in Fig. 8. The neighboring vertices of $M_1$ are $M_2, M_4$ and $M_9$ as shown in Fig. 9. Since $M_2, M_4$ and $M_9$ are connected to $M_1$ by edges, each of them bears a fixed spatial relationship to $M_1$, regardless of the actual spatial orientation and position of $M_1$. Therefore, in a 2-D projection of the 3-D object, the junction types which occur for vertices $M_2, M_4$ and $M_9$ are constrained by the junction type for vertex $M_1$.

Let us denote a junction which is hidden (occluded) in a 2-D projection by the symbol "$\phi$" and include this in our set of junction types. Vertex $M_1$, at viewpoints $VP_1, VP_2, VP_3$ and $VP_4$ as indicated in Fig. 10a will have a corresponding $v_1$ junction and 4 different combinations of junction types for vertices $M_2, M_4$ and $M_9$ as shown in Fig. 10b. We call each of these combinations a *neighbor-constraint-list*. All over viewpoints at which vertex $M_1$ projects into a $v_1$ junction type will have combinations of junction types for vertices $M_2, M_4$ and $M_9$ to be one of these 4 lists. Note that the *neighbor-constraint-list* is an ordered list of three elements, for which conventions are defined to order the elements of the list for each junction type. For a $V$ type junction, the ordering convention is that if we orient the $V$ junction to resemble the letter "V", then the neighboring junction connected to the left line forming the V junction would be ordered first and the neighboring junction connected to the right line would be ordered second. The third element of the list is a hidden junction type and will be ordered last. Conventions we adopted for the other junction types are indicated in Fig. 4. We define the set of all distinct *neighbor-constraint-lists* associated with a particular junction type $x$ at a given vertex to be the

$v_1$          $w_1$          $y_1$          $t_2$

Fig. 8. Possible junction types for vertex $M_1$ in Fig. 5a.

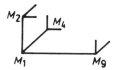

Fig. 9. Neighboring vertices of $M_1$ for the 3-D object in Fig. 5a.

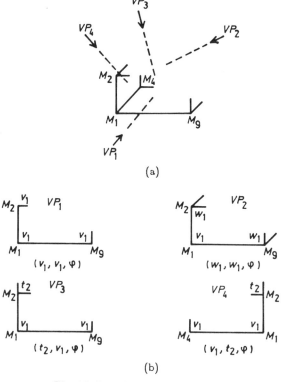

(a)

(b)

Fig. 10. Junction constraint propagation.

*neighbor-constraint-set* for junction type $x$ at the given vertex. Therefore for each allowable junction type at a vertex we have a *neighbor-constraint-set* associated with the junction type. The allowable-junction-type and their neighbor-constraint-sets for vertex $M_1$ is shown in Table 1. We call the allowable-junction-types at a given vertex *attribute* 1 of its corresponding node in the model graph, and we call the neighbor-constraint-sets *attribute* 2 of the node. The above analysis is repeated for each vertex of a 3-D object and we generate a model graph for the object, where each node of the graph has its two attributes of allowable-junction-types and neighbor-constraint-sets. The complete model graph for the 3-D object in Fig. 5a is shown in Fig. 5b and c.

Table 1. Allowable-junction-types and neighbor-constraint-sets for vertex $M_1$ in Fig. 5a.

| Allowable junction set | $\{v_1, t_2, w_1, y_1\}$ |
|---|---|
| Neighbor-constraint-sets | Junction type $v_1$: $$\begin{cases} (v_1, v_1, \varphi) \\ (t_2, v_1, \varphi) \\ (w_1, w_1, \varphi) \\ (v_1, t_2, \varphi) \end{cases}$$ Junction type $t_2$: $\{(v_1, t_2, v_1)\}$ Junction type $w_1$: $\{(v_1, y_1, v_1)\}$ Junction type $y_1$: $\{(w_1, w_1, w_1)\}$ |

## 2.3. Projection Graphs

In this section, the 2-D projections of a 3-D object are modeled as graphs and they can be shown to be subgraph isomorphisms of the model graph. Model matching then becomes the problem of searching whether an input projection graph is a subgraph of the model graph.

We define a projection graph to be a graph constructed from the 2-D line drawing projected from a 3-D object by the following procedure. We create a node for each junction in the 2-D line drawing which is a projection of a vertex in the 3-D object. The junction type that occurs is incorporated as an attribute of the node. We then connect two nodes by a branch if their corresponding junctions are connected by a line in the line drawing. Note that we do not create a node for junction types $t_1, t_2, t_3$ and $t_4$ since they are the projections of one edge occluding the other in the 3-D space, and therefore are not projections of a vertex in the 3-D space. We use an *open arc* to represent the occluded line and do not connect it to any node since it is actually connected to a hidden junction. We do not create nodes for type $A$ and type $S$ virtual junctions since they do not correspond to any node in the model graph. We do not create branches for lines connecting two virtual junctions since they are virtual edges and do not correspond to branches in the model graph. A projection of the 3-D object in Fig. 5a is shown in Fig. 11a and its projection graph is shown in Fig. 11b and c. Also, a projection of the curved object in Fig. 6a is shown in Fig. 12a and its projection graph is as shown in Fig. 12b and c. We observe that two vertices connected by an edge in 3-D space project into two junctions connected by a line in 2-D space. The projection from 3-D space to 2-D space does not change the topology of how the vertices or the junctions are connected. The projection only hides some of the lines and junctions in 2-D space. These are called hidden lines and hidden junctions in computer graphics literature[22]. For example, vertices $M_4$ and $M_8$ of the 3-D object in Fig. 5a are projected as hidden junctions invisible in the 2-D line drawing of Fig. 11a. Since every node in a projection graph corresponds to a unique node in its model graph and every branch connecting two nodes in a projection graph corresponds to a unique branch connecting the corresponding nodes in its model graph, we have the following lemma:

**Lemma 6.** The projection graphs constructed from the 2-D projections of a 3-D object are subgraph isomorphisms of the model graph constructed from the 3-D object.

Note that the number of branches emerging from a projection graph node is at most three and the total number of nodes in a projection graph cannot be larger than the total number of nodes in its model graph. In fact, we can prove a stronger condition on the relationship between the number of nodes in a projection graph and the number of nodes in its model graph as follows.

By Lemma 4, a model graph has at least the same number of nodes $n$ in its projection graph if $n$ is even; or it has at least $n + 1$ nodes if $n$ is

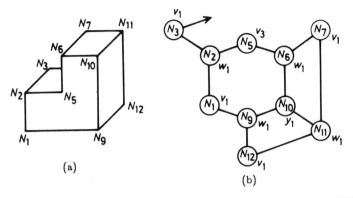

| Node | Junction type | Neighbor-junction-list |
|------|---------------|------------------------|
| $N_1$ | $v_1$ | $(w_1, w_1, \varphi)$ |
| $N_2$ | $w_1$ | $(v_1, v_3, v_1)$ |
| $N_3$ | $v_1$ | $(\varphi, w_1, \varphi)$ |
| $N_5$ | $v_3$ | $(w_1, w_1, \varphi)$ |
| $N_6$ | $w_1$ | $(v_1, y_1, v_3)$ |
| $N_7$ | $v_1$ | $(w_1, w_1, \varphi)$ |
| $N_9$ | $w_1$ | $(v_1, y_1, v_1)$ |
| $N_{10}$ | $y_1$ | $(w_1, w_1, w_1)$ |
| $N_{11}$ | $w_1$ | $(v_1, y_1, v_1)$ |
| $N_{12}$ | $v_1$ | $(w_1, w_1, \varphi)$ |

(c)

Fig. 11. (a) A 2-D projection, (b) its projection graph and (c) neighbor-junction-list.

odd. The minimum number of branches in a model graph is thus $3\left\lceil\frac{n}{2}\right\rceil$ by Lemma 5. Let us denote the total number of branches (not including open arcs) in a projection graph by $B$. The number of hidden line segments $L_{\text{hid}}$ (an occluded line is considered a hidden line segment since part of it is hidden) is then bounded below by

$$L_{\text{hid}} \geq 3\left\lceil\frac{n}{2}\right\rceil - B .\tag{4}$$

Since at most three hidden lines are needed to form a junction, the number of hidden junctions is bounded below by

$$J_{\text{hid}} \geq \left\lceil\frac{L_{\text{hid}}}{3}\right\rceil = \left\lceil\frac{n}{2}\right\rceil - \left\lfloor\frac{B}{3}\right\rfloor .\tag{5}$$

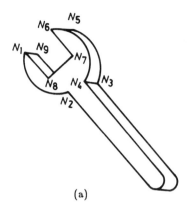

(a)

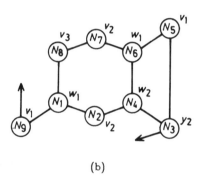

(b)

| Node | Junction type | Neighbor-junction-list |
|------|---------------|------------------------|
| $N_1$ | $w_1$ | $(v_1, v_3, v_2)$ |
| $N_2$ | $v_2$ | $(w_2, w_1, \varphi)$ |
| $N_3$ | $y_2$ | $(\varphi, w_2, v_1)$ |
| $N_4$ | $w_2$ | $(w_1, y_2, v_2)$ |
| $N_5$ | $v_1$ | $(y_2, w_1, \varphi)$ |
| $N_6$ | $w_1$ | $(v_1, w_2, v_2)$ |
| $N_7$ | $v_2$ | $(v_3, w_1, \varphi)$ |
| $N_8$ | $v_3$ | $(w_1, v_2, \varphi)$ |
| $N_9$ | $v_1$ | $(\varphi, w_1, \varphi)$ |

(c)

Fig. 12. (a) 2-D projection of a convex-curved object "wrench," (b) its projection graph, and (c) neighbor-junction-list.

For example, in the projection graph of Fig. 11b,

$$L_{\text{hid}} \geq 3 \left\lceil \frac{10}{2} \right\rceil - 12 = 3$$

and

$$J_{\text{hid}} \geq \left\lceil \frac{3}{3} \right\rceil = 1 \ .$$

In fact, we have six hidden lines and two hidden junctions. Since the number of visible junctions plus the minimum number of hidden junctions must be less than or equal to the number of nodes in the model graph, the following lemma holds:

**Lemma 7.** The number of nodes $n$ in a projection graph and the number nodes $m$ in its model graph satisfies

$$n + \left\lceil \frac{n}{2} \right\rceil - \left\lfloor \frac{B}{3} \right\rfloor \leq m \tag{6}$$

where $B$ is the total number of branches in the projection graph not including the open arcs.

Care must be taken if there are more than one object in the scene and objects are occluding each other. If we assume no accidental alignment of a vertex and an edge (as in Fig. 7), then the junction formed by the occlusion of edges from different objects are always "T" type junctions. Since we use open arcs to represent occluded lines and do not create nodes for "T" type junctions, a separate projection graph will be created for each of the overlapping line drawings of different objects. Each of the projection graphs constructed can then be matched against the stored model graphs, as described in the following section.

## 2.4. Model Matching as Subgraph Searching

Since all possible projection graphs constructed from the 2-D projections of a 3-D object are subgraph isomorphisms of the model graph, it is necessary that an input projection graph be a subgraph of the model graph for the input projection to match the model. Figure 13 gives an example for a cube, where the projection graphs for all the possible views of the cube are shown to be subgraph isomorphisms of its model graph. Note that this is not a sufficient condition for model matching since two 2-D line

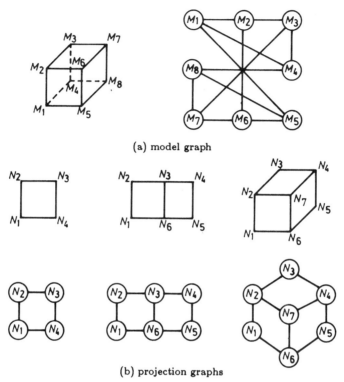

(a) model graph

(b) projection graphs

Fig. 13. Subgraph isomorphism of the model graph for a cube.

drawings may have the same projection graph, yet representing different objects. That is, a projection graph could match more than one model graph. The projection graph only conveys information about the topology of how vertices and edges are connected in a 3-D object. We thus have the following lemma:

**Lemma 8.** The subgraph isomorphism of a projection graph to a model graph is a necessary but not sufficient condition for a 2-D projection to match a 3-D object. We call this a *topological match.*

For final verification, the 3-D geometric model of a 3-D object must be projected onto the 2-D plane by an estimated camera transform between the input 2-D line drawing and the 3-D object. The projected image is then compared with the input 2-D image. We call this *hypothesis verification.* Model matching then becomes two sub-problems — topological matching and hypothesis verification. Topological matching becomes a problem of searching for subgraph isomorphism between a projection graph and a model graph in our approach. Known algorithms for subgraph searching can be found in Ref. 23. The time complexity can be as high as $M^N$ in the general case where $M$ is the number of nodes in the bigger graph and $N$ is the number of nodes in the smaller graph. However, we are dealing with a special case of the subgraph searching problem. Since each node in the model graph has only three branches, and we further allow junction types propagation between neighboring nodes to serve as constraints in the matching process, the time complexity is greatly reduced.

Similar to the constructions of model graphs, we define the *neighbor-junction-list* for each node in the projection graph to be an ordered list which consists of the junction types of its neighboring junctions. The ordering conventions follow those in Fig. 4. A "$\phi$" is used to denote a hidden junction. A node $i$ in the projection graph is said to satisfy the neighbor-constraints at a node $j$ in the model graph if the junction type $x$ of node $i$ is an allowable-junction-type of node $j$ and the neighbor-junction-list for node $i$ is in the neighbor-constraint-set for junction type $x$ at node $j$. In order for a node $i$ in the projection graph to match a node $j$ in the model graph, this constraint must be satisfied.

The algorithm for subgraph searching proceeds as follows. We label the projection graph nodes from $N_1$ to $N_n$ and the model graph nodes from $M_1$ to $M_m$. We try to match node $N_1$ to one of nodes $M_1$ to $M_m$. Then we try to match the neighboring nodes of $N_1$ to the neighboring nodes of the node matched to $N_1$ in the model graph. For each node $N_i$ matched in the projection graph, we try to match its neighboring nodes to the neighboring nodes of the node matched to node $N_i$ in the model graph. We repeat this process until all nodes in the projection graph are matched to some nodes in the model graph. If an error occurs, we backtrack until all possible matching combinations are exhausted.

We analyze the time complexity of the algorithm as follows. There are at most $m$ choices for $N_1$, at most three choices for the first neighboring node of $N_1$, at most two choices for the second neighboring node of $N_1$ and one choice for the third neighboring node. The remaining nodes other than $N_1$ have at most two choices for their first neighboring node and one choice for their second neighboring node since one of the neighboring nodes was matched previously. This is depicted in Fig. 14. The time complexity is therefore

$$t_{topol} = O(m2^{\lceil \frac{n}{2} \rceil}) \,. \tag{7}$$

match $n$ nodes against $m$ nodes

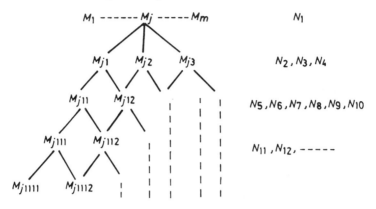

| Subgraph nodes | No. of choice |
|:---:|:---:|
| $N_1$ | $m$ |
| $N_2$ | 3 |
| $N_3$ | 2 |
| $N_4$ | 1 |
| $N_5$ | 2 |
| $N_6$ | 1 |
| $N_7$ | 2 |
| $N_8$ | 1 |
| $N_n$ | 1 |

Time complexity

$$= 6m2^{\lceil \frac{n-4}{2} \rceil}$$

$$= \tfrac{3}{2}m2^{\lceil \frac{n}{2} \rceil}$$

Fig. 14. Time complexity of searching algorithm.

It is expected that a highly regular and symmetric object would have a higher time complexity than an irregular object since the constraint propagations between neighboring nodes take greater effect in an irregular object.

### 2.5. Search Time Speed-Up

Since time is a crucial factor in many practical applications, it is desirable to speed-up the search process. The procedures described below do not improve the time complexity but substantially reduce the matching time in many instances.

The first procedure is by use of Lemma 7. We count the number of nodes and branches in the projection graph and the number of nodes in the model graph (this can be done once and the values stored). If Eq. (6) is not satisfied, we conclude that the projection does not match the model without going into subgraph searching.

The second procedure is to hierarchically rank the allowable-junction-types in the model graph. A junction type which is an allowable-junction-type in a lesser number of model graph nodes is given a higher precedence than one which is an allowable-junction-type in a larger number of model graph nodes. The ranking of junction types in the model graph of Fig. 5b and c is shown in Table 2. Note that junction types $y_2, v_2, v_3$ and $w_2$ are ranked the highest since they can occur only at two nodes (nodes $M_5$ and $M_8$). In subgraph searching, the projection graph is first searched for the next highest precedence junction types, attempts are then made to match them with the nodes in the model graph at which these junction types could occur. This considerably reduces the search space.

Table 2. Ranking of junction types for the model graph in Fig. 5b and c.

| Junction types | Nodes at which it occurs | Number of Occurrences | Rank |
|---|---|---|---|
| $w_2, y_2, v_2, v_3$ | $M_5, M_8$ | 2 | 1 |
| $y_1, v_1, w_1$ | $M_1, M_2, M_3, M_4, M_6, M_7,$ $M_9, M_{10}, M_{11}, M_{12}$ | 10 | 2 |
| $t_2$ | $M_1 - M_{12}$ | 12 | 3 |

The above procedures can be incorporated as initial steps in a recognition scheme in the block diagram of Fig. 15. This scheme has the effect of optimizing the model search time with the proposed method.

As an example, we demonstrate the subgraph searching of the 2-D projection in Fig. 11a against the model graph in Fig. 5b. We construct the projection graph for the 2-D line drawing in Fig. 11b, and the neighbor-junction-list for each node in the projection graph in Fig. 11c. The number of branches $B$ (excluding the open arc emerging from node $N_3$) in the projection graph is 12 and the number of visible junctions $n$ is 10. The number

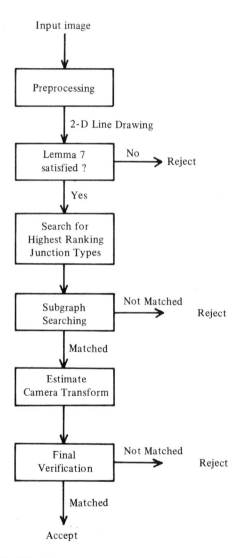

Fig. 15. Block diagram of a recognition scheme.

of nodes $m$ in the model graph is 12. Applying Lemma 7, we obtain

$$n + \left\lceil \frac{n}{2} \right\rceil - \left\lfloor \frac{B}{3} \right\rfloor \leq m$$

$$10 + \left\lceil \frac{10}{2} \right\rceil - \left\lfloor \frac{12}{3} \right\rfloor \leq 12$$

$$10 + 5 - 4 \leq 12$$

$$11 \leq 12 \ .$$

Thus, the first procedure is satisfied. The second procedure is then applied by searching for the highest ranking junction types in the projection graph. From Table 2, the highest ranking junction types are $w_2, y_2, v_2$ and $v_3$ and they can occur only at nodes $M_5$ and $M_8$ of the model graph. Of the four junction types, only junction type $v_3$ occurs at node $N_5$ in the projection graph. Thus node $N_5$ is matched against nodes $M_5$ and $M_8$. Suppose node $N_5$ is matched against node $M_5$ first, then there is a match since the junction type of $N_5, v_3$, is an allowable-junction-type for node $M_5$ and the neighbor-junction-list for node $N_5$ $(w_1, w_1, \phi)$, is in the neighbor-constraint-set for junction type $v_3$ at node $M_5$ (see Fig. 5c). Next, the neighboring node of node $N_5$, node $N_2$, is matched against node $M_6$. There is a match. Next, the other neighboring node of node $N_5$, node $N_6$, is matched against node $M_2$. There is a mismatch since the neighbor-junction-list for node $N_6$ $(v_1, y_1, v_3)$ is not in the neighbor-constraint-set for junction type $w_1$ at node $M_2$. Therefore, the algorithm backtracks and matches node $N_2$ against node $M_2$ and node $N_6$ against node $M_6$ and there is a match. The algorithm proceeds until all nodes in the projection graph are matched to some nodes in the model graph.

## 2.6. Parallel Search Algorithm

For 2-D projections with up to 50 junctions (the projection in Fig. 11a has 10 junctions), the time complexity is not a crucial factor since $n$ is small. For very complex objects for which $n$ is large, we do not need to match every node in the projection graph. We only have to match a small set of nodes (six is all that is sufficient[17]) to estimate the transform of the object with respect to the camera. The other unmatched junctions can be verified by projection of their corresponding 3-D object vertices in the geometric model onto the 2-D plane by the estimated camera transform.

However, there may be more than one distinct set of six nodes in the model graph to which a set of six nodes in the projection graph can be matched. This occurs in highly regular objects having many identical substructures. Only one of these sets of six nodes in the model graph is the correct matching set. To find the correct matching set, a camera transform is estimated and a final verification is performed with each set.

We propose a parallel algorithm for the exhaustive search of the set of six matching nodes in the model graph, given a set of six connected nodes in the projection graph. A set of six connected nodes in the projection graph is numbered from $N_1$ to $N_6$. $N_1$ is matched against each of the $m$ nodes in the model graph, in parallel. $N_1$ should be chosen as the highest precedence node in the projection graph, as discussed in the last section. From the $m$ parallel search processes, let $k$ be the number of sets of six nodes matched, where

$$k \leq m \ . \tag{8}$$

For each of these $k$ sets of nodes matched, the camera transform is estimated and a final verification is performed. This is carried out by $k$ parallel processes.

The time complexity for the parallel algorithm can be analyzed as follows. Since there is a set of six nodes, $n$ equals 6 in Eq. (7). Since the search process is carried out in parallel at each of the $m$ model graph nodes, the factor of $m$ in Eq. (7) is cancelled out. Thus,

$$t_{\text{topol}} = O(2^{\lceil \frac{6}{2} \rceil}) = O(8) = O(\text{constant}) \ . \tag{9}$$

Therefore, the time complexity is constant in the topological stage of model matching. For final verification, assuming that it is sufficient to verify the projections of the $m$ vertices of the 3-D geometric model onto the 2-D image plane, the time complexity is linear with respect to $m$. Therefore,

$$t_{\text{verify}} = O(m) \ . \tag{10}$$

Thus, the total time complexity, that of topological match and final verification is still linear in $m$.

$$t_{\text{total}} = t_{\text{topol}} + t_{\text{verify}} = O(m) \ . \tag{11}$$

## 3. INCOMPLETE LINE DRAWINGS

Because of noise and lighting conditions, sometimes we are unable to get a perfect line drawing after preprocessing. There may be junctions or part or all of a line segment missing (see Fig. 16a). The inherent nature of our modeling scheme allows us to model imperfect line drawings. We construct the projection graph of an incomplete line drawing as usual. We represent each line segment not meeting at a junction by an open arc (see Fig. 16b). A missing line segment causes a missing branch in the projection graph. A missing junction causes a missing node in the projection graph. An open line segment corresponds to an open arc. Missing line segments or junctions do not change the topology of interconnections between junctions and line segments which are present. The obtained projection graph will still be a subgraph isomorphism of the model graph and we can still carry out the subgraph searching algorithm described before. Therefore, we have the following lemma:

**Lemma 9.** An incomplete line drawing projection of a 3-D object can be modeled as a subgraph isomorphism of the projection graph obtained from the complete line drawing at the same viewpoint. And, consequently, the projection graph obtained from an incomplete line drawing is still a subgraph isomorphism of the model graph.

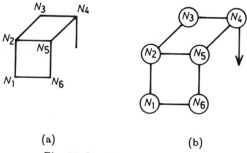

(a)                        (b)

Fig. 16. Imperfect line drawing.

As long as we have a minimum of six connected nodes in the projection graphs from an incomplete line drawing, we can still estimate the camera transform and perform final verification.

Note that in the approach where visible regions or surfaces are extracted as key matching features[6], a missing line or a missing junction from the outline of a region may totally invalidate the recognition procedure or lead to misrecognition. In the approach using characteristic views[2], a single missing junction or line could also lead to failure of the recognition procedure.

## 4. CAMERA TRANSFORM ESTIMATION AND HYPOTHESIS VERIFICATION

After topological matching using the subgraph searching method as discussed in Sec. 2.4, the 3-D geometric model must be projected onto the 2-D plane for final verification. Let

$V'' = \{v_1'', v_2'', \ldots, v_n''\}$ be the junctions in the image,
$V = \{v_1, v_2, \ldots, v_n\}$ be the matching model vertices and
$V^p = \{v_1^p, v_2^p, \ldots, v_n^p\}$ be the predicted vertices under a transformation $H$.

We seek to choose $H$ to minimize the error function

$$E = \sum_{i=1}^{n} \|v_i'' - v_i^p\| \, . \qquad (12)$$

A geometric model is said to match a given image if the computed error is less than some threshold $T$, that is

$$E < T \, . \qquad (13)$$

It was mentioned in Sec. 2.4 that there may be more than one model that is topologically matched to the input image. In such cases, we choose the model which produces the minimum matching error $E$, from all the models whose computed error satisfies Eq. (13). Also, when projected onto the 2-D plane, the 2-D coordinates of the unmatched vertices must not fall outside the 2-D line drawing; that is, they must be predicted to be hidden or else the model is an unacceptable match. This method is called *hypothesis verification* by picture synthesis, first used in Ref. 6 and discussed in Ref. 17.

Let us define a model point to be a 3-D coordinate in the geometric model of a 3-D object, an object point to be a 3-D coordinate in a 3-D object, and an image point to be the 2-D coordinates of the 2-D projection of a model point or an object point. In the subgraph searching procedure discussed in Sec. 2.4, each pair of nodes matched between the projection graph and the model graph establishes a pair of correspondence points between the 2-D image and the 3-D model. Since the coordinates of each point are known in their respective spaces, the camera transformation relating the model points and the image points can be estimated. One method used in Ref. 6 and discussed in Ref. 17 is as follows.

The model points are given in 4-dimensional homogeneous coordinates by column vector $(x_i, y_i, z_i, w_i)^t$ and the image points are given in 3-dimensional homogeneous coordinates by column vector $(x_i'', y_i'', w_i'')^t$. The model points are given in a coordinate system attached to the model, chosen for the convenience of measuring model coordinates, and the image points are given in a coordinate system with $x$ and $y$ axes in the image plane. The equation relating the image points to the model points is given by

$$HV = V''D \qquad (14)$$

where $V$ is a $4 \times n$ matrix whose $n$ columns are the homogeneous coordinates of the $n$ model points, $V''$ is a $3 \times n$ matrix whose $n$ columns are the homogeneous coordinates of the $n$ corresponding points in the image. $H$ is a $3 \times 4$ matrix representing the transformation of model points to image points and D is an $n \times n$ diagonal matrix which allows the scaling coordinate of $HV$ to differ from the $w_i$ of $V''$. Since we have 12 unknowns in $H(3 \times 4)$ and $n$ unknowns in $D(n \times n)$, a minimum of six pairs of correspondence points are necessary for a nondegenerate solution of Eq. (14). The *pseudo-inverse* solution is given in Ref. 6 as

$$H = V'' D V^T (V V^T)^{-1} \ . \qquad (15)$$

$D$ can be solved by letting

$$Q = V''^T V''$$
$$A = V^T (V V^T)^{-1} V - I \qquad (16)$$

where $I$ is the identity matrix. If we define a new matrix such that $s_{ij} = a_{ij} q_{ji}$, then the diagonal terms of $D, \{d_1, \ldots, d_n\}$, can be formed by solving the linear equation

$$S d = 0 \qquad (17)$$

where $d$ is a column vector formed by the diagonal elements of $D$. That is,

$$d = (d_1, d_2, \ldots, d_n)^t \ . \qquad (18)$$

It should be noted that this solution ignores the interdependence of the elements of matrix $H$. Therefore, the solution may be inaccurate. The elements of matrix $H$ are related to each other by the parameters of the camera — *focal length* and the *pan, tilt* and *swing* of the image plane relative to the object. More accurate but computationally expensive estimates can be obtained by using nonlinear optimization techniques as in Refs. 24-26. Also, a set of three correspondence points between the 3-D model and the 2-D image are sufficient for estimating the solution of $H$ if nonlinear techniques are used, rather than the six needed for the linear solution of Eq. (14).

## 5. EXPERIMENTAL RESULTS

The digitized image of a 3-D object "bracket" is shown in Fig. 17. Local edges of the digitized image are detected using a first order gradient operator and thresholding is done to produce a binary image as in Fig. 18. A thinning and a line completion algorithm are then used to thin lines that are too thick and to complete lines that are slightly broken due to preprocessing errors. The image after the thinning and line completion operations is shown in Fig. 19. A junction detection algorithm is then applied to detect the junctions and their coordinates in the image plane. The projection graph is then constructed from the junctions and lines detected. This is shown in Fig. 20. The subgraph searching algorithm is used to match the projection graph against the model graph and a topological match is found. Six of the nodes matched are used to estimate the camera transform using Eq. (15) and the result is shown in Table 3. The wire-frame geometric model is then projected onto the image plane using this estimated transform, and the result is shown. in Fig. 21. This is seen to be in close resemblance to Fig. 19.

Table 3. Estimated camera transform for the line drawing in Fig. 19.

| | | | |
|---|---|---|---|
| 0.72009 | -0.65208 | -0.04062 | 77.52967 |
| -0.29116 | -0.29906 | -1.01573 | 181.96817 |
| 0.00000 | -0.00000 | 0.00000 | 1.00000 |

## 6. ADDITIONAL ATTRIBUTES

The model graph representation described in the previous sections does not consider the physical dimensions and type of edges of a 3-D object. In the verification stage of the recognition procedure, the geometric model of a 3-D object is projected onto the 2-D image plane. In this section, we discuss

Fig. 17. Digitized image of a 3-D object "bracket".

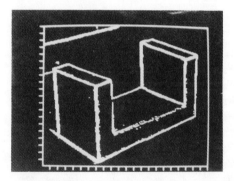

Fig. 18. Digitized image after gradient operation and thresholding.

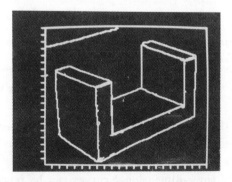

Fig. 19. Line drawing after thinning and line completion operation.

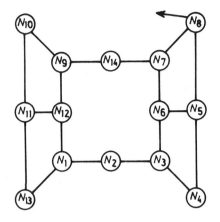

| Node | Junction type | Neighbor-junction-list |
|------|---------------|------------------------|
| $N_1$ | $w_1$ | $(v_1, y_1, v_1)$ |
| $N_2$ | $v_1$ | $(w_1, w_1, \varphi)$ |
| $N_3$ | $w_1$ | $(v_1, y_1, v_1)$ |
| $N_4$ | $v_1$ | $(w_1, w_1, \varphi)$ |
| $N_5$ | $w_1$ | $(v_1, y_1, y_2)$ |
| $N_6$ | $y_1$ | $(w_1, w_1, w_2)$ |
| $N_7$ | $w_2$ | $(v_3, y_2, y_1)$ |
| $N_8$ | $y_2$ | $(w_1, w_2, \varphi)$ |
| $N_9$ | $w_1$ | $(v_3, y_1, v_1)$ |
| $N_{10}$ | $v_1$ | $(w_1, w_1, \varphi)$ |
| $N_{11}$ | $w_1$ | $(v_1, y_1, v_1)$ |
| $N_{12}$ | $y_1$ | $(w_1, w_1, w_1)$ |
| $N_{13}$ | $v_1$ | $(w_1, w_1, \varphi)$ |
| $N_{14}$ | $v_3$ | $(w_1, w_2, \varphi)$ |

Fig. 20. Projection graph constructed from line drawing in Fig. 19.

the inclusion of 3-D coordinate values for object vertices, edge length for straight object edges and parametric cubic representation for curved object edges as attributes of the model graph.

A large class of three-dimensional curves can be represented by parametric cubic curves which are third-order polynomials of some parameter $t$

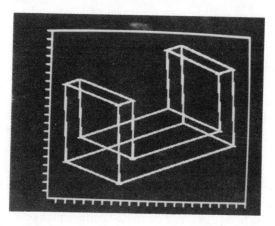

Fig. 21. Projection of wire frame model onto image plane using estimated camera transform.

(Ref. 22). Curved edges in a 3-D object can be represented by this representation with parameter $t$ in the range $0 \leq t \leq 1$. Hence,

$$
\begin{aligned}
x(t) &= a_x t^3 + b_x t^2 + c_x t + d_x \ , \\
y(t) &= a_y t^3 + b_y t^2 + c_y t + d_y \ , \\
z(t) &= a_z t^3 + b_z t^2 + c_z t + d_z
\end{aligned}
\tag{19}
$$

where $0 \leq t \leq 1$ will completely describe the 3-D curved edges of a large class of 3-D objects.

A cubic parametric curve can be defined in many ways. One method is to define the positions and tangents at the curve's endpoints. This definition is called the *Hermite Form*[22] and can be described by the vectors $P_1, P_4, R_1$ and $R_4$ where vectors $P_1$ and $P_4$ specify the 3-D coordinates at the end points and vectors $R_1$ and $R_4$ specify the tangent at the end points.

For each branch $b$ of a 3-D object, an attribute $e$ from the attribute set $V_B$, defined as

$$
V_B = \{(s, l), (c, P)\}
\tag{20}
$$

can be assigned to represent the type of edge branch $b$ represents, where $e = (s, l)$ denotes a straight edge with length $l$ and $e = (c, P)$ denotes a curved edge with cubic parameter

$$
P = (P_1, P_4, R_1, R_4)
\tag{21}
$$

With this representation, if branch $b$ connects nodes $i$ and $j$, the parameter $t$ of the cubic curve goes from 0 to 1 along the 3-D edge between vertices $i$ and $j$.

For each node $i$ of a model graph, the attribute $a = (x_i, y_i, z_i)$ can be added to node $i$ where $(x_i, y_i, z_i)$ are the coordinate values of vertex $i$ in the 3-D geometric model of a 3-D object.

With the added attributes in the model graph representation and similar attributes that can be added to a projection graph[27], more discrimination power can be obtained in the topological match stage of the recognition procedure. An input projection graph can be rejected if the attribute of its branches do not match that of the model graph. Some examples for rejection are: a straight line in the input image does not match a curved edge attribute, the length of a line on the 2-D image plane exceeds the length of an edge in the 3-D object, and others. Details of this are discussed in Ref. 27. For the verification stage of the recognition procedure, the model graph contains complete geometric information of the vertices and edges of a 3-D object. The 3-D coordinate values of the vertices and selected points from the parametric representation of the curved edges can be projected onto the 2-D image plane for comparison with the input image.

## 7. CONCLUDING REMARKS

We have presented a graph-theoretic modeling scheme for 3-D planar and curved objects, which was shown to be useful in the recognition of 3-D objects. We have shown that the junction semantics of a 2-D line drawing and junction constraints propagation between neighboring junctions are useful in the recognition of 3-D objects. Determination of correspondence points between the input image and the 3-D geometrical model is crucial in estimating the camera transform between the image plane and the 3-D object. The intrinsic nature of our modeling scheme allows us to pose this problem as a subgraph-matching procedure between the projection graph and the model graph. The proposed scheme is efficient in memory requirement, as it requires one model graph for each model. A parallel search algorithm has been devised based on the proposed scheme and was shown to have time complexity of $O(1)$ in the topological match stage and time complexity of $O(m)$ in the final verification. The projection graph from an imperfect line drawing can also be shown to be a subgraph isomorphism of the model graph and therefore the scheme is effective in noisy and poorly lighted environments where perfect line drawings cannot be extracted. Finally, we discussed the addition of 3-D coordinate values (for vertices), the edge length (for straight edges) and parametric cubic curves representation (for curved edges) as additional attributes in the model graph. This results in a more complete representation and, consequently, a better recognition procedure can be developed based on it.

## REFERENCES

1. R.C. Bolles, J.H. Kremers and R.A. Cain, "A simple sensor to gather three-dimensional data", Tech. Note 249, SRI International, Inc., Menlo Park, CA, 1981.
2. I. Chakravarty and H. Freeman, "Characteristic views as a basis for three-dimensional object recognition", *SPIE, Vol. 336 Robot Vision*, 1982, pp. 37-45.
3. S.E. Yam, "Three-dimensional pattern analysis for industrial robotic systems", Ph.D. thesis, School of Electrical Engineering, Purdue University, August, 1976.
4. W.A. Perkins, "A model-based vision system for industrial parts", *IEEE Trans. on Computers* **27** (1978) 126-143.
5. Aristides A.G. Requicha, "Representation for rigid solids: theory, methods and systems", *Computing Surveys* **12** (1980) 437-464.
6. L.G. Roberts, "Machine perception of three-dimensional solids", in *Optical and Electro-Optical Information Processing*, ed. J. Tipett (MIT Press, Cambridge, MA 1965) pp. 159-197.
7. R.A. Brooks, R. Greiner and T.O. Binford, "The ACRONYM model-based vision system", *Proc. IJCAI*, **6**, Tokyo, 1979, pp. 105-113.
8. R.C. Bolles, "Verification vision for programmable assembly", *Proc. of IJCAI-77*, Cambridge, Aug. 1977, pp. 569-575.
9. P.G. Mulgaonkav, L.G. Shapiro and R.M. Haralick, "Recognizing three-dimensional objects from single perspective views using geometric and relational reasoning", in *Proc. IEEE Computer Society Conf. Pattern Recognition and Image Processing*, 14-17 June, 1982, pp. 479-484.
10. E.K. Wong and K.S. Fu, "A graph-theoretic approach to model-matching in computer vision", *Second IEEE Computer Society Workshop on Computer Vision: Representation and Control*, Annapolis, MD, 30 April-2 May 1984, pp. 106-111.
11. A. Sanfeliu and K.S. Fu, "Distance between attributed relational graphs for pattern recognition", *IEEE Trans. Syst., Man, Cybern.* **13** (1983) 353-362.
12. A. Sanfeliu, "An application of a distance measure between graphs to the analysis of muscle tissue patterns", Purdue Univ., West Lafayette, IN, TR-EE, 81-15, May 1981.
13. W.H. Tsai and K.S. Fu, "Error-correcting isomorphism of attributed relational graphs for pattern analysis", *IEEE Trans. Syst. Man, Cybern.* **9** (1979) 757-768.
14. W.H. Tsai and K.S. Fu, "Subgraph error-correcting isomorphism for syntactic pattern recognition", *IEEE Trans. Syst., Man, Cybern.* **13** (1983) 48-62.
15. M.A. Eshera, "A graph distance measure for image analysis", *IEEE Trans. Syst., Man, Cybern.* **14** (1984) 398-408.
16. O.D. Faugeras and M. Berthod, "Scene labeling: An optimization approach", *Proc. of IEEE Conf. Pattern Recognition and Image Processing*, Chicago, August, 1979, pp. 318-326.
17. R. Nevatia, *Machine Perception* (Prentice-Hall, NJ, 1982).

18. R. Shapira, "Computer reconstruction of bodies bounded by quadric surfaces from a set of imperfect projections", Tech. Rep. CRL-48, Rensselauer Polytechnic Inst., Troy, NY, 1976.

19. I. Chakravarty, "A generalized line and junction labeling scheme with application to scene analysis", *IEEE Trans. Patt. Analy. Mach. Intell.* 1 (1979) 202-205.

20. M.B. Clowes, "On seeing things", *Artificial Intelligence* 1 (1970) 79-116.

21. D.A. Huffman, "Impossible objects as nonsense sentences", in *Machine Intelligence, Vol. 6*, eds., B. Meltzer and D. Michie, (American Elsevier, New York, 1971) pp. 295-323.

22. J.D. Foley and A. Van Dam, *Fundamentals of Interactive Computer Graphics* (Addison Wesley, 1984).

23. J.A. Bondy and U.S.R. Murty, *Graph Theory with Applications* (North-Holland, 1981).

24. I. Sobel, "On calibrating computer controlled cameras for perceiving 3-D scenes", *Artificial Intelligence* 5 (1974) 185-198.

25. D.B. Gennery, "Modeling the environment of an exploring vehicle by means of stereo vision", Stanford Artificial Intelligence Laboratory Memo AIM-339 (Ph.D. thesis), June 1980.

26. M.A. Fischler and R.C. Bolles, "Random samples consensus: A paradigm for model filtering with applications to image analysis and automated cartography", *Commun. ACM* 24 (1981) 381-396.

27. E.K. Wong, "A graph-theoretic approach to 3-D objects representation and recognition", in preparation for submission to *IEEE Trans. on Pattern Analysis and Machine Intelligence*.

# 15

# CHINESE CHARACTER RECOGNITION

J.W. TAI and Y. J. LIU
*Institute of Automation*
*Academia Sinica, Beijing*
*China*

By means of attribute grammar, a syntactic-semantic method which unifies the statistical and syntactic approaches to pictorial pattern recognition is proposed in this chapter. In addition, the application of the method to character description and on-line hand-written Chinese character recognition is discussed. A fuzzy attributed finite-state automaton is introduced for stroke recognition. According to the intrinsic structure of Chinese characters a two-dimensional character is transformed into a one-dimensional attributed string on the basis of order arrangements of Chinese characters. Such strings can be easily recognized by template matching. Finally, the implementation of an on-line handwritten Chinese character recognition system is described.

## 1. INTRODUCTION

Chinese character recognition is a key problem for information process-ing in China. Recent work on this topic has been reported in Refs. 1–7. Actually, Chinese characters are pictorial patterns consisting of curve seg-ments as well as straight-line segments. A Chinese character which consists of one part with several strokes is called a single component character. In contrast, a Chinese character which consists of a few parts, with each part having several strokes is called a compound character. Two strokes of a character may be unconnected, or one stroke of a character may contain some connecting points which join the stroke to other strokes. An example of two kinds of Chinese characters are shown in Fig. 1.

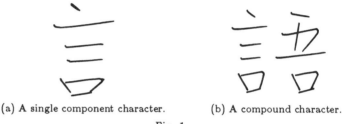

(a) A single component character.    (b) A compound character.

Fig. 1.

Obviously, the structural properties of Chinese characters are important and can be applied to Chinese character recognition, especially for on-line Chinese character recognition. The structure of Chinese characters can be divided into four levels. They are: (1) whole character level, (2) parts of character level, (3) stroke level and (4) line segments level. In the Chinese language we can find 7000–10000 whole characters, 200–500 parts of character, 40–80 strokes and 4–8 straight-line segments. Level 1 is the highest level with complex structure and level 4 is the lowest level with simple structure.

In fact, a structural (or syntactic) approach for Chinese character recog-nition is satisfactory. A set of strokes or straight-line segments can be considered as a set of primitives, and production rules can also be found according to the properties of characters. In this chapter, first, some rela-tions between two curve segments or straight-line segments are discussed. The position of a curve segment relative to another curve segment plays an important role in the construction of Chinese characters. The operations of PDL[8] are extended by introducing attributes. We know PDL is efficient in describing some kinds of pictorial pattern such as photographs in particle physics, but it is not sufficient for describing Chinese characters with several connecting points of a stroke, which connect to other strokes.

Secondly, an attributed grammar approach is introduced. Comparing the attributed grammar approach with the statistical and the classical syntactic approaches, one may find that the statistical approach is unable to describe complex pattern structures and subpattern relations, and the classical syntactic approach is weak in handling noisy patterns and numerical semantic information[9-12]. These shortcomings can be overcome if the attributed grammar approach is applied. We define in Sec. 3, that an attributed grammar includes two parts, a syntactic part represented by a phrase structure grammar, and a semantic part consisting of three sets: (1) a set of primitive attributes, (2) a set of relations with attributes, and (3) a set of semantic rules. The former is used to specify language syntax, and the latter to add contextual semantics. Besides, not only an attributed string grammar but also a two dimensional attributed tree grammar is defined. Such an "attributed grammar approach" is termed as "syntactic-semantic approach". Then based on the fact that the normal form of an attributed grammar is in a finite state form, some examples of describing Chinese characters by attributed finite state grammars are given in Sec. 4. In addition, a distance measure consisting of syntactic and semantic parts is defined for the recognition of pictorial patterns by a minimum distance criterion.

Finally, on-line Chinese character recognition is the main topic of the last section. For Chinese characters, strokes are basic units, and a stroke is composed of curve segments and straight-line segments, or it can be approximated by straight-line segments. The straight-line segments are chosen as primitives. A fuzzy attributed finite-state automaton is given for recognizing straight-line segments. Another interesting problem is that when one writes a Chinese character on an input, a sequence of strokes is obtained. The order of strokes is an important piece of information in recognizing the character, but different writers may have a different order of strokes because it is impossible for them to have the same educational background and culture, etc. According to the intrinsic structural properties of Chinese characters, a method for order arrangement of stroke, independent of writers, is provided. By means of order arrangement, two-dimensional pictorial patterns such as Chinese characters can be transformed into one-dimensional stable strings of primitives, and can then be processed by a syntactic-semantic approach.

## 2. SOME RELATIONS BETWEEN TWO CURVE SEGMENTS

A Chinese character is composed of strokes, and strokes are curve segments or straight-line segments. In fact, the latter is a special case of the former, so curve segments can be considered as the basic units or primitives and the relationships between strokes of a character reflect the structural information of the character. In this section, we focus on the relation between a pair of curve segments. Some definitions are briefly reviewed[11,12], and the new definitions are given.

**Definition 2.1.** A simple curve segment is a curve segment with either $f(l) > 0$ or $f(l) < 0$ for $0 < l < L$, where

$$f(l) = \lim_{\Delta l \to 0} \frac{1}{\Delta l} \left[ \begin{matrix} \text{angle between the tangent line to the} \\ \text{curve segment at } 1 - \frac{1}{2}\Delta l \text{ and } 1 + \frac{1}{2}\Delta l \end{matrix} \right].$$

**Definition 2.2.** A curve segment $\overset{\frown}{X_1 X_2}$ is denoted as a 2-tuple

$$\overset{\frown}{X_1 X_2} = (a, \ x)$$

where $a$ is a syntactic symbol denoting the structure of $\overset{\frown}{X_1 X_2}$ and $x = A(a) = (L, \ \phi, \ R)$ is an attribute vector, where

$$L = \int_0^L dl, \quad \phi = \int_0^L f(l) dl, \quad R = \int_0^L \left( \int_0^S f(l) dl \frac{\phi}{2} \right) ds$$

and $c$ is a vector which connects $X_1$ to $X_2$.

**Definition 2.3.** A binary relation REL between a pair of curve primitives $A$ and $B$ is denoted as a 2-tuple

$$\text{REL} \ (A, \ B) = (u, \ x)$$

where $u$ is a syntactic symbol denoting the structure of REL, and $x$ represents the semantic information of REL. It might be a numerical or logical attribute of REL, or some other semantic constraint.

Two curve segments $A$ and $B$ are connected, if the distance between $a \in A$ and $b \in B$ is minimum and equals to $d$, where $0 < d < e$; $e$ is a positive real number. One connecting point of $A$ is labelled $P_a$ if the distance between this point and $a$ is a minimum. In addition, one connecting point of $B$ is labelled $P_b$ if the distance between this point and $b$ is a minimum. The relation between $A$ and $B$ is called $P_a P_b$ concatenation relation.

Each curve segment has two end points, one is called the head and the other is called the tail. The vectors from tail to head are denoted by $f$ and $g$ respectively for $A$ and $B$. A curve segment can be linked or concatenated to other curve segments at its tail and/or head.

Four binary concatenation operators like PDL[8] are defined as follows:

| Syntactic and semantic description | Interpretation | Graph |
|---|---|---|
| $\text{REL}(A,\ B) = (+,\ \theta)$ | head $(A)$ CATtail $(B)$; $((h,\ t),\ \theta)$ <br> $\theta$ is the angle between $f$, $g$ | |
| $\text{REL}(A,\ B) = (\times,\ \theta)$ | tail $(A)$ CATtail $(B)$; $((t,\ t),\ \theta)$ <br> $\theta$ is the angle between $f$, $g$ | |
| $\text{REL}(A,\ B) = (-,\ \theta)$ | head $(A)$ CAThead $(B)$; $((h,\ h),\ \theta)$ <br> $\theta$ is the angle between $f$, $g$ | |
| $\text{REL}(A,\ B) = (\div,\ \theta)$ | tail $(A)$ CAThead $(B)$; $((t,\ h),\ \theta)$ <br> $\theta$ is the angle between $f$, $g$ | |

**Definition 2.4.** A primitive $P$ is denoted as $P = (\alpha,\ x)$, where $\alpha$ is a syntactic symbol denoting the structure of $P$, which might be a simple curve segment with $n$ connecting points. $x$ is a set of attributes which includes three kinds of attributes.

(1) $n$ connecting vectors of $p$, $p(1)$, $p(2),\ldots,p(n)$, where $p(k)$ is the vector from the point $k-1$ to point $k$, $k = 2, 3,\ldots,n$ and $p(1) = p(2)$,

(2) the rank of $p(i)$ $i = 1, 2,\ldots,n$. $r(p) = N^{+} \cup 0$,

(3) the primitive attributes of $p$, $A(p) = (l_1,\ l_2,\ldots,l_n)$, where $l_k$ is the length of the curve segment from point $k$ to point $k+1$.

A special case is $p$ which has only two connecting points, a tail and a head, then $x = (c,\ r(c),\ L)$ where $c$ is the vector from tail to head. $r$ is the rank of $c$, and $L$ is the length of the curve segment.

**Definition 2.5.** A generalized concatenation relation between two primitives $A$ and $B$ is denoted as $\text{REL}(A,\ B) = (E = (k,\ m), \theta)$, where $(k,\ m)$

represents the linking styles between vector $p(k-1)$ of $A$ and vector $p(m-1)$ of $B$. And $\theta$ is the angle between $p(k-1)$ and $p(m-1)$. $E$ can be written as

$$E = (k,\ m) = \begin{cases} + & \text{if } k = n_1,\ m = 1 \\ \times & \text{if } k = m = 1 \\ - & \text{if } k = 1,\ m = n_2 \\ \div & \text{other cases .} \end{cases}$$

If two segments $A$ and $B$ are unconnected, and $m_1$ and $m_2$ are two middle points of $A$ and $B$ respectively then the projection of $A$ and $B$ on $x, y$ axes are $X_a, X_b, Y_a$ and $Y_b$, and the length of $X_a, X_b, Y_a$ and $Y_b$ are $x_a, x_b, x_c$ and $x_d$ respectively. Let $x = \max[x_a, x_b], y = \max[y_a, y_b]$, the $x$ axis is divided into three parts i.e. left part, middle part and right part, by the two end points of $x$. And the $y$ axis is divided into three parts i.e. the part above $y$, the middle part and the part below $y$, by the two end points of $y$. We determine which parts the coordinates of the middle point of the relative curve segment ($A$ relative to $B$, $B$ relative to $A$) are located in. For coordinate $x$, consider $A$ relative to $B$; one case is $\max[x_a,\ x_b] = x_b$, where the location of the middle point of $A$ on the $x$ axis can be easily verified and is labelled by $Q$. Another case is $\max[x_a,\ x_b] = x_a$ for which we can find out the location of the middle point of $B$ on the $x$ axis. Suppose it belongs to part $\overline{Q}$, then we transfer it by the rules: left $\longrightarrow$ right, right $\longrightarrow$ left, and middle $\longrightarrow$ middle to get the part name $Q_a$ ($A$ relative to $B$) on the $x$ axis, as shown in Fig. 2. Similarly we can get the part name $Q_b$ ($A$ relative to $B$) on the $y$ axis. The relation between $A$ and $B$ is called a $Q_a Q_b$ relation.

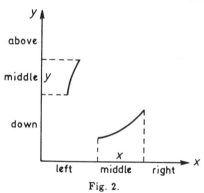

Fig. 2.

For two curve segments $A$ and $B$ which are unconnected, if the middle point of $B$ is the reference point, eight directions including left above (la), middle above (ma), right above (ra), left middle (lm), right middle (rm), left down (ld), middle down (md) and right down (rd) can be applied to represent a position with $A$ relative to $B$.

To sum up, the relative position of two unconnected curve segments is given in the following:

**Definition 2.6.** For a pair of unconnected primitives $A$ and $B$, the position where $A$ is relative to $B$ is defined as

$$\text{REL}\,(A,\ B) = (E,\ re^{i\theta})$$

where $E \in$ (la, ma, ra, lm, rm, ld, md, rd); $re$ is the vector from the middle point of $B$ to the middle point of $A$. The relation REL $(A,\ B)$ is represented as

$$\text{REL}(A,\ B) = \begin{cases} \text{rm if } r \neq 0 & -\frac{\pi}{8} < \theta \leq \frac{\pi}{8} \\ \text{ra if } r \neq 0 & \frac{\pi}{8} < \theta \leq \frac{3}{8}\pi \\ \text{ma if } r \neq 0 & \frac{3}{8}\pi < \theta \leq \frac{5}{8}\pi \\ \text{la if } r \neq 0 & \frac{5}{8}\pi < \theta \leq \frac{7}{8}\pi \\ \text{lm if } r \neq 0 & \frac{7}{8}\pi < \theta \leq \frac{9}{8}\pi \\ \text{ld if } r \neq 0 & \frac{9}{8}\pi < \theta \leq \frac{11}{8}\pi \\ \text{md if } r \neq 0 & \frac{11}{8}\pi < \theta \leq \frac{13}{8}\pi \\ \text{rd if } r \neq 0 & \frac{13}{8}\pi < \theta \leq \frac{15}{8}\pi \end{cases}$$

and shown in Fig. 3.

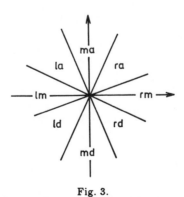

Fig. 3.

## 3. A SYNTACTIC-SEMANTIC APPROACH TO PICTORIAL PATTERN RECOGNITION

A syntactic-semantic approach (attributed grammar approach) to pictorial pattern recognition is presented in this section. Attributed grammars were first formulated by Knuth[13] from the computational linguistics point of view. The description and recognition of patterns by means of attributed grammars have recently been advocated by several investigators[9-12]. As a matter of fact, not only the shortcomings of statistical and classical syntactic approaches have been overcome, but these approaches can also be unified by an attributed grammar approach. First, we define an attributed context-free string grammar as follows:

**Definition 3.1.** An attributed context-free string grammar is a 4-tuple

$$G = (V_N,\ V_T,\ P,\ S)$$

where $V_N$ is a set of nonterminals, $V_T$ is a set of terminals and $S$ is the start symbol. For each $X \in (V_N \cup V_T)$, there exists a finite set of attributes $A(X)$ with each $a$ of $A(X)$ having a set (either finite or infinite) of possible values $D_l$. $P$ is a set of productions each of which consists of two parts: (1) a syntactic rule and (2) a semantic part including a concatenation relation (or a set of concatenations relations) and a semantic rule. The syntactic rule is of the following form

$$X_0 \longrightarrow X_1 X_2 \ldots X_m$$

where $X_0 \in V_N$ and each $X_i \in V_N \cup V_T$ for $1 \leq i \leq m$. The concatenation relation is

$$\mathrm{CAT}\,(a_i,\ a_j) \in \mathrm{R}(a_i,\ a_j)$$

where $a_i, a_j \in V_T$. The semantic rule is a set of expressions of the following form

$$l_1 \longrightarrow f_1(l_{11},\ l_{12}, \ldots, l_{1n_1})$$
$$l_2 \longrightarrow f_2(l_{21},\ l_{22}, \ldots, l_{2n_2})$$
$$\vdots$$
$$l_m \longrightarrow f_m(l_{m1},\ l_{m2}, \ldots, l_{mn_m})$$

where $(l_1, l_2, \ldots, l_m) = A(X_0) \cup A(X_1) \ldots A(X_m)$. Each $l_{ij}(1 \leq i \leq m, 1 \leq j \leq n_i)$ is an attribute of some $X_k$ for $0 \leq k \leq m$, and each $f_i(1 < i < m)$

is an operator which may be in one of the following forms:

(a) a mapping $f_i$; $D_{l_{i1}} \times D_{l_{i2}} \times \ldots \times D_{l_{im}} - D_{l_i}$,

(b) a closed-form function i.e. $l_i$ may be expressed functionally in terms of the value of $l_{i1}, l_{i2}, \ldots, l_{in}$, or

(c) an algorithm which takes $l_{i1}, l_{i2}, \ldots, l_{in}$ and any other available information or data as the input and generates $l_i$ as the output.

**Definition 3.2.** For an attributed context-free grammar, a concatenation relation between two nonterminals $N_1$ and $N_2$ of a derivation tree is defined as follows

$$\text{CAT } (N_1, \ N_2) = \text{CAT } (a, \ b)$$

where $a$ is the leftmost terminal of a subtree with root $N_1$ in the derivation tree, and $b$ is the rightmost terminal of a subtree with root $N_2$ in the derivation tree.

It is well-known that a context-free language (cfl) generated by a context-free grammar (cfg) often consists of infinitive strings. From the pumping lemma for cfl[14]: for any cfl, there exists a constant $n$ depending on $L$, such that if $z$ is in $L$ and $|z| \geq n$ then we may write $z = uvwxy$ such that (1) $|vx| \geq 1$, (2) $|vwx| \leq n$, and (3) for all $i \geq 0, uv^i wx^i y$ is in $L$. If each terminal (primitive) of a cfg consists of straight-line segments, and the length of the line segments as attributes are added to the grammar then the attributes of $v$ and $x$ are represented by $A(v)$ and $A(x)$ respectively. And it is obvious $A(v) = iA(v), A(x) = iA(x)$. $v^i$ and $x^i$ can be considered the same as syntactic symbols $v$ and $x$ as long as proper attributes $iA(v)$ and $iA(x)$ are assigned to $v$ and $x$ from the semantic part of the grammar. The strings $uv^i wx^i y$ might be considered to have the same structure as $uvwxy$ but their semantic contents are different. From this point of view, we can get the following conclusion.

A context-free language generated by a context-free grammar is a finite set of strings if terminals are straight lines, and attributes are added to the grammar.

The proof of this conclusion is omitted as it can be found in Ref. 15. An example is given in the following:

**Example 3.3.**[16]

(1) A context-sensitive grammar $G_1$ is used to describe a set of right-angled triangles.

$$G_1 = (\{S,\ A,\ B\},\ \{a,\ b,\ c\},\ P,\ S)\ ,$$

where $\{a,\ b,\ c\} = \{\rightarrow,\ \searrow,\ \downarrow\}$.

$P$:

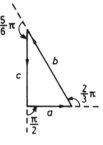

1. $S \longrightarrow aSBA$    5. $bB \longrightarrow bb$
2. $S \longrightarrow aBA$    6. $bA \longrightarrow bc$
3. $AB \longrightarrow BA$    7. $cA \longrightarrow cc$
4. $aB \longrightarrow ab$

$$L(G_1) = \{a^n b^n c^n | n \geq 0\}\ .$$

(2) An attributed cfg $G_2$ can be constructed to generate $L(G)$. We first introduce the attributes for the primitives and relations:

a. The length of the primitive: $A(a) = 1,\ A(b) = 2,\ A(c) = \sqrt{3}$.

b. The concatenation attributes: $\mathrm{CAT}(a,\ b) = (+,\ \frac{2}{3}\pi),\ \mathrm{CAT}(b,\ c) = (+,\ \frac{5}{6}\pi)$ and $\mathrm{CAT}(c,\ a) = (+,\ \frac{\pi}{2})$. Consider the cfg $G_2$.

$$\tilde{G}_2 = (\{S,\ A,\ B,\ C\},\quad \{a,\ b,\ c\},\quad P,\ S)$$

where $P$:

1. $S \longrightarrow ABC$    5. $A \longrightarrow a$
2. $A \longrightarrow aA$    6. $B \longrightarrow b$
3. $B \longrightarrow bB$    7. $C \longrightarrow c$ .
4. $C \longrightarrow cC$

We can add a set of concatenation relations to $G_2$ in order that the grammar might generate $L(G_1)$. In this example, the different primitives are $a$, $b$ and $c$. The syntactic symbol of string $a^n$ is considered the same as $a$ but with length $n$ and $b^n$ is considered the same as $b$ but with length $2n$, and $c^n$ the same as $c$ but with length $\sqrt{3}n$. The concatenation relations between terminals are that $a$ can only concatenate with $b$, $b$ only with $c$ and $c$ only with $a$, and $\mathrm{CAT}(a,\ b) + \mathrm{CAT}(b,\ c) + \mathrm{CAT}(c,\ a) = 2\pi$ must be satisfied. The semantic rules are simple because the attributes of primitives are the lengths of $a$, $b$ and $c$. The attributed cfg $G_2$ is given in the following.

$$G_2 = (\{S,\ A,\ B,\ C\},\quad \{a,\ b,\ c\}\ P,\ S)$$

**where $P$:**

| syntactic part | semantic part | |
|---|---|---|
| | (concatenation relation) | (semantic rule) |

| | | |
|---|---|---|
| $S \longrightarrow ABC$ | $\mathrm{CAT}(S,\ A) = \mathrm{CAT}(c,\ a) = (+,\ \frac{\pi}{2})$ | $A(S) = A(A) + A(B) + A(C)$ |
| $A \longrightarrow aA$ | $\mathrm{CAT}(A,\ B) = \mathrm{CAT}(a,\ b) = (+,\ \frac{2}{3}\pi)$ | $A(A) = 1 + A(A)$ |
| $B \longrightarrow bB$ | $\mathrm{CAT}(B,\ C) = \mathrm{CAT}(b,\ c) = (+,\ \frac{5}{6}\pi)$ | $A(B) = 2 + A(B)$ |
| $C \longrightarrow cC$ | $\mathrm{CAT}(C,\ A) = \mathrm{CAT}(c,\ a) = (+,\ \frac{\pi}{2})$ | $A(C) = \sqrt{3} + A(C)$ |
| $A \longrightarrow a$ | | $A(A) = 1$ |
| $B \longrightarrow b$ | | $A(B) = 2$ |
| $C \longrightarrow c$ | | $A(C) = \sqrt{3}$ |

The grammar $G_2$ is actually a context-free programmed grammar. The concatenation relations can be equivalently intepreted by the following context-free programmed grammar

$$G'_2 = (\{S,\ A,\ B,\ C\},\quad \{a,\ b,\ c\},\quad P,\ S)$$

**where $P$ :**

| label | core | success field | failure field |
|---|---|---|---|
| 1. | $S \longrightarrow ABC$ | $\{2,\ 5\}$ | $\{0\}$ |
| 2. | $A \longrightarrow aA$ | $\{3\}$ | $\{0\}$ |
| 3. | $B \longrightarrow bB$ | $\{4\}$ | $\{0\}$ |
| 4. | $C \longrightarrow cC$ | $\{5,\ 2\}$ | $\{0\}$ |
| 5. | $A \longrightarrow a$ | $\{6\}$ | $\{0\}$ |
| 6. | $B \longrightarrow b$ | $\{7\}$ | $\{0\}$ |
| 7. | $C \longrightarrow c$ | $\{0\}$ | $\{0\}$ |

(3) Furthermore, an attributed finite-state grammar can be constructed to describe a set of right-angled triangles if concatenation attributes between a pair of primitives and node attributes are introduced into the grammar. Such an attributed finite-state grammar $G_3$ is given in the following.

$$G_3 = (\{S,\ N_1,\ N_2\},\quad \{a,\ b,\ c\},\quad P,\ S)$$

where $a, b, c$ and straight-line segments are as follows:

$$\overline{a} \qquad b\backslash \qquad c|$$

*P:*

|  | syntactic part | semantic part | |
|---|---|---|---|
|  |  | (concatenation relation) | (semantic rule) |
| 1. | $S \longrightarrow aN$ | CAT $(a,\ b) = (+, \frac{2}{3}\pi)$ | $A(a) = n$ |
| 2. | $N \longrightarrow bN$ | CAT $(b,\ c) = (+, \frac{5}{6}\pi)$ | $B(b) = 2n$ |
| 3. | $N \longrightarrow c$ | CAT $(c,\ a) = (+, \frac{1}{2}\pi)$ | $A(c) = \sqrt{3}n$ |

If $n$ is assigned various positive integers, a set of right-angled triangles is obtained and

$$L(G_3) = L(G_1) \ .$$

The grammars mentioned above are string grammars which generate attributed strings. A tree grammar with attributes is defined[16,17] in terms of the properties of concatenation relations referred to in PDL tree grammar and plex grammar[18].

**Definition 3.4.** A relational attributed tree grammar (RATG) is a 4-tuple $G = (N, V, P, S)$ where $N$ is a finite set of nonterminals, $V$ is a finite set of terminals with attributes, $S$ is the starting symbol, and $P$ is a finite set of productions. Each production has the following form:

syntactic part                          semantic part

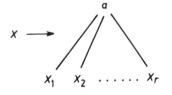

$$X \longrightarrow$$

CAT$(a,\ X_i) = $ CAT$(a,\ b_i)$ where $b_i$ is the root of subtree $T_i$ generated by $G$ starting from $X_i$.

$a, b \in V; X, X_i \in N; i = 1, 2, \ldots r.$

**Example 3.5.** An RATG in expansive form (context-free form) is applied to describe the Chinese character 扔

$$G = (N, V, P, S)$$

where

$$N = \{S, A_1, A_2, \ldots, A_m\}$$

$$V = \left\{ \; \begin{matrix} a_0 \end{matrix} \;, \; \begin{matrix} a_1 \end{matrix} \;, \; \begin{matrix} a_2 \end{matrix} \;, \; \begin{matrix} a \end{matrix} \; \right\}$$

$A(a_0) = (l_1, l_2), \quad A(a_1) = (l_1, l_2), \quad A(a_2) = (l_1, l_2, l_3), \quad A(a_3) = (l_1, l_2)$

$r(a_0) = \{1, 0\}, \quad r(a_1) = \{3, 2, 0\}, \quad r(a_2) = \{2, 1, 0\}, \quad r(a_3) = \{1\}$

$P:$

| syntactic part | semantic part |
|---|---|
| $S \longrightarrow \begin{matrix} a_1 \\ \mid \\ A_1 \end{matrix}$ | $A(a_1) = (\frac{1}{2}, \frac{1}{2})$ <br> $\mathrm{CAT}(a_1, A_1) = \mathrm{CAT}(a_1, a_0) = ((3, 1)(+, \frac{2}{3}\pi))$ |
| $A_1 \longrightarrow \begin{matrix} a_0 \\ \mid \\ A_2 \end{matrix}$ | $A(a_0) = (\frac{1}{2}, \frac{1}{2})$ <br> $\mathrm{CAT}(a_0, A_2) = \mathrm{CAT}(a_0, a_3) = ((2, 2)(-, \frac{1}{2}\pi))$ |
| $A_2 \longrightarrow \begin{matrix} a_3 \\ \mid \\ A_3 \end{matrix}$ | $A(a_3) = (\frac{1}{2}, \frac{1}{2})$ <br> $\mathrm{CAT}(a_3, A_3) = \mathrm{CAT}(a_3, a_1) = ((3, 2)(\times, \frac{1}{6}\pi))$ |
| $A_3 \longrightarrow \begin{matrix} a_1 \\ \diagup \mid \diagdown \\ A_5 \quad A_4 \quad A_6 \end{matrix}$ | $A(a) = (1, 1)$ <br> $\mathrm{CAT}(a_1, A_4) = \mathrm{CAT}(a_1, a_2) = ((2, 1)(+, \frac{1}{2}\pi))$ <br> $\mathrm{CAT}(a_1, A_5) = \mathrm{CAT}(a_1, a_2) = ((1, 1)(\times, \frac{1}{2}\pi))$ <br> $\mathrm{CAT}(a_1, A_6) = \mathrm{CAT}(a_1, a_2) = ((3, 1)(+, \frac{1}{2}\pi))$ |
| $A_4 \longrightarrow \begin{matrix} a_2 \\ \diagup \mid \diagdown \\ A_7 \; A_8 \; A_9 \; A_{10} \end{matrix}$ | $A_5 \longrightarrow a_2, \; A(a_2) = (1, 1, \frac{1}{8}), \; A(a_2) = (1, 0, 1)$ <br> $A_6 \longrightarrow a_2, \; A(a_2) = (1, 0, 1)$ <br> $\mathrm{CAT}(a_2, A_7) = \mathrm{CAT}(a_2, a_1) = ((4, 2)(\times, -\frac{\pi}{2}))$ <br> $\mathrm{CAT}(a_2, A_8) = \mathrm{CAT}(a_2, a_1) = ((3, 2)(\times, -\frac{\pi}{2}))$ <br> $\mathrm{CAT}(a_2, A_9) = \mathrm{CAT}(a_2, a_1) = ((2, 2)(\times, -\frac{\pi}{2}))$ <br> $\mathrm{CAT}(a_2, A_{10}) = \mathrm{CAT}(a_2, a_0) = ((4, 1)(+, -\frac{\pi}{6}))$ |
| $A_7 \longrightarrow \begin{matrix} a_1 \\ \mid \\ A_{11} \end{matrix}$ | $A_8 \longrightarrow a_1, \; A(a_1) = (1, 1), \; A(a_1) = (\frac{4}{5}, \frac{4}{5})$ <br> $A_9 \longrightarrow a_1, \; A_{10} \longrightarrow a_0, \; A(a_1) = (\frac{4}{5}, \frac{4}{5}),$ <br> $A(a_0) = (1, 1)$ <br> $\mathrm{CAT}(a_1, A_{10}) = \mathrm{CAT}(a_1, a_0) = ((3, 1)(+, \frac{\pi}{6}))$ |
| $A_{11} \longrightarrow \quad a_0$ | $A(a_0) = (1, 1)$ |

The Chinese character 甬 is represented by an attributed tree in Fig. 4.

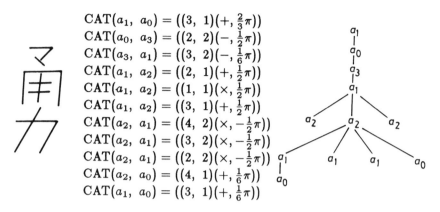

$$\begin{aligned}
\mathrm{CAT}(a_1,\ a_0) &= ((3,\ 1)(+,\tfrac{2}{3}\pi))\\
\mathrm{CAT}(a_0,\ a_3) &= ((2,\ 2)(-,\tfrac{1}{2}\pi))\\
\mathrm{CAT}(a_3,\ a_1) &= ((3,\ 2)(-,\tfrac{1}{6}\pi))\\
\mathrm{CAT}(a_1,\ a_2) &= ((2,\ 1)(+,\tfrac{1}{2}\pi))\\
\mathrm{CAT}(a_1,\ a_2) &= ((1,\ 1)(\times,\tfrac{1}{2}\pi))\\
\mathrm{CAT}(a_1,\ a_2) &= ((3,\ 1)(+,\tfrac{1}{2}\pi))\\
\mathrm{CAT}(a_2,\ a_1) &= ((4,\ 2)(\times,-\tfrac{1}{2}\pi))\\
\mathrm{CAT}(a_2,\ a_1) &= ((3,\ 2)(\times,-\tfrac{1}{2}\pi))\\
\mathrm{CAT}(a_2,\ a_1) &= ((2,\ 2)(\times,-\tfrac{1}{2}\pi))\\
\mathrm{CAT}(a_2,\ a_0) &= ((4,\ 1)(+,\tfrac{1}{6}\pi))\\
\mathrm{CAT}(a_1,\ a_0) &= ((3,\ 1)(+,\tfrac{1}{6}\pi))
\end{aligned}$$

Fig. 4. The attributed tree of character.

If the concatenation attributes (angle between two connecting vectors) and primitive attributes (length of primitive) are considered as parameters, we can get the various distorted versions of a Chinese character. Three distorted versions of character 甬 are given in Fig. 5.

Fig. 5. Different versions of a character.

For an RATG if the terminal in $V$ has only two connecting points, a tail (point 1) and a head (point 2), then the connecting vector is the vector from point 1 to point 2, and the concatenation relations between $a$ and $X_k$ means CAT $(a,\ X_k) = $ CAT $(a,\ a_k)$, where $a_k$ is the root of the subtree generated by $G$ from $X_k$. Let $i$ and $i_k$ denote the unit vectors of $a$ and $a_k$ respectively, then the geometric interpretation of the concatenation relation can be given as follows:

1. $\mathrm{CAT}(a,\ a_k) = (+,\ \cos^{-1}(i \cdot i_k))$    2. $\mathrm{CAT}(a,\ a_k) = (-,\ \cos^{-1}(i \cdot i_k))$

3. $\text{CAT}(a, a_k) = (\times, \cos^{-1}(i \cdot i_k))$  4. $\text{CAT}(a, a_k) = (+, \cos^{-1}(-i \cdot -i_k))$

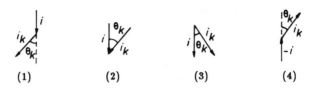

(1)  (2)  (3)  (4)

An example is given in the following to illustrate that the "directed triangles" generated by a context-sensitive web grammar[18] can be generated by an RATG in context-free form[16].

**Example 3.6.** An RATG which generates directed triangles is given as

$$G = (N, V, A, P)$$

where

$$N = \{A_1, A_2\}$$

$$V = \{a : \quad \|s\| = \|t\| = 1, \quad s \cdot t = \cos\theta\}$$

*P:*

| syntactic | | semantic part |
|---|---|---|
| 1. $A_1 \longrightarrow$ | $a$, $A_1$ $A_2$ | $\text{CAT}(a, A_1)$ $\text{CAT}(a, A_2)$ |
| 2. $A_2 \longrightarrow$ | $a$, $A_2$ | $\text{CAT}(a, A_2)$ |
| 3. $A_1 \longrightarrow$ | $a$ | |
| 4. $A_2 \longrightarrow$ | $a$ | |

A typical sentence of $L(G)$ is generated by the derivation

$$\text{CAT}(a,\ a) = ((2,\ 1), s \cdot s = 1)$$

$$\text{CAT}(a,\ a) = ((2,\ 1), s \cdot s = 1)$$

$$\text{CAT}(a,\ a) = ((3,\ 1), t \cdot t = \theta)$$

$$\text{CAT}(a,\ a) = ((3,\ 1), t \cdot t = \theta)$$

$$\text{CAT}(a,\ a) = ((3,\ 1), t \cdot t = \theta).$$

## 4. DESCRIBING CHINESE CHARACTERS BY MEANS OF ATTRIBUTED FINITE-STATE GRAMMARS

As mentioned above, an important property of attributed grammars is that there exists a trade-off between syntactic and semantic complexities in grammar definition. In other words, semantic information can be applied to achieve lower syntax in pattern description. Thus, a finite state form, as the syntactic part of an attributed grammar, is sufficient for describing Chinese characters, if some kinds of semantic information are added to the grammar.

To sum up, an attributed finite-state grammar might be applied to describe Chinese characters consisting of connected (crossed) or unconnected strokes.

Three examples are given below. To put it in a simple way, suppose that the strokes are straight-line segments.

**Example 4.1.** An attributed finite-state grammar $G$ is applied to describe the Chinese character

$$G = (\{\overrightarrow{a}, \nearrow b, \downarrow c, \searrow d\}, \{N_0, \dots, N_4\}, P, N)$$

$P$:

$$N_0 \longrightarrow aN_1 \qquad A(a) = 1$$
$$\mathrm{REL}(a, a) = (\mathrm{md}, r_1 e^{i\theta_1})$$

$$N_1 \longrightarrow aN_2 \qquad A(a) = 2$$
$$\mathrm{REL}(a, b) = (\mathrm{ld}, r_2 e^{i\theta_2})$$

$$N_2 \longrightarrow bN_3 \qquad A(b) = 1.5$$
$$\mathrm{REL}(b, c) = (\mathrm{rm}, r_3 e^{i\theta_3})$$

$$N_3 \longrightarrow cN_4 \qquad A(c) = 1.5$$
$$\mathrm{REL}(c, d) = (\mathrm{rm}, r_4 e^{i\theta_4})$$

$$N \longrightarrow d \qquad A(d) = 2$$

**Example 4.2.** This example illustrates that Chinese characters with both unconnected strokes and crossed strokes can also be described by an attributed finite-state grammar $G$ as follows:

$$G = (\{\searrow a, \quad \xrightarrow{\phantom{x}} b, \quad {}_2\!\nearrow^1\!c, \quad \searrow^1_2 d\}, \quad \{N_0, N_1, N_2, N_3\}, \ P, N)$$

$P$:

$$N_0 \longrightarrow aN_1 \qquad A(a) = 0.2$$
$$\mathrm{REL}(a, b) = (\mathrm{ld}, r_1 e^{i\theta_1})$$

$$N_1 \longrightarrow bN_2 \qquad A(b) = 1$$
$$\mathrm{REL}(b, c) = (\mathrm{md}, r_2 e^{i\theta_2})$$

$$N_2 \longrightarrow cN_3 \qquad A(c) = 1$$
$$\text{REL}(c,\ d) = ((2,\ 2), \tfrac{\pi}{2})$$

$$N_3 \longrightarrow d \qquad A(d) = 1$$

It is obvious that the above description of a Chinese character is independent of translation and rotation.

**Example 4.3.** The Chinese character 勇 is generated by an RATG in finite-state form with more complex concatenation relations.

$$G = (N,\ V,\ S,\ P)$$

where

$$N = \{N_1, N_2, \ldots, N_{11}, S\}$$

$V$ is the same as $V$ of Ex. 3.5.

$P$:

| syntactic part | semantic part |
|---|---|
| $S \longrightarrow a_1 N_1$ | $\text{CAT}(a_1, a_0) = ((3,\ 1)(+,\ \tfrac{2}{3}\pi))$ |
| $N_1 \longrightarrow a_0 N_2$ | $\text{CAT}(a_0, a_3) = ((3,\ 2)(-,\ \tfrac{1}{2}\pi))$ |
| $N_2 \longrightarrow a_3 N_3$ | $\text{CAT}(a_3, a_1) = ((3,\ 2)(-,\ \tfrac{1}{6}\pi))$ |
| $N_3 \longrightarrow a_1 N_4$ | $\text{CAT}(a_1, a_2) = ((1,\ 1)(\times,\ \tfrac{1}{2}\pi))$ |
| $N_4 \longrightarrow a_2 N_5$ | $\text{CAT}(a_1, a_2) = ((3,\ 1)(+,\ \tfrac{1}{2}\pi))$ |
| $N_5 \longrightarrow a_2 N_6$ | $\text{CAT}(a_1, a_2) = ((2,\ 1)(+,\ \tfrac{1}{2}\pi))$ |
| $N_6 \longrightarrow a_2 N_7$ | $\text{CAT}(a_2, a_1) = ((2,\ 2)(-,\ -\tfrac{1}{2}\pi))$ |
| $N_7 \longrightarrow a_1 N_8$ | $\text{CAT}(a_2, a_1) = ((3,\ 2)(-,\ -\tfrac{1}{2}\pi))$ |
| $N_8 \longrightarrow a_1 N_9$ | $\text{CAT}(a_2, a_0) = ((4,\ 2)(+,\ \tfrac{1}{6}\pi))$ |
| $N_9 \longrightarrow a_0 N_{10}$ | $\text{CAT}(a_0, a_1) = ((1,\ 2)(-,\ \tfrac{2}{3}\pi))$ |
| $N_{10} \longrightarrow a_1 N_{11}$ | $\text{CAT}(a_1, a_0) = ((3,\ 1)(+,\ \tfrac{2}{3}\pi))$ |
| $N_{11} \longrightarrow a_0$ | |

In this example, unlike conventional attributed string grammar[19], the concatenation relations are not defined between two consecutive primitives. Although the grammar is finite-state grammar, the concatenation relations are more complicated than that in expansive tree grammar form.

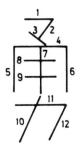

An attributed string is generated by $G$ as follows

$a_1 \ a_0 \ a_3 \ a_1 \ a_2 \ a_2 \ a_2 \ a_1 \ a_1 \ a_0 \ a_1 \ a_0$ .

Most Chinese characters are compound characters, i.e. composed of several parts. A printed compound Chinese character can be viewed as a square. Precisely, a printed compound Chinese character is located in a square. And each part of the character is located in a polygon. Actually, the relative position of one part to another part of a character is the same as the relative position of the polygon around part A to the polygon around part B. From *Xin Hua* Dictionary, more than 7000 Chinese character were analysed. A square is composed of various combinations of two polygons as follows:

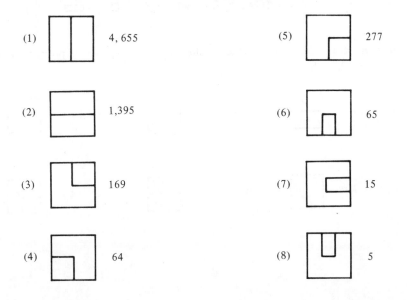

(1)    4, 655

(2)    1,395

(3)    169

(4)    64

(5)    277

(6)    65

(7)    15

(8)    5

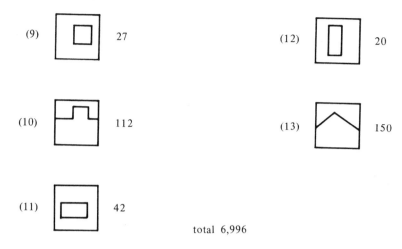

(9)    27

(12)   20

(10)   112

(13)   150

(11)   42

total 6,996

We choose the symbols AB, LR, HA, CA to represent above-below, left-right, half around, and around respectively. The relations between two polygons $P$ and $Q$ are denoted as

$$
\text{REL}(P,\ Q) = \begin{cases}
(\text{AB}, \varepsilon, K) & \text{where } \varepsilon \in \{ \llcorner , \sqcap , \wedge \} \\
(\text{LR},\ \delta,\ K) & \text{where } \delta \in \{0, \tfrac{\pi}{4}, -\tfrac{\pi}{4}\} \\
(\text{HA},\ \gamma, K) & \text{where } \gamma \in \{0, \tfrac{\pi}{2}, -\tfrac{\pi}{2}\} \\
(\text{CA},\ \beta, K) & \text{where } \beta \in \{\square ,\ \square ,\ \square \}
\end{cases}
$$

$0 < K < 1$, where $K$ represents the ratio of the area of polygon $P$ to the area of the whole square.

(AB, $\llcorner$, $K$):  ,  (AB, $\sqcap$, $K$):  ,  (AB, $\wedge$, $K$):  .

(LR, 0, $K$):  ,  (LR, $\frac{\pi}{4}$, $K$):  ,  (LR, $-\frac{\pi}{4}$, $K$):  .

$(HA, 0, K)$:  ,  $(HA, \frac{\pi}{2}, K)$:  ,  $(HA, -\frac{\pi}{2}, K)$:  .

$(CA, 0, K)$:  ,  $(CA, \square, K)$:  ,  $(CA, \blacksquare, K)$:  .

A compound Chinese character consists of several parts. After the segmentation, it is divided into two parts, and one part or both parts can be segmented again. For example,

The square around a compound character is thus segmented into several polygons. It is easy to describe the structure of a square, which consists of several polygons, by $G$ as follows:

$$G = (V_N = \{U, V, \ldots\}, \quad V_T = \{A, B, \ldots\}, P, S) .$$

The production forms are

$$U \longrightarrow DW \quad REL(D, W) \quad A(U) = A(D) + A(W)$$

or

$$U \longrightarrow E \qquad\qquad A(U) = A(E) .$$

It is obvious that a derivation tree of $G$ is a two-branch tree. A primitive (a terminal) is a polygon $P$ and the attribute $A(P)$ is the area of the polygon $P$. The relational attribute represents the relative position between two polygons. The structure of a compound Chinese character is the same as the structure of the polygons which the parts of a character are located in. A polygon corresponds to a terminal.

An example is given to illustrate the structure of a compound character. The character is located in a square which is composed of several rectangles. Each part of the character is located in a rectangle. The structure of the square is described by $G$ as follows:

$$G = (\{X, Y, Z, S\}, \quad \{B, C, D, E\}, \quad P, S) .$$

*P*:

| syntactic part | semantic part | |
|---|---|---|
| $S \longrightarrow BX$ | $\mathrm{REL}(B,\ X) = (\mathrm{AB},\ -,\ \frac{1}{3})$ | $A(S) = A(B) + A(X)$ |
| $X \longrightarrow CY$ | $\mathrm{REL}(C,\ Y) = (\mathrm{LR},\ 0,\ \frac{1}{2})$ | $A(X) = A(C) + A(Y)$ |
| $Y \longrightarrow DZ$ | $\mathrm{REL}(D,\ Z) = (\mathrm{AB},\ -,\ \frac{1}{2})$ | $A(Y) = A(D) + A(Z)$ |
| $Z \longrightarrow E$ | | |

where terminal $B, C, D, E$ are rectangles of different sizes.

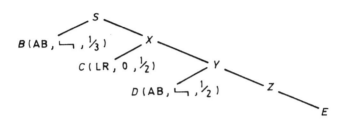

The above derivation tree provides a geometrical relation between parts of the character 鎬 which could also be represented by a string of terminals with relational attributes.

$$B_{(\mathrm{AB},\ -,\frac{1}{3})}\left(C_{(\mathrm{LR},0,\frac{1}{2})}\left(D_{(\mathrm{AB},\ -,\frac{1}{2})}\ E\right)\right)$$

As shown in this example, four terminals denote four rectangles. $A(B)$ is the area of $B$. It is obvious that the semantic rules are linear. According to the semantic rules, from the leaves of the derivation tree to the root, a square corresponding to the root is formed by rectangles corresponding to the nodes of the derivation tree. The area of the square is equal to the total area of the rectangles.

If capital letter $B'$ denotes the starting symbol of an attributed finite-state grammar which generates one part of a compound character located in rectangle $B$, then four parts of the compound character 鎬 are generated by $G_1, G_2, G_3$ and $G_4$ respectively.

From the above discussion, a single component Chinese character corresponds to an attributed string. By means of an attributed representation, we can give a quantitative distance measure between two Chinese characters.

**Definition 4.4.** If a single Chinese character is represented by an attributed string $C_1$

$$C_1 = a_{1_{\text{CAT}(a_1, a_2)}} a_2 \cdots a_{i_{\text{CAT}(a_i, a_{i+1})}} \qquad a_{i+1} \cdots a_n$$

and the structure of a distorted version of $C_2$ is the same as $C_1$

$$C_2 = \tilde{a}_{1_{\text{CAT}(\tilde{a}_1, \tilde{a}_2)}} \tilde{a}_2 \cdots \tilde{a}_{i_{\text{CAT}(\tilde{a}_i, \tilde{a}_{i+1})}} \qquad \tilde{a}_{i+1} \cdots \tilde{a}_n$$

then a distance measure between $C_1$ and its distorted version $C_2$ is

$$d(C_1, \ C_2) = \sum_{i=1}^{n} \left[ \left( \alpha_i \| (A(a_i) - A(\tilde{a}_i)) \|^2 + \beta_i (\theta_i - \tilde{\theta}_i)^2 \right) \right]$$

where $\alpha_i, \beta_i > 0$ are weighting factors.

For compound characters, a character is composed of several parts. Two characters $C_1$ and $C_2$ are considered with the same structure if the number of parts as well as the relative position between two corresponding parts are the same. For two characters with the same structure, a distance similar to the distance between two single component characters can also be given.

Thus a minimum distance criterion can be applied for Chinese character recognition.

## 5. ON-LINE CHINESE CHARACTER RECOGNITION

Stroke extraction is one of the basic problems for on-line Chinese character recognition. Various methods such as dynamic programming, comparison of sequence, finite-state automaton, etc. have been suggested. It is known that a stroke is composed of a straight-line sequence or can be approximated by a straight-line sequence. According to statistical data, there are probably 38 kinds of regular strokes, but many people cannot write in regular stroke form when they write Chinese characters. Even though handwriting is constrained, there are more than 38 kinds of strokes. In

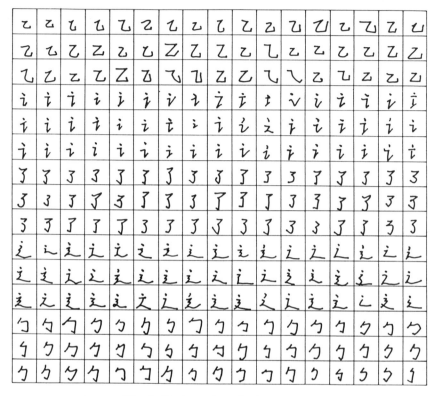

Fig. 6. Strokes written by fifty persons.

fact, there has to be extracted 70 kinds of strokes at least. Some examples of strokes written by fifty persons are given in Fig. 6.

The stroke samples can be decomposed into a sequence of straight-line segments. Regular strokes of constrained handwritten Chinese characters are composed of 11 kinds of generalized line segments as follows:

Four of the 11 line segments are more basic, and others can be approximated by these four basic line segments.

Most approximated Chinese characters consisting of four basic line segments can be classified by computer. If a line segment has three connecting points, named tail, middle and head, see Defs. 2.4 and 2.5, the 17 relations between two straight-line segments are those as listed in Table 1.

Making a comparison between strokes in Fig. 6 and regular strokes, we find that most of the strokes in Fig. 6 include line segments which appear in the corresponding regular strokes. The difference is that some line segments may be added into those strokes, especially at the starting position and inflexional position of the strokes, and the proportion of length of segments in main directions may be different. We consider that the handwritten strokes are distorted versions of regular strokes. For stroke recognition, both conventional template matching techniques and attributed finite-state grammar approach as well as fuzzy set[20] are used.

If a regular stroke is considered as a template which consists of $n$ line segments $a_1, a_2, \ldots, a_n$, the length of $a$ is $A(a_i) = l_i, i = 1, \ldots, n$. The noisy strokes and distorted versions are derived from two kinds of variations. One is that there may be some new short line segments added into the starting position and concatenation position of two consecutive line segments of the regular stroke. Another one is that the lengths of the segments of the regular stroke may be varied. Such a set of distorted versions of a regular stroke is suitably described by an attributed finite-state grammar $G$. In this grammar, the selection of production is controlled by some conditions of attributes. $G$ is given as follows:

$$G = (V_N, V_T, N_0, P, J, H, K)$$

where $V_N$ is a finite set of nonterminals, $V_T$ is a finite set of terminals, $N_0$ is the start symbol, $P$ is a finite set of productions, $J$ is a finite set of integers, $H$ is a finite set of given functions, and $K$ is a finite set of referential attributes from a template.

$P$ :

1. $N_0 \longrightarrow a_1 N_0$, $\quad a_1 \overline{\in} V_{T_1}, \quad V_{T_1} \subset V_T, \quad A(a_1) = l_1$
   or $a_1 \in V_{T_1}, \quad f_1(A(a_1)) \nleqslant 0, \quad A(a_1) = l_1$

2. $N_0 \longrightarrow a_1 N_1$, $\quad a_1 \in V_{T_1}, \quad f(A(a_1)) \leq 0, \quad A(a_1) = l_1$

$2n - 1$. $N_{n-1} \longrightarrow a_n N_{n-1}$, $\quad a_1 \overline{\in} V_{T_n}, \quad V_{T_n} \subset V_T, \quad A(a_n) = l_n$
   or $a \in V_{T_n}, \quad f_{n-1}(A(a_n)) \nleqslant 0, \quad A(a_n) = l_n$

$2n$. $N_{n-1} \longrightarrow a_n$, $\quad a_1 \in V_{T_n}, \quad f_n(A(a_n)) \leq 0, \quad A(a_n) = l_n$

Table 1. Seventeen relations between two line segments.

| No. | Name of relation | Interpretation | Dual relation |
|-----|------------------|----------------|---------------|
| 1   | (h, h)           |                | (h, h)        |
| 2   | (h, m)           |                | (m, h)        |
| 3   | (h, t)           |                | (t, h)        |
| 4   | (m, t)           |                | (t, m)        |
| 5   | (t, t)           |                | (t, t)        |
| 6   | (t, m)           |                | (m, t)        |
| 7   | (t, h)           |                | (h, t)        |
| 8   | (m, h)           |                | (h, m)        |
| 9   | (m, m)           |                | (m, m)        |
| 10  | (l, a)           |                | (n, d)        |
| 11  | (m, a)           |                | (m, d)        |
| 12  | (r, a)           |                | (l, d)        |
| 13  | (r, m)           |                | (l, m)        |
| 14  | (r, d)           |                | (l, a)        |
| 15  | (m, d)           |                | (m, a)        |
| 16  | (l, d)           |                | (r, a)        |
| 17  | (l, m)           |                | (r, m)        |

There are $2n$ productions. The productions corresponding to odd labels describe new segments which may be added into the starting position and concatenation positions of two consecutive segments, or to attributes which do not satisfy condition $f(A(a)) \leq 0$. On the other hand, productions corresponding to even labels describe segments of a regular stroke with length variation in allowable intervals. The grammar $G$ generates the language

$$L(G) = \{X | N_o \overset{\pi}{\Longrightarrow} x\}$$

where $\pi$ is a sequence of production labels. The number of symbols in $X$ is equal to or greater than $n$.

From the recognition point of view, corresponding to the above grammar, we can define an attributed finite-state automaton $T$ as follows:

$$T = (\Sigma, \ Q, \ \delta, \ q_0, \ H, \ q_f)$$

where $\Sigma$ is a finite set of input symbols with attributes represented by $(a_i, \ l_i)$, $Q$ is a finite set of states, each state being associated with a reference value, $\delta$ is a mapping of $Q \times \Sigma$ into $Q$, $q_0 \in Q$ is the initial state, $H$ is a finite set of functions and $q_f \in Q$ is the final state.

The difference between an attributed finite-state automaton and a conventional finite-state automaton is the transition condition $\delta$. The interpretation of

$$\delta(q, \ (a, \ A(a)) = q' \quad \text{if} \quad f(A(a)) = 0, \quad q, q' \in Q, \quad a \in \Sigma$$

is that the automaton $T$, in state $q$ and scanning the symbol with attribute $A(a)$ goes to state $q'$ if $A(a)$ satisfies the condition $f(A(a)) < 0$. The state transition diagram corresponding to $\delta(q, \ a, \ A(a)) = q', f(A(a)) < 0$ is shown as follows:

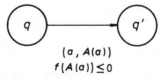

$$(a, A(a))$$
$$f(A(a)) \leq 0$$

**Example 5.1.** For a regular stroke given in Fig. 7 (strokes are coded by five directions), an attributed finite state automaton $T$ is constructed for recognising handwritten strokes which are similar to regular strokes

$$T = (\Sigma, \; Q, \; \delta, \; q_0, \; H, \; q_f)$$

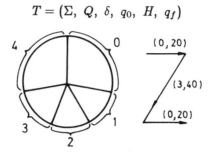

Fig. 7. A regular stroke.

where $\Sigma = \{(0, \; l), (1, \; l)(2, \; l)(3, \; l)(4, \; l)\}$ and $l_i, i = 0, 1, \ldots 4$ are real numbers. The lengths of segments of regular strokes are $\bar{l}_0 = 20, \bar{l}_1 = 40, \bar{l}_2 = 20$. These data are considered as attributes of state $Q$ where $Q = \{q_0(20), \; q_1(40), \; q_2(20), \; q_f(0)\}$ and

$H = \{\bar{l}_0/2 \leq A(a) \leq 3\bar{l}_0/2, \quad \bar{l}_1/2 \leq A(a) \leq 3\bar{l}_1/2, \quad \bar{l}_2/2 \leq A(a) \leq 3\bar{l}_2/2\}$ .
The transition rules are:

$$\delta[q_0, \; (a, \; l)] = \begin{cases} q_1, & \text{if } a = 0, \text{ and } 10 < l < 30 \\ q_0, & \text{if otherwise} \end{cases}$$

$$\delta[q_1, \; (a, \; l)] = \begin{cases} q_2, & \text{if } a = 2 \vee 3, \text{ and } 20 \leq l \leq 30 \\ q_1, & \text{if otherwise} \end{cases}$$

$$\delta[q_2, \; (a, \; l)] = \begin{cases} q_f, & \text{if } a = 0, \text{ and } 10 \leq l \leq 30 \\ q_2, & \text{if otherwise} \end{cases}$$

The transition diagram of $T$ is shown in Fig. 8

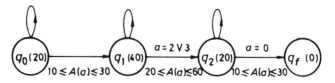

Fig. 8. A transition diagram of $T$.

A string $x = (1, \; 4)(0, \; 14)(1, \; 3)(2, \; 24)(1, \; 8)(0, \; 19)$ is accepted by $T$. The stroke corresponding to $x$ is shown in Fig. 9. According to the rules of transition, the sequence of transition for the input $X$ is:

$$
\begin{array}{ll}
(1,\ 4)\colon & \delta[q_0,\ (1,\ 4)] = q_0 \\
(0,\ 14)\colon & \delta[q_0,\ (0,\ 14)] = q_1 \\
(1,\ 3)\colon & \delta[q_1,\ (1,\ 3)] = q_1 \\
(2,\ 24)\colon & \delta[q_1,\ (2,\ 24)] = q_2 \\
(1,\ 8)\colon & \delta[q_2,\ (1,\ 8)] = q_2 \\
(1,\ 19)\colon & \delta[q_2,\ (1,\ 19)] = q_f
\end{array}
$$

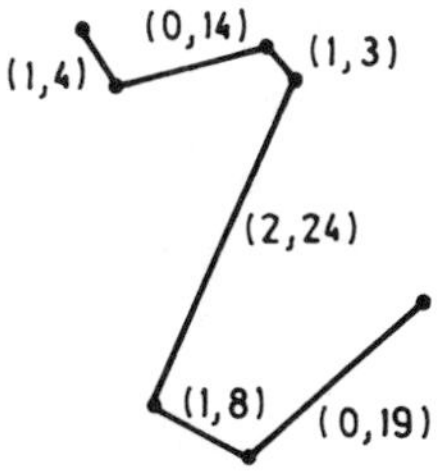

Fig. 9. An input stroke.

The strokes accepted by $T$ are those with a regular stroke as template and the order of direction of the main line segment is in keeping with the regular stroke.

An attributed finite-state automaton is simple, and its function is better than a finite-state automaton. Actually, attributed finite-state automata are not sufficient for recognising handwritten strokes. The reason is that a state transition has only two possibilities: it stays at the state or goes to the next state; no context information can be used. Many strokes which are similar to regular strokes, for instance the two strings $Y$ and $Z$ given in Fig. 10, cannot be accepted by $T$.

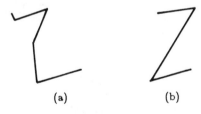

(a)      (b)

$$Y = (1,4)(0,17)(3,18)(2,19)(0,20)$$
$$Z = (0,19)(3,41)(0,19)(3,1)$$

Fig. 10. Two strokes.

From the above discussion, we conclude that an attributed finite-state automaton is not so powerful for recognising handwritten strokes. It is reasonable to realise that a set of similar handwritten strokes is a fuzzy set, and by means of fuzzy information processing technique, both a fuzzy attributed finite-state grammar as well as a fuzzy attributed finite-state automaton can be defined as follows[21].

**Definition 5.2.** A fuzzy attributed finite-state grammar $G_f$ is an eight-tuple

$$G_f = (V_N, \ V_T, \ N_0, \ P, \ J, \ K, \ H, \ L)$$

where $V_N$, $V_T$, $N_0$, $P$, $J$, $K$, $H$, are the same as $G$, $V_{T_i} \subset V_T (i = 1, 2, \ldots, n)$ are subsets of $V$; $L = \{l_i, \ i = 1, 2, \ldots, n\}$ is a finite set of positive real attributes corresponding to nonterminals, and $P$ includes a syntactic part as well as a semantic part given as follows:

$P$ :

| syntactic part | semantic part |
|---|---|

1. $N_0 \rightarrow a_1 N_0 \begin{cases} \text{if } \ a_1 \overline{\in} V_{T_1} \ \text{ and } \ l_1 = 0 \\ \text{if } \ a_1 \in V_{T_1} \ \text{ and } \ l_1 = \min[\tilde{l}_1 + A(a), \tilde{l}_1] \end{cases}$ ⟶ $\begin{array}{l} g_1 = A(a_1) \\ g_1 = A(a_1) \end{array}$

2. $N_0 \rightarrow a_1 \begin{cases} \text{if } \ a_1 \overline{\in} V_{T_1} \ \text{ and } \ l_1 = 0 \\ \text{if } \ a \in V_{T_1} \ \text{ and } \ l_1 = \min[\tilde{l}_1 + A(a_1), \tilde{l}_1] \end{cases}$ ⟶ $\begin{array}{l} g_1 = A(a_1) \\ g_1 = A(a_1) \end{array}$

3. $N \rightarrow aN$, if $a_2 \in V_{T_2}$ and $f_1(A(a_2)) \leq 0$

$\vdots$

$3n - 2$. $N_{n-1} \rightarrow a_n N_{n-1} \begin{cases} \text{if } \ a_n \overline{\in} V_{T_n} \ \text{ and } \ l_n = 0 \\ \text{if } \ a_n \in V_{T_n} \ \text{ and } \ l_n = \min[\tilde{l}_n + A(a_n), \tilde{l}_n] \end{cases}$ ⟶ $\begin{array}{l} g_n = A(a_n) \\ g_n = A(a_n) \end{array}$

$3n - 1$. $n_{n-1} \rightarrow a_n \begin{cases} \text{if } \ a_n \overline{\in} V_{T_n} \ \text{ and } \ l_n = 0 \\ \text{if } \ a_n \in V_{T_n} \ \text{ and } \ l_n = \min[\tilde{l}_n + A(a_n), \tilde{l}_n] \end{cases}$ ⟶ $g_n = A(a_n)$

The membership of a string $x$ derived by $G_f$ is

$$\mu(x) = \frac{\sum_{\pi} l_i}{\sum_{\pi} g_i}$$

and the language generated by $G_f$ is

$$L(G_f) = \{X | N_0 \overset{\pi}{\Longrightarrow} X, \ \mu(X)\} \ .$$

From this definition, each nonterminal $N_i (i = 1, 2, \ldots, n)$ has three rewriting forms describing possible distorted versions of the $(i+1)$th line segment of a template. The semantic rules play an important role, for $N_{i-1} \longrightarrow a_i N_{i-1}$ and $N_{i-1} \longrightarrow a_i$. A corresponding rule $l_i = \min[\tilde{l}_i + A(a_i), \bar{l}_i]$, where $\tilde{l}_i$ represents the attribute of $N_{i-1}$ before the current production, is selected, and $\bar{l}_i$ is the attribute of the $(i+1)$th line segment of the template, the symbol min means the minimum value of the two quantities in square brackets. This semantic rule shows that attribute $l_i$ is dependent on productions which have been selected, so it gives some context information implicitly.

Corresponding to $G_f$, a fuzzy attributed finite-state automaton is also defined.

**Definition 5.3.** A fuzzy attributed finite-state automaton is an eight-tuple $I_f = (\Sigma,\ Q,\ F,\ \delta,\ H,\ K,\ L,\ q_0)$, where $\Sigma$, $Q$ and $q_0$ are the same as $T$, $H$ is a finite set of given functions, $K$ is a finite set of referential attributes, and $L = \{l_i\}$ is a finite set of positive real attributes corresponding to the states.

$F$ is a mapping of $\Sigma \times Q \times L$ to $L$; the interpretation of $F[q_i,\ \tilde{l_i},\ (a,\ u)] = l_i$ is that $\tilde{l_i}$ represents attributes accumulated by transitions at state $q_i$ before the current transition, $(a,\ u)$ is one symbol $a$ with attribute $u$ as input, the transition rule is

$$l \xrightarrow[(a,\ u)]{} \begin{cases} \tilde{l_i} + 0 & \text{if } a \overline{\in} \Sigma_i, \quad \Sigma_i \subset \Sigma \\ \min[(\tilde{l_i} + u),\ \bar{l_i}] & \text{if } a \in \Sigma_i, \quad \Sigma_i \subset \Sigma \end{cases}$$

where $\bar{l_i}$ is the attribute of the line segment of template, and $\delta$ is a mapping of $\Sigma \times Q \times L$ to $Q$.

The membership of a string $x$ is

$$\mu(x) = \frac{\displaystyle\sum_i l_i}{\displaystyle\sum_j g_j}$$

where the numerator represents the summation of attributes corresponding to the main segments of the template, and the denominator represents the summation of attributes of the input string. All $g \in Q$ can be the final state.

**Example 5.4.** An example is given to illustrate how a handwritten stroke is recognised by $T_f$. The regular stroke $\angle$ is considered as the template, $Q = (q_0,\ q_1,\ q_2)$, $\Sigma = \{0,\ 1,\ 2,\ 3,\ 4\}$, and a positive constant $K$ is introduced for normalisation purposes. The transition rules of attributes and the transition rules of state are given as follows:

$$F[q_0,\ l_0,\ (a,\ u)] = \begin{cases} l_0 + 0 \longrightarrow l_0, & \text{if } a \neq 0 \\ \min[(\tilde{l_0} + u),\ k\bar{l_0}] \longrightarrow l_0, & \text{if } a = 0 \end{cases}$$

$$F[q_1, \, l_1, \, (a, \, u)] = \begin{cases} l_1 + 0 \longrightarrow l_1, & \text{if } a \neq 2, \; a \neq 3 \\ \min[(\bar{l}_1 + u), k\bar{l}_1] \longrightarrow l_1, & \text{if } a = 2 \text{ or } 3 \end{cases}$$

$$F[q_2, \, l_2, \, (a, \, u)] = \begin{cases} l_2 + 0 \longrightarrow l_2, & \text{if } a \neq 0 \\ \min[(l_2 + u), \; k\bar{l}_2] \longrightarrow l_2, & \text{if } a = 0 \end{cases}$$

$$\delta[(q_0, \, l_0, \, (a, \, u)] = \begin{cases} q_0, & \text{if } a = 0 \text{ or } l_0 < (k\bar{l}_0/2) \\ q_1, & \text{if } a \neq 0 \text{ and } l_0 \geq (k\bar{l}_0/2) \end{cases}$$

$$\delta[(q_1, \, l, \, (a, \, u)] = \begin{cases} q_1, & \text{if } a = 2 \vee 3, \text{ or } l_1 < (k\bar{l}_1/2) \\ q_2, & \text{if } a \neq 2, a \neq 3 \text{ and } l_1 \geq (k\bar{l}_1/2) \end{cases}$$

$$\delta[q_2, \, l, \, (a, \, u)] = q_2, \quad \text{if} \quad a = 0 \text{ or } a = 1 \, .$$

For an input string $x = (1, \, 4)(0, \, 17)(3, \, 18)(2, \, 19)(0, \, 22)$, the stroke corresponding to $x$ is shown in Fig. 10a. We chose $k = (\Sigma_j g_j)/16 = (4 + 17 + 18 + 19 + 22)/16 = 5$. So $k\bar{l}_0/2 = 10, k\bar{l}_1/2 = 20, k\bar{l}_2/2 = 10$.
The transitions of $x$ accepted by $T$ are explained as follows:

$(1, 4) : a \neq 0, \, l_0 = 0$, $\qquad$ $F[q_0, \, l_0, \, (1, \, 4)] = 0 + 0$
$\qquad\qquad\qquad\qquad\qquad\qquad\qquad\qquad\quad = l_0$
$\qquad l_0 < 10$, $\qquad\qquad\qquad$ $\delta[q_0, \, l_0, \, (1, \, 4)] = q_0$, the input head moves one
$\qquad\qquad\qquad\qquad\qquad\qquad\qquad\qquad\qquad\qquad\qquad\quad$ square to the right.

$(0, 17) : a = 0, \, l_0 = 0$, $\qquad$ $F[q_0, \, l_0, \, (1, \, 17)] = \min[(0, \, 17), \, 20)] = 17$
$\qquad\qquad\qquad\qquad\qquad\qquad\qquad\qquad\qquad\quad = l_0$
$\qquad a = 0, \, l_0 = 17$, $\qquad\quad$ $\delta[q_0, \, l, \, (1, \, 17)] = q_0$, the input head moves one
$\qquad\qquad\qquad\qquad\qquad\qquad\qquad\qquad\qquad\qquad\qquad\quad$ square to the right.

$(3, 18) : a \neq 0, \, l_0 = 17$, $\quad$ $F[q_0, \, l_0, (3, \, 18)] = 17 + 0 = 17$
$\qquad\qquad\qquad\qquad\qquad\qquad\qquad\qquad\qquad\quad = l_0$
$\qquad a = 0, \, l_0 = 10$, $\qquad\quad$ $\delta[q_0, \, l_0, \, (3, \, 18)] = q_1$, the transition of state
$\qquad\qquad\qquad\qquad\qquad\qquad\qquad\qquad\qquad\qquad\qquad\quad$ reads $(3, 18)$ again.

$(3, 18) : a = 3, \, l_1 = 0$, $\qquad$ $F[q, \, l_1, (3, \, 18)] = \min[(0 + 18), \, 40] = 18$
$\qquad\qquad\qquad\qquad\qquad\qquad\qquad\qquad\qquad\quad = l_0$
$\qquad a = 3, \, l_1 = 18$, $\qquad\quad$ $\delta[q, \, l_1, (3, \, 18)] = q$, the input head moves one
$\qquad\qquad\qquad\qquad\qquad\qquad\qquad\qquad\qquad\qquad\qquad\quad$ square to the right.

$(2, 19) : a = 2, l_1 = 18,$ $\quad F[q_1, l_1, (2, 19)] = \min[(18 + 19), 40] = 37$
$$= l_1$$
$\quad\quad\quad a = 2, l_1 = 37,$ $\quad \delta[q_1, l_1, (2, 19)] = q_1,$ the input head moves one
square to the right.

$(0, 22) : a \neq 2$ or $3, l_1 = 37,$ $\quad F[q_1, l_1, (0, 22)] = 37 + 0 = 37$
$$= l_1$$
$\quad\quad\quad a = 2$ or $3, l \geq 20,$ $\quad \delta[q_1, l_1, (0, 22)] = q_2,$ the transition of state
reads (0.22) again.

$(0, 22) : a = 0, l = 0,$ $\quad F[q, l, (0, 22)] \quad = \min[(0 + 22), 20] = 20$
$$= l_2$$
$\quad\quad\quad a = 0, l_2 = 20,$ $\quad [q_2, l_2, (0, 22)] \quad = q_2$

and

$$\mu(x) = \frac{17 + 37 + 20}{4 + 17 + 18 + 19 + 22} = 0.95 \ .$$

A positive real number $r$ is chosen as threshold, $r < 1$. If $\mu(x)$ is greater than $r$ for an input string $x$, then $x$ is recognised as the referential regular stroke of the automaton.

From previous discussion, straight-line segments of a Chinese character can be extracted by fuzzy attributed finite-state automaton. Another interesting point is how to get an order of line segment in order for recognising Chinese characters. We know that when someone writes a Chinese character on an input tablet, an order of stroke is obtained, but different writers may have different orders of stroke. A method for order arrangement independent of writers is proposed in Ref. 22. For two line segments of a Chinese character, according to the intrinsic structural properties of the character, some criteria are given to verify which line segment takes precedence over another. If the appearance of two line segments satisfies the structural criteria, an index 1 is assigned to the relation between two line segments, otherwise an index 0 is assigned. For instance, consider a set of four basic line segments as primitives, two segments are connected and the relation between them is $(m, m)$, by structure properties of Chinese characters. A precedence matrix is given in Fig. 11.

| A \ B | — | \ | │ | / |
|---|---|---|---|---|
| — | 0 | 1 | 1 | 1 |
| \ | 0 | 0 | 0 | 0 |
| │ | 0 | 1 | 0 | 0 |
| / | 0 | 1 | 1 | 0 |

Fig. 11. A precedence matrix of four basic line segments.

From the order of appearance of line segments, two samples of Chinese character 禾 written by different persons are given in Fig. 12a and b. The order of line segments $s_1$ is different from the order of line segments $s_2$, where

$$s_1 = /, \quad —, \quad │, \quad /, \quad \backslash$$

$$s_1 = /, \quad │, \quad —, \quad /, \quad \backslash$$

According to intrinsic structural properties, the order of line segments is

$$s = /, \quad —, \quad /, \quad │, \quad \backslash$$

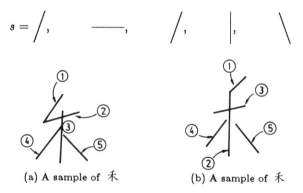

(a) A sample of 禾          (b) A sample of 禾

Fig. 12.

We can transform the different order of line segments to $s$ but we shall not discuss the procedure of transformation here. It can be found in Ref. 22.

An on-line Chinese character recognition system has been implemented by the syntactic semantic approach described above. The system consists of a small input tablet, an interface board and an IBM-PC/XT. The software is written using 8086 assembly language. The program (16KB) and the data (64KB) are within the interface card in the form of EPROM. The interface card is designed as a standard plug-in card of the IBM-PC. It is inserted into a slot on the 62 Bus of the PC connecting the small input tablet. This approach is especially convenient to input Chinese characters into IBM-PC/XT/AT.

The system can recognize over 7000 on-line handwritten Chinese characters with irregular script. The processing time required is not more than 300 ms for one character. Over 1000 people have tried the system. After a 30-minute period of training, the average error rate is approximately 5%. The system is shown in Fig. 13.

Fig. 13. An on-line Chinese character recognition system.

# REFERENCES

1. Ye Pei Jian, "Reconnaissance Automatique en Temps Real des Caracteres Chinois Manusents", Thése, Université de Neuchatel, Suisse, 1985.

2. Zhang Xinzhong and Xia Ying," "The automatic recognition of handprinted Chinese characters — A method of extracting an ordered sequence of strokes", *Pattern Recognition Lett.* 1 (1983) 259-265.

3. C.Y. Suen, Y.Y. Tang and Q.R. Wang, "Feature extraction in the recognition of Chinese characters printed in difference fonts", *Proc. Int. Conf. on Chinese Computing*, Singapore, 1986, pp. 136-143.

4. Q.R. Wang and C.Y. Suen, "Analysis and design of a decision tree based on entropy reduction and its application to large character set recognition", *IEEE, Trans. PAMI* 6 (1984) 4066-4170.

5. Q.R. Wang and C.Y. Suen, "Large tree classifier with heuristic search and global training", *IEEE Trans. PAMI* 9 (1987) 91-102.

6. Y.X. Gu, Q.R. Wang and C.Y. Suen, "Application of a multiplayer decision tree in computer recognition of Chinese character", *IEEE. Trans. PAMI* 5 (1983) 83-89.

7. Shu Wenhao, Guo Qing and Li Lan, "A study of on-line Chinese characters recognition", *Proc. 1985 Int. Conf. on Chinese Computing*, San Francisco, 1985.

8. A.C. Shaw, "The formal picture description scheme as a basis for picture processing systems", *Info. and Control* 14 (1969) 9-52.

9. K.C. You and K.S. Fu, "A syntactic approach to shape recognition using attributed grammars", *IEEE Trans. Syst. Man and Cybern.* 9 (1979) 334-345.

10. W.H. Tsai and K.S. Fu, "Attributed grammar — a tool for combining syntactic and statistical approaches to pattern recognition", *IEEE Trans. Syst. Man and Cybern.* 10 (1980) 873-885.

11. W.H. Tsai and K.S. Fu, "A syntactic-statistical approach to recognition of industrial objects", *Proc. 5th Int. Conf. Pattern Recognition*, Miami Beach, FL, 1-4 Dec., 1980, pp. 251-259.

12. W.H. Tsai and K.S. Fu, "Error-correcting isomorphisms of attributed relational graphs for pattern analysis", *IEEE Trans. Syst. Man and Cybern.* 9(1979) 757-768.

13. D.E. Knuth, "Semantics of context-free languages", *J. Math. Syst. Theory* 2 (1978) 127-146.

14. A. V. Aho and J. Ullman, *The Theory of Parsing, Translation and Compiling, Vol. 1*, (Prentice-Hall, Englewood Cliffs, NJ, 1972).

15. J.W. Tai and K.S. Fu, "Semantic syntax-directed translation for pictorial pattern recognition", *Proc. 6th Int. Conf. Pattern Recognition*, Munich, 1982, pp. 169-171.

16. J.W. Tai, "A kind of attributed grammar for pattern recognition", *Acta Automatica Sinica* 9 (1983) 90-98.

17. J.W. Tai, "A syntactic-semantic approach for Chinese character description", *Computer Processing of Chinese and Oriental Languages* 1 (1984) 186-194.

18. K.S. Fu, *Syntactic Methods in Pattern Recognition* (Academic Press, 1974).

19. J.W. Tai, "A line drawing pattern recognition method", *Acta Automatica Sinica* 11 (1984) 225-233.

20. A. Kandel, *Fuzzy Techniques in Pattern Recognition* (John Wiley and Sons, 1982).

21. Y.J. Liu and J.W. Tai, "A fuzzy attributed finite state automaton for on-line Chinese character recognition", Technical Report of Institute of Automation, Chinese Academy of Sciences, 1986. To be published in *Acta Automatica Sinica*.

22. Y.J. Liu and J.W. Tai, "A method of stroke order arrangement for on-line Chinese character recognition", Technical Report of Institute of Automation, Chinese Academy of Sciences, 1986. To be published in *Acta Automatica Sinica*.

23. J.W. Tai, "A syntactic-semantic distance measure for pattern recognition", *Acta Automatica Sinica* **10** (1984) 2-7.

24. J.W. Tai and C.H. Hu, "The investigation of handwritten character recognition methods", *Acta Automatica Sinica* **5** (1979) 39-46.

# 16

# TABLE DRIVEN PARSING FOR SHAPE ANALYSIS

T.C. HENDERSON and A. SAMAL
*Department of Computer Science*
*The University of Utah*
*Salt Lake City, UT 84112*
*USA*

Compiler generation tools have been used quite successfully to produce parsers for certain classes of string grammars. Such techniques can also be applied to the development of syntactic shape parsers. We present a generalization of LR parsing to shape grammars based on the use of geometrical relations between the symbols. The components of this approach are: a grammar for defining classes of 2-D and 3-D shapes; a shape grammar compiler which produces a tabular representation of the explicit and implicit constraints between the parts of the shape; and a general parsing mechanism which uses these tables of constraints to perform the analysis of unknown shapes.

## 1. INTRODUCTION

We believe that the syntactic method offers many advantages for shape analysis. The major advantage is the possibility of defining logical relations between anthropomorphically significant parts of a shape. Moreover, formal techniques allow both the automatic generation of constraint relations for grammatical descriptions of shape and the application of these constraints during the analysis of shape. Shaw[1], Fu[2], Rosenfeld[3] and others[4-7] have proposed various approaches to syntactic or grammatical shape models, but in general, the parsing methods for these models are standard string parsers, e.g. Earley's algorithm. In order to obtain the most advantage from the grammatical approach, however, the relation between the shape grammar and the shape parsing method must be formally established. In this paper, we consider a bottom-up parsing mechanism and its relation to a particular class of shape grammars. Our goal is to outline a framework for a coherent approach to syntactic pattern recognition.

In choosing the parsing mechanism for a given shape grammar, the problem is much the same as that faced by a compiler writer trying to choose a recognizer for a string grammar. In the traditional bottom-up parsing approach[8,9], a recognizer is implemented in a general way using tables. These tables are derived from the given grammar and describe relations between the vocabulary symbols of the grammar. A constructor is designed which, given a grammar, checks it for suitability and builds the necessary tables for the recognizer (see Fig. 1). That is, to implement the recognizer for a given grammar, the constructor is run with the grammar as data, and the output is merged with the recognizer. We will show how this technique can be extended from string grammars to shape grammars.

Our general shape grammar scheme is to produce a shape parsing mechanism by means of a shape grammar compiler from a high-level shape grammar description. This is analogous to using an automatic parser generator to produce a string parser from a high-level programming language description. Note that this contrasts with most syntactic methods where use is made of a general context-free parser. (However, for an approach which is similar in spirit, see Bunke's attributed programmed graph grammar transformation system[10].) The shape parsing mechanism performs the actual analysis of unknown shapes and outputs an organization imposed on the shape primitives in terms of the underlying grammar.

Most proposed syntactic shape analysis methods have dealt with the

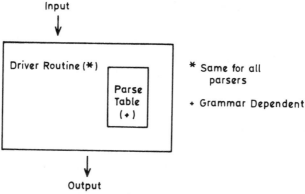

Fig. 1. Parts of an LR parser.

shape grammar (or model) at length, while the corresponding parsing algorithm has been chosen *ad hoc* and from a string grammar perspective, e.g. You[11] uses Earley's algorithm. The shape parsing mechanism has usually been constructed manually. Finally, in most formalisms it is a tedious process to produce the shape grammar for any interesting class of shapes.

This provides an impetus for developing more suitable user-oriented languages for describing a shape grammar. Thus, one problem faced is the design of suitable shape grammar description languages, and the subsequent problem is the construction of correct and efficient compilers for such languages.

As an example of one approach to syntactic shape analysis, we propose a generalization of LR parsing as the framework within which to define shape grammars and their parsers. The major motivation for this choice is that methods exist for automatically deriving the shape parsing mechanism. In particular, we have:

- a shape grammar formalism which accounts for most structural aspects of 2-D and 3-D shape,
- a table-driven parsing mechanism which uses constraints between pieces of the shape, and
- an automatic method to compute constraint relations between the vocabulary symbols of the grammar.

This process can be viewed as a generalization of traditional table-driven grammar techniques in that the grammars involve constraints between string grammar symbols. With string grammars, bottom-up parsing involves scanning from left to right until the tail of the handle is found, then scanning right to left from the tail until the head of the handle is found. This works well enough for string grammars, but shape grammars pose the problem of complicated relations between the symbols, and these relations must be accounted for and taken advantage of by the shape parsing mechanism.

## 2. DETAILS OF THE APPROACH

Most syntactic approaches which consider the parsing problem at all typically use parsing algorithms which are applicable to the entire class of context-free grammars, e.g. the Cocke-Younger-Kasami algorithm or Earley's algorithm. Although these are general parsing methods, they are computationally expensive even for string grammars, and they require on the order of $n^3$ time and the order of $n^2$ space. On the other hand, it is possible that for specific grammars, these requirements can be reduced. Other methods such as $LR(k)$ parsing are available, though, which do not suffer from these deficiencies, and are the recommended technique for implementing parsers for programming languages. It is in this vein that we explore the extension of the $LR(k)$ approach to shape grammar parsing and the automatic generation of parsers from shape grammar descriptions.

### 2.1. LR Parsing

The $LR(k)$ grammars are a class of context-free grammars which can be parsed deterministically[8]. The parse uses a left-to-right scan (the L in LR) of the input to produce (the reverse of) a right sentential parse (the R in LR) and can scan $k$ input symbols ahead. Suppose that

$$S = \alpha_0 \xrightarrow[rm]{p_1} \alpha_1 \xrightarrow[rm]{p_2} \ldots \xrightarrow[rm]{p_m} \alpha_m = w \; ,$$

is a rightmost derivation of $w$, where rm means rightmost and $p_i$ means production $i$ is applied. Then an $LR(k)$ parser produces $p_m, p_{m-1}, \ldots, p_1$. Basically, the parser shifts input symbols onto a pushdown list. When a handle appears at the top of the pushdown list, the handle is reduced. This process continues until the start symbol is produced or an error is detected. For $LR(k)$ grammars, it is possible to determine which nonterminal should replace the handle by scanning at most $k$ symbols to the right of the handle.

Thus, an LR($k$) parser must decide whether to shift a new input symbol onto the pushdown list or whether a handle is present already. Once it is determined that a handle is present, it is necessary to find the left end of the handle. Finally, the appropriate nonterminal to replace the handle must be chosen (this involves finding the right production to apply).

An LR($k$) parser is a table which encodes the current state of the parse in terms of (1) a *parsing action function* and (2) a *goto function*. A parse proceeds by applying the parsing action to the head of the pushdown list. The four possible actions are: **shift, reduce, error** or **accept**. If it is **shift**, then the next input symbol is shifted onto the pushdown list. If it is **reduce**, then the indicated production is used to remove the symbols on the top of the pushdown list which correspond to the right hand side of the production. The left hand side of the production is placed on the pushdown list. If it is **error**, the parse is halted with an error message, or some kind of recovery may be attempted. If it is **accept**, the parse is halted and the parse is known.

One advantage of LR($k$) parsing is that it is possible to optimize LR($k$) parsers. LR($k$) grammars represent one of the largest classes (of unambiguous grammars) for which deterministic parsers can be constructed, and LR parsers can compete quite well with other kinds of parsers. The basic problem of producing an LR($k$) parser is to generate the LR($k$) table which controls the parsing. Although it is possible to automatically produce these tables, they are often too large to be practicable. However, since LR($k$) parsers have the desirable properties of being fast and capable of early error-detection, the return is high if an optimizing step is taken.

## 2.2. Extending LR Techniques for Shape Grammars

Now let us consider how this approach applies to shape grammars. First of all, it is possible to encode a class of shapes directly as an LR($k$) grammar using terminal symbols which correspond to some shape primitives. Such parsers can be produced using standard parser generators such as *lex* (lexical analyzer generator) and *yacc* (yet another compiler compiler). For the examples given below, we have used these tools running under Berkeley Unix 4.2. Thus, for any class of shapes which can be described by LR(0) grammars. It is quite straightforward to generate the corresponding recognizers using such parser generator tools.

First, parsers can be produced rather easily for any class describable by regular expressions. For example, normal ECGs (see Fig. 2) can be characterized by the following regular expression (from Ref. 5):

$$[prbt \ (b|bb|bbb)] + \ .$$

The input to lex is given in Appendix A. This is all that is required to produce the finite state recognizer.

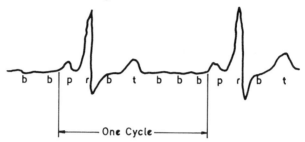

Fig. 2. The regular pattern appearing in a normal ECG.

Context-free grammars require the use of yacc. Consider the following two examples from Fu[4], one for median chromosomes and the other for acrocentric chromosomes. These shapes are shown in Figs. 3 and 4.

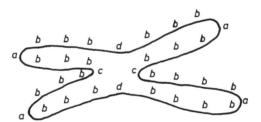

Fig. 3. Median chromosome shape.

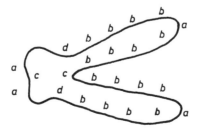

Fig. 4. Acrocentric chromosome shape.

*Grammar for median chromosome*

$$G_1 = (T, N, P, S)$$
$$T = \{a, b, c, d\} \quad N = \{S, A, B, D, E, F, H, J\}$$

where $a, b, c$ and $d$ correspond to $\curvearrowright$, $|$, $\curvearrowleft$, $\{$, respectively.

*Productions (P):*

$$S \longrightarrow A\,A$$
$$A \longrightarrow c\,B$$
$$B \longrightarrow F\,B\,E \mid H\,D\,J$$
$$D \longrightarrow F\,D\,E \mid d$$
$$E \longrightarrow b$$
$$F \longrightarrow b$$
$$H \longrightarrow a$$
$$J \longrightarrow a$$

The LR parsing table produced for this grammar is given in Appendix B.

*Grammar for acrocentric chromosome*

$$G_2 = (T, N, P, S)$$
$$T = \{a, b, c, d\} \quad N = \{S, A, B, D, E, F, G, H, J, L, R, W\}$$

*Productions (P):*

$$S \longrightarrow A\,A$$
$$A \longrightarrow c\,B$$
$$B \longrightarrow F\,L \mid R\,E$$
$$D \longrightarrow F\,G \mid W\,E$$
$$E \longrightarrow b$$
$$F \longrightarrow b$$
$$G \longrightarrow F\,G \mid d$$
$$H \longrightarrow a$$
$$J \longrightarrow a$$
$$L \longrightarrow H\,D\,J \mid F\,L$$

$$R \longrightarrow H D J \mid R E$$
$$W \longrightarrow W E \mid d$$

The LR parsing table for this grammar is given in Appendix C.

However, for more complex geometrical shape grammars, the extension to $LR(k)$ parsing must be more general. It is important to note that $LR(k)$ tables form the basis for $LR(k)$ parsing. Moreover, $LR(k)$ tables encode the structure of the strings of a language in terms of their neighborhood relations, e.g. PRECEDES and FOLLOWS. That is, the $LR(k)$ tables represent in a finite deterministic way the combinatorics of these relations. This suggests that one generalization of LR grammars to shape grammars can be based on the use of relations between symbols, where these relations include geometrical relations between the shape primitives. Several issues must be dealt with:

1. the definition and use of the parsing tables,
2. the generalization of "left-to-right" scanning,
3. the nature of the parse which is produced, i.e. the control of the parse, and
4. the noise and ambiguity in the data and shape primitives.

The goal of this paper is to define the general advantages and disadvantages of this approach and to indicate how some of the previous work in syntactic pattern recognition addresses these issues. It is clear that many possibilities exist for tackling these problems.

The automatic generation of parsing tables is at the heart of the approach. It is possible to define table-driven shape parsing methods, where the tables encode various geometric relations of interest between symbols in a convenient way. Even though a deterministic parsing method does not necessarily result, it is possible to apply intrinsic shape constraints during a parse. This approach can exploit the mechanism of table-driven methods in two fundamental ways.

First, it is possible to use the tables directly defined in a similar way as string grammar tables. For example, we have already seen that shapes can be defined as strings. Typically this approach is possible if a complete, finite, unambiguous set of shape primitives is available. Moreover, simple extensions to more general shapes are possible (and the left-to-right scan can be appropriately modified). In general, however, this direct approach runs into too many problems with missing or ambiguous shape primitives, noise, etc.

Alternatively, the tables (which define the shape relations) can be used to drive a parsing process which is based on using the error information in the tables. In fact, the hierarchical constraint process (HCP) implements just this notion. The process works as follows:

- Shape primitives are assigned a set of possible terminal symbol interpretations.
- These multiple labelings give rise to a host of possible shapes depending on which combination of labels is chosen.
- The failure of a constraint on a given vocabulary hypothesis for a particular shape primitive causes that hypothesis to be removed.

The major idea is that the tables encode general 2-D and 3-D shape relations and can be used by a shape parser to eliminate invalid hypotheses. Thus, the parse proceeds in two modes:

- a "disprover" mode in which inconsistent hypotheses are discarded, and
- an "apply productions" mode in which higher-level vocabulary symbols are produced from the current set of symbols.

The table techniques can be used in both of these modes. The tables used in this process can be automatically produced from the shape grammar which defines the class of shapes to be recognized. (Methods for producing tables of the second mode can be found in Ref. 8 and table generation methods for the "disprover" mode can be found in Ref. 12.)

In general, it is not possible to talk about or define a "left-to-right-scan" for a set of shape primitives, unless the shapes are described as silhouettes. Even in this case, it is not easy to define a unique starting primitive. In our previous work on HCP, we have actually defined and used grammars for silhouettes. However, in order to take noise and ambiguity into account (also see below), no left-to-right scan was defined or used. Thus, in the most general case, the vocabulary symbols are considered in parallel. (Note that for a shape grammar, a vocabulary symbol corresponds to a part of the shape, where terminal symbols define the lowest level granularity of shape description, and the start symbol represents a complete shape.) Also, no uniquely appropriate sentential parse has been defined.

Finally, the problem of noise and ambiguity must be addressed in applying syntactic techniques to shape analysis, especially if real world images are to be analyzed. Several solutions have been proposed for this problem, including:

- relax the conditions for extracting the shape primitives,
- introduce probabilities on the productions and strings which describe the shapes, and
- allow multiple hypotheses for the shape primitives and delete inconsistent or unsupported hypotheses.

All of these approaches can be used within the shape grammar compiler paradigm proposed here. Our work with HCP has concentrated on the last of these approaches. The choice of one of these methods should be made on the basis of the kind of data that will be available, the class of shapes to be recognized, and the desired robustness.

Other important issues, such as the control of the parse, the choice of constraints, etc. can be discussed once a particular method is chosen. For example, if the shapes can be modeled by an LR string grammar, then the parse is a deterministic LR parse, and the constraints are determined by the handles of the language. On the other hand, HCP can use a wide range of constraints and control the parse through hypothesis elimination.

## 3. A 3-D SHAPE GRAMMAR EXAMPLE

To illustrate these ideas in the context of 3-D shape modeling, we first review the hierarchical constraint process and then give an example. We present a grammar for the "cup" shape (compare, for example, the grammar in Ref. 13), where the shape primitives are certain generalized cylinders.

Stratified shape grammars have been described elsewhere in detail[12]. We give only a brief summary here. A stratified context-free grammar $G$ is quadruple $(T, N, P, S)$, where $T$ is the set of terminal symbols, $N$ is the set of non terminal symbols, $P$ is the set of productions, and $S$ is the start symbol. Let $V = (N \cup T)$ be the set of all vocabulary symbols. Associated with every symbol $v \in V$ is a level number, $ln(v) : V \longrightarrow \{0, 1, \dots, n\}$ where $ln(S) = n$ and $\forall v \in T, ln(v) = 0$.

$T$ consists of symbols which correspond to relatively large pieces of the shapes modeled by the grammar. In particular, each terminal symbol corresponds to one of the following: a circle, a cylinder, or a curve segment.

$N$ consists of symbols each of which has a level number from 1 to $n$ associated with it. In any rule $v := \alpha$ (the rewrite part of a production), if $ln(v) = k$ then every symbol in the string $a$ is at level $k - 1$. Furthermore,

$\forall v \in \mathbf{V}$

$$v = \langle \text{name part} \rangle \{ \text{attachment part} \} [\text{semantic part}],$$

where

$\langle \text{name part} \rangle$ is a unique name by which the symbol $v$ is known ,
$\{ \text{attachment part} \}$ is a set of attachment points of the symbol ,
$[\text{semantic part}]$ is a set of predicates which describes certain aspects of the symbol.

$\mathbf{P}$ consists of productions of the form $(v := \alpha, A, C, G_a, G_s)$ and $v := \alpha$ is the rewrite part that indicates the replacement of the symbol $v$ by the group of symbols $\alpha$, where $v \in \mathbf{N}$ and $\alpha = v_1 v_2 \ldots v_k$ such that $v_i \in \mathbf{V}$ and $ln(v_i) = (ln(v) - 1)$ for $i = 1k$ : $A$ is a set of applicability conditions on the syntactic arrangement of the $v_i$; $C$ is a set of semantic consistence conditions on the $v_i$ and consists of various predicates describing geometric and other properties of the $v_i$; $G_a$ is a set for generating the attachment part of $v$, the new symbol; $G_s$ is a set of rules for generating the semantic part of $v$, the new symbol.

What is important to note about such grammars is that it is possible to derive very useful geometric constraints from them, and that such constraints can be used in a table-driven way. In fact, the constraints are nothing but relations implemented as tables.

We will not go through the details of the constraint compilation techniques. From the shape grammar, these techniques produce an enlarged set of relations which are only partially explicit in the grammar. For example, it may be possible to discover that two pieces of a shape (more technically, their syntactic symbols) are indeed parallel, even though no explicit statement of that is given in the productions.

Such relations can be used to significantly reduce the amount of work necessary to determine if an unknown shape is in the class defined by the shape grammar. The mechanism which performs this function is the Hierarchical Constraint Process. HCP uses the hypothesis elimination mode to account for ambiguity and noise in the data. In fact, the ambiguity of the underlying data is a major problem faced by any syntactic shape analysis method, but not by string parsers.

Usually no clear-cut decision can be made in associating the terminal symbols of a grammar with the shape primitives. Thus, the parsing mechanism must not only overcome the problem of parsing a complicated arrangement of symbols (i.e. concatenation is no longer the only relation between symbols), but must also make clear the interpretations of a given shape primitive. HCP solves this in the following way. Given a set of shape primitives (i.e. circles, cylinders, or curve segments detected in a scene), and a stratified shape grammar for the class of shapes, HCP performs the following actions:

- associate with each shape primitive a set of possible interpretations, i.e. terminal symbols,
- determine the initial network of hypotheses, that is, for each possible interpretation of each shape primitive, insert a node in the network; two nodes of the network are connected if their underlying shape primitives are physically adjacent,
- apply procedures to the network until the network is empty or the start symbol is produced.

The association of terminal symbols with shape primitives will (in the limit) be to hypothesize every terminal symbol for each primitive. However, methods for reducing the number of hypotheses include using a more global analysis to derive indications of appropriate scale, orientation, etc. from simple global properties; e.g. one can histogram selected features of the primitives themselves to infer properties of particular vocabulary symbols.

The network of hypotheses represents all possible sentential forms for the given shape primitives. Every path in the network represents a distinct set of interpretations of the primitives and must be parsed. However, this is usually much too large a set to be parsed one after the other. The hierarchical constraint process computes a bottom-up parse of all the paths in parallel. This is done by applying the constraints to the network and it can be described by specifying three simple procedures and two sets which these procedures manipulate.

BUILD — Given level $k$ of the network, BUILD uses the productions of the grammar to construct level $k+1$ nodes. Physically adjacent hypotheses are linked, and a record is kept of which nodes are used to construct each level $k+1$ node. All level $k+1$ nodes are put into the CONSTRAIN-SET, and all level $k$ nodes are put into the COMPACT-SET (both of these sets are initially empty).

CONSTRAIN — While the CONSTRAIN-SET is not empty, CON-STRAIN examines each member of that set; if a node fails to satisfy the constraints, then its neighbors are put into the CONSTRAIN-SET, any nodes it helped produce and the nodes used to produce it are put into the

COMPACT-SET, and it is deleted from the network.

COMPACT — While the COMPACT-SET is not empty, COMPACT examines each member of that set; given a node $n$ from the COMPACT-SET, if one of the lower level nodes used to produce $n$ has been deleted, or if $n$ has not helped produce a node at the level above it, (and that level has been built), then $n$'s neighbors are put into the CONSTRAIN-SET. Any nodes it helped produce and the nodes used to produce $n$ are put into the COMPACT-SET, and $n$ is deleted from the network.

This then is the shape parsing mechanism. The constraint propagation is based on the discrete relaxation techniques developed by Waltz[14] and Rosenfeld[15]. As an example of this approach, consider the following 3-D shape grammar for the class "cup".

$$T = \{\text{bottom, cylinder, handle}\}$$
$$N = \{\text{cup, body}\}$$
$$S = \{\text{cup}\}, \text{ and}$$
$$P = \{$$

*Production 1:*

⟨cup⟩{ }[vertical_axis diameter height] :=

⟨body⟩{contact$_1$ contact$_2$} [vertical_axis' diameter' height']

+⟨handle⟩{end$_1$' end$_2$'} [height'' vertical_axis'']

$A$ : [(contact$_1$ = end$_1$) and (contact$_2$ = end$_2$)
or (contact$_1$ = end$_2$) and (contact$_2$ = end$_1$)]

$S$ : [(vertical_axis' = vertical_axis'') and (height' = height'')]

$G_a$: [ ]

$G_s$: [(vertical_axis := vertical_axis') (diameter := diameter')
(height := height')]

*Production 2:*

⟨body⟩{contact$_1$ contact$_2$}{vertical_axis diameter height] :=

⟨bottom⟩{end'}[normal'diameter']

+⟨cylinder⟩{end'}[axis'' diameter'' height'']

$A$: [end' = end'']

$S$: [(normal' = axis'') and (diameter'' ⟩ = diameter)]

$G_a$: [(contact$_1$ := "free") (contact$_2$ := "free")]
$G_s$: [(vertical_ axis := axis') (diameter := diameter')
         (height := height')]
}

where "free" is on the cylinder and matches anything.

*Identities:*

$$\langle\text{bottom}\rangle\{\text{end}\}[n\ d] \equiv \langle\text{circle}\rangle\{\text{end}\}[n\ d]$$
$$\langle\text{handle}\rangle\{e_1\ e_2\}[h\ a] \equiv \langle\text{curve segment}\rangle\{e_1\ e_2\}[h\ a]$$

The compiled constraints "Neighbors" and "Parallel" are:

*Neighbors:*

|     | bot | cyl | bod | han | cup |
| --- | --- | --- | --- | --- | --- |
| bot |     | 1   |     |     |     |
| cyl | 1   |     |     |     |     |
| bod |     |     |     | 1   |     |
| han |     |     | 1   |     |     |
| cup |     |     |     |     |     |

*Parallel:*

|     | bot | cyl | bod | han | cup |
| --- | --- | --- | --- | --- | --- |
| bot |     | 1   | 1   | 1   | 1   |
| cyl | 1   |     | 1   | 1   | 1   |
| bod | 1   | 1   |     | 1   | 1   |
| han | 1   | 1   | 1   |     | 1   |
| cup | 1   | 1   | 1   | 1   |     |

where a blank in the table means zero. Also, 0 means the relation does not hold, while a 1 means that it does. These tables can then be used in the normal manner by HCP as described in Ref. 12. Note that the parallel constraint is quite powerful since every symbol is parallel to every other one. This makes it possible to detect errors very quickly.

## 4. DISCUSSION

We have shown one possible approach to constructing a framework for shape parsing, and have shown how to implement a bottom-up, constraint-driven parsing mechanism. In addition, we have explained how it relates to traditional string parser theory. For the syntactic approach to prove useful, it is necessary that a clear conceptual relation should exist between the grammar and the parser. Moreover, parser generators must be made available to make the development of shape grammars and their parsers feasible and effective.

In analyzing a class of shapes, we proceed as follows:

- define a shape grammar for the class of shapes,
- derive the syntactic and semantic constraints between the vocabulary symbols of the grammar, and
- apply the parsing procedure to a set of shape primitives using the constraints to produce a parse (perhaps by eliminating incorrect hypotheses).

Successful experiments have been run for detecting various kinds of shapes. However, several problems have been encountered. Shape grammars can have many productions, and so a convenient means for defining a grammar has yet to be developed. Thus, at present, shape grammars are a major source of error and usually require much debugging. One solution to this is an interactive, graphical shape grammar specification system; another attractive approach is to generate such grammars directly from a CAD design.

There are two other critical issues which we are now studying. First, we would like to be able to provide deterministic parse tables for shape grammars. This could tremendously speed up the parsing process. The second issue is the choice of constraints (perhaps even the combination of several constraints). Currently, this is guided directly by the kinds of relations specified in the grammar (e.g. parallel, relative length, etc.). However, a deeper analysis might radically reduce the size and number of tables used in the parser.

## ACKNOWLEDGEMENT

This work was supported in part by NSF Grants MCS-8221750, DCR-8506393, and DMC-8502115.

## REFERENCES

1. A.C. Shaw, "A formal picture description scheme as basis for picture processing systems", *Information and Control* **14** (1969) 9-52.
2. K.S. Fu and B.K. Bhargava, "Tree systems for syntactic pattern recognition", *IEEE Trans. Computers* **22** (1973) 1087-1099.
3. A. Rosenfeld and D. Milgram, "Web automata and web grammars", in *Machine Intelligence*, eds. B. Melrzer and D. Michie (Edinburgh University Press, Edinburgh, 1972) pp. 3307-3324.
4. K.S. Fu, *Syntactic Methods in Pattern Recognition* (Academic Press, 1974).
5. Rafael C. Gonzalez and Michael G. Thomason, *Syntactic Pattern Recognition* (Addison-Wesley, 1978).
6. T. Pavlidis, *Structural Pattern Recognition* (Springer-Verlag, 1977).
7. Q.Y. Shi and K.S. Fu, "Parsing and Translation of (attributed) expansive graph languages for scene analysis", *IEEE Trans. Pattern Analysis and Machine Intelligence* **5** (1983) 472-484.
8. A.V. Aho and J.D. Ullman, *The Theory of Parsing, Translation and Compiling* (Prentice Hall, New Jersey, 1973).
9. D. Gries, *Compiler Construction for Digital Computers* (John Wiley, New York, 1969).
10. H. Bunke, "Attributed programmed graph grammars and their application to schematic diagram interpretation", *IEEE Trans. Pattern Analysis and Machine Intelligence* **4** (1982) 574-582.
11. K. You and K.S. Fu, "Syntactic Shape Recognition", Technical Report in Image Understanding and Information Extraction, Summary Report, Purdue University, Purdue, March, 1977.
12. T. Henderson and L. Davis, "Hierarchical models and analysis of shape", *Pattern Recognition* **14** (1981) 197-206.
13. W.C. Lin and K.S. Fu, "A syntactic approach to 3-D object representation", *IEEE Trans. Pattern Analysis and Machine Intelligence* **6** (1984) 351-364.
14. D. Waltz, "Understanding line drawings of scenes with shadows", in *The Psychology of Computer Vision*, ed. P.H. Winston, (McGraw-Hill, New York, 1975) pp. 19-91.
15. A. Rosenfeld, R. Hummel and S. Zucker, "Scene labeling by relaxation operations", *IEEE Trans. Syst. Man, and Cybern.* **6** (1976) 420-433.

## APPENDIX A

The input to lex for the ECG waveform grammar is:

```
%%
[(prbt)(b|bb|bbb)]+      { printf("Normal ECG Pattern\ n"); };
[a-z]+                   { printf("Abnormal ECG Pattern\ n"); };
%%
```

## APPENDIX B

The states generated by yacc for the median chromosome grammar are:

state 0

$accept: _S $end

c  shift 3
.  error

S  goto 1
A  goto 2

state 1

$accept: _S $end

$end  accept
.  error

state 2

S: A_ A

c  shift 3
.  error

A  goto 4

state 3

A: c_ B

a  shift 9
b  shift 8
.  error

B  goto 5
F  goto 6
F  goto 7

state 4

S: AA_    (1)

.  reduce 1

state 5

A: cB_    (2)
.  reduce 2

**state 6**

       B: F_ BE

       a  shift 9
       b  shift 8
       .  error

       B  goto 10
       F  goto 6
       H  goto 7

**state 7**

       B: H_ D J

       b  shift 8
       d  shift 13
       .  error

       F  goto 12
       D  goto 11

**state 8**

       F: b_    (7)

       .  reduce 7

**state 9**

       H: a_    (9)

       .  reduce 9

**state 10**

       B: F B_ E

       b  shift 15
       .  error

       E  goto 14

**state 11**

       B: H D_ J

       a  shift 17

. error

J goto 16

state 12

D: F_D E

b shift 8
d shift 13
. error

F goto 12
D goto 18

state 13

D: d_   (6)

. reduce 6

state 14

B: F B E_(3)

. reduce 3

state 15

E: b_   (8)

. reduce 8

state 16

B: H D J_   (4)

. reduce 4

state 17

J: a_   (10)

. reduce 10

state 18

D: F D_E

b shift 15
. error

E goto 19

state 19

D: F D E_   (5)

. reduce 5

7/127 terminals, 8/300 nonterminals
11/600 grammar rules, 20/750 states
0 shift/reduce, 0 reduce/reduce conflicts reported
8/350 working sets used
memory: states, etc. 84/12000, parser 16/12000
11/600 distinct lookahead sets
3 extra closures
13 shift entries, 1 exceptions
14 goto entries
2 entries saved by goto default
Optimizer space used: input 48/12000, output 27/12000
27 table entries, 6 zero
maximum spread: 260, maximum offset: 259

## APPENDIX C

The states generated by yacc for the acrocentric chromosome grammar
are:

state 0

$accept: _S $end

c shift 3
. error

S goto 1
A goto 2

state 1

$accept: S_$end

$end accept
. error

state 2

S: A_ A

c shift 3
. error

A goto 4

state 3

A: c_ B

a shift 10
b shift 8
. error

B goto 5
F goto 6
R goto 7
H goto 9

state 4

S: A A_   (1)

. reduce 1

state 5

A: c B_   (2)

. reduce 2

state 6

B F_ L

a shift 10
b shift 8
. error

F goto 13
L goto 11
H goto 12

state 7

       B: R_E
       R: R_E

       b  shift 15
       .  error

       E  goto 14

state 8

       F: b_    (12)

       .  reduce 12

state 9

       R: H_DJ

       b  shift 8
       d  shift 19
       .  error

       F  goto 17
       D  goto 16
       W  goto 18

state 10

       H: a_    (17)

       .  reduce 17

state 11

       B: F L_    (3)

       .  reduce 3

state 12

       L: H_D J

       b  shift 8
       d  shift 19
       .  error

       F  goto 17
       D  goto 20
       W  goto 18

state 13

      L: F_L

      a shift 10
      b shift 8
      . error

      F goto 13
      L goto 21
      H goto 12

state 14

      B: R E_   (4)
      R: R E_   (14)

      b reduce 14
      . reduce 4

state 15

      E: b_   (7)

      . reduce 7

state 16

      R: H D_J

      a shift 23
      . error

      J goto 22

state 17

      D: F_G

      b shift 8
      d shift 26
      . error

      F goto 25
      G goto 24

state 18

      D: W_E

W: W_ E

b  shift 15
.  error

E  goto 27

state 19

W: d_    (16)

.  reduce 16

state 20

L: H D_ J

a  shift 23
.  error

J  goto 28

state 21

L: F L_    (11)

.  reduce 11

state 22

: H D J_    (13)

.  reduce 13

state 23

J: a_    (18)

.  reduce 18

state 24

D: F G_    (5)

.  reduce 5

state 25

G: F_ G

b  shift 8
d  shift 26
.  error

F  goto 25
G  goto 29

state 26

  G: d_ (9)

  . reduce 9

state 27

  D: W E_ (6)

  W: W E_ (15)

  b reduce 15

  . reduce 6

state 28

  L: H D J_ (10)

  . reduce 10

state 29

  G: F G_ (8)

  . reduce 8


7/127 terminals, 12/300 nonterminals

19/600 grammar rules, 30/750 states

0 shift/reduce, 0 reduce/reduce conflicts reported

12/350 working sets used

memory: states, etc. 142/12000, parser 29/12000

12/600 distinct lookahead sets

2 extra closures

20 shift entries, 3 exceptions

24 goto entries

3 entries saved by goto default

Optimizer space used: input 78/12000, output 37/12000

37 table entries, 4 zero

maximum spread: 260, maximum offset: 259

# 17

# A GENERAL PURPOSE LINE DRAWING ANALYSIS SYSTEM

ROGER MOHR[†]
*LIFIA, Institut IMAG*
*46 Avenue Felix Viallet*
*38031 Grenoble Cedex*
*France*

This chapter illustrates how the syntactical method allows building of a flexible general recognition system. The class of inputs here is two-dimensional line drawings. For this purpose we designed in our laboratory a system called MIRABELLE. From a model and a graphic tablet input the system is able to recognize a hand-drawn sketch and to provide labeling of each of its part.

The first section describes the goal of this system. The language which is used to define the shape models is given in Sec. 2. The next section details the recognition process: it is a parsing which proceeds alternatively in a top-down and in a bottom-up manner. This algorithm has to adapt its recognition strategy and Sec. 4 explains how models and inputs are taken into account by the parser. The algorithm was tailored for correcting distorted inputs; Sec. 5 describes the different error corrections that are possible and the corresponding mechanism implemented. Finally the last section discusses the features of this system, its strong points and its weaknesses, what can be extended easily and what are the main changes needed for doing industrial drawing recognition.

---

[†]This work was done when the author was with the Computer Research Institute of Nancy.

## 1. PURPOSES OF OUR SYSTEM

The MIRABELLE system was designed to be flexible and to be able to recognize different line drawing classes. These goals imply:

- the possibility to acquire a model which will provide the labeling and interpretation of the drawing;
- a language for describing this input mode;
- a general recognition algorithm which is able to match the input data with the model and also which is able to deal with the average noise present in this kind of input;
- the choice of standard tools for line drawing acquisition. To simplify the preprocessing, the graphic tablet input was chosen.

We want the model to be able to describe large classes of patterns. Figure 1 for instance provides some samples we would like to recognize (and therefore describe) in the class "hammer". Hand-drawn inputs necessarily imply errors and noise. Therefore the recognition process must handle distorted patterns like those shown in Fig. 2. Systematic blind error recovery is not possible and only contextual recognition allows correction of these kinds of input errors.

Fig. 1. Samples from the class "hammer".

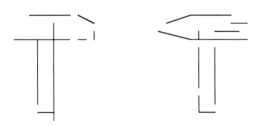

Fig. 2. Distorted inputs for the class "hammer".

These different constraints oriented the project towards the syntactic approach:

- syntax allows contextual recognition,
- grammars provide description languages,
- parsing is a general purpose recognition mechanism.

## 2. THE DESCRIPTION LANGUAGE

In the chosen approach shapes are decomposed into subshapes down to the primitive shape level. The retained primitives were restricted to straight line segments called $L$ and to circular arcs called $C$. Each shape is provided with two particular points: the *head* which is symbolized on the figures with the sign ○, the *tail* symbolized by the sign ×. It has to be pointed out that these points have only a theoretical existence and that no special sign has to be put on the drawings.

The primitives are grouped into classes according to the angle between the line segment joining the head to the tail and the tolerance factor which is allowed for this angle. So the primitive $L(45, 35)$ designates the class of line segments with a 45±35 degree angle with the horizontal base line (see Fig. 3). To describe a given universe the user determines the given classes he wants to handle and gives them a name by typing for instance:

*horizontal:* $L(0, 10)$.

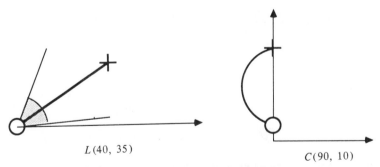

$L(40, 35)$

$C(90, 10)$

Fig. 3. The definition of primitives classes.

Length and curvature were not taken into account in the characterization of our primitives. Therefore the description will be invariant by scaling. In some applications metric information like size are very informative: for a fixed scale, a short line cannot be the border line of a door but can be the border line of a book; in such a case this information should be added into the definition of the primitives.

Subshapes are assembled into more complex shapes by using assembly operators. Five such operators were designed; all of them were inspired by the work done by Shaw[1]. These operators specify how two of the specific primitives points (head or tail) have to be put in coincidence. Let $v, h$ and $c$ be the primitives defined in Fig. 4. The expression $h + v$ designates the shape obtained with $h$ and $v$ having the tail of $h$ in coincidence with the head of $v$. Figure 4 illustrates all the five operators: $+, \times, \circ, *$ and $-$. Notice that only "$-$" permutes tail and head, and that "$*$" implies a double coincidence. The tail of the resulting pattern is always the tail of the second operand and the head of the first. This allows associativity of the four binary operators. For these reasons the formula $(-h) + (v + h)$ is written $-h + v + h$ with standard convention of higher priority for unary operators.

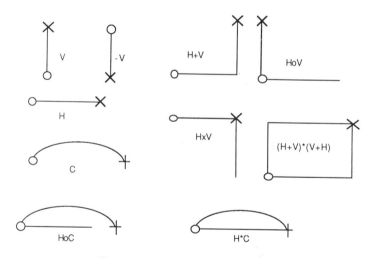

Fig. 4. The five algebraic operators.

Topographic operators allow more imprecise assembly by specifying only topographical relationship on the subshapes. Seventeen such operators were implemented; they allow description of positional relations like *above*, *inside*,... . For instance *above* $(A, B)$ will be the shape composed of $A$ and $B$ with $A$ placed above $B$. The operators refer to the extreme abscissae $(x_m, x_M)$ and ordinates $(y_m, y_M)$ of the concerned subshapes; *above* $(A, B)$

means that the condition

$$y_{Am} > y_{BM}$$

is fulfilled. Consequently, the plane is divided into seventeen regions corresponding to these relations (see Fig. 5). This introduces some limitations in the descriptive power of our language. For instance Fig. 6 displays a rabbit and a bird for which the relation *inside* holds instead of the relation *above* which people would usually prefer.

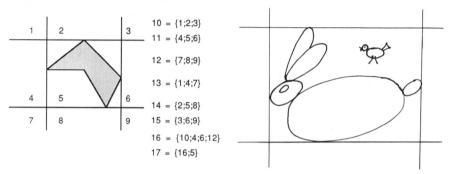

10 = {1;2;3}
11 = {4;5;6}
12 = {7;8;9}
13 = {1;4;7}
14 = {2;5;8}
15 = {3;6;9}
16 = {10;4;6;12}
17 = {16;5}

Fig. 5. The different regions.        Fig. 6. *inside (rabbit, bird)*.

A set of different rewriting rules — also called description rules — gives the different possible definitions of the subshapes composing the sketch to be recognized. The definition of the classes of primitives and the set of rules are named the description system. The left-hand side of the first rule represents the final goal of the recognition.

As in any grammar, different rules with the same left-hand side shape name allow description of different variants of this shape. For instance the following description system has two rules for the shape box, which correspond to the two sketches of Fig. 7 $(h, v$ and $c$ are from Fig. 4).

$$\text{rule 1: box: } U * h$$
$$\text{rule 2: box: } U * h * c$$
$$\text{rule 3: } U : -v + h + v \, .$$

To illustrate the power of such a system, let us consider a more complex example. The primitives first typed in are the following:

$H : L(0, 10)$; a horizontal line

$V : L(90, 10)$; a vertical line
$RO : L+45, 30)$; a right oblique line
$LO : L(135, 30)$; a left oblique line

The rules are:

1  *HOUSE* ⟶ *upon* (*ROOF, FRONT*)
2  *ROOF* ⟶ *inside* (*ATTIC-SEQUENCE, ROOF-SIDES*)
3  *ATTIC-SEQUENCE* ⟶ *ATTIC*
4  *ATTIC-SEQUENCE* ⟶ *on-the-left* (*ATTIC, ATTIC-SEQUENCE*)
5  *ATTIC* ⟶ *inside* (*WINDOW,  ATTIC-SIDES*)
6  *WINDOW* ⟶ *H * U*
7  *U* ⟶ *-V + H + V*
8  *ATTIC-SIDES* ⟶ *upon* (*ATTIC-ROOF, U*)
9  *ATTIC-ROOF* ⟶ *RO + -LO*
10  *ROOF-SIDES* ⟶ (*RO + ROOF-TOP + -LO*) * H
11  *ROOF-TOP* ⟶ *upon* (*CHIMNEY, forward*(CHIMNEY, H))
12  *CHIMNEY* ⟶ *V + H + -V*
13  *FRONT* ⟶ *inside* (*WINDOW-SEQUENCE, WALLS*)
14  *WINDOW-SEQUENCE* ⟶ *WINDOW*
15  *WINDOW-SEQUENCE* ⟶ *on-the-right* (*WINDOW,*
                                         *WINDOW-SEQUENCE*)
16  *WALLS* ⟶ *-V + H + -LO + DOOR-AUX + RO + DOOR-AUX +V*
17  *DOOR-AUX* ⟶ *upon* (*DOOR, H*)
18  *DOOR* ⟶ *CHIMNEY*

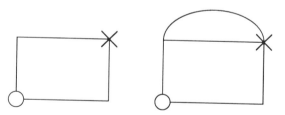

Fig. 7. Two different boxes.

Notice that *CHIMNEY* described by rule 12 is an arch. For this reason
rule 18 is able to use this arch for the definition of *DOOR*. No reference
to the pattern size makes this possible: a chimney is an arch of any size.
However this shortcut in description allows a strange interpretation: each
door can be seen as a chimney! Figure 8 displays some of the subshapes.

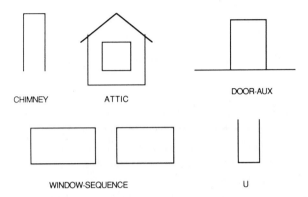

CHIMNEY    ATTIC    DOOR-AUX

WINDOW-SEQUENCE    U

Fig. 8. Subshapes from house description.

## 3. RECOGNITION

The handwritten input is sampled through a graphic tablet device. The point sequences are first divided into straight lines and curves. We used Berthod's algorithm[2]; however better methods are now available (see Ref. 3 for instance). This set of line drawing primitives is then sent to the parser.

Most of the algorithms introduced for parsing pictures are derived from algorithms given for strings and proceed from left to right (cf. Chapter 3 of this book). But our two dimensional patterns are not linear and therefore have no left or right. Global parsing algorithms[4] proceed in parallel with all the primitives and therefore can be applied without this left to right constraint. However such an algorithm runs by taking into account all the possible constructions and therefore needs a hugh memory space, even if this one is only polynomial in the input size.

An algorithm that is able to start at any part of the pattern was developed by Miller[5]. It was designed for strings and applied to speech recognition. The algorithm we shall present here is related to Miller's one. It is also able to start with any primitive of a given picture. From this anchor point it proceeds alternatively bottom-up and top-down; having recognized a subpattern $A$, it chooses in a bottom-up manner a rule

$$B \longrightarrow \mu$$

in which $A$ occurs.

For instance having an $H$ when recognizing a *HOUSE*, the system may choose rule 7:

$$U \longrightarrow -V + H + V \ .$$

When a *ROOF* is recognized the system chooses rule 1

$$HOUSE \longrightarrow upon \ (ROOF, \ FRONT) \ .$$

In this particular case it is the only possible rule.

The parsing algorithm proceeds then in a top-down manner in order to recognize the missing parts of $\mu$ and so complete the pattern $B$. In the last example the missing part is a shape *FRONT* such that the relation *upon* (*ROOF, FRONT*) holds.

This second step depends on the operators which are used in the rule. If it is a coincidence operator such as $A + C$ or $A * C$, it is possible to analyze the missing pattern $C$ in a top-down manner starting from the head of $A$. If a topographical operator is used, for instance *contains (A, C)*, the whole parsing process starts again in order to recognize $C$: a starting primitive $P$ is chosen which may belong to $C$, and a rule is chosen

$$D \longrightarrow \mu'$$

in which $P$ occurs.

Obviously we must keep all the information that can be used for reducing the number of choices at the different steps. So we remember the subregion in which the partial analysis has to be performed, the goal of this partial analysis and the known locations of tails or heads.

In order to specify how this algorithm works we will give the procedures for a restricted description language: at most one operator is allowed in each rule. The extension to the full language is easily programmed.

There are three parsing procedures which cooperate. As we have already seen, one proceeds bottom-up. It has four input parameters and produces as a result a recognized shape with its tail and head. The inputs are:

- the goal **G** of the current recognition; for the first call it will be the starting symbol, such as *HOUSE* in our last example;
- the subpattern **A** already recognized and from which we want to identify our goal pattern;
- **H** and **T**: the location of the head and tail of $A$;
- the region **R** which has to be considered for this parsing; at the first call this region is the whole drawing, but for latter calls it may be

reduced through constraints introduced by topographical operators.

For the first call, we first choose a starting primitive $P$; from there the analysis is done by the call

BOTTOM-UP (Starting-symbol, $P$, head($P$), tail($P$), whole-drawing) .

The procedure BOTTOM-UP is detailed in Fig. 9. There are several choices to be made in this algorithm. They could be solved through a standard backtracking mechanism. However, contextual information can be introduced in order to limit the possible choices and even to reduce them to a single possibility. This point will be discussed in the next section.

```
BOTTOM-UP (G, A, H, T, R)
        if A = G then {the goal is reached}
        else
(2)         choice of a rule B ——→ μ
                case  B ——→ A + C then TAIL-TO-HEAD(C, H, H', R);
                                       T' := T
                      B ——→ C + A then HEAD-TO-TAIL(C, T, T', R);
                                       H' := H
(a)                   B ——→ C * A then HEAD-TO-TAIL(C, H, T', R);
                                       if T ≠ T' then error { coincidence of
                                                              tails are verified}
                                       else H' :=H; T' := T
                      B ——→ relation (A,C)   then let R' be the subregion
                                             delimited by relation;
(3)                                          choice of a starting
                                                   primitive P in R';
                                             BOTTOM-UP (C, P, head(P), tail(P, R'));
                                             h' := H; T' := T
                end case
            { the right-hand side μ is now analyzed, we continue bottom-up}
                BOTTOM-UP (G, B, H', T', R)
end
```

Fig. 9. The bottom-up parsing procedure.

The two top-down parsers are very similar: one works by knowing the tail point of the pattern to be analyzed and returns its head, the second one starts with the head and ends by returning the tail. It is similar to two string parsers, one analyzing from left to right, as they are usually running, the other analyzing from right to left. Because of the obvious symmetry of these two algorithms, only the "head-to-tail" procedure will be explained.

HEAD-TO-TAIL has three inputs:

- the pattern $C$ to be parsed,
- the location $H$ of its head,
- the subregion $R$ where the analysis has to be performed.

As a result it provides the location $T$ of the recognized shape $C$. Figure 10 details this procedure.

HEAD-TO-TAIL $(A, H, R, T)$

if $A$ is a primitive then

        if there is an occurrence of a primitive $A$ whose

            head coincides with $H$ and which is contained in $R$

                then $T := \text{tail}(A)$

                else error

else

    (1)   choice of a rule $A \longrightarrow \mu$;

          case $A \longrightarrow B + C$ then HEAD-TO-TAIL$(C, H, R, T')$;

                                HEAD-TO-TAIL$(B, H', R, T'')$; $T := T''$

    (a)       $A \longrightarrow B * C$  then HEAD-TO-TAIL$(C, H', R, T')$;

                                  HEAD-TO-TAIL$(B, H', R, T'')$;

                if $T' \neq T''$ then error

                    else $T := T'$

          $A \longrightarrow B$       then HEAD-TO-TAIL $(B, H, R, T')$; $T := T'$

          $A \longrightarrow relation\ (B, C)$ then HEAD-TO-TAIL $(B, H, R, T')$;

                Let $R'$ be the subregion of $R$ specified by $relation$;

    (3)               choice of a starting primitive $P$ in $R'$;

                BOTTOM-UP $(C, P,\ \text{head}(P),\ \text{tail}(P))$;

                $T := T'$

end

Fig. 10. The top-down parser HEAD-TO-TAIL.

The special case of operator "$*$" has to be pointed out. It implies a double coincidence. Therefore, having to recognize $A * B$ and knowing $A$, the recognition of $B$ may start from the head or from the tail of $A$. Only the first case is indicated in Fig. 10 line (a). However if noise occurs at the head, the recognition algorithm has to start at the tail. This remark applies also for BOTTOM-UP at the line (a).

## 4. TOWARDS DETERMINISTIC RECOGNITION

As it was already said, if we are solving the choice through a backtracking mechanism we will run the parsing in exponential time. MIRABELLE implements the choice in this way, but using careful tests which restrict considerably the number of choices. So in practical cases the algorithm runs almost deterministically: usually 3 to 5 backtracking points for practical examples. This section discusses what kind of information can be extracted from the grammar in order to allow such a testing.

We will discuss all the choices in the algorithms. They are indicated by numbers (1) to (3) in Fig. 9 and Fig. 10.

**Choice (1).** In HEAD-TO-TAIL we have to recognize $A$ and decide which rule $A \rightarrow \mu$ has to be applied. The only information we have about $A$ is its head point $H$ and the region $R$ in which it has to be contained. Therefore an easy test can be performed by looking at what occurs at point $H$. At least one of the primitives appearing at this point has to belong to $A$ in accordance with $\mu$.

So for each expression $\mu$ we define $head(\mu)$ which is the set of all possible sets of primitives which can appear at the head of a shape described by $\mu$. For instance if $\mu = H * V$,

$$head(\mu) = \{ \ \{head(H), \ head(V)\} \ \} \ .$$

If $\mu = X + Y$ and $X \rightarrow -H, X \rightarrow C * V$, then

$$head(\mu) = \{ \ \{tail(H)\} \ , \ \{head(C), \ head(V)\} \ \} \ .$$

The details of the definition of the relation head and the way it is computed can be found in Ref. 6. Similarly $tail(\mu)$ is defined for the TAIL-TO-HEAD algorithm. If a set $S$ of primitives is then present at the location $H$, the rule $A \rightarrow \mu$ can be chosen only if

$$head(\mu) \subseteq S \ .$$

This test is very similar to what is done for LL(1) parsing by testing one primitive ahead. It is just generalized by working in the two directions and by considering not only elements but sets.

**Choice (2).** Having recognized a subshape $A$, we have to choose the rule we want to use in BOTTOM-UP. It is a rule $B \rightarrow \mu$ such that $A$ occurs in $\mu$. The available information for making such a decision are the head and tail positions of $A$ which have to be connected to the remaining shapes. We need therefore to know the possible couple of primitive sets that are admissible with $A$ in this rule. Let $Cont_r(\mathbf{A})$ be this set of couples — $Cont_r$ like context in the rule $r$. For instance in the following grammar where $A, B$ and $C$ are primitive shapes

(1) $X \longrightarrow Y + A + Z$
(2) $Z \longrightarrow A + V$
(3) $Y \longrightarrow B * C$
(4) $V \longrightarrow B$
(5) $V \longrightarrow Y$

the possible contexts we have for $A$ are:

$$Cont_1(A) = \{ \ (\{head(B), \ head(C)\} \ , \ \{tail(A)\} \ ) \ \}$$
$$Cont_2(A) = \{ \ (\{head(A)\} \ , \ \{tail(B)\} \ ) \ ,$$
$$( \ \{head(A)\} \ , \ \{tail(B) \ , \ tail(C)\} \ ) \ \} \ .$$

Figure 11 illustrates the different shapes described by such a grammar and what the contexts are. In this case it is obvious that a quick look at the primitives occurring at the head and tail locations allows only one possible choice. It should also be noticed that even if due to noise, one of these primitives has disappeared, the decision still remains unambiguous: if at the tail of $A$ appears the head of a $B$ and of a $C$ and simultaneously at its head there appears the tail of an $A$, then $A$ is in the context of rule 1; if at its tail and head there appear respectively either a head of $A$ and a tail of $B$, or a head of $A$ and a tail of $B$ with a tail of $C$, then $A$ is in the context of rule 2.

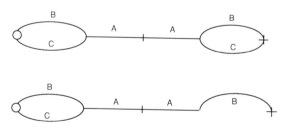

Fig. 11. Different contexts of shape $A$.

Here again we are not going to detail the way the context is computed (see Ref. 6 for more explanations). The MIRABELLE system extracts them automatically from the grammar and stores them in tables in order to speed up the parser.

**Choice (3).** The choice of a starting primitive for a partial analysis leading to a shape $C$ which must be contained in the region $R'$. The primitive has of course to be a possible subshape of $C$. The possible subshapes are easily computed from the grammar: let $\lceil$ be the relation defined by

$$A \lceil B \text{ iff } \exists \mu A \longrightarrow \mu \text{ and } B \text{ occurs in } \mu \, ,$$

let $\lceil^*$ be the transitive closure of $\lceil$, then $\lceil^*(A)$ is the set of subshapes of $A$.

Such a simple consideration only avoids obvious bad choices for $P$. In order to find a primitive which leads to $C$ we define the set $\mathrm{CHAR}(C)$ — CHAR like characteristic — to be the set of primitives which have only occurrences in $C$ or in a proper subshape of $C$. In the absence of noise which could introduce wrong primitives, the presence of such a characteristic primitive guarantees the presence of $C$.

A characteristic primitive may not be present: for instance a steeple may be characteristic of a church, but there are churches without steeples. So we introduce also the set of primitives necessarily present in a shape: $\mathrm{NEC}(C)$ is the set of primitives that occur in all $C$s. From these two sets the program chooses a starting primitive in $\mathrm{NEC}(C) \cap \mathrm{CHAR}(C)$.

Unfortunately this intersection is usually empty: CHAR is generally a subset of very specific primitives and NEC a set of very common ones. So in such a case the algorithm tries for a primitive in $\mathrm{CHAR}(C)$; if $\mathrm{CHAR}(C)$ is empty or no primitive of $\mathrm{CHAR}(C)$ occurs in the region $R'$ the algorithm looks for a primitive which belongs to $\mathrm{NEC}(C)$. If $\mathrm{NEC}(C)$ is empty then finally any primitive of $\lceil^*$ is a good candidate.

## 5. RECOGNITION OF DISTORTED INPUT

In Chapter 3 of this book, E. Tanaka has presented error correcting parsers. Another possible approach for this problem is to modify the grammar so it can accept distorted input (see for instance Chapter 6 of Ref. 7). In the latter case the errors are incorporated in the model, in the former case they are taken into account by the algorithm.

We preferred the first approach because it allows more flexibility for the control of error recovery. However the way it was implemented is more pragmatic than the systematic techniques presented in Chapter 3. Therefore we can also explicitly manage the special kind of errors introduced for hand line drawing input. This also allows us to take into account all the special operators; we have already mentioned in the previous section that the double coincidence operator "*" leads to an immediate strategy: if some noise occurs at one of the coincidence points (tail or head) the system continues analysis from the other point.

## 5.1. The Different Corrections

We are considering four types of corrections; each of them has a scoring which is used to measure the level of correction:

- addition of a missing primitive (scoring $S_1$);
- splitting of a primitive into a sub-primitive (scoring $S_2$); often we have one input line which corresponds to several shorter segments in the description;
- prolongation or shortening of primitives in order to have exact coincidence (scoring $S_3$ which is adapted to the length of the modification);
- removal of extra primitives $(S_4)$.

Figure 12 illustrates all these possible corrections.

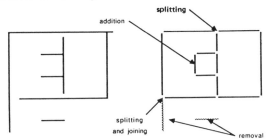

Fig. 12. Different kinds of corrections.

We have to define what an admissible corrected input is. All the score values are summed up and averaged by the number $N$ of primitives of the recognized pattern and give the correction value $C$

$$ C = (n_1 S_1) + n_2 S_2 + n_3 S_3 + n_4 S_4)/N \ . $$

$C$ is then compared to a threshold for the acceptance or rejection of the recognition.

Figure 13a gives a very distorted input. The correction threshold was therefore very high to allow many corrections. Several parsings were successful, however one parsing analyzed the drawing as illustrated by Fig. 13b. The parser started with the segment $[A - B]$. The head and tail context of this primitive was exactly the context of the bottom of DOOR and therefore the erroneous door was recognizd after a few corrections. From there, in a top-down manner the system looked for the wall lines which were also recognized after adding one more vertical line. And from there the error was propagated to the complete drawing. It has to be noticed that with a lower threshold the system backtracks: too many corrections give a correction rate which is too high. Then the correct recognition is performed.

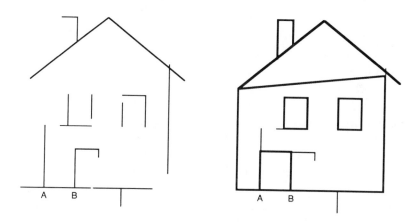

Fig. 13. A wrong parsing through corrections.

## 5.2. The Parsing Strategy

Acceptance of corrections leads to several possible answers for the recognition. Usually the number of possible corrected recognitions is very large and leads the programs to combinatorial explosion. Therefore we implemented a parsing strategy which usually provides as a result a good corrected parsing but which does not look for the best corrected parsing. It can be seen as a search for a good solution in the search space of all the partial analyses of the input drawing. The search tree is pruned when the local analysis has a correction rate which does not allow a final recognition.

It was obvious after some experiments that the key point was the right choice of a starting primitive. Such a primitive must lead to a right and unambiguous analysis starting. When a large enough subpart of the drawing is correctly recognized it introduces many constraints to the remaining recognition. All these constraints keep the remaining corrections almost always in the right track.

The choice of the starting primitive was already discussed in the previous section. Strategy considerations add a new constraint to the choice of the starting primitive, i.e. it must lead to an almost deterministic parsing. So two more conditions were introduced:

- the context of the primitive must be exactly one of the possible contexts $Cont_r$ computed from the grammar, and
- only one rule can be chosen deterministically with the help of this context.

When several primitives meet this criterion the primitive with least occurrence in the grammar is kept.

We ran this strategy and the strategy of random choice on various examples. Processing time was reduced by an average factor of 4 and for some parsings the random strategy ran more than 20 times slower. It has to be pointed out that the choice of the horizontal $[A - B]$ of Fig. 13 is not discarded by the two additional conditions expressed here. However one of the oblique lines of the roof has also a right context and has fewer occurrences in the grammar and therefore is chosen by this strategy.

In the top-down procedures one extra rule was programmed. It concerns the choice between two rules with the same sets of primitives that can occur at the head or the tail (point (a) of Fig. 10). This happens for instance with recursive rules like:

$WINDOW\text{-}SEQUENCE \longrightarrow WINDOW$
$WINDOW\text{-}SEQUENCE \longrightarrow on\text{-}the\text{-}right$
$(WINDOW, \ WINDOW\text{-}SEQUENCE)$ .

In such a case the rule which leads to the deepest analysis is chosen first. It can be seen as a way for trying to analyze the largest part of the input.

## 6. DISCUSSION AND CONCLUSION

MIRABELLE is a system able to recognize hand-drawn sketches. Examples of successful recognition are given in Fig. 14. Recognition time is usually between 1 and 2 seconds CPU time by using the strategy previously described. The input language allows description of large classes of patterns. Compilation of this language takes more time, typically 10 seconds CPU time for the HOUSE example given in Sec. 2. However it should be noticed that this processing occurs only once for an input grammar and this step is the key for the high speed recognition; in fact quasi-deterministic

Fig. 14. Some input for the **MIRABELLE** system.

recognition is possible only by using the tables provided by this compilation.

The error correcting mechanism was encoded in the parser. This enables the system to take into account specific kinds of errors for these inputs and explains also the good results that were obtained. So it does not provide a general error recovery mechanism for other applications. However we applied general ideas for this programming that can be generalized:

- keeping maximum information at each point of the analysis helps the making of correction decisions and the elimination of some choices;
- allowing flexibility lets the algorithm tailor its strategy, for instance to parse first where it is the easiest; information collected there can thus help in the making of decisions in more critical parts;
- designing of parsing strategy by clearly stating the different choices that have to be done helps to reach the two former points.

The system has to be considered as an experiment for testing the power and the generality of the syntactic approach. The conclusion is very positive. However MIRABELLE is not applicable for industrial applications and there are several reasons for this:

*Assembly operators.* Only two coincidence points are available for describing shapes and there are shapes for which this is insufficient (see Ref. 6). Extension to more than two coincidence points is easy but in industrial drawings some assembly from sub-shapes into super-shape are not made by coincidence of points but through coincidence of lines; such a possibility is not offered here. Even some more complex rules are sometimes needed; they may look like expert system rules, for instance "Houses are approximately aligned in a line parallel to the road border".

*Primitives classes.* Elementary lines are the only primitives: it would be very easy to add more complex drawings if they can be isolated in the whole input. However we have no tool for handling 2-dimensional primitives like hatched areas.

*Noisy input analysis.* MIRABELLE is able to parse only one drawing and the results are satisfactory both in time and output if the noise is limited. Plan reading needs to recognize overlapping structures which introduce a lot more noise. Thus the context which was used for ambiguity removal will be probably insufficient in such applications. More contextual information will be necessary.

*Description style.* This system is purely syntactic and therefore the shapes have nice hierarchical description. Real shapes do not have such deep recursive structures and look more like large flat networks. So our description language is not really adapted for such kind of descriptions. Bunke[8] suggests attributed graph grammars for solving some of these problems.

*Input.* Graphic tablet input simplifies the segmentation of lines into primitives. However sketches are usually printed on paper. Therefore a hard preprocessing work is here necessary in order to extract the primitives[9,10].

## REFERENCES

1. A.C. Shaw, "Parsing of graph representable pictures", *J. ACM* **17** (1970) 453-481.
2. M. Berthod and P. Jancenne, "Le prétraitement des tracés manuscrits sur une tablette graphique", *Proc. of 2nd Conference AFCET-RFIA*, Paris, 1979, pp. 195-209.
3. K. Wall, "Curve fitting based on polygonal approximation", *Proc. of the 8th International Conference on Pattern Recognition*, Paris, 1986, pp. 1273-1275.
4. D.M. Younger, "Recognition and parsing of context free languages in time $n^3$", *Inform. Control* **10** (1967) 189-200.
5. P.L. Miller, "A locally organized parser for spoken input", *Comm. ACM* **17** (1974) 621-630.
6. R. Mohr, "Precompilation of syntactical descriptions and knowledge directed analysis of patterns", *Pattern Recognition* **19** (1986) 255-266.
7. K.S. Fu, *Syntactic Methods for Pattern Recognition* (Academic Press, 1974).

8. H. Bunke, "Attributed programmed graph and application to diagram interpretation", *IEEE Trans. on Pattern Anal. and Mach. Intell.* **6** (1982) 574-582.

9. U. Cugini, G. Ferri, P. Mussio and M. Protti, "Pattern-directed restoration and vectorization of digitized engineering drawings", *Computers and Graphics* **8** (1984) 337-350.

10. E. Meynieux, S. Seisen and K. Tombre, "Bilevel information recognition and coding in office paper documents", *Proc. 8th International Conference on Pattern Recognition*, Paris, 1986, pp. 442-445.

11. G. Masini and R. Mohr, "MIRABELLE, a system for structural analysis of line drawings", *Pattern Recognition* **16** (1983) 363-372.

# 18

# ECG ANALYSIS

E. SKORDALAKIS

*Department of Electrical Engineering*
*Division of Computer Science*
*National Technical University of Athens*
*15773 Zographou, Athens, Greece*

The electrocardiogram (ECG) contains diagnostic information and for this reason it is of great value in clinical practice. The process of extracting this information is performed in two phases: the first phase is the pattern recognition and measurement phase and the second is the interpretation phase. Work done in our laboratory in employing the syntactic approach to the pattern recognition and measurement phase of ECG analysis is presented in this paper.

## 1. INTRODUCTION

The electrocardiogram (ECG) contains diagnostic information which concerns the human heart and for this reason it is of great value in clinical practice for diagnosing certain heart diseases and abnormalities. The process by which this information is extracted manually from the ECG is as follows: (1) certain patterns on the ECG are recognized and some of their characteristics are measured; (2) the recognized patterns and their measurements are used in conjunction with some empirically established diagnostic criteria for deriving a diagnosis in the form of a set of diagnostic statements. The first phase is called "the pattern recognition and measurement phase" while the second is called the "interpretation phase" of ECG processing.

Millions of ECGs are analysed every year worldwide. It is obvious that automating the corresponding process for deriving the diagnostic information from ECGs is worthwhile. Attempts towards this end started in the late 1950s with the result of having now many ECG processing systems with satisfactory performance. A description of many of such systems can be found in Refs. 1 and 2. All of them employ the non-syntactic approach in the pattern recognition and measurement phase.

The non-syntactic approach is based on a transformation that is applied to the original ECG data. The purpose of this transformation is to enhance the patterns we are interested in recognizing while suppressing all the other patterns as well as the noise. In the transformed ECG data a detection function is applied for detecting the presence or the absence of the patterns to be recognized. An approximation of the regions, where the patterns are located, is calculated. Having these results, one goes back to the original ECG data where one can utilize this information and perform a more detailed study for the recognition and the classification of the various patterns as well as for taking measurements of the various parameters. Usually the patterns that are detected in the transformed ECG data are the QRS complexes. Once these patterns are recognized, search regions are established for the other complexes using *a priori* knowledge.

In contrast, the syntactic approach considers the ECG as a composite pattern that is decomposed into other subpatterns which in turn are decomposable into other subpatterns etc. until no more decomposition is possible. These final subpatterns are called primitive patterns. The primitive patterns have to be recognized first and then in a bottom-up fashion they are combined to recognize higher order subpatterns, these higher order subpatterns are combined with primitive patterns to recognize still higher order subpatterns etc. until the ECG as a whole is recognized. This approach seems more natural and more human than the non-syntactic one. The resultant programs that implement this approach are expected to be more readable, understandable, testable and modifiable. Because of these expected benefits it is apparent that the application of the syntactic approach to the pattern recognition and measurement phase of the ECG analysis is worthwhile.

Attempts towards this direction have been made. However, these attempts have not addressed the whole problem but parts of it[3-6]. Another attempt to apply the syntactic approach to the same problem but in an integrated manner is therefore well justified. This is exactly what we tried to do. In the following sections we present our work in this problem area.

## 2. ELECTROCARDIOGRAPHIC PATTERNS

The ECG is composed of a series of electrical phenomena resulting from atrial and ventricular depolarization and repolarization. Graphically, the ECG is a set of waveforms, which are taken by an instrument called the "electrocardiograph". Each one of these waveforms is a recording of the electrical activity of the heart within a certain time period corresponding to a certain placement of the electrodes on the human body. Thus, the ECG gives us a number of different views of the electrical activity of the heart within a specific time period. The number of the different views is usually either 12 or 3. In the first case, the ECG is called 12-lead ECG whereas in the second case it is called vector-cardiogram (VCG). The leads of the 12-lead ECG are named I, II, III, AVR, etc. while the leads of the VCG are named X, Y and Z.

The relation between the ECG signal and the functioning of the human heart is as follows[7]. A cyclic pacemaking impulse normally originates in the sino-atrial (S-A) node which is located high in the right atrium, and ends at the ventricles. This impulse initiates a wave of cellular depolarization that moves across both atria resulting in the contraction of the atria and the filling of the ventricles with blood. The impulse travels down to the atrio-ventricular (A-V) node where a delay is introduced before it is passed to the ventricles. The arrival of the impulse in the ventricles initiates a wave of cellular depolarization which results in the contraction of the ventricles and the expelling of blood into the pulmonary and systematic circulations. After the contraction of the ventricles, a recovery period follows (repolarization), which lasts until the heart reaches its resting state. At this point, a cardiac cycle has been completed and a new cycle can be initiated through a new impulse generated at the S-A node etc. Thus, within a cardiac cycle we normally observe three complexes on the ECG waveform (Fig. 1). The P complex which corresponds to the depolarization of the atria, the QRS complex which corresponds to the depolarization of the ventricles and the T complex which corresponds to the repolarization of the ventricles. No visible complex corresponds to the repolarization of the atria. In some cases a wave is seen after the T complex. This is called the U wave and its origin is unknown.

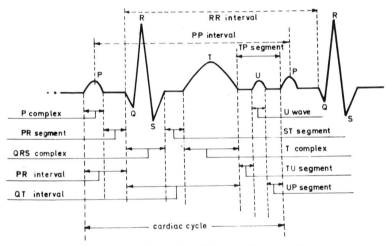

Fig. 1. A cardiac cycle and its constituent patterns.

Each cardiac complex is composed of one or more cardiac waves. For example, the component waves of the QRS complex in Fig. 1 are the Q, R and S waves. The number of various component waves of the cardiac complexes varies from lead to lead and from patient to patient. Other patterns within a cardiac cycle are the interwave segments (PR, ST, TU, UP, TP) and the cardiac intervals (PR, QT, RR, PP) as shown in Fig. 1. Thus, the electrocardiographic patterns of interest listed in a bottom-up fashion are: waves, segments, intervals, complexes, cardiac cycles, leads and ECGs. The commonly used measurements of electrocardiographic patterns are amplitudes and durations for the complexes, and durations for the segments and intervals.

The cardiac events of atrial depolarization and ventricular depolarization form an ordered pair of events which do not overlap in time. Although this is true in most cases, there are some cases in which this assumption is not valid. In the second case the corresponding ECGs are composed of complexes in various orderings and with possible overlap. Let us call these ECGs category B ECGs and the ones of the first case category A ECGs. Irregularities in the formation of the impulse and/or irregularities in the conduction system which propagates the impulse are responsible for the generation of the category B ECGs.

This categorization of ECGs is important from the pattern recognition point of view. In category A ECGs the problem of pattern recognition is difficult because some waves are hardly recognizable due to small amplitude or to noise, but at least the structural relationships of the cardiac complexes, as well as of the waves within the cardiac complexes, are known *a priori*. In category B ECGs we have all the problems of the category A ECGs plus the problem of not knowing the structural relationships of the cardiac complexes *a priori*, as well as the problem of the overlapping of the cardiac complexes.

Another aspect of electrocardiographic patterns is that their size and shape may change in time, that is, a certain pattern does not necessarily have the same size and shape in all cardiac cycles. In other words, electrocardiographic patterns can be time varying patterns.

## 3. RECOGNITION OF ELECTROCARDIOGRAPHIC PATTERNS

In order to apply the syntactic approach to a pattern recognition problem the following subproblems have to be solved: (1) primitive pattern selection, (2) primitive pattern extraction, (3) primitive pattern encoding, and (4) formulation of a pattern grammar. The solutions given to these subproblems with respect to the recognition of the electrocardiographical patterns are described.

### 3.1. Primitive Pattern Selection

The main electrocardiographic patterns are the complexes and the segments. Each one of the complexes is a series of peaks of alternating signs. The segments have the shape of a straight line or a parabola. Because of this, three primitive patterns were chosen: the "peak", the "straight line segment", and the "parabolic segment".

The peak pattern is shown in Fig. 2. This pattern is that part of a signal which is demarcated by three characteristic points. The first point is called the "left peak boundary", the second the "peak extremum", and the third the "right peak boundary". The peak extremum is the highest point in positive peaks and the lowest in negative peaks. The sample points between the left peak boundary and the peak extremum form the "left arm" of the peak. The sample points between the peak extremum and the right boundary form the "right arm" of the peak. Peaks are symbolized as $P_1$, $P_2, \ldots$, where $P_i$ is the name of the peak $i$.

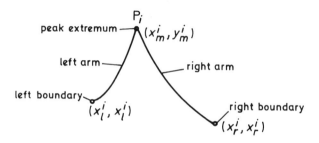

Fig. 2. Illustration of the peak pattern.

A set of attributes is assigned to each one of the primitive patterns as follows:

A set of twelve attributes is assigned to each peak $P_k$. This set is symbolized as: $\{x_l^k, y_l^k, x_m^k, y_m^k, x_r^k, y_r^k, x_{la}^k, v_{la}^k, x_{ra}^k, v_{ra}^k, A^k, E^k\}$ where

$(x_l^k, y_l^k)$    is the left boundary of the peak $P_k$,

$(x_m^k, y_m^k)$    is the peak extremum of the peak $P_k$,

$(x_r^k, y_r^k)$    is the right boundary of the peak $P_k$,

$x_{la}^k$    is the x-coordinate of the point in the left arm of the peak $P_k$ where the maximum (absolute) slope occurs,

$v_{la}^k$    is the value of the slope at the point with x-coordinate equal to $x_{la}^k$,

$x_{ra}^k$    is the x-coordinate of the point in the right arm of the peak $P_k$ where the maximum (absolute) slope occurs,

$v_{ra}^k$    is the value of the slope at the point with x-coordinate equal to $x_{ra}^k$,

$A^k$    is the angle at the peak extremum,

$E^k$ is the energy of the peak $k$ defined as $\Sigma_{i=p}^{q}(y_i - y_{i-1})^2, p = x_l + 1, \; q = x_r$.

A set of six attributes is assigned to each straight line segment $k$. This set is symbolized as: $(x_b^k, \; y_b^k, \; x_e^k, \; y_e^k, \; B^k, \; C^k)$ where

$(x_b^k, \; y_b^k)$    is the start point of the line segment,
$(x_e^k, \; y_e^k)$    is the end point of the line segment,
$B^k$ and $C^k$ are the coefficients in the equation $y = B^k x + C^k$.

A set of seven attributes is assigned to each parabolic segment $K$. This set is symbolized as: $\{x_b^k, \; y_b^k, \; x_e^k, \; y_e^k, \; B^k, \; C^k, \; D^k\}$ where

$(x_b^k, \; y_b^k)$    is the start point of the parabolic segment,
$(x_e^k, \; y_e^k)$    is the end point of the parabolic segment,
$B^k, \; C^k, \; D^k$ are the coefficients in the equation $y = B^k x^2 + C^k x + D^k$.

## 3.2. Primitive Pattern Extraction

The extraction of the primitive patterns is centered on the extraction of the peaks[8]. This is because if the peaks are extracted then the segments are extracted too. The boundaries of the peaks are also boundaries of the segments in the following sense: when the right boundary of the peak $P_i$ is very close to the left boundary of the peak $P_{i+1}$ then no segment exists between the peaks $P_i$ and $P_{i+1}$ otherwise a segment exists which has as left boundary the right boundary of the peak $P_i$ and as right boundary the left boundary of the peak $P_{i+1}$.

### 3.2.1. Peak extraction

The extraction of peaks from noise-free ECG waveforms is an easy task. In real practice, ECG waveforms are contaminated by noise. One of the effects of noise is the introduction of new (noisy) peaks in the ECG waveforms. Because of this, the extraction of the real peaks from the ECG waveforms is a very difficult task.

The procedure which has been adopted for the extraction of peaks and their attributes is based on the philosophy of direct methods[9]. Existing methods for recognition of peaks belong to two categories: the direct methods and the indirect methods. In the indirect methods the real peaks are recognized by smoothing the sample data and accepting that the noisy peaks are suppressed by the smoothing. In the direct methods, the noisy peaks are recognized directly using *ad hoc* techniques and then the real peaks are recognized by subtracting from the set of all peaks the noisy ones.

This procedure performs its task in seven steps as follows:

*Step 1:* It recognizes the set of all peaks in a given ECG waveform.

*Step 2:* It recognizes noisy peak pairs. A noisy peak pair is a pair of adjacent peaks that satisfy a certain set of criteria. The criteria for recognizing the peak pair $(P_{i-2}, P_{i-1})$ as noisy (Fig. 3) when the peak $P_i$ is positive are the following:

criterion 1: $y_l^{i-2} \leq y_l^{i-1} \wedge y_r^{i-1} \geq y_r^{i-2}$,

criterion 2: $\Delta t_m \leq \delta$ where $\delta = \delta_2$ *when* $\left| y_m^{i-1} - y_m^{i-2} \right| < \delta_1$
   *else* $\delta = \delta_3$,

criterion 3: $\Delta t_m \geq \Delta t_l \wedge \Delta t_m \leq \Delta t_r$ *when* $\Delta t_m > \delta_4$.

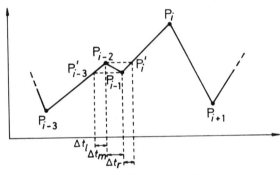

Fig. 3. Noisy peak pair.

When the peak $P_i$ is negative the inequalities in the first criterion are reversed. $\delta_1, \delta_2, \delta_3$ and $\delta_4$ denote threshold values.

The first of these criteria demands that the peak pair $(P_{i-2}, P_{i-1})$ is located (nested) within the peak pair $(P_{i-3}, P_i)$. The second and third are duration criteria.

It has been found[9] that, on average, 84% of the noisy peaks in an ECG waveform can be recognized by this step.

The noisy peaks recognized in this step are subtracted from the set of all peaks found in Step 1 and the set of the remaining peaks is given as input to Step 3.

*Step 3:* It recognizes noisy peak pairs but in contrast to Step 2 these noisy peak pairs satisfy another set of criteria. It is noted that the noisy peak pairs recognized in this step are located near the baseline while the ones recognized in Step 2 are located everywhere. The criteria for recognizing the peak pair $(P_i, P_{i+1})$ as noisy are the following:

criterion 4: $x_m^{i+1} - x_m^i < \delta_5$,
criterion 5: $\left| y_m^{i+1} - y_m^i \right| < \delta_6$,
criterion 6: $\left| y_l^i - y_m^i \right| < \delta_7$,
criterion 7: $\left| y_r^{i+1} - y_m^{i+1} \right| < \delta_8$.

The first is a duration criterion while the others are height criteria. A pair of adjacent peaks which have small duration and amplitude are rejected as noisy. This is the meaning of these criteria. $\delta_5, \delta_6, \delta_7$ and $\delta_8$ denote threshold values. The peaks recognized as noisy are subtracted from the input set of peaks given to this step and the set of the remaining peaks is given as input to Step 5. This set still contains noisy peaks that have to be recognized and rejected.

*Step 4:* It calculates an approximation to the baseline. The reason for this is that after Step 3 the remaining noisy peaks are located around the baseline and an approximation to the baseline together with a sets of criteria (Step 5) are needed for recognizing and rejecting these remaining noisy peaks. The method used for the calculation of an approximation to the baseline is based on the assumption that: (1) the variance of each arm in small peaks close to the baseline is small (Fig. 4a), (2) the variance of one of the arms, on peaks close to the baseline and with the one arm close to the baseline as in Fig. 4b and Fig. 4c, is also small.

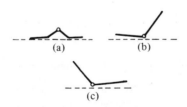

(a)          (b)

(c)

Fig. 4. Peaks close to the baseline that can be used for finding fiducial points.

Such peaks which are close to the baseline are identified and used for finding fiducial points from which the approximation to the baseline passes. To each such peaks $P_i$, a fiducial point $j$ is associated with coordinates

$(x'_j, y'_j)$ where $x'_j = x^i_m$ and $y'_j$ as defined below. The approximation to the baseline is denoted by the ordered set of fiducial points

$$((x'_1, y'_1), (x'_2, y'_2), \ldots, (x'_n, y'_n))$$

where $n$ is the number of fiducial points found. The actual approximation to the baseline is formed by joining these fiducial points by line segments.

For identifying that the peak $P_i$ can be used for finding a fiducial point the following criterion is used

criterion 8: $Z = Z_1 \vee Z_2,$

where

$Z$ is a predicate variable,
$Z_1$ and $Z_2$ are predicate variables with values given by the formulae:

$$Z_1 = \sigma_l^2 < \delta_9 ,$$
$$Z_2 = \sigma_r^2 < \delta_9 ,$$

$$\sigma_l^2 = \sum_{k=b}^{e}(y_k - \overline{y}_l)^2, \quad e = x^i_m, \quad b = e - \delta_{10}, \quad \overline{y}_l = \left(\sum_{k=b}^{e} y_k\right)/(\delta_{10} + 1) ,$$

$$\sigma_r^2 = \sum_{k=b}^{e}(y_k - \overline{y}_r)^2, \quad b = x^i_m, \quad e = b + \delta_{10}, \quad \overline{y}_r = \left(\sum_{k=b}^{e} y_k\right)/(\delta_{10} + 1) ,$$

$y_i$, $i = 1(1)n$ are the amplitudes of the sample points of the ECG waveform,
$\delta_q$, $\delta_{10}$    are threshold values.

A variable $q$ is defined according to: $q = 1$ when both $Z_1$ and $Z_2$ are true, $q = 2$ when only $Z_1$ is true, and $q = 3$ when only $Z_2$ is true. The $y'_j$ coordinate of the corresponding fiducial point is calculated according to:

$$y'_j = (\overline{y}_l + \overline{y}_r)/2 \quad \text{when } q = 1 ,$$
$$y'_j = \overline{y}_l \quad \text{when } q = 2 ,$$
$$y'_j = \overline{y}_r \quad \text{when } q = 3 .$$

*Step 5:* It recognizes noisy peaks around the baseline. This is accomplished by employing the approximation to the baseline calculated in Step 4 and applying the following criteria to each peak $P_i$:

criterion 9: $\sim Z,$

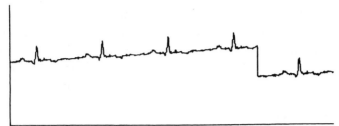

Fig. 5. Illustration of a jump.

criterion 10: $x_r^i - x_l^i < \delta_{11}$,
criterion 11: $\left| y_m^i - y_b^i \right| < \delta_{12}$,

where
$Z, Z_1, Z_2$ are predicate variables with values given by the formulae:

$$Z_1 = \left| y_m^i - y_l^i \right| > \delta_{13} \wedge \left| y_m^i - y_r^i \right| > \delta_{14}$$
$$Z_2 = \left| y_m^i - y_l^i \right| > \delta_{14} \wedge \left| y_m^i - y_r^i \right| > \delta_{13}$$
$$Z = Z_1 \vee Z_2 .$$

$y_b^i$ is the amplitude of the baseline (found from its approximation) at the point with x-coordinate equal to the one of the peak $P_i$. $\delta_{11}, \delta_{12}, \delta_{13}, \delta_{14}$ are threshold values.

The criteria have the following meaning. Criterion 9 protects small Q waves and small S waves from rejection as noisy peaks. Criterion 10 demands that noisy peaks have small duration. Criterion 11 states that peaks close to the baseline are considered as noisy.

The peaks recognized as noisy are subtracted from the input set of peaks given to this step and the set of the remaining peaks is given as input to Step 6. This set may still contain noisy peaks that have to be recognized and rejected.

*Step 6:* It recognizes jumps. A jump is a noisy peak (an artifact). As illustrated in Fig. 5, in a jump there is a sudden and large deviation from a base level, that does not return within a short time interval. The net effect of this artifact is that the baseline changes level. A peak $P_k$ is considered to be a jump when it fulfills the following two criteria:

criterion 12: $V_{la}^k > \delta_{15} \cdot V_{ra}^k \vee V_{ra}^k > \delta_{15} \cdot V_{la}^k$
criterion 13: $\max\left\{ \left| y_m^k - y_l^k \right|, \ \left| y_m^k - y_r^k \right| \right\} > \delta_{16}$

where $\delta_{15}, \delta_{16}$ are threshold values.

Criterion 12 expresses the property that the maximum slope in one arm of a peak is considerably greater than the maximum slope of the other arm. Criterion 13 expresses the high amplitude characteristic of the jumps.

The peaks recognized as jumps are subtracted from the input set of peaks given to this step and the set of the remaining peaks is given as input to Step 7. This set may still contain noisy peaks that have to be recognized and rejected.

*Step 7:* It recognizes high spikes. A high spike is a sequence of consecutive noisy peaks (an artifact). As illustrated in Fig. 6, in a high spike there is a sudden large deviation from a base level with return to it within a short time interval. The characteristics of a high spike are steep slopes, high amplitudes and small durations. A sequence of consecutive peaks is considered to be a high spike when each peak fulfills the following criteria:

criterion 14: $\left|y_m^k - y_l^k\right| \le \delta_{17*}\left|V_{la}^k\right| \vee \left|y_m^k - y_r^k\right| \le \delta_{17*}\left|V_{ra}^k\right|$
criterion 15: $\min\left\{\left|y_m^k - y_l^k\right|,\ \ \left|y_m^k - y_r^k\right|\right\} > \delta_{18}$
criterion 16: $x_r^k - x_l^k < \delta_{19}$

where $\delta_{17}, \delta_{18}, \delta_{19}$ are threshold values.

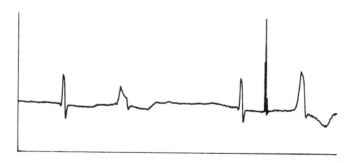

Fig. 6. Illustration of a spike.

Criterion 14 expresses the steep slope characteristic, criterion 15 the high amplitude characteristic and criterion 16 the small duration characteristic.

The peaks recognized as high spikes are subtracted from the input set of peaks given to this step and the set of the remaining peaks in the set of the real peaks.

The number of the required threshold values is really large. One might expect that the estimation of proper values for them would be a difficult problem. Fortunately, this is not the case. This may be attributed to the fact that these thresholds are independent of each other because they concern different features of the patterns. We experienced that proper values for them can be estimated by simple experimentation. The values we found and which are used in our runs are the following:

$$\delta_1 = 25, \quad \delta_2 = 16, \quad \delta_3 = 20, \quad \delta_4 = 4, \quad \delta_5 = 15, \quad \delta_6 = 65,$$
$$\delta_7 = \delta_8 = 200, \quad \delta_9 = 5, \quad \delta_{10} = 30, \quad \delta_{11} = 8, \quad \delta_{12} = 50, \quad \delta_{13} = 200,$$
$$\delta_{14} = 20, \quad \delta_{15} = 6, \quad \delta_{16} = 250, \quad \delta_{17} = 2, \quad \delta_{18} = 250, \quad \delta_{19} = 15 .$$

### 3.2.2. Segment extraction

The segment lies by definition between the cardiac complexes. The grouping of peaks into complexes is done easily because within a complex the right boundary of a peak (except the last) nearly coincides with the left boundary of the next peak. Once the start-point and the end-point of a segment are found then by a least-squares fit a decision can be made as to whether it is a straight line or a parabola.

### 3.2.3. An illustrative example

An illustrative example is given in Fig. 7 where the results of the various steps of the extraction procedure can be observed. The initial ECG waveform is given in Fig. 7a. The set of noisy peaks, recognized at Step 2 were subtracted from the set of all peaks recognized at Step 1 and the remaining peaks are shown in Fig. 7b, where the peaks are marked by the symbol '+'. From this set the noisy peaks recognized at Step 3 were subtracted and the remaining peaks are shown in Fig. 7c. The approximation to the baseline calculated at Step 4 is shown in Fig. 7d, where the symbol '×' is used to mark a fiducial point. From the set of peaks of Fig. 7c the noisy peaks recognized at Step 5 were subtracted and the remaining peaks are shown in Fig. 7e. No noisy peaks were recognized at Step 6 and Step 7.

Thus, the real peaks are the ones shown in Fig. 7e, where the boundaries of the peaks are marked by upward arrows. The segments can be identified in this figure too. The primitive patterns found in this example together with some of their attributes are given in tabular form in Table 1.

It is noted that errors can be introduced in the primitive extraction step. These errors are of two kinds. The first kind corresponds to the case of real peaks which are not identified as such (false negative errors). The second kind corresponds to the case of noisy peaks which are identified as real peaks (false positive errors).

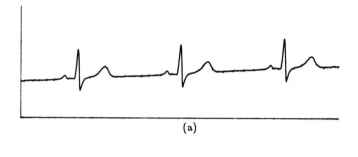

(a)

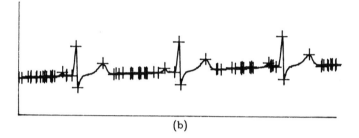

(b)

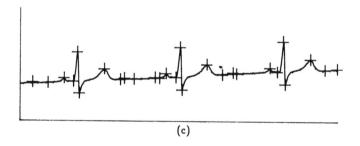

(c)

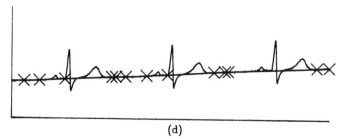

(d)

Fig. 7. An illustrative example of the extraction of the primitive patterns.

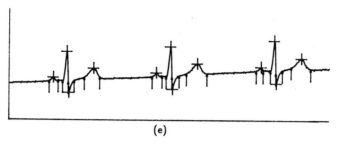

(e)

**Fig. 7.** Cont'd.

### 3.3. Linguistic Representation

The alphabet of symbols $\Sigma = \{K^+, K^-, E, \Pi\}$ has been adopted, where $K^+$ represents positive peak, $K^-$ negative peak, $E$ straight line segment and $\Pi$ parabolic segment, for encoding ECG waveforms. Thus, an ECG waveform is linguistically represented as a string of symbols from the alphabet $\Sigma$.

**Example.** The linguistic representation of the waveform of Fig. 7a is the following:

$$EK^+\Pi K^+ K^- EK^+\Pi K^+ EK^+ K^- \Pi K^+\Pi K^+\Pi K^+ K^- EK^+\Pi .$$

### 3.4. Pattern Grammar

An attribute grammar suitable for the recognition of category A ECGs, as well as for the classification of the QRS complexes, is given in Appendix A. This grammar is an enhanced version of the one given in Ref. 10 and can be processed by any non-deterministic attribute grammar evaluator that finds the first solution only. It recognizes the electrocardiographic patterns and calculates their measurements as required in the pattern recognition and measurement phase of an ECG processing system.

The grammar has been formulated in such a way that it can be used to parse error-free input strings as well as erroneous input strings. The errors which can be handled by this grammar are those due to noisy peaks at the interwave segments that have been recognized as real peaks during the primitive extraction phase (false positive errors). The syntactic rules in the grammar are written in such a way that the alternatives for an error-free input string are applied first. If this does not lead to a solution then the alternatives, that assume errors, are applied next.

The attribute grammar notation used has been augmented with a global

Table 1. Primitives and their attributes.

| Primitive | Begin | | Peak | | End | | Angle | Energy | Coefficients | | |
|---|---|---|---|---|---|---|---|---|---|---|---|
| | X | Y | X | Y | X | Y | | | A | B | C |
| LINE+ | 1 | -278 | | | 190 | -215 | | | 0.04 | -2.76 | |
| PEAK+ | 190 | -215 | 211 | -141 | 232 | -204 | 113.8 | 1939 | | | |
| PARABOLA+ | 232 | -204 | | | 253 | -220 | | | 0.23 | -5.69 | 32.88 |
| PEAK+ | 253 | -220 | 275 | 461 | 280 | -246 | 11.1 | 158466 | | | |
| PEAK- | 280 | -246 | 284 | -492 | 308 | -211 | 27.7 | 34405 | | | |
| LINE+ | 308 | -211 | | | 356 | -144 | | | 0.28 | -6.50 | |
| PEAK+ | 356 | -144 | 401 | 72 | 428 | -130 | 79.9 | 4326 | | | |
| PARABOLA+ | 428 | -130 | | | 672 | -111 | | | 0.00 | -0.16 | 0.18 |
| PEAK+ | 672 | -111 | 693 | -30 | 718 | -99 | 113.4 | 2166 | | | |
| LINE- | 718 | -99 | | | 737 | -109 | | | -0.07 | 1.64 | |
| PEAK+ | 737 | -109 | 759 | 582 | 764 | -124 | 11.0 | 162693 | | | |
| PEAK- | 764 | -124 | 768 | -407 | 798 | -91 | 29.4 | 44257 | | | |
| PARABOLA+ | 798 | -91 | | | 832 | -38 | | | 0.08 | -6.84 | 132.75 |
| PEAK+ | 832 | -38 | 885 | 186 | 928 | -45 | 92.7 | 6603 | | | |
| PARABOLA+ | 928 | -45 | | | 1158 | 22 | | | 0.00 | -0.03 | -0.67 |
| PEAK+ | 1158 | 22 | 1182 | 113 | 1190 | 22 | 76.5 | 2054 | | | |
| PARABOLA- | 1190 | 22 | | | 1224 | 34 | | | -0.02 | 3.45 | -102.47 |
| PEAK+ | 1224 | 34 | 1244 | 727 | 1250 | -29 | 10.4 | 177737 | | | |
| PEAK- | 1250 | -29 | 1253 | -268 | 1281 | 37 | 28.2 | 35542 | | | |
| LINE+ | 1281 | 37 | | | 1323 | 123 | | | 0.30 | -19.33 | |
| PEAK+ | 1323 | 123 | 1372 | 315 | 1413 | 74 | 92.3 | 5689 | | | |
| PARABOLA+ | 1413 | 74 | | | 1501 | 91 | | | 0.00 | -0.27 | 9.24 |

attribute called "FLAG" that takes only the values 0 and 1. When FLAG takes the value 0 during the syntactic evaluation of a BNF rule, the parser considers that matching of the input substring with the corresponding syntactic structure has not been successful. Thus, FLAG directs the parsing (recognition) through the semantics.

Twenty attributes are used, namely:

| | |
|---|---|
| *iw* | denoting the number of waves, inherited |
| *sw* | denoting the number of waves, synthesized |
| *ic* | denoting the number of classes, inherited |
| *sc* | denoting the number of classes, synthesized |
| *iqrs*[*i*] | denoting the number of QRSs in class *i*, inherited |
| *sqrs*[*i*] | denoting the number of QRSs in class *i*, synthesized |
| *type* | denoting the QRS morphology, synthesized |
| *beg* | denoting the begin point of a pattern, synthesized |
| *end* | denoting the end point of a pattern, synthesized |
| *xm* | denoting the x-coordinate of the extremum of a peak, synthesized |
| *ybeg* | denoting the y-coordinate of the point with x-coordinate *beg*, synthesized |
| *yend* | denoting the y-coordinate of the point with x-coordinate *end*, synthesized |
| *yxm* | denoting the y-coordinate of the extremum of a peak, synthesized |
| *te* | denoting the energy of a peak, synthesized |
| *ang* | denoting the angle of a peak, synthesized |
| *ldur* | denoting the duration of the left arm of a peak, synthesized |
| *rdur* | denoting the duration of the right arm of a peak, synthesized |
| *lh* | denoting the height of the left arm of a peak, synthesized |
| *rh* | denoting the height of the right arm of a peak, synthesized |
| *tp-flag* | denoting the candidacy of a peak as a P or T (sub)pattern, inherited and synthesized. |

The attributes *beg, end, xm, ybeg, yend, yxm, te* and *ang* take as initial values the ones of the attributes of the corresponding terminal symbols which were symbolized previously, i.e. $x_l^k, x_r^k, x_m^k, y_l^k, y_r^k, y_m^k, E^k, A^k$, respectively.

The semantic rules for each BNF rule are given below it. For the sake of brevity the semantic rules for the computation of the begin and end points of the interwave segments (ST for example) have been omitted. A notation was also adopted concerning the evaluation of the attributes *iqrs*[*i*] and

$sqrs[i]$. Where no index is present in these attributes (symbolically, $iqrs[\ ]$ and $sqrs[\ ]$), it is assumed that a loop is performed, with the index varying from 1 to $K$ where $K$ is the maximum value of the index.

The details of the various tasks of the grammar are as follows:

*QRS detection and recognition.* A series of consecutive peaks — one to seven — is considered as a QRS complex if (a) the energy of at least one peak is greater that $\varepsilon_1$, (b) the angle of each peak is less than $\varepsilon_5$, and (c) the angle between the right arm of peak $i$ and the left arm of peak $i + 1$ is less than $\varepsilon_2$. The alternative of the BNF rule that matches the QRS pattern specifies its morphology.

*P, T detection and recognition.* One or two consecutive peaks are considered as a $P$ or a $T$ complex when the height and the duration of each arm in every peak is greater than $\varepsilon_3$ and $\varepsilon_4$, respectively, depending on the syntactic rule being evaluated. The discrimination between $P$ and $T$ complexes and other (noisy) peaks is accomplished by comparing their energies. Noisy peaks in a region between two QRSs are demanded to have energy less than the energy of the $P$ and $T$ complexes in that region. The alternative of the BNF rule that matches the $P$ or $T$ pattern specifies its morphology. It is noted that $P$ and $T$ complexes before the first QRS complex found and after the last QRS complex found are not detected.

*QRS classification.* It is performed by a nearest neighbor classification algorithm. The distance between a QRS complex and a class of QRS complexes is computed as the average of the distances between the QRS complex and each QRS complex in the class. The distance between two QRS complexes is expressed using the "city block" metric and the features used are the normalized duration and height of each wave component of a QRS complex. An alignment between the two QRS complexes is performed so that their distance is minimized.

$\varepsilon_1, \varepsilon_2, \varepsilon_3, \varepsilon_4$ and $\varepsilon_5$ denote threshold values.

## 4. EXPERIMENTAL RESULTS

The stage of testing this approach to the pattern recognition and measurement phase of an ECG analysis system has not been finished yet. For this reason no quantitative results concerning the performance of this approach will be presented. Work is underway for completing this stage[11] and taking corrective action where it would be appropriate. Nevertheless, from the results taken so far it can be stated that the performance of this approach is satisfactory.

Three illustrative examples are given below with real ECG data taken from the standard CSE ECG library[12].

## 4.1. Illustrative Example 1

This example is shown in Fig. 8. The initial ECG waveform is given in Fig. 8a. The primitive patterns that were extracted at the primitive extraction step are given in Fig. 8b. The corresponding linguistic representation of this ECG waveform is the following:

$$\Pi K^+ \Pi K^- \Pi K^+ \Pi K^+ \Pi K^- \Pi K^+ \Pi K^+ \Pi K^- \Pi K^+ \Pi .$$

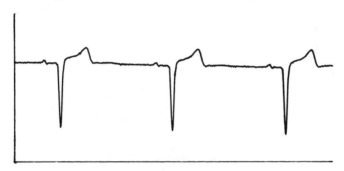

(a) Initial ECG waveform.

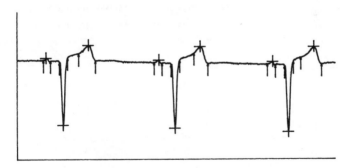

(b) Extracted primitive patterns.

Fig. 8.

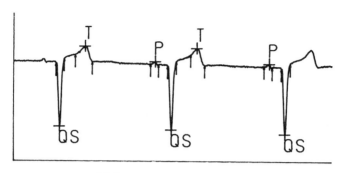

(c) Recognized ECG patterns.

Fig. 8. Cont'd.

The recognition results are given in Fig. 8c. The QRS classification results are as follows:

NUMBER OF CLASSES = 1

CLASS [1]: NUMBER OF QRS'S = 3

QRS 1 BEGIN = 202    END = 241    MORPHOLOGY: QS

QRS 2 BEGIN = 728    END = 769    MORPHOLOGY: QS

QRS 3 BEGIN = 1262    END = 1304    MORPHOLOGY: QS

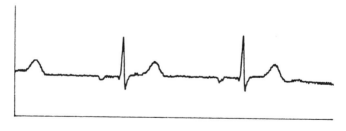

(a) Initial ECG waveform.

Fig. 9.

(b) Extracted primitive patterns.

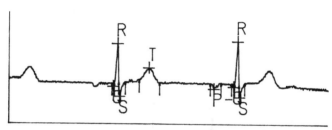

(c) Recognized ECG patterns.

Fig. 9. Cont'd.

## 4.2. Illustrative Example 2

This example is shown in Fig. 9. The initial ECG waveform is given in Fig. 9a. The primitive patterns that were extracted at the primitive extraction step are given in Fig. 9b. In this example the primitive extractor has erroneously recognized a noisy peak as a real peak. This peak is identified by a downward arrow and it is located at an ST segment. The corresponding linguistic representation of this ECG waveform is the following:

$$\Pi K^+ \Pi K^- E K^- K^+ K^- E \underset{\uparrow}{K}^+ \Pi K^+ \Pi K^- \Pi K^- K^+ K^- \Pi K^+ \Pi \ ,$$

where the false positive symbol is marked with an upward arrow. The recognition results are given in Fig. 9c where it can be observed that the false positive pattern has been ignored and the recognition of the ECG waveform was performed correctly. The QRS classification results are as follows:

NUMBER OF CLASSES = 1

CLASS [1]: NUMBER OF QRS'S = 2
QRS 1 BEGIN = 488    END = 550     MORPHOLOGY: QRS
QRS 2 BEGIN = 1048   END = 1110   MORPHOLOGY: QRS

## 4.3. Illustrative Example 3

This example is shown in Fig. 10. The initial ECG waveform is given in Fig. 10a. The primitive patterns that were extracted at the primitive extraction step are given in Fig. 10b and the corresponding linguistic representation of this ECG waveform is the following:

$$\Pi K^+ \Pi K^+ K^- \Pi K^+ \Pi K^+ \Pi K^+ K^- \Pi K^+ \Pi K^+ E K^- \Pi K^+ E K^+ K^- \Pi K^+ E \ .$$

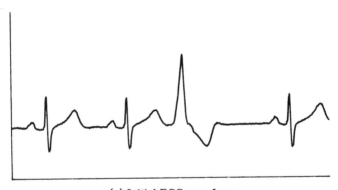

(a) Initial ECG waveform.

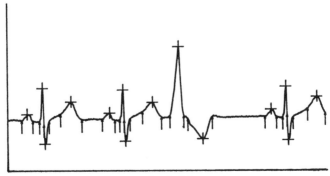

(b) Extracted primitive patterns.

Fig. 10.

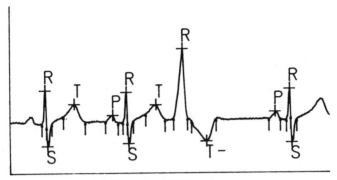

(c) Recognized ECG patterns.

Fig. 10. Cont'd.

The recognition results are given in Fig. 10c. The QRS classification results are as follows:

NUMBER OF CLASSES = 2

CLASS [1]: NUMBER OF QRS'S = 3

QRS 1 BEGIN = 152    END = 198    MORPHOLOGY: RS

QRS 2 BEGIN = 532    END = 581    MORPHOLOGY: RS

QRS 3 BEGIN = 1300    END = 1384    MORPHOLOGY: RS

CLASS [2]: NUMBER OF QRS'S = 1

QRS 1 BEGIN = 770    END = 835    MORPHOLOGY: R

## REFERENCES

1. J.H. van Bemmel and J.L. Willems, *Trends in Computer Processed Electrocardiograms* (North-Holland, Amsterdam, 1976).
2. J.L. Willems, J.H. van Bemmel and C. Zywietz, *Computer ECG Analysis: Towards Standardization* (North-Holland, Amsterdam, 1986).
3. S.L. Horowitz, "A syntactic algorithm for peak detection in waveforms with applications to cardiography", *Comm. ACM* 18 (1975) 281-285.
4. G. Belforte, R. De Mori and F. Ferraris, "A contribution to the automatic processing of electrocardiograms using syntactic methods", *IEEE Trans. Biomed. Eng.* 26 (1979) 125-136.
5. J.K. Udupa and I.S.N. Murthy, "Syntactic approach to ECG rhythm analysis", *IEEE Trans. Biomed. Eng.* 27 (1980) 370-375.
6. G. Papakonstantinou, E. Skordalakis and F. Gritzali, "An attribute grammar for QRS detection", *Pattern Recognition* 19 (1986) 297-303.
7. E. Skordalakis, "Syntactic ECG Processing: A review, *Pattern Recognition* 19 (1986) 306-313.

8. E. Skordalakis and P. Trahanias, "Primitive pattern selection and extraction in ECG waveforms", *Proc. 8th ICPR*, Paris, Oct. 1986, pp. 380-382.

9. E. Skordalakis, "Recognition of noisy peaks in ECG waveforms", *Comp. Biomed. Res.* **17** (1984) 208-221.

10. P. Trahanias, G. Stamatopoulos and E. Skordalakis, "Error detection and correction in linguistic representation of ECG waveforms", *Proc. 1st European Workshop on Fault Diagnostics, Reliability and Related Knowledge-Based Approaches*, Island of Rhodes, Greece, 1986 (in press).

11. P. Trahanias, Syntactic ECG Recognition, Ph.D. Thesis, under preparation.

12. J.L. Willems *et al.*, "Establishment of a reference library for evaluating computer ECG measurement programs", *Comp. Biomed. Res.* **18** (1985) 439-457.

# APPENDIX

An attribute grammar for the description of category A ECG waveforms.

1. $\langle \text{ECG LEAD} \rangle_1 \longrightarrow \langle \text{INITIAL PART} \rangle_2 \langle \text{CARDIAC CYCLES} \rangle_3$
$\langle \text{FINAL PART} \rangle_4$
$\text{num\_waves} := sw_4; \ iw_3 : 0, \ iw_4 := sw_3;$
$\text{num\_classes} := sc_4; \ \text{num\_qrs}[\ ] := sqrs[\ ]_4;$
$ic_3 := 0; \ iqrs[\ ]_3 := 0;$
$ic_4 := sc_3; \ iqrs[\ ]_4 := sqrs[\ ]_3;$

2. $\langle \text{INITIAL PART} \rangle \longrightarrow \langle \text{SEGMENT} \rangle \langle \text{INITIAL PART} \rangle$
$\longrightarrow \varepsilon$
$\longrightarrow \langle \text{PEAK} \rangle \langle \text{INITIAL PART} \rangle$

3. $\langle \text{FINAL PART} \rangle_1 \longrightarrow \langle \text{QRS} \rangle_2 \langle \text{REST PART} \rangle_3$
$sw_1 := sw_2; \ iw_2 := iw_1;$
$sc_1 := sc_2; \ sqrs[\ ]_1 := sqrs[\ ]_2;$
$ic_2 := ic_1; \ iqrs[\ ]_2 := iqrs[\ ]_1;$

4. $\langle \text{REST PART} \rangle \longrightarrow \langle \text{SEGMENT} \rangle \langle \text{REST PART} \rangle$
$\longrightarrow \langle \text{PEAK} \rangle \langle \text{REST PART} \rangle$
$\longrightarrow \varepsilon$

5. $\langle \text{CARDIAC CYCLES} \rangle_1 \longrightarrow \langle \text{CARDIAC CYCLE} \rangle_2$
$\langle \text{CARDIAC CYCLES} \rangle_3$
if $(sw_3 = 0)$ then
$\qquad sw_1 := sw_2;$
else
$\qquad sw_1 := sw_3;$
$iw_2 := iw_1; \ iw_3 := sw_2;$
if $(sc_3 = 0)$ then
$\quad$ begin
$\qquad sc_1 := sc_2;$
$\qquad sqrs[\ ]_1 := sqrs[\ ]_2;$
$\quad$ end
else
$\quad$ begin
$\qquad sc_1 := sc_3;$
$\qquad sqrs[\ ]_1 := sqrs[\ ]_3;$
$\quad$ end

$$ic_2 := ic_1; \; iqrs[\;]_2 := iqrs[\;]_1;$$
$$ic_3 := sc_2; \; iqrs[\;]_3 := sqrs[\;]_2;$$
$$\longrightarrow \varepsilon$$
$$sw_1 := 0;$$
$$sc_1 := 0; \; sqrs[\;]_1 := 0;$$

6. $\langle \text{CARDIAC CYCLE} \rangle_1 \longrightarrow \langle \text{QRS} \rangle_2 \langle \text{NON\_QRS} \rangle_3$
$$sw_1 := sw_3; \; iw_2 := iw_1; \; iw_3 := sw_2;$$
$$sc_1 := sc_2; \; sqrs[\;]_1 := sqrs[\;]_2;$$
$$ic_2 := ic_1; \; iqrs[\;]_2 := iqrs[\;]_1;$$

7. $\langle \text{QRS} \rangle_1 \longrightarrow \langle \text{Q} \rangle_2 \langle \text{R} \rangle_3 \langle \text{S} \rangle_4 \langle \text{R}' \rangle_5 \langle \text{S}' \rangle_6 \langle \text{R}'' \rangle_7 \langle \text{S}'' \rangle_8$
$$type_1 := 1;$$
semantic routine 1 (7, 0);
$$\longrightarrow \langle \text{Q} \rangle_2 \langle \text{R} \rangle_3 \langle \text{S} \rangle_4 \langle \text{R}' \rangle_5 \langle \text{S}' \rangle_6 \langle \text{R}'' \rangle_7$$
$$type_1 := 2;$$
semantic routine 1 (6, 0);
$$\longrightarrow \langle \text{R} \rangle_2 \langle \text{S} \rangle_3 \langle \text{R}' \rangle_4 \langle \text{S}' \rangle_5 \langle \text{R}'' \rangle_6 \langle \text{S}'' \rangle_7$$
$$type_1 := 3;$$
semantic routine 1 (6, 1);
$$\longrightarrow \langle \text{R} \rangle_2 \langle \text{S} \rangle_3 \langle \text{R}' \rangle_4 \langle \text{S}' \rangle_5 \langle \text{R}'' \rangle_6$$
$$type_1 := 4;$$
semantic routine 1 (5, 1);
$$\longrightarrow \langle \text{Q} \rangle_2 \langle \text{R} \rangle_3 \langle \text{S} \rangle_4 \langle \text{R}' \rangle_5 \langle \text{S}' \rangle_6$$
$$type_1 := 5;$$
semantic routine 1 (5, 0);
$$\longrightarrow \langle \text{Q} \rangle_2 \langle \text{R} \rangle_3 \langle \text{S} \rangle_4 \langle \text{R}' \rangle_5$$
$$type_1 := 6;$$
semantic routine 1 (4, 0);
$$\longrightarrow \langle \text{R} \rangle_2 \langle \text{S} \rangle_3 \langle \text{R}' \rangle_4 \langle \text{S}' \rangle_5$$
$$type_1 := 7;$$
semantic routine 1 (4, 1);
$$\longrightarrow \langle \text{R} \rangle_2 \langle \text{S} \rangle_3 \langle \text{R}' \rangle_4$$
$$type_1 := 8;$$
semantic routine 1 (3, 1);
$$\longrightarrow \langle \text{Q} \rangle_2 \langle \text{R} \rangle_3 \langle \text{S} \rangle_4$$
$$type_1 := 9;$$
semantic routine 1 (3, 0);

$\longrightarrow \langle Q \rangle_2 \langle R \rangle_3$

    $type_1 := 10;$

    semantic routine 1 (2, 0);

$\longrightarrow \langle R \rangle_2 \langle S \rangle_3$

    $type_1 := 11;$

    semantic routine 1 (2, 1);

$\longrightarrow \langle R \rangle_2$

    $type_1 := 12;$

    semantic routine 1 (1, 1);

$\longrightarrow \langle QS \rangle_2$

    $type_1 := 13;$

    semantic routine 1 (1, 7);

8. $\langle NON\_QRS \rangle_1 \longrightarrow \langle SR \rangle_2$

    if $(tp\_flag_2 \neq 0)$ then FLAG:=0;

    $sw_1 := iw_1;$

    $\longrightarrow \langle ST \rangle_2 \langle T \rangle_3 \langle TR \rangle_4$

    if $(tp\_flag_2 \neq 0 \;\vee\; tp\_flag_4 \neq 0)$

        then FLAG:0;

    if $\neg\ (te_2 < te_3 \wedge te_4 < te_3 \wedge dur_2 \leq dur_4)$

        then FLAG:=0;

    $sw_1 := sw_3;\ iw_3 := iw_1;$

    $\longrightarrow \langle SP \rangle_2 \langle P \rangle_3 \langle PR \rangle_4$

    if $(tp\_flag_2 \neq 0 \;\vee\; tp\_flag_4 \neq 0)$

        then FLAG:=0;

    if $\neg\ (te_2 < te_3 \wedge te_4 < te_3 \wedge dur_2 > dur_4)$

        then FLAG:=0;

    $sw_1 := sw_3;\ iw_3 := iw_1;$

    $\longrightarrow \langle ST \rangle_2 \langle T \rangle_3 \langle TP \rangle_4 \langle P \rangle_5 \langle PR \rangle_6$

    if $(tp\_flag_2 \neq 0 \vee tp\_flag_4 \neq 0 \vee tp\_flag_6$
    $\neq 0)$ then

        if $\neg\ (te_2 < te_2 \wedge te_2 < te_5 \wedge te_4 < te_3 \wedge$

            $te_4 < te_5 \wedge te_6 < te_3 \wedge te_6 < te_5)$

            then FLAG:=0;

    $sw_1 := sw_5;\ iw_3 := iw_1;\ iw_5 := sw_3;$

9. $\langle ST \rangle_1 \longrightarrow \langle INTERWAVE\ SEGMENT \rangle_2$
$$te_1 := te_2;\ \ tp\_flag_1 := tp\_flag_2;$$

10. $\langle TP \rangle_1 \longrightarrow \langle INTERWAVE\ SEGMENT \rangle_2$
$$te_1 := te_2;\ \ tp\_flag_1 := tp\_flag_2;$$

11. $\langle PR \rangle_1 \longrightarrow \langle INTERWAVE\ SEGMENT \rangle_2$
$$te_1 := te_2;\ \ tp\_flag_1 := tp\_flag_2;$$

12. $\langle TR \rangle_1 \longrightarrow \langle INTERWAVE\ SEGMENT \rangle_2$
$$te_1 := te_2;\ \ tp\_flag_1 := tp\_flag_2;$$

13. $\langle SP \rangle_1 \longrightarrow \langle INTERWAVE\ SEGMENT \rangle_2$
$$te_1 := te_2;\ \ tp\_flag_1 := tp\_flag_2;$$

14. $\langle SR \rangle_1 \longrightarrow \langle SEGMENT \rangle_2 \langle INTERWAVE\ SEGMENT \rangle_3$
$$tp\_flag_1 := tp\_flag_3;$$
$\longrightarrow \langle PEAK \rangle_2 \langle INTERWAVE\ SEGMENT \rangle_3$
<u>if</u> $(ldur_2 > \varepsilon_4 \wedge rdur_2 > \varepsilon_4 \wedge$
$\quad lh_2 > \varepsilon_3 \wedge rh_2 > \varepsilon_3)$ <u>then</u>
$$tp\_flag_1 := 1 + tp\_flag_3;$$
<u>else</u>
$$tp\_flag_1 := tp\_flag_3;$$

15. $\langle INTERWAVE\ SEGMENT \rangle_1 \longrightarrow \langle SEGMENT \rangle_2 \langle INTERWAVE$
$$SEGMENT \rangle_3$$
$$tp\_flag_1 := tp\_flag_3;\ \ te_1 := te_3;$$
$\longrightarrow \varepsilon$
$$tp\_flag_1 := 0;\ \ te_1 := 0;$$
$\longrightarrow \langle PEAK \rangle_2 \langle INTERWAVE$
$$SEGMENT \rangle_3$$
<u>if</u> $(ldur_2 > \varepsilon_4 \wedge rdur_2 > \varepsilon_4 \wedge$
$\quad lh_2 > \varepsilon_3 \wedge rh_2 > \varepsilon_3)$ <u>then</u>
$$tp\_flag_1 := 1 + tp\_flag_3;$$
<u>else</u>
$$tp\_flag_1 := tp\_flag_3;$$
$$te_1 := \max(te_2,\ te_3);$$

16. $\langle T \rangle_1 \longrightarrow \langle T\_OR\_P \rangle_2$
semantic routine 2;
$$iw_2 := iw_1;\ \ tp\_flag_2 := -1;$$

17. $\langle P \rangle_1 \longrightarrow \langle T\_OR\_P \rangle_2$
         semantic routine 2;
         $iw_2 := iw_1; \ tp\_flag_2 := -2;$

18. $\langle T\_OR\_P \rangle \longrightarrow K^+ K^-$
              semantic routine 3 $(3, 1, -1)$;
         $\longrightarrow K^- K^+$
              semantic routine 3 $(3, -1, 1)$;
         $\longrightarrow K^+$
              semantic routine 3 $(2, 1, 0)$;
         $\longrightarrow K^-$
              semantic routine 3 $(2, 0, -1)$;

19. $\langle R \rangle \longrightarrow K^+$
         semantic routine 4;

20. $\langle R' \rangle \longrightarrow K^+$
         semantic routine 4;

21. $\langle R'' \rangle \longrightarrow K^+$
         semantic routine 4;

22. $\langle Q \rangle \longrightarrow K^-$
         semantic routine 4;

23. $\langle QS \rangle \longrightarrow K^-$
         semantic routine 4;

24. $\langle S \rangle \longrightarrow K^-$
         semantic routine 4;

25. $\langle S' \rangle \longrightarrow K^-$
         semantic routine 4;

26. $\langle S'' \rangle \longrightarrow K^-$
         semantic routine 4;

27. $\langle PEAK \rangle \longrightarrow K^+$
         semantic routine 5;
         $\longrightarrow K^-$
         semantic routine 5;

28. $\langle \text{SEGMENT} \rangle \longrightarrow E$

$$\longrightarrow \Pi$$

semantic routine 1 $(k,\ l)$

<u>begin</u>

/ * semantic checks for the acceptance of a */

/ * series of peaks as a qrs complex */

flag1:=0;

flag2:=1;

flag3:=1;

for $i = 1$ <u>to</u> $k$ <u>do</u>

    <u>begin</u>

        <u>if</u> $(te_{i+1} > \varepsilon_1)$ <u>then</u> flag1:=1;

        <u>if</u> $(ang_{i+1} > \varepsilon_5)$ <u>then</u> flag2:=0;

    <u>end</u>

<u>for</u> $i = 1$ <u>to</u> $k - 1$ <u>do</u>

    <u>begin</u>

        <u>if</u> $(\text{angle (i)} > \varepsilon_2)$ <u>then</u> flag3:=0;

    <u>end</u>

FLAG:=flag1 * flag2 * flag3;

/ *_ _ _ _ _ _ _ _ _ _ _ _ _ _ _ _ _ _ _ _ * /

/ * store the component waves of a qrs complex */

$n := iw_1$;

<u>for</u> $i = 1$ <u>to</u> $k$ <u>do</u>

    <u>begin</u>

        $n := n + 1$;

        store_wave $(n,\ \text{wave\_class}[i + l])$;

    <u>end</u>

$sw_1 := n$;

$beg_1 := beg_2$;

$end_1 := end_{k+1}$;

/ * _ _ _ _ _ _ _ _ _ _ _ _ _ _ _ _ _ _ _ _ _ * /

/ * compute features needed for qrs classification * /

<u>for</u>   $i = 1$ <u>to</u> 7 <u>do</u>

    <u>begin</u>

        $d_x[i]_1 := 0$

        $d_y[i]_1 := 0$

    <u>end</u>

```
base1:=ybeg₂;
```
$\text{base1}:=ybeg_2;$

if      ($l = 1$) then
    begin
        $i_1 := 2;\ i_2 := k + 1;\ m := 0;$
    end
else
    begin
        $i_1 := 1;\ i_2 := k;\ m := 1;$
    end
for   $i = i_1$ to $i_2$ do
    begin
        $d_x[i]_1 := end_{i+m} - beg_{i+m};$
        $d_y[i]_1 := |yxm_{i+m} - base1|;$
    end

/ * _ _ _ _ _ _ _ _ _ _ _ _ _ _ _ _ _ _ _ _ _ _ * /
/ * compute distances of the qrs complex from the    * /
/ * classes; find the class with the minimum          * /
/ * distance from the qrs and the minimum distance * /

min_dist:=∞;
$n := ic_1;$
for $i = 1$ to $n$ do
    begin
        if (distance(qrs, $i$) < min_dist) then
            begin
                min_dist:=distance(qrs, $i$);
                index:=$i$;
            end
    end

/ * _ _ _ _ _ _ _ _ _ _ _ _ _ _ _ _ _ _ _ _ _ * /
/ * if minimum distance less than a preset       * /
/ * threshold $t$ assign qrs in that class otherwise * /
/ * initiate a new class for that qrs            * /

if (min_dist< $t$) then
  $iqrs=[\text{index}]_1 := iqrs[\text{index}]_1 + 1;$
else
    begin
        $n : n + 1$
        $iqrs[n]_1 := 1;$

```
      end
sc₁ := n;
sqrs[ ]₁ := iqrs[ ]₁;
cluster[sc₁,  sqrs[sc₁]₁] ⟵ qrs;
end
```

semantic routine 2
```
begin
te₁ := te₂;
sw₁ := sw₂;
beg₁ := beg₂;
end₁ := end₂;
end
```

semantic routine 3 $(k,\ i_1,\ i_2)$
```
begin
/ * semantic checks for the acceptance of a peak or        * /
/ * two peaks with alternating signs as a T or P complex * /
te₁ := 0;
for i = 2 to k do
      begin
            if ¬ (te_i < ε₁ ∧ lh_i > ε₃ ∧ rh_i > ε₃∧
                  ldur_i > ε₄ ∧ rdur_i > ε₄) then FLAG:=0;
            te₁ := max(te₁,  te_i);
      end
beg₁ := beg₂;
end₁ := end_k;
/ * _ _ _ _ _ _ _ _ _ _ _ _ _ _ _ _ _ _ _ _ _ _ * /
/ * store the component waves of a T or P complex * /
n := iw₁ + 1;
if (tp_flag₁ = -1) then m := 0;
else  m := 2;
if (i₁ = 1 ∧ i₂ = -1) then
      begin
            store_wave (n, wave_class [9+m]);
            n := n + 1;
            store_wave (n, wave_class[10 + m]);
      end
```

```
else if (i₁ = -1 ∧ i₂ = 1) then
   begin
         store_wave (n, wave_class[10 + m]);
         n := n + 1;
         store_wave (n, wave_class[9 + m]);
   end
else if (i₁ = 1 ∧ i₂ = 0) then
         store_wave (n, wave_class[9 + m]);
else
         store_wave (n, wave_class[10 + m]);
sw₁ := n;
end
```

semantic routine 4
```
begin
beg₁ := beg₂;
end₁ := end₂;
xm₁ := xm₂;
yxm₁ := yxm₂;
ybeg₁ := ybeg₂;
te₁ := te₂;
ang₁ := ang₂;
end
```

semantic routine 5
```
begin
lh₁ := |yxm₂ - ybeg₂|;
rh₁ := |yxm₂ - yend₂|;
ldur₁ := xm₂ - beg₂;
rdur₁ : end₂ - xm₂;
te₁ := te₂;
end
```

*Auxiliary routines*

function angle($i$): Computes the angle between the right arm of the peak $i$ and the left arm of the peak $i + 1$.

function distance(qrs, $i$): Computes the distance between the qrs complex and the $i$ class.

routine store_wave ($n$, wave_class [$i$]): Stores in the $n$th position of a matrix the wave "wave_class [$i$]" and its attributes, where the matrix wave_class[ ] is defined as:

wave_class[1]:= 'Q',    wave_class[2]:= 'R',    wave_class[3]:= 'S',
wave_class[4]:= 'R''',    wave_class[5]:= 'S''',    wave_class[6]:= 'R''''',
wave_class[7]:= 'S''''',    wave_class[8]:= 'QS',    wave_class[9]:= 'T',
wave_class[10]:= 'T−',    wave_class[11]:= 'P',    wave_class[12]:= 'P−'.

# AUTHOR INDEX

Abe, K., 133, 227, 229

Adachi, H., 79, 81

Agin, G., 373

Aho, A.V., 56, 57, 62, 71, 79, 81, 250, 356, 423, 454, 456, 461

Akinniyi, F.A., 198

Ali, F., 46

Allermann, G., 342

Añaños, M., 176

Angluin, D., 7, 238, 241, 262, 264, 277

Aoki, K., 77, 161

Au, T., 199, 233

Aurbach, J., 77

Aygun, B.O., 225, 229


Bahl, L.R., 271

Ballard, D.H., 328, 342

Bandler, W., 336

Barr, A., 323, 326, 328

Belforte, G., 501

Berthod, M., 313, 373, 384, 485

Bhanu, B., 322

Bhargava, B.K., 31, 146, 277, 454

Biermann, A.W., 241, 260, 264

Binford, T.O., 384

Birkhoff, G., 4, 15

Biswas, G., 283

Bobrow, D.G., 325, 328

Bolles, R.C., 374, 382, 384, 408

Bondy, J.A., 399

Boorman, S.A., 146, 148

Booth, T.L., 292, 296, 302, 357, 363

Bourlard, H., 271

Boyer, K.L., 15

Boyle, J., 324

Brachman, R.J., 328

Bratko, I., 329, 331

Brauneg, D.J., 287

Brayer, J.M., 277, 283

Brewka, G., 331

Brooks, R.A., 384

Brown, C.M., 328, 342

Brownston, L., 327, 330, 334

Buchanan, B.G., 326

Bunke, H., 7, 13, 30, 31, 39, 43, 44, 316, 318, 328, 330, 332, 334, 341, 342, 362, 454, 496

Burt, S., 374

Buttleman, H.W., 9

Cain, R.A., 374, 382
Carr, J.W., III, 257
Casacuberta F., 63
Case, J., 241
Cayla, C., 265, 272
Chakravarty, I., 382, 383, 384, 386, 406
Chan, T.Y.T., 321
Chandrasekaran, B., 323, 335, 350
Chang, C., 324
Chen, C.H., 15
Cheng, J.K., 321
Cheng, Y.C., 146, 174
Chirathamjaree, C., 272, 277
Chou, S.M., 285
Chowkwanyun, R., 325
Claus, V., 86
Clocksin, W.F., 324, 331
Clowes, M.B., 386
Cohen, D.N., 225, 229
Coldren, B., 374
Cook, C.M., 274
Cook C.R., 291, 292, 294
Corneil, D.G., 148
Covvey, H.D., 328
Crespi-Reghizzi, S., 272, 287
Cugini, U., 496

Dai, X.W., 283
Damestoy, J.P., 328
Dattatreya, G.R., 336
Davis, L., 461, 462, 466
Davis, L.S., 318, 322
Davis, R., 326
De Mori, R., 268, 327, 501
Delauney, B., 376
Deliyanni, A., 330
Devijver, P.A., 120, 129, 131, 310,

322, 350
Di Primio, F., 331
Don, H.S., 318
Dowling, G.R., 126
Du Bois, D., 268
Duane, G.S., 327
Dubes, R.C., 283
Duda, R.O., 41, 45, 310, 330, 336
Duerr, B., 351
Dvorak, J., 332, 334

Ebert, W., 376
Ehrig, H., 86, 103
Erman, L.D., 340
Eshera, M.A., 384
Evans, T.G., 283
Ezure, K., 18, 56, 63, 81

Fan, T.I., 12, 358, 363
Farrell, R., 327, 330, 334
Faugeras, O.D., 313, 319, 322, 384
Feder, T., 47, 50
Feigenbaum, E.A., 323, 326, 328
Feistel, H., 328, 330, 341
Feldman, J.A., 241, 260, 276, 328
Ferraris, F., 501
Ferrate, G., 30
Ferri, G., 496
Feustel, D.C., 321
Filipski, A., 357
Findler, N.V., 328
Fischer, M.J., 126, 132, 355, 359
Fischler, M.A., 408
Fitzer, M., 376
Foley, J.D., 394, 411
Freeman, H., 382, 383, 384, 406
Friedman, J.H., 131
Fu, K.S., 6, 8, 9, 12, 13, 14, 18, 19,

20, 30, 31, 39, 42, 46, 51, 56, 68, 77, 79, 80, 81, 86, 103, 113, 121, 132, 141, 146, 149, 169, 171, 172, 174, 198, 227, 229, 233, 240, 241, 268, 276, 277, 283, 285, 286, 287, 291, 292, 296, 302, 315, 318, 322, 331, 334, 336, 342, 350, 351, 353, 354, 355, 356, 357, 358, 359, 360, 361, 362, 363, 377, 384, 417, 418, 422, 423, 426, 454, 455, 458, 462, 491

Fukunaga, K., 131, 150, 321

Fung, L.W., 68, 356, 363

Galiano, I., 264, 287

Gallagar, R., 215

Garcia, P., 264, 287

Garey, M.R., 312

Gaschnig, J., 330

Gennery, D.B., 408

Georgeff, M., 326

Gernert, D., 315

Ghahraman, D.E., 198, 199, 201, 233

Ghosh, J., 325

Ginsburg, S., 56

Gips, J., 276

Gleason, G., 373

Gold, E.M., 241

Goldfarb, L., 198, 233, 321

Goldstein, I.P., 328

Gonzalez, R.C., 4, 6, 8, 9, 13, 18, 20, 39, 42, 56, 58, 277, 283, 287, 310, 356, 363, 454, 458

Gorn, S., 278

Gotlieb, C.C., 148

Graham, S.L., 63, 81

Granum, E., 18, 20, 21, 287

Gray, F., 194

Grebner, K., 39, 43, 318

Green, P.D., 328

Greibach, S., 332

Greiner, R., 384

Grenander, U., 350

Gries, D., 454

Gritzali, F., 501

Groen, F.C.A., 322

Grosky, 292

Gu, Y.X., 416

Guo, Qing, 416

Gupta, M.M., 336

Haettich, W., 351

Hall, P.A.N., 341

Hall, P.A.V., 126

Hanson, A.R., 322, 328

Haralick, R.M., 6, 14, 18, 185, 189, 194, 199, 233, 313, 321, 322, 342, 379, 384

Harmon, P., 327, 329, 331

Harrison, M.A., 63, 81

Hart, P.E., 41, 45, 310, 330, 336

Harvey, W.A., 327

Haton, J.-P., 328

Hayes, P.H., 330

Hayes-Roth, F., 340

Henderson, T.C., 313, 318, 461, 462, 466

Hitaka, T., 80

Hofmann, I., 328, 330, 341

Holland, S.W., 374

Hopcroft, J.E., 34, 292, 311, 332

Horning, J.J., 276

Horowitz, S.L., 501

Huang, T.S., 321, 351, 354, 357, 360, 363

Huffman, D.A., 386
Hummel, R.A., 189, 313, 465
Hung, M.J., 135
Hwang, K., 325

Ikeda, M., 18, 56, 63, 77, 80, 81
Illingworth, J., 313
Ip, D.J., 376
Ishizuka, M., 336
Itoga, S.Y., 264

Jancenne, P., 485
Jelinek, F., 271
Johnson, D.S., 312
Joynson, R.E., 374
Juang, B.H., 271

Kak, A.C., 15
Kakusho, O., 77
Kamata, K., 79, 80, 81
Kamp, Y., 271
Kanal, L.N., 336, 341, 342, 350
Kandel, A., 333, 336, 439
Kant, E., 327, 330, 334
Kasai, T., 66, 79, 81
Kaul, M., 317
Kayser, K., 376
Kim, J.H., 327
King, D., 327, 329, 331
Kirsch, R.A., 292
Kiszka, J.B., 336
Kitchen, L., 321
Kittler, J., 120, 129, 131, 310, 313,
    322, 350
Kleene, S.C., 248
Knuth, D.E., 46, 422
Kobayashi, H., 81
Korns, M., 373
Kowalski, R.A., 330

Krause, K., 374
Kremers, J.H., 382
Kruskal, J.B., 135
Kruskal, J.R., 121
Kubichek, R.F., 322
Kuklinski, T., 373
Kuno, S., 79, 81

Lam, L., 327
Lan, Li, 416
Lee, H.C., 286, 357, 363
Lee, H.S., 328
Lee, R.C., 324
Lemmer, J.F., 336
Lennig, M., 135
Lesser, V.R., 340
Leveshtein, A., 152
Levine, B., 277
Levine, M.D., 327, 340
Levinson, S.E., 271, 341
Liberman, M., 135
Lichten, L., 287
Lin, H.J., 291, 292
Lin, W.C., 51, 462
Liu, Y.J., 443, 447, 448
Lowerre, B.T., 341
Lowrance, R., 355
Lu, S.Y., 121, 132, 146, 148, 149, 156,
    165, 169, 171, 172, 174, 276, 286,
    356, 358, 360, 361, 363
Luneau, P., 265, 272
Lusk, E., 324
Lyon, G., 71, 81

MacLane, S., 4, 15
Majumdar, A.K., 268
Malpas, J., 330, 331
Martin, N., 327, 330, 334

Masek, W.J., 140
Massone, L., 327
Matsuyama, T., 327, 340
McAllister, D.F., 4, 15, 22
McCall, J.T., 194
McCormick, W.M., 194
McCracken, D.L., 327
McDermott, J., 327
McKeown, D.M., 327
Medici, A., 372
Melkanoff, M.A., 287
Mellish, C.S., 324, 331
Mercer, A., 291, 293
Mercer, R.L., 271
Mermelstein, P., 135
Meynieux, E., 496
Miclet, L., 6, 8, 9, 18, 20, 30, 240, 241, 254, 256, 258, 262
Milgram, D.L., 13, 454
Miller, P.L., 485
Miyazawa, O., 81
Moayer, B., 287
Mohr, R., 489, 490, 495
Moret, B.M.E., 336
Mori, S., 372, 373
Morita, K., 291
Mott, D.H., 324
Mui, J.K., 336
Mulgaonkav, P.G., 384
Mundy, J.L., 374
Murthy, I.S.N., 501
Murty, U.S.R., 399
Mussio, P., 496
Mylopoulos, J., 328

Nagao, M., 327, 340
Nagasawa, T., 82
Nagin, P.A., 322

Nagl, M., 13, 14, 86, 103
Nakamura, A., 291
Nakamura, T., 80
Narendra, P.M., 131, 321
Nazif, A.M., 327
Nevatia, R., 385, 403, 406, 407
New, H., 77
Ney, H., 271
Niemann, H., 233, 328, 330, 341
Nilsson, N.J., 324, 329, 330, 332, 341
Niyogi, D., 324

Ohmori, K., 148
Ohta, Y., 327
Okuda, T., 66
Olin, K.E., 327
Oliver, D., 146, 148
Osherson, D.N., 243
Oshika, B., 77
Ouriachi, K., 285
Overbeek, R., 324
Ozeki, K., 82

Page, C., 357
Pao, T.W., 257
Papakonstantinou, G., 501
Pasche, D., 39, 43, 44
Paterson, M.S., 140
Pavlidis, T., 13, 14, 30, 46, 198, 291, 377, 378, 454
Payton, D.W., 327
Pearl, J., 341
Perkins, W.A., 374, 382
Peterson, T.G., 71, 356
Post, E., 325
Potter, H.H.S., 376
Prade, H., 268
Price, K.E., 319, 379

Probst, D., 327
Protti, M., 496
Pyster, A., 9

Quincy, E.A., 322
Quinqueton, J., 240

Rabiner, L.R., 271, 341
Reddy, R., 340
Reder, S., 276
Reichert, T.A., 225, 229
Requicha, Aristides A.G., 382
Richetin, M., 256, 265, 272, 286
Richter, D.J., 327
Riseman, E.M., 322, 328
Roberts, L.G., 383, 405, 406, 407
Roberts, R.B., 328
Robinson, J.A., 324
Rodger, R.S., 256
Rosebrugh, R.D., 256
Rosenfeld, A., 13, 86, 103, 189, 274,
    283, 291, 292, 293, 313, 454, 465
Rosenkrantz, D.J., 276
Rossol, L., 374
Roy, A.K., 268
Rozenberg, G., 86, 103
Rubin, S.M., 341
Rulot, H., 264
Ruzzo, W.L., 63, 81

Safranek, R.J., 15
Sagerer, G., 39, 43, 318, 328, 330, 341
Sakuramoto, K., 79, 81
Saloma, A., 357
Sanderson, A.C., 322
Sanfeliu, A., 13, 19, 30, 31, 146, 176,
    177, 198, 362, 384
Sankoff, D., 121, 135

Sarman, V.V.S., 336
Schantz, H.F., 372
Schlag, J.F., 322
Schmolze, J.G., 328
Schurmann, J., 372
Segarra, E., 264, 287
Seisen, S., 496
Selkow, S.M., 148
Shaheen, S.I., 340
Shank, R.C., 328
Shapira, R., 385, 386
Shapiro, G., 321
Shapiro, L.G., 6, 14, 18, 131, 185, 189,
    194, 199, 233, 321, 342, 384
Shaw, A.C., 9, 47, 50, 198, 291, 361,
    416, 419, 454, 482
Shi, Q.Y., 362, 454
Shillman, R., 373
Shortliffe, E.A., 323, 326, 336
Shu, Wenhao, 416
Skordalakis, E., 501, 505, 506, 513
Smith, A.R., III., 291
Smith, C.-H., 7, 238, 241
Sobel, I., 408
Solomonoff, R., 260, 272, 276
Sondhi, M.M., 271, 341
Srihari, S.N., 324
Stacey, D., 198
Stamatopoulos, G., 513
Stanat, D.F., 4, 15, 22
Stockman, G., 342
Straub, M., 243
Stute, H., 376
Suen, C.Y., 297, 373, 416
Sugata, K., 291
Sugita N., 133, 227, 229
Swain, P., 376
Sze, T.W., 132

Tai, J.W., 315, 354, 360, 361, 362, 363, 423, 426, 429, 432, 443, 447, 448

Tai, K.C., 148, 156, 158

Tamada, I., 82

Tamura, T., 268

Tanaka, E., 18, 56, 63, 66, 68, 75, 77, 79, 80, 81, 82, 138, 148, 156, 161, 356, 363

Tanaka, K., 268

Tang, G.Y., 46, 351, 354, 360, 363, 416

Thacher, J.W., 148

Thakor, N.V., 328

Thomason, M.G., 6, 8, 9, 10, 13, 18, 20, 21, 30, 39, 42, 56, 58, 277, 283, 287, 356, 358, 363, 454, 458

Thompson, R.A., 357, 358, 363

Tilove, R., 374

Tombre, K., 496

Tomek, I., 375

Tonomura, T., 68, 81

Tou, J.T., 4, 310

Trahanias, P., 505, 513, 516

Tront, J., 194

Tropf, H., 351

Tsai, W.H., 6, 9, 14, 18, 121, 142, 198, 233, 350, 351, 354, 358, 359, 360, 361, 362, 363, 384, 417, 418, 422

Tsatsoulis, C., 334

Tsotsos, J.K., 328

Turner, R., 323

Udupa, J.K., 501

Ullman, J.D., 34, 56, 57, 62, 79, 81, 250, 292, 311, 423, 454, 456, 461

Ullman, J.R., 148, 194

Van Bemmel, J.H., 500

Van Dam, A., 394, 411

Veelenturf, L.P.J., 265

Venable, S.F., 327

Vere, S.A., 335

Vernadat, F., 256, 286

Vidal, E., 264, 287

Wagner, R.A., 126, 132, 355, 359

Wakahara, K., 82

Wall, K., 485

Waltz, D., 313, 465

Wang, C.Y., 322

Wang, P.S.P., 283, 291, 292, 294

Ward, J., 373

Ward, M.R., 374

Weeks, V., 77

Weinstein, S., 243

Wellekens, C.J., 271

Wiedemann, A.M., 327

Wilhelm, R., 148

Willems, J.L., 500, 517

Winkler, G., 351

Winograd, T., 328

Winston, P.H., 286, 325, 329, 335

Wolf, F., 328, 330, 341

Wong, A.K.C., 15, 23, 198, 199, 201, 219, 223, 225, 229, 233

Wong, E.K., 384

Wood, A.R., 328

Woods, W.A., 79, 283

Wos, L., 324

Xia, Y., 416

Xie, H.C., 322

Yam, S.E., 382

Yamamoto, K., 372

Yamamoto, Y., 291

Yamasaki, S., 68, 81

Yang, H.S., 15

Yang, Y.H., 132

Yao, T.P., 336

Yasuda, M., 372

Ye, Pei Jian, 416

Yoshida, S., 80

Yoshino, K., 77

You, K.C., 46, 351, 354, 355, 360,
    361, 363, 417, 422, 455

You, M.L., 15, 23, 198, 199, 201, 219,
    223, 227, 233

Young, T.Y., 350

Younger, D.M., 485

Yu, S.S., 9, 121, 142, 354, 358, 363

Zadeh, L.A., 333

Zhang, T.Y., 297

Zhang, X., 416

Zimmermann, H.J., 333

Zisman, M.O., 326

Zucker, S.W., 189, 313, 328, 465

Zue, V., 77

Zywietz, C., 500

# SUBJECT INDEX

*a priori* probability, 309
accepting state, 104
acceptor, 103
  array, 105-111
  finite-state, 105
  graph, 111-113
  monotonic, 105
  string, 104-105
  tape-bounded, 105
ACRONYM, 384
admissible class, 241, 242
aerial image understanding, 319
alphabet, 31
ambiguous (word), 35, 40
AND/OR-graph, 336, 341
AND/OR-tree, 341
array, 47, 100, 112, 120
array acceptor, 105-111
array grammar, 86, 96-100, 292, 297
  context-free, 292
  inference of, 296
  isometric, 99, 293
  monotonic, 292
array language, 106, 297
  context-free, 294

array pattern, 297
ART, 331
artificial intelligence, 323, 331, 382
attribute, 14, 45, 121, 140, 337, 352,
  354, 408, 422, 504, 515
  inherited, 46
  synthesized, 46
attribute grammar, 513
attributed finite-state automaton,
  441, 443
attributed grammar, 45-46, 114,
  360, 361, 417, 422, 430
attributed graph, 198, 199-201, 224,
  384
attributed relation, 187
attributed relational description, 188
attributed string, 140, 355, 358, 361
attributed string matching, 140-142
augmented transition network (ATN),
  283, 285
automaton (automata), 9-10, 103
  attributed finite-state, 441, 443
  canonical, 254, 257, 280
  canonical tree, 280
  derived, 247, 254
  deterministic, 245

deterministic finite, 286

error-correcting tree, 19, 169

finite, 243-252, 264, 285; properties
   of, 249-252; stochastic, 267-268

fuzzy attributed finite-state, 445

fuzzy, inference of, 268

non-deterministic, 244-245

probabilistic, 241, 268

pushdown, 56

stack, 285

stochastic, 265; inference of, 268

tree, 279

axiom, 324


BABYLON, 331

backtracking, 189, 325, 331, 487, 488

backtracking tree search, 189-190

backward-chaining, 326

Bayes-classifer, 322

Bayes-classification, 309, 322

Bayes' decision rule, 357, 361

Bayes' formula, 41

beam search, 341

best-first search, 341

bidirectional search, 341

bijection, 15

binary search, 321

binary tree, 101

binary tree grammar, 171

biomedical applications, 376

biomedicine, 370

biomolecules, 225

blackboard model, 340

blank symbol, 90, 104

bottom-up error-correcting parser, 68,
   80

bottom-up inference, 326

bottom-up parser, 56, 68, 75, 79

bottom-up parsing, 36, 78, 318, 454,
   486

bottom-up recognition, 46

branch, 169

branch-and-bound search, 341

breadth-first search, 123, 156, 341

brute force approach, 317


C language, 332

CAD, 376, 378

CAD/CAM, 374

camera transform, 406

canonical automaton, 254, 257, 280

canonical context-free grammar, 273

canonical grammar, 253, 260, 273

canonical tree automaton, 280

cardiac complex, 502

certainty, 42

certainty factors, 336

chain code, 174

character recognition, 224, 372-373
   *see also* Chinese character, recog-
      nition

characteristic grammar, 40, 267

characteristic views, 382, 383

Chinese character, 416, 417, 418, 433
   compound, 435
   recognition, 415-449
   single component, 437

Chomsky normal form, 34, 57, 68

chromosome, 4, 9, 11, 458, 459

CKY, *see* Cocke-Kasami-Younger
   method

classification, 120, 223, 308, 309, 322
   Bayes, 309, 322
   diagnostic, 323, 335
   hierarchical, 335, 336

nearest neighbor, 129, 309, 321

nonparametric, 309

parametric, 309

pattern, 37, 308

statistical, 309, 361, 376

clustering, 132, 199, 223, 321

Cocke-Kasami-Younger method (CKY), 56

Cocke-Kasami-Younger parser (CKY), 63

Cocke-Younger-Kasami algorithm (CYK), 456

Cocke-Younger-Kasami parser (CYK), 342, 356

common subsequence, 132

compatibility, 312, 322

completeness, 324

COMPLETER, 63, 74

complexity measure, 22, 274

computational complexity, 22-24, 67, 121, 126, 133, 134, 139, 140, 311, 312

computer vision, 328, 382

concatenation, 31, 418, 419, 422

concepts, 327, 337

CONCLUSION, 326, 329, 331

connective, 323

consistency, 41, 324

consistent labeling, 18

constant, 323

constrained hand-print machine, 372

constraint compilation, 463

constraint list, 391

constraint propagation, 389

constraints, 312

constructive solid geometry, 382

context dependent costs, 138

context dependent distance, 139

context-free array grammar, 292

context-free array language, 294

context-free grammar, 33, 43, 89, 99, 102, 241, 276-277, 353, 423, 456

inference of, 272

parallel, 93

context-free language, 56, 58, 63, 66, 68, 75, 242, 356, 423

context-free programmed grammar, 276

context-free programmed language, 356

context-sensitive grammar, 33, 89, 96

context-sensitive language, 77, 356

continuous relaxation, 312

contour-fitting, 370

control, 339

control sets, 326

Cook's method, 274

coordinate grammar, 115

corrections, 492

cost path, 123

cost sequence, 123

costs, 19, 122

*see under* deletion, insertion and substitution

Crespi-Reghizzi algorithm, 272

curve segment, 418, 419

curves, 485

cycle, 101

cyclic tree, 177

cylinder representations, 382

3-d objects, 382

data driven inference, 326

data structure, 192

database, 326

decision function, 120, 309

decision tree, 336

decision-theoretic approach, 4

decision-theoretic method, 308, 310, 321, 350, 371

default values, 330

deletion, 18, 22, 66, 68, 73, 121, 135, 142, 165, 169, 353, 356

  costs of, 138

  error, 68

Dempster/Shafer's theory, 336

denumerable, 241

depth-first search, 325, 341

derivation, 8, 32, 40, 87, 114

  graph, 35

  tree, 9, 33, 34, 37, 38, 314

derived automaton, 247, 254

deterministic automaton, 245

deterministic finite automaton, 286

deterministic parser, 457

diagnostic classification, 323, 335

diagnostic information, 500

digraph, 14, 15, 101

direct parsing, 63

directed graph, 14, 47, 101, 283

discrepancy measure, 274

discrete relaxation, 191, 312, 317

discriminant grammar, 357

disjunction, 275

distance, 66, 123

distance measure, 6, 15, 19, 120, 132, 151, 152, 199, 213, 218

distorted input, 491

distribution, 120

divide-and-conquer strategy, 167

dynamic programming, 23, 80, 123, 161, 318, 341, 342

dynamic programming matrix, 23

Earley's algorithm, 454, 456

Earley's parser, 58, 63, 71, 75, 342

ECG, *see* electrocardiogram

ECG analysis, 499-530

edge, 385

edge-finding, 370

edit operations, 121, 122, 123, 135, 138, 142, 152, 157, 165, 169

elastic matching, 133

electrocardiogram (ECG), 328, 457, 500, 501, 503

electrocardiographic pattern, 503

  complex, 503

  segment, 503

embedding, 103

embedding rule, 14

empty string, 121

empty word, 31

entropy, 20, 198, 203, 205, 207

  increment of, 213, 216

  measure, 198

epimorphism, 16

error-correcting, 174

error-correction, 10, 19

error-correcting matching, 311, 353, 355

error-correcting parser, 66, 75, 318, 491

  bottom-up, 68, 80

  top-down, 71, 80

error-correcting parsing, 18, 39, 353, 356, 358, 359

error-correcting tree automaton, 19, 169

error-tolerant recognition, 6

error detection, 374

error transformation, 353

exhaustive search, 404

expanded grammar, 171, 172
expert system shell, 326

face, 385
fact, 325
feature extraction, 370, 373
feature space, 120, 308
feature vector, 45, 308
features, 308, 310, 350, 352
finite automaton, 243-252, 264, 285
  properties of, 249-252
finite language, 252
finite-state acceptor, 105
finite-state grammar, 90, 92, 100, 318
finite-state machine, 243
first order random graph, 205-208,
  211
flexible matching, 18
forest, 162
formal grammar, 6, 8, 30, 31-34, 36,
  120, 147, 314, 315, 333, 338
formal language, 10, 31-34
formal logic, 323, 331
FORTRAN, 332
forward-chaining, 326
forward checking, 190
frames, 327, 328, 330
Freeman's chain code primitives, 294
FRL, 328
function, 15, 323
future error table (ftab), 192
fuzzy attributed finite-state
  automaton, 445
fuzzy automaton, inference of, 268
fuzzy logic, 333
fuzzy set, 333, 443

generalized substitution, 135-138, 142

generation, 95
generic matching, 148, 149
generic tree, 149
goal driven inference, 326
grammar, 32, 292, 352
  array, 86, 96-100, 292, 297; context-
    free, 292; inference of, 296; iso-
    metric, 99, 293; monotonic, 292
  attribute, 513
  attributed, 45-46, 114, 360, 361,
    417, 422, 430
  binary tree, 171
  canonical, 253, 260, 273
  canonical context-free, 273
  characteristic, 40, 267
  context-free, 33, 43, 89, 99, 102, 241,
    276-277, 353, 423, 456; inference
    of, 272; parallel, 93; stochastic,
    274
  context-free programmed, 276
  context-sensitive, 33, 89, 96
  coordinate, 115
  definition of, 8, 9
  discriminant, 357
  expanded, 171, 172
  finite, stochastic, 268
  finite-state, 90, 92, 100, 318
  for non-string languages, 13-14
  formal, 6, 8, 30, 31-34, 36, 120, 147,
    314, 315, 333, 338
  graph, 13, 86, 100-103, 315, 316
  isometric, 90-93
  linear, 90, 110
  matrix, 96-97
  monotonic, 89, 99
  multi-dimensional, 241, 277
  parallel, 93-96
  parameterized, 113, 114-115

parsing, 295, 298
pattern, 513
plex, 50, 51, 426
programmed, 113-114; stochastic, 334
regular, 33, 43, 239, 241, 243, 246,
    255, 258, 260; stochastic, 268
scattered-context, 332
shape, 374, 454, 455, 457, 462;
    stratified, 462
stochastic, 9, 39, 41, 265, 266-267,
    268, 357, 358
string, 13, 31, 86, 87-89, 426
tree, 12, 86, 103, 113, 277, 287, 426;
    stochastic, 286
type 0, 33, 89
type 1, 33
type 2, 33, 89
type 3, 33
unambiguous, 457
universal, 252
unrestricted, 33
web, 429
weighted, 357
grammatical inference, 7, 252, 277,
    292, 296, 298, 314
applications of, 285-288
definition of, 238-239
different approaches, 240-241
in pattern recognition, 239-240
problem of, 254
graph, 47, 120, 311, 351
AND/OR, 341
attributed, 198, 199-201, 224, 384
derivation, 35
directed, 14, 47, 101, 283
hierarchical, 315, 337
labeled, 100
model, 385-389, 394, 395, 397

projection, 393-397
prototype, 337
random, 15, 198, 199, 201-205, 322;
    first order, 205-208, 211
solution, 342
graph acceptor, 111-113
graph grammar, 13, 86, 100-103,
    315, 316
graph matching, 121, 148, 319
graph morphism, 200
graph parser, 317
graph synthesis, 199, 208-213,
    219-222
graph-theoretic matching, 384
Greibach normal form, 34

handprinted characters, 373
handwritten input, 485
head, 47, 481
heuristic method, 242, 255-256
heuristic search, 274
heuristics, 241, 243, 252
hidden Markov model, 241, 265, 266,
    269-272
    *see also* Markov model
hierarchical classification, 335, 336
hierarchical constraint process (HCP),
    461, 463, 464
hierarchical graph, 315, 337
hierarchical relaxation, 318
high spike, 510
histogram, 322
homomorphism, 15, 16, 181
Hough transforms, 370
hybrid approaches, 7
hybrid expert system shells, 330
hybrid method, 307-342
hybrid system, 339

hypothesis verification, 398, 406

identifiable in the limit, 242
image creation, 360
image interpretation, 327
image processing, 376
image segmentation, 327
image understanding, 327, 328, 341
inductive inference, 238, 264
industrial applications, 370-379
inexact matching, 6, 18, 20, 311
inference, 328
  bottom-up, 326
  data driven, 326
  goal driven, 326
  grammatical, *see* grammatical infer-
    ence
  inductive, 238, 264
  regular, methods, 256; theorem, 254;
    theory of, 252
  top-down, 326
inference algorithm, 20
inference learning, 7, 19
inference methods, 20
inference rule, 324
information-theoretic measures, 15
inheritance, 328, 330, 337
inherited attribute, 46
initial state, 104
initial symbol, 32, 87
injection, 15
input vocabulary, 104,
insertion, 18, 22, 66, 68, 73, 121, 135,
  142, 165
  costs of, 138
  error, 68

inspection, 374-375, 377
instances, 328
interpreter, 326
isometric array grammar, 99, 293
isometric grammar, 90-93
isomorphism, 16, 182, 200, 218, 223

joint distribution, 201
joint probabilities, 201
jump, 509
junction set, 391
junction type, 386, 389, 391, 393, 401

k-equivalence, 249, 250, 260
k-nearest neighbor classifier, 151
k-reversible language, 262, 263
k-tails, 249, 262, 264, 268, 280, 285,
  287
k-tails method, 260
KEE, 331
KL-ONE, 328
Kleene's theorem, 248
knowledge representation, 323
KRL, 328

L-systems, 96
labeled graph, 100
labeling scheme, 386
language, 8, 32, 33, 36, 41, 87, 90, 95,
  99
  array, 106, 297; context-free, 294
  context-free, 56, 58, 63, 66, 68, 75,
    242, 356, 423
  context-free programmed, 356
  context-sensitive, 77, 356
  finite, 252
  formal, 10, 31-34

k-reversible, 262, 263
matrix, 107
non-string, 13
parallel, 94, 95
rational, 247, 248
regular, 242, 248, 252, 258
reversible, 262
stochastic, 267
zero-reversible, 263
learning, 270-271, 292
inference, 7, 19
machine, 7
unsupervised, 199
learning machine, 19
left-hand side, 32
left-recursion, 56
levenshtein distance, 19, 66, 126, 355, 356
weighted, 126
lexical analyzer generator (lex), 457
line drawing analysis, 479-495
line drawing, incomplete, 405-406
linear grammar, 90, 110
local distortion, 149, 150
logic programming, 324-325, 332
logic
formal, 323, 331
fuzzy, 333
non-monotonic, 325
loop detection, 78
LR parsing, 455, 456-457
LR(k) parsing, 456
Lyon parser, 71, 75

M.1, 327
machine learning, 7, 19
machine vision, applications, 371
mapping, 157

Markov chain, 20, 269
Markov model, 287,
*see also* hidden Markov model
Markov network, 21
Markov process, 269
match, 18, 22
matched filtering, 370
matching, 143, 332, 350, 351, 372, 382
attributed string, 140-142
elastic, 133
error correcting, 311, 353, 355
flexible, 18
generic, 148, 149
graph, 121, 148, 319
graph-theoretic, 384
inexact, 6, 18, 20, 311
model, 397
partial, 148
perfect, 148
prototype, 313, 314, 332, 334, 342
relational, 180, 189
string, 121, 342
structural, 120, 121, 321
structural pattern m., 311
tree, 146, 147, 148, 149-152, 156, 165, 169, 172, 176, 177
tree to tree m., *see* tree m.,
tree to tree-grammar m., 169
matrix grammar, 96-97
matrix language, 107
maximum likelihood classification, 199, 223
medical image, 341
mensuration, 374
merge, 359
metarules, 326
minimum distance classification, 199, 223

MIRABELLE, 480, 488, 490, 495
model graph, 385-389, 394, 395, 397
model matching, 397
monomorphism, 16, 182, 200
monotonic acceptor, 105
monotonic array grammar, 292
monotonic grammar, 89, 99
monotony, 325, 327
Moore's algorithm, 250
multidimensional grammar, 241, 277
multigraphs, 102

n-attaching point entity, 50
nape, 50
natural language understanding, 328
nearest common predecessor (NCP),
    165
nearest neighbor, 19, 142
nearest neighbor classification, 129,
    309, 321
neighbors, 97
node, 112
node deletion, 152, 154, 156, 165
node insertion, 152, 154, 156, 165
node label substitution, 152, 156
node merging, 152, 165, 176
node splitting, 152, 154, 165, 176
noisy patterns, 358, 360
noisy peak, 505, 506, 507, 508, 509
non-deterministic automaton, 244-245
non-monotonic logic, 325
non-string language, 13
nonparametric classification, 309
nonterminal, 8, 36, 422
nonterminal symbol, 32, 352
NP-complete, 312

OCR, *see* optical character

recognition,
OL-systems, 96
omnifont machines, 372
operators, 482
OPS5, 327, 330
optical character recognition (OCR),
    370, 372, 377, 379

page reader, 372
Pao-Carr method, 257
parallel context-free grammar, 93
parallel grammar, 93-96
parallel language, 94, 95
parallel search, 403
parameterized grammar, 113, 114-115
parametric classification, 309
parse table, 57
parser, 56, 63, 378
    bottom-up, 56, 68, 75, 79
    Cocke-Kasami-Younger (CKY), 63
    Cocke-Younger-Kasami (CYK), 342,
        356
    deterministic, 457
parser
    Earley's, 58, 63, 71, 75, 342
    error-correcting, 66, 75, 318, 491;
        bottom-up, 68, 80; top-down,
        71, 80
    graph, 317
    Lyon, 71, 75
    top-down, 58, 71, 75, 79, 331, 487
parsing, 18, 34-36, 42, 43, 56, 95, 314,
    350, 351, 354, 360
    bottom-up, 36, 78, 318, 454, 486
    direct, 63
    error-correcting, 18, 39, 353, 356,
        358, 359
    LR, 455, 456-457

LR(k), 456
  stochastic, 353
  top-down, 36
parsing grammar, 295, 298
parsing table, 460
partial matching, 148
PASCAL, 332
pattern analysis, 37
pattern class, 309
pattern classification, 37, 308
pattern grammar, 513
pattern primitives, 4, 201
peak extraction, 505
peak pattern, 504
perfect matching, 148
Petri-nets, 326
pictorial pattern recognition, 422
picture description language (PDL),
    9, 47, 315, 416
planning, 333
plex grammar, 50, 51, 426
plex structures, 50
polynomial classifier, 372
positive information sequence, 242
predicate, 323
predicate calculus, 323, 324, 325, 328,
    329, 330, 332, 333, 341
  first order, 323, 325
PREDICTOR, 62
PREMISE, 326, 329, 331
primitive elements, 146
primitive pattern, 500, 504
  extraction, 505
primitive representations, 354
primitives, 4, 36, 47, 147, 172, 174,
    350, 351, 352, 481, 489
  starting, 493-494
probabilistic automaton, 241, 268

probabilistic relaxation, 312, 317, 318
probability, 40, 41, 120, 203, 205, 317
probability distribution, 198, 223, 309
probability updating, 313
production system, 325, 327, 328,
    329, 330, 333, 334, 341
  relational, 334
programmed grammar, 113-114
projection graph, 393-397
Prolog, 324, 329, 330, 331, 332, 334,
    341
prototype, 120, 129
  structural, 314
prototype graph, 337
prototype matching, 313, 314, 332,
    334, 342
pseudometric, 321
pumping lemma, 252, 258
pushdown automaton, 56

quantifier, 323

random arcs, 201
random graph, 15, 198, 199, 201-205,
    322
  first order, 205-208, 211
random variables, 201
random vertices, 201
rational language, 247, 248
reasoning, 328
recognition, 382
  bottom-up, 46
  character, 224, 372-373
  error-tolerant, 6
  pictorial pattern r., 422
  shape, 141
  speech, 327, 328, 341
  spoken language, 138

statistical pattern r., 45, 355
structural pattern r., 310
top-down, 46
recognizer, 56
reduction, 275
reference tree, 155
regular expression, 244, 247, 248, 258, 286
regular grammar, 33, 43, 239, 241, 243, 246, 255, 258, 260
stochastic, 268
inference of, 243
regular inference, 247
methods, 256
theorem, 254
theory of, 252
regular language, 242, 248, 252, 258
regular structures, 264
relation, 4-6, 18, 180, 352
relational description, 180, 184
attributed, 188
relational distance, 185
relational matching, 180, 189
relational structures, 121
relaxation, 312, 313, 317, 319, 322, 332, 334, 384
continuous, 312
discrete, 191, 312, 317
hierarchical, 318
probabilistic, 313, 317, 318;
syntax-directed, 318
remote sensing, 370, 376
resolution, 324
resource, 22
RETE matching algorithm, 327
reversible language, 262
rewriting rule, 32

right-hand side, 32
rightmost derivation, 456
robotic assembly, 15
robotic vision, 373-374, 378
rule, 87, 326

sample, 252, 296
negative, 252, 264, 296
positive, 264, 296
sample set condensation, 321
sample set editing, 322
satellite imagery, 376
SCANNER, 63, 74
scattered-context grammar, 332
schematic diagrams, 316
search, 399, 341
backtracking tree, 189-190
beam, 341
best-first, 341
bidirectional, 341
binary, 321
branch-and-bound, 341
breadth-first, 123, 156, 341
depth-first, 325, 341
exhaustive, 404
heuristic, 274
parallel, 403
tree, 189
search technique, 340
segmentation, 373, 376
semantic nets, 327, 328, 329, 330, 337-339
semantic rule, 9, 354
sequential machine, 264
definition of, 265
shape, 481
shape analysis, 372, 373, 375, 454, 455

shape grammar, 374, 454, 455, 457, 462
  stratified, 462
shape grammar compiler, 454
shape primitive, 461
shape recognition, 141
similarity, 66
similarity measure, 120, 147, 149, 151, 218, 220
slots, 328, 337
solution graph, 342
space complexity, 56, 57, 62, 70, 75, 318
speech recognition, 327, 328, 341
speech understanding, 340
split, 169
spoken language recognition, 138
stack automaton, 285
start symbol, 352, 422
starting symbol, 32
state set, 104
state-space search problem, 155
statistical classification, 309, 361, 376
statistical classifier, 120
statistical decision theory, 333
statistical methods, 308, 321, 350, 371
statistical pattern recognition, 45, 355
stereo vision, 15
stochastic automaton, 265
  inference of, 268
stochastic context-free grammar, 274
stochastic finite automaton, 267-268
stochastic grammar, 9, 39, 41, 265, 266-267, 268, 357
stochastic language, 267
stochastic parsing, 353
stochastic production rule, 353
stochastic programmed grammar, 334

stochastic regular grammar, 268
stochastic schema, 13
stochastic tree grammar, 286
straight lines, 485
straight-line segment, 418
stratified shape grammar, 462
stretch, 169
string, 86, 100, 101, 112, 120, 121, 227, 311, 351
  attributed, 140, 355, 358, 361
string acceptor, 104-105
string alignment, 225
string analysis method, 352
string distance, 121, 129
string grammar, 13, 31, 87-89, 426
string matching, 121, 342
string mutation, 225
STRIPS, 332, 335
stroke, 418, 437, 438, 439
stroke extraction, 437
structural description, 120
structural distortion, 149
structural matching, 120, 121, 321
structural method, 321, 350, 355
structural pattern matching, 311
structural pattern recognition, 310
structural prototype, 311, 313, 319, 337
structural representation, 30
structure, 4
subgraph isomorphism, 319, 342, 398
subgraph searching, 397, 399, 401
subpattern, 4, 6, 351, 352, 353
subpattern representation, 354
subsequence, 132
substitution, 18, 22, 66, 68, 73, 121, 135, 142, 165, 169, 275, 353, 358
  costs of, 138, 151

error, 67, 361
  generalized, 135-138, 142
substring, 6, 20
subtree, 150
subtree matching, 148
successor method, 256
surface, 385
surface representation, 382
surjection, 15
symbolic learning, 239
syntactic approach, 6, 30
syntactic method, 310, 313, 317, 350
syntactic tree, 56
syntactic/structural approach, 4
syntax, 8
syntax analysis, 351
syntax-directed parser, error-correcting, 318
syntax-directed probabilistic relaxation, 318
syntax-directed translation, 10-13, 358, 360
syntax-directed translation schema, 10, 11
synthesized attribute, 46

Tai distance, 157
Tai distance measure, 158, 159
tail, 47, 249, 481
tail-clustering method, 262
tape vocabulary, 104
tape-bounded acceptor, 105
template-matching, 372
terminal, 8, 9, 36, 422
terminal profile, 272, 273
terminal symbol, 32, 352, 461
terminal vocabulary, 87

theoretic decision methods, 150
thinning, 370
threshold, 24, 506, 509, 510
thresholding, 220, 322
time complexity, 56, 57, 62, 70, 75, 190, 299, 317, 318, 399, 404
  exponential, 325, 331
time-varying images, 12
time varying pattern, 503
time warping, 133
top-down error correcting parsers, 80
top-down inference, 326
top-down parser, 58, 71, 75, 79, 331, 487
top-down parsing, 36
top-down recognition, 46
topological match, 398, 412
topological matching, 399
transition function, 104
transition network
  augmented, 283, 285
  basic, 283, 285
translation, 10-13
transposition, 353
tree, 47, 101, 120, 146, 150, 311, 351
  AND/OR, 341
  binary, 101
  cyclic, 177
  decision, 336
  derivation, 9, 33, 34, 37, 38, 314
  generic, 149
  reference, 155
  syntactic, 56
tree automaton, 279
tree correction method, 161
tree correction problem, 152, 157
tree domain, 277
tree grammar, 12, 86, 103, 113, 277, 287, 426

stochastic, 286
tree matching, 146, 147, 148, 149-152,
    156, 165, 169, 172, 176, 177
tree search, 189
tree structure, 146, 149
tree to tree matching,
    *see* tree matching
tree to tree-grammar matching, 169
Turing machines, 334
type 0 grammar, 33, 89
type 1 grammar, 33
type 2 grammar, 33, 89
type 3 grammar, 33

unambiguous (word), 35, 40
unambiguous grammar, 457
universal grammar, 252
unrestricted grammar, 33
unsupervised classification, 223
unsupervised learning, 199

variable, 323
vertices, 385
vision workstation, 375
VLSI, 375-376
vocabulary, 32, 87
    input, 104
    tape, 104
    terminal, 87
volumetric representation, 382

warping, 133
waveforms, 501, 505
web grammar, 429
webs, 101
weighted grammar, 357
word, 31

yet another compiler compiler (yacc),
    457

zero-reversible language, 263

## About the Editors

**Horst Otto Bunke** received the Dipl.-Inf. and Dr.-Ing. degree from the University of Erlangen, West Germany in 1974 and 1979, respectively. He was with the University of Erlangen from 1974—1984. From 1980—1981 he was on leave visiting Purdue University, West Lafayette, Indiana. In 1983 he held a temporary appointment at the University of Hamburg, West Germany. In 1984 he joined the University of Berne, Switzerland where he is now a full professor of Computer Science.

From 1982—1986 he was the chairman of the technical committee on Syntactical and Structural Pattern Recognition of the International Association for Pattern Recognition. Currently, he is a member of the executive committee of the Swiss Group for Artificial Intelligence and Cognitive Science, and the Swiss Information Society.

Prof. Bunke is editor-in-charge of the *International Journal of Pattern Recognition and Artificial Intelligence.* He has about 80 publications including six books. Prof. Bunke is a member of the American Association for Artificial Intelligence, the IEEE Computer Society, the Pattern Recognition Society, the European Association for Signal Processing, and other scientific organizations. His current research interests include pattern recognition, machine vision, and knowledge-based systems.

**Alberto Sanfeliu** received the diploma and the Ph.D. from the Polytechnical University of Cataluña (UPC), Spain, in 1978 and 1982, respectively. From 1975 to 1979 he was at the Instituto de Cibernética (UPC—CSIC) de Barcelona. For a period of two years (1979—1981) he visited the Department of Electrical Engineering , Purdue University (USA) and worked with Prof. K. S. Fu. He is now Professor Titular at the Polytechnical University of Cataluña and is doing research at the Instituto de Cibernética. He is the present Chairman of the IAPR Technical Committee on Syntactic and Structural Pattern Recognition and the President of the Spanish National Society for Pattern Recognition and Image Processing.

Prof. Sanfeliu is an associate editor of the *International Journal of Pattern Recognition and Artificial Intelligence* and was the co-guest editor (with H. Bunke) in the special issue "Advances in Syntactic Pattern Recognition" of the *Pattern Recognition* journal. His areas of interest in research are syntactic and structural pattern recognition and artificial intelligence, mainly related to robotics and computer vision.